Silver Nanoparticles for Antibacterial Devices

Biocompatibility and Toxicity

Silver Nanoparticles for Antibacterial Devices

Biocompatibility and Toxicity

Edited by
Huiliang Cao

CRC Press
Taylor & Francis Group
Boca Raton London New York

CRC Press is an imprint of the
Taylor & Francis Group, an **informa** business

CRC Press
Taylor & Francis Group
6000 Broken Sound Parkway NW, Suite 300
Boca Raton, FL 33487-2742

Printed on acid-free paper

International Standard Book Number-13: 978-1-4987-2532-3 (Hardback)

Library of Congress Cataloging-in-Publication Data

Names: Cao, Huiliang, editor.
Title: Silver nanoparticles for antibacterial devices : biocompatibility and toxicity / [edited by] Huiliang Cao.
Description: Boca Raton : CRC Press, [2017] | Includes bibliographical references and index.
Identifiers: LCCN 2016051829| ISBN 9781498725323 (hardback : alk. paper) | ISBN 9781498725330 (ebook)
Subjects: | MESH: Nanoparticles | Silver | Biocompatible Materials--toxicity | Anti-Infective Agents | Nanoparticles--therapeutic use
Classification: LCC RS420 | NLM QT 36.5 | DDC 615.1/9--dc23
LC record available at https://lccn.loc.gov/2016051829

Visit the Taylor & Francis Web site at
http://www.taylorandfrancis.com

and the CRC Press Web site at
http://www.crcpress.com

Contents

Preface

Millions of patients worldwide derive benefits from various implantable biomedical devices, such as fracture fixations, prosthetic joints, pacemakers, vascular grafts, dental implants and stents, whereas these devices are challenged by biomaterial-associated infections (BAIs) in relation to their extended stay in vivo. Recognising the ever-increasing importance of anti-BAI and the seriousness of antibiotic resistance, the probe into the development of silver nanoparticles (Ag NPs) for antibacterial applications is in a renaissance, producing thousands of papers concerning their antibacterial actions in the past 10 years. On the other hand, many studies demonstrated that Ag NPs have potential risk to mammalian cells and touched off a highly debated issue on the benefits of using the material. Accordingly, *Silver Nanoparticles for Antibacterial Devices: Biocompatibility and Toxicity* brings together the synthesis, the physicochemical properties, the biological behaviours of Ag NPs and the clinical demands for fabricating antibacterial medical devices, discussing how to suppress the side effects of Ag NPs and make them inhibit bacterial adhesion without injuring the functions of mammalian cell (selective toxicity).

The book has 15 chapters and is divided into four sections, namely Synthesis and Assembling, The Risk of Silver, Techniques and Concepts for Risk Control and Clinical Demands. The section on Synthesis and Assembling focuses on the bioinspired synthesis of Ag NPs, tuning the properties of silver monolayers for biological applications, synergistic antimicrobial activity of silver and chitosan, titania nanotubes as Ag NP carriers to prevent implant-associated infection, as well as the preparation, characterisation and antibacterial mechanism of polymer–silver nanocomposites. The second section, The Risk of Silver, includes the dissolution of Ag NPs, the resistance issue of silver as an antimicrobial agent, the risks of Ag NPs to the human body and the immunomodulatory activities of Ag NPs in human neutrophils. The section on Techniques and Concepts for Risk Control discusses evaluating the interactions of Ag NPs and mammalian cells by using biomics technologies, the methods and tools for assessing nanomaterials and uses and regulation of nanosilver in Europe, as well as the concepts toward selectively toxic Ag NPs. The last section illuminates pathogenesis, clinical presentation and management of orthopaedic implant-associated infections, the typical causes and control of dental implant infection and the guidelines for nanosilver-based antibacterial devices.

These chapters, written by leading experts in their respective fields, attempt to present the latest techniques in synthesis and processing of Ag NPs, introduce the mechanisms on controlling the physicochemical behaviours of nanoparticles, sketch the basic concepts for designing safe antibacterial medical devices and consequently lay out the valuable status and significance of the book to the biomaterials and biomedical engineering community. Moreover, although the book focuses on Ag NPs, the general principles on managing the risks of nanotoxicity are applicable to other materials.

I would like to express my sincere thanks to all the contributors who devoted their valuable time and effort to write these excellent chapters and made the book a reality. I also acknowledge the joint support from Youth Innovation Promotion Association CAS, Shanghai Rising-Star Program, and National Natural Science Foundation of China.

Huiliang Cao
Shanghai, P. R. China

Editor

Huiliang Cao earned his PhD in materials science and engineering from South China University of Technology in 2008. After having worked for 2 years as a postdoctoral research scientist and another 2 years as an assistant professor at Shanghai Institute of Ceramics, Chinese Academy of Sciences (SICCAS), in 2012, he was promoted to associate professor. Dr Cao, as a member of the Chinese Society for Biomaterials and the Chinese Mechanical Engineering Society, centres on exploring the cellular responses to materials engineered with distinctive surface or interface properties, especially on developing antibacterial materials with selective toxicity.

Contributors

Long Bai
Research Institute of Surface Engineering
Taiyuan University of Technology
Taiyuan, China

Uttam C. Banerjee
Department of Pharmaceutical Technology (Biotechnology)
National Institute of Pharmaceutical Education and Research
Punjab, India

Jayeeta Bhaumik
Department of Pharmaceutical Technology (Biotechnology)
National Institute of Pharmaceutical Education and Research
Punjab, India

Huiliang Cao
State Key Laboratory of High Performance Ceramics and Superfine Microstructure
Shanghai Institute of Ceramics
Chinese Academy of Sciences
Shanghai, China

Paul K. Chu
Department of Physics and Materials Science
City University of Hong Kong
Hong Kong, China

Bharat P. Dwivedee
Department of Pharmaceutical Technology (Biotechnology)
National Institute of Pharmaceutical Education and Research
Punjab, India

Ang Gao
Department of Physics and Materials Science
City University of Hong Kong
Hong Kong, China

Denis Girard
Laboratoire de recherche en inflammation et physiologie des granulocytes
Université du Québec, INRS-Institut Armand-Frappier
Laval, Quebec, Canada

Yingxin Gu
Department of Oral and Maxillo-facial Implantology
Shanghai Key Laboratory of Stomatology
Shanghai Ninth People's Hospital
Shanghai Jiao Tong University
Shanghai, China

Michael R. Hamblin
Wellman Center for Photomedicine
Massachusetts General Hospital
and
Department of Dermatology
Harvard Medical School
Boston, Massachusetts

and

Harvard-MIT Division of Health Sciences and Technology
Cambridge, Massachusetts

Ruiqiang Hang
Research Institute of Surface Engineering
Taiyuan University of Technology
Taiyuan, China

Steffen Foss Hansen
Department of Environmental Engineering
Technical University of Denmark
Lyngby, Denmark

Yan Huang
State Key Laboratory of Bioelectronics
School of Biological Science and Medical Engineering
Southeast University
Nanjing, China

Ying-Ying Huang
Wellman Center for Photomedicine
Massachusetts General Hospital
and
Department of Dermatology
Harvard Medical School
Boston, Massachusetts

Gitika Kharkwal
NAC-SCRT Secretariat
ICMR Headquarters
New Delhi, India

Feng Li
American Advanced Nanotechnology
Houston, Texas

Wirginia Likus
Department of Anatomy
School of Health Science in Katowice
Medical University of Silesia
Katowice, Poland

Xiaoying Lü
State Key Laboratory of Bioelectronics
School of Biological Science and Medical Engineering
Southeast University
Nanjing, China

Aiga Mackevica
Department of Environmental Engineering
Technical University of Denmark
Lyngby, Denmark

Lin Mei
Key Laboratory of Functional Polymer Materials of Ministry of Education
Institute of Polymer Chemistry
Nankai University
Tianjin, China

and

School of Materials and Chemical Engineering
Zhongyuan University of Technology
Zhengzhou, China

Erchao Meng
School of Material and Chemical Engineering
Zhengzhou University of Light Industry
Zhengzhou, China

Kristel Mijnendonckx
Unit of Microbiology
Expert Group Molecular and Cellular Biology
Belgian Nuclear Research Centre (SCK·CEN)
Mol, Belgium

Magdalena Oćwieja
Jerzy Haber Institute of Catalysis and Surface Chemistry
Polish Academy of Sciences
Krakow, Poland

Tanya S. Peretyazhko
Jacobs, NASA Johnson Space Center
Houston, Texas

Pier Paolo Pompa
Istituto Italiano di Tecnologia
Genoa, Italy

Shichong Qiao
Department of Oral and Maxillo-facial Implantology
Shanghai Key Laboratory of Stomatology
Shanghai Ninth People's Hospital
Shanghai Jiao Tong University
Shanghai, China

Loris Rizzello
Department of Chemistry
University College London
London, U.K.

Sulbha K. Sharma
Laser Biomedical Section and Application Division
Raja Ramanna Centre for Advanced Technology
Indore, India

Krzysztof Siemianowicz
Department of Biochemistry
School of Medicine in Katowice
Medical University of Silesia
Katowice, Poland

Neeraj S. Thakur
Department of Pharmaceutical Technology (Biotechnology)
National Institute of Pharmaceutical Education and Research
Punjab, India

Rob Van Houdt
Unit of Microbiology
Expert Group Molecular and Cellular Biology
Belgian Nuclear Research Centre (SCK·CEN)
Mol, Belgium

Qingbo Zhang
Department of Chemistry
Rice University
Houston, Texas

Xinge Zhang
Key Laboratory of Functional Polymer Materials of Ministry of Education
Institute of Polymer Chemistry
Nankai University
Tianjin, China

Werner Zimmerli
Basel University Medical Clinic
Liestal, Switzerland

Section I

Synthesis and Assembling

1

Bioinspired Synthesis of Silver Nanoparticles: Characterisation, Mechanism and Applications

Neeraj S. Thakur, Bharat P. Dwivedee, Uttam C. Banerjee and Jayeeta Bhaumik

CONTENTS

1.1 Introduction

Metal nanoparticles have been studied and applied in many areas including the biomedical, agricultural and electronic fields (Mittal et al. 2013). Several products of colloidal silver are already in the market. Research on new, eco-friendly and cheaper methods has been initiated. Biological production of metal nanoparticles has been studied by many researchers owing to the convenience of the method that produces small particles stabilised by protein. However, the mechanism involved in this production has not yet been elucidated, although hypothetical mechanisms have been proposed in the literature (Mittal et al. 2014). Thus, this chapter discusses the various mechanisms provided for the biological synthesis of silver nanoparticles (AgNPs) by plants, fungi and bacteria. One thing that is clear is that the mechanistic aspects in some of the biological systems need more detailed studies.

Research on nanoparticles is currently an area of intense scientific interest owing to a wide variety of potential applications in the biomedical, agricultural, optical and electronic fields (Ravindran et al. 2013; Tran et al. 2013). An important type of material that has been studied is metal nanoparticles because of their physicochemical and optoelectronic properties (Mittal et al. 2013). There are various physical and chemical methods employed for the synthesis of metal nanoparticles (Mittal et al. 2013). However, these methods have certain disadvantages as a result of the involvement of toxic chemicals and radiation. Therefore, research is shifting towards biological methods of synthesis of metal nanoparticles, as these are rapid, cost-effective and eco-friendly.

A constant demand exists for economic, commercially viable as well as environment-friendly synthetic routes to nanoparticles (Mittal et al. 2013). Bio-enthused synthesis of nanoparticles provides advantages over chemical and physical methods as it is environmentally-friendly, does not need high pressure and high temperature and no toxic chemicals are needed in biological methods (Mittal et al. 2014). Biomaterials such as bacteria, yeast, fungi and various parts of plants are used in nanoparticle synthesis (Mittal et al. 2013; Narayanan and Sakthivel 2010). Currently, most of the applications of AgNPs are in the biotechnology field as antibacterial and antifungal agents, in textile engineering, in wastewater treatment and as silver-based consumer products (Gade et al. 2010). Nanoparticles, which are mainly utilised in biomedical applications, fall within the size range of 1–100 nm. The bioinspired method is considered to be ideal, amongst different synthetic routes to nanoparticle formation, since it avoids the use of toxic chemicals (Mittal et al. 2014).

The biosynthesis of AgNPs incorporated with therapeutic and imaging agents involves theranostic activities (Bhaumik et al. 2015). These multifunctional nanotheranostic agents can be used in the treatment of cancer, microbial infection and many other diseases (Bhaumik et al. 2014, 2016). The antioxidant capability of the biosynthesised nanoparticle is dependent on the properties of phytochemicals with which the surface of the nanoparticles is coated (Mittal et al. 2014). These phytochemicals mainly consist of flavonoids and phenolic compounds that possess strong reducing properties. Additionally, the presence of functional groups (such as hydroxyl and amine) makes them useful for conjugation. Bioinspired theranostic agents can be further developed using AgNPs developed through the following strategies: (1) selection and screening of plant extracts for the synthesis of nanoparticles, (2) optimisation of various physicochemical parameters for biosynthesis, (3) functionalisation of the synthesised nanoparticles with the therapeutic and imaging agents and (4) characterisation of nanoconjugates using various analytical techniques.

1.2 Biosynthesis of AgNPs

1.2.1 Biosynthesis of AgNPs Using Plant Extracts

The main advantage of using plant extracts for the synthesis of AgNPs is that they can be used as reducing and stabilising agents simultaneously. Plant extracts frequently offer good manipulation and control over crystal growth and stabilisation (Bhaumik et al. 2015; Mittal et al. 2014). However, using different plant extracts and reductants in the synthesis of metal nanoparticles is challenging. In order to obtain nanoparticles with the desired shape, size and dispersity, biosynthesis was performed using plant extracts.

Reduction of silver ions to nanoparticles using an extract of *Desmodium triflorum* was ascribed to the presence of H^+ ions, NAD^+ and ascorbic acid in the extract (Ahmad et al. 2011). Synthesis of highly stable AgNPs (16–40 nm) using the leaf extract of *Datura metel* has been reported (Kesharwani et al. 2009). The extract contained alkaloids, proteins, enzymes, amino acids, alcoholic compounds and polysaccharides, which were said to be responsible for the reduction of the silver ions to nanoparticles (Kesharwani et al. 2009). Quinol and chlorophyll pigments present in the extract also contributed to the reduction of silver ions and stabilisation of the nanoparticles. Sukirtha et al. (2012) synthesised AgNPs using a leaf extract of *Melia azedarach*, which exhibited anti-cancer properties. Synthesis of AgNPs using a methanolic extract of *Eucalyptus hybrida* (safeda) leaves has been reported (Dubey et al. 2009). Flavonoid and terpenoid compounds present in the extract were claimed to be responsible for the stabilisation of nanoparticles. Banerjee and Narendhirakanan (2011) used an extract of *Syzygium cumini* (jambul) seeds to produce AgNPs. The seed extract had antioxidant properties *in vitro*. The nanoparticles formed using the extract were found to have higher antioxidant activity compared with the seed extract. This may have been attributed to a preferential adsorption of the antioxidant material from the extract onto the surface of the nanoparticles. Extract of banana (*Musa paradisiaca*) peels has been used to generate AgNPs (Bankar et al. 2010), which displayed excellent antifungal and antibacterial activity against a wide range of pathogens. Ahmad et al. (2010) used extracts of the legume *Desmodium triflorum* to synthesise AgNPs in the size range of 5–20 nm. MubarakAli et al. (2011) reported the synthesis of AgNPs using *Mentha piperita* (peppermint), which showed antibacterial activity. Babu and Prabu (2011) synthesised 35-nm AgNPs using a flower extract of *Calotropis procera*. Kouvaris et al. (2012) used a leaf extract of *Arbutus unedo* to produce nanoparticles with a narrow size distribution. AgNPs produced using the peel extract of *Citrus sinensis* were found to have broad-spectrum antibacterial activity (Kaviya et al. 2011). The particles formed at 60°C had an average size of around 10 nm, but reducing the reaction temperature to 25°C increased the average size to 35 nm (Kaviya et al. 2011). Vijayaraghavan et al. (2012) reported a one-step synthesis of silver nano/microparticles using *Trachyspermum ammi* and *Papaver somniferum* extracts. The extracts of *T. ammi* produced nanoparticles (87–998 nm) of various triangular shapes, and the extract of *P. somniferum* resulted in spherical-shaped microparticles (3–8 μm). Dwivedi and Gopal (2010) used extracts of *Chenopodium album* leaves to produce AgNPs. The particles had quasi-spherical shapes and were in the size range of 10–30 nm.

Production of spherical- and triangular-shaped AgNPs using fruit extracts of *Tanacetum vulgare* has been reported (Dubey et al. 2010b). A Fourier transform infrared (FTIR) study revealed that the carbonyl groups were involved in the reduction of metal ions to nanoparticles. The zeta potential of the AgNPs was shown to vary with pH: a low zeta potential at strongly acidic pH (Dubey et al. 2010b). A larger particle size could be achieved by reducing the pH of the reaction (Dubey et al. 2010b). Silver ions could be reduced to AgNPs using a leaf extract of *Cinnamomum camphora* (Huang et al. 2007).

We earlier reported the simultaneous bioinspired synthesis of AgNPs using *Camellia sinensis* followed by surface engineering to construct nanotheranostic agents (Bhaumik et al. 2015). This procedure avoided the use of toxic chemicals since plant extracts were used in entire nanomaterial formation (reduction of metal, aggregation and stabilisation). The phytochemicals present in the plants used in nanoparticle preparation mainly consisted of polyphenols and flavonoids that are rich in hydroxyl moieties. Thus, any potential molecule (a drug or an imaging agent) with counter functionality (such as the -COOH group) can be reacted to form an ester bond and attach

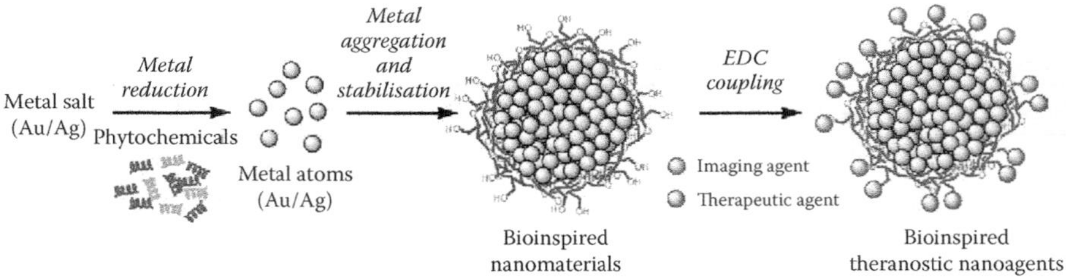

SCHEME 1.1
(See colour insert.) Diagrammatic representation of bioinspired synthesis and surface functionalisation of the theranostic nanoagents. (Reproduced with permission from Bhaumik, Thakur et al. *ACS Biomat Sci Eng*, 1:382–392. Copyright 2015 American Chemical Society.)

on the phytochemical surface. Because of the presence of carboxylic acid groups, rhodamine B and rose bengal could be conjugated to the surface of bioinspired nanoparticles by the aid of EDC-mediated coupling (Scheme 1.1). The nanomaterials were completely characterised by means of various spectroscopic techniques. Bioinspired nanoconstructs were further subjected to antioxidant assays to determine whether the phytochemicals retained their antioxidant properties after forming nanoformulations. Drug loading on the surface of the nanoconjugates was also estimated by UV–vis spectroscopy and high-performance liquid chromatography (HPLC) analysis. Overall, these bioinspired nanotheranostic agents have potential applications in nanomedicine. The use of various plant extracts to synthesise AgNPs of different sizes and shapes is summarised in Table 1.1.

1.2.2 Biosynthesis of AgNPs Using Fungi

Fungi have been explored for the synthesis of AgNPs (Table 1.2). Fungi are advantageous because they can withstand flow, pressure and agitation; in addition, they are easy to grow, fabricate and handle. The downstream processing of secretory reducing protein is easy. The mycosynthesis of AgNPs may be inside or outside the cell. A list of fungi used in the formation of AgNPs is urnished in Figure 1.1 and Table 1.2.

1.2.2.1 Intracellular Synthesis

It has been observed that the size of intracellularly formed nanoparticles is smaller than that of extracellularly formed nanoparticles. The selective accumulation and absorption of silver by Phoma PT35 (Pighi et al. 1989) and Phoma sp. 3.2883 (Chen et al. 2003), respectively, have been reported. The exposure of the fungal biomass of *Verticillium* sp. to the aqueous silver nitrate solution resulted in AgNP accumulation inside the fungal cell surface with a negligible amount in the solution (Mukherjee et al. 2001). The incubation of *Aspergillus flavus* with silver nitrate solution accumulates the AgNPs on

TABLE 1.1

Biosynthesis of AgNPs Using Plant Extracts

S. No.	Plant Type	Size and Shape	Reference
1	*Acalypha indica*	20–30 nm; spherical	Krishnaraj et al. 2010
2	*Allium sativum* (garlic clove)	4–22 nm; spherical	Ahamed et al. 2011
3	*Boswellia ovalifoliolata* Ag	30–40 nm	Ankanna et al. 2010
4	*Calotropis procera*	150–1000 nm	Babu and Prabu 2011
5	*Camelia sinensis*	30–40 nm	Bhaumik et al. 2015; Vilchis-Nestor et al. 2008
6	*Carica papaya*	25–50 nm	Jain et al. 2009
7	*Catharanthus roseus*	48–67 nm	Kannan et al. 2011; Ponarulselvam et al. 2012
8	*Chenopodium album*	10–30 nm; quasi-spherical shape	Dwivedi and Gopal 2010
9	*Cinnamomum camphora*	55–80 nm	Huang et al. 2007
10	*Citrus sinensis* peel	35 ± 2 nm (at 25°C), 10 ± 1 nm (at 60°C); spherical	Kaviya et al. 2011
11	*Coleus amboinicus* Lour	25.8 ± 0.8 nm	Subramanian 2012
12	*Coleus aromaticus*	44 nm	Vanaja and Annadurai 2012
13	*Curcuma longa*	–	Sathishkumar et al. 2010
14	*Datura metel*	16–40 nm; quasi-linear superstructures	Kesharwani et al. 2009
15	*Desmodium triflorum*	5–20 nm	Ahmad et al. 2011
16	*Eclipta prostrate*	35–60 nm; triangles, pentagons, hexagons	Rajakumar and Abdul Rahuman 2011
17	*Emblica officinalis*	10–20 nm	Ankamwar et al. 2005
18	*Eucalyptus hybrida*	50–150 nm	Dubey et al. 2009
19	*Garcinia mangostana* (mangosteen leaf)	35 nm	Veerasamy et al. 2011
20	*Gelidiella acerosa*	22 nm	Vivek et al. 2011
21	*Memecylon edule*	20–50 nm; triangular, circular, hexagonal	Elavazhagan and Arunachalam 2011
22	*Melia azedarach*	–	Sukirtha et al. 2012
23	*Mentha piperita* (peppermint)	5–150 nm; spherical	MubarakAli et al. 2011; Parashar 2009
24	*Moringa oleifera*	57 nm	Prasad and Elumalai 2011
25	*Mucuna pruriens*	6–17.7 nm; spherical	Arulkumar and Sabesan 2010
26	*Musa paradisiacal*	20 nm	Bankar et al. 2010
27	*Nelumbo nucifera* (lotus)	25–80 nm; spherical, triangular	Santhoshkumar et al. 2011
28	*Rhododedendron dauricam*	25–40 nm; spherical	Mittal et al. 2012
29	*Rosa rugosa*	30–60 nm	Dubey et al. 2010a

(Continued)

TABLE 1.1 (CONTINUED)

Biosynthesis of AgNPs Using Plant Extracts

S. No.	Plant Type	Size and Shape	Reference
30	*Sesuvium portulacastrum*	5–20 nm; spherical	Nabikhan et al. 2010
31	*Swietenia mahogani* (mahogany)	pH 7; 20 nm	Mondal et al. 2011
32	*Syzygium cumini*	29–92 nm; spherical	Banerjee and R.T. 2011; Kumar et al. 2010; Mittal et al. 2014
33	*Tanacetum vulgare* (tansy fruit)	16 nm	Dubey et al. 2010b
34	*Trachyspermum copticum*	6–50 nm	Vijayaraghavan et al. 2012

Source: Reprinted from *Biotech Adv* 31, Mittal et al., Synthesis of metallic nanoparticles using plant extracts, 346–356, Copyright 2013, with permission from Elsevier.

the surface of its cell wall (Vigneshwaran et al. 2007). The intracellularly synthesised AgNPs showed spherical, quasi-hexagonal and rod-shaped morphologies with a size range of 8–25 nm (Mukherjee et al. 2001; Vigneshwaran et al. 2007).

1.2.2.2 Extracellular Synthesis

The extracellular synthesis of nanoparticles has many applications because of the negation of redundant adjoining cellular machineries from the cell. Most of the fungi have enormous secretory components involved in the reduction and capping of nanoparticles, considered as the organisms that produce nanoparticles extracellularly. Many authors reported the extracellular synthesis of AgNPs using various strains of fungi. They reported the silver salt reduced by the secretory components (enzymes) in the presence of suitable electron donors (4-hydroxyquinolone) and cofactors (NADPH) (Ahmad et al. 2003; Anil Kumar et al. 2007; Durán et al. 2005; Ingle et al. 2009). The synthesised nanoparticles were stabilised by the secretory proteins. Extracellularly, different strains of fungi formed different sizes of nanoparticles; also, the time of reaction varied from strain to strain (Table 1.2). Most of the synthesised nanoparticles were spherical, but some of the nanoparticles were rods, hexagons, cubes, stars and so on (Amerasan et al. 2016; Verma et al. 2010).

1.2.3 Biosynthesis of AgNPs Using Bacteria

The bacterial synthesis of nanoparticles involves both nanotechnology and biotechnology (Kalishwaralal et al. 2008). The biogenesis of nanoparticle biosynthesis originated from a biosorption study of metals with different bacterial strains. Nanoscale production of silver was launched in the age of nanotechnology. Nanoparticles were not in focus even when many

TABLE 1.2
Biosynthesis of AgNPs Using Fungi

Name	Size/Shape	Time of Synthesis	Reference
Fusarium oxysporum	5–15 nm	72 h	Ahmad et al. 2003
Aspergillus fumigatus	5–25 nm	72 h	Bhainsa and D'Souza 2006
Fusarium oxysporum sp.	20–50 nm	28 h	Durán et al. 2011
Fusarium semitectum	10–60 nm	120 h	Basavaraja et al. 2008
Penicillium brevicompactum	23–105 nm	72 h	Shaligram et al. 2009
Alternaria alternata	20–60 nm	48 h	Gajbhiye et al. 2009
Verticillium	25 ± 12 nm	72 h	Mukherjee et al. 2001
Streptomyces hygroscopicus	20–30 nm	96 h	Sadhasivam et al. 2010
Aspergillus niger	3–30 nm	72 h	Jaidev and Narasimha 2010
Trichoderma viride	5–40 nm	24 h	Fayaz et al. 2010a
Coriolus versicolor	25–75 nm	1 h	Sanghi and Verma 2009
Penicillium fellutanum	5–25 nm	24 h	Kathiresan et al. 2009
Penicillium sp.	58.35 ± 17.88 nm	72 h	Hemath Naveen et al. 2010
Trichoderma reesei	5–50 nm	72 h	Vahabi et al. 2011
Cladosporium cladosporioides	10–100 nm	24 h	Balaji et al. 2009
Fusarium solani USM-3799	5–35 nm	24 h	Ingle et al. 2009
Aspergillus flavus	8.92 ± 1.61 nm	48 h	Vigneshwaran et al. 2007
Chrysosporium tropicum	20–50 nm	72 h	Soni and Prakash 2012
Amylomyces rouxii KSU-09	5–27 nm	72 h	Musarrat et al. 2010
Aspergillus clavatus	10–25 nm, hexagonal	72 h	Verma et al. 2010
Aspergillus flavus NJP08	17 ± 5.9 nm	72 h	Jain et al. 2011
Cochliobolus lunatus	3–21 nm	72 h	Salunkhe et al. 2011
Humicola sp.	5–25 nm	96 h	Syed et al. 2013
Phoma gardeniae ITCC 4554	10–30 nm	72 h	Gade et al. 2015
Cryphonectria sp.	30–70 nm	24 h	Dar et al. 2013
Epicoccum nigrum	1–22 nm	24 h	Qian et al. 2013
Penicillium citrinum	90–120 nm	24 h	Honary et al. 2013
Ganoderma neo-japonicum	2–10 nm	12 h	Gurunathan et al. 2013
Metarhizium anisopliae	28–38 nm, rod	72 h	Amerasan et al. 2016
Neurospora crassa	3–50 nm, sphere	24 h	Castro-Longoria et al. 2011
Aspergillus terreus	1–20 nm	24 h	Li et al. 2012
Geotricum sp.	30–50 nm	96 h	Jebali et al. 2011
Fusarium oxysporum	25–50 nm	72 h	Korbekandi et al. 2013

(*Continued*)

TABLE 1.2 (CONTINUED)

Biosynthesis of AgNPs Using Fungi

Name	Size/Shape	Time of Synthesis	Reference
Fusarium culmorum MTCC-2090	5–25 nm	2 h	Bawaskar et al. 2010
Streptomyces sp.	15–25 nm	24 h	Alani et al. 2012
Bipolaris nodulosa	10–60 nm	72 h	Saha et al. 2010
Aspergillus foetidus MTCC8876	20–40 nm	96 h	Roy 2013
Trichoderma viride	2–4 nm	24 h	Fayaz et al. 2010b
Penicillium purpurogenum	–	72 h	Pradhan et al. 2011
Fusarium solani	3–8 nm	48 h	El-Rafie et al. 2010
Phytophthora infestans	5–80 nm	1 h	Thirumurugan et al. 2011
Aspergillus niger	5–35 nm	4 h	Kathiresan et al. 2010
Pestalotia sp.	10–40 nm	72 h	Raheman et al. 2011
Aspergillus tubingensis	35 ± 10 nm	96 h	Rodrigues et al. 2013
Bionectria ochroleuca	35 ± 10 nm	96 h	Rodrigues et al. 2013
Pencillium sp	25 nm, sphere	24 h	Singh et al. 2013
Penicillium diversum	5–45 nm	24 h	Ganachari et al. 2012
Aspergillus niger 2587	20–70 nm, sphere	72 h	Soni and Prakash 2013
Aspergillus clavatus	550–650 nm	120 h	Saravanan and Nanda 2010
A. solani GS1	5–20 nm	72 h	Devi et al. 2014
P. funiculosum GS2	5–10 nm	72 h	Devi et al. 2014
Fusarium oxysporum	10–20 nm	45 min	Birla et al. 2013
Aspergillus terreus CZR-1	1.0–5.0	24 h	Raliya and Tarafdar 2012

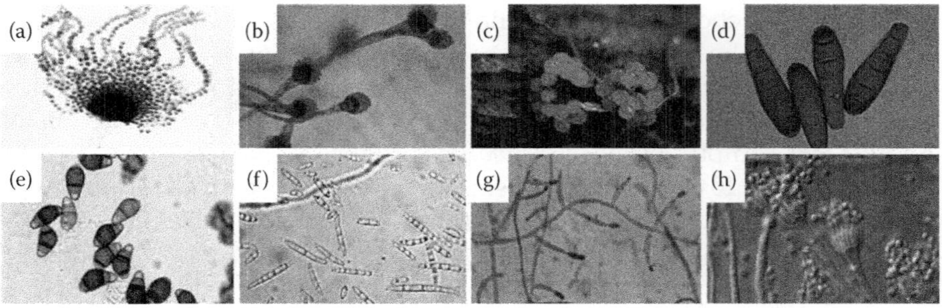

FIGURE 1.1

(See colour insert.) Image of fungi used in the biosynthesis of AgNPs: (a) *Aspergillus flavus*, (b) *Aspergillus fumigatus*, (c) *Bionectria ochroleuca*, (d) *Bipolaris nodulosa*, (e) *Cochliobolus lunatus*, (f) *Fusarium oxysporum*, (g) *Fusarium semitectum*, (h) *Penicillium fellutanum*. (Picture courtesy of Google images.)

microbial remediation of metals were reported (Beveridge 1976; Beveridge and Fyfe 1985).

Biosynthesis of AgNP was first reported in 1984 through *Pseudomonas stutzeri* AG259 (Haefeli et al. 1984; Zhang et al. 2005). This opened new avenues towards the preparation of nanostructured materials. Biological methods are gaining impetus because they are performed under normal conditions to achieve synthesis that enables control over the size and shape of the nanoparticles.

Microbial production of metal nanoparticles gave birth to a new era of nanomaterial development. Bacterial cells are noticeably used as biomachinery for AgNPs synthesis (Malhotra et al. 2013; Mittal et al. 2013; Poulose et al. 2014). Bacteria can take part in the synthesis of nanoparticles through either the intracellular or extracellular route. In general, bioreduction processes are mainly involved in the microbial production of nanoparticles. Extracellular reductase enzymes of microorganisms reduce the silver ions and form particles in the nanometer-size range. Scientific studies reveal an NADH-dependent reductase enzyme role in the bioreduction of silver; in some cases, nitrate-dependent reductase is also reported. The bacteria *P. stutzeri* produced silver nanocrystals of size 200 nm (Klaus et al. 1999). *P. stutzeri* shows resistance to silver; a possible explanation for this is the deposition of the particles in periplasm granules followed by metal efflux and metal binding. *Cornebacterium* sp. can synthesise AgNPs with a size range of 10–15 nm after treatment with diamine silver complex (Zhang et al. 2005). The bioreduction of the ions to nanoparticles is probably caused by the reducing nature of the carboxyl group of amino acid residues, amide linkage and other reducing groups. The microbial production of nanoparticles can be explained by the oxidation–reduction-mediated modulation of solubility, toxicity, the absence of a particular metal transport system, the complexation or precipitation of metals, biosorption, efflux system and bioaccumulation (Husseiny et al. 2007). Nanoparticles produced via biological routes show similarities in chemical routes and in the size and shape of particles, which can also be controlled by these bacterial strains.

The effect of silver ion concentration was studied, and it was found that higher concentrations of silver ions are sensitive for the production of AgNPs; for example, *Bacillus licheniformis* produce AgNPs at 1 mM concentration. Beyond 10 mM, the organism undergoes cell death within minutes (Kalimuthu et al. 2008; Pandian et al. 2010). Often, silver is labelled as an 'element with a dual behaviour' at lower concentrations as it acts as an inducer for nanoparticles synthesis and its higher concentration leads to induction of cell death. Figure 1.2 and Table 1.3 provide a list of organisms that were reported for synthesis of AgNPs.

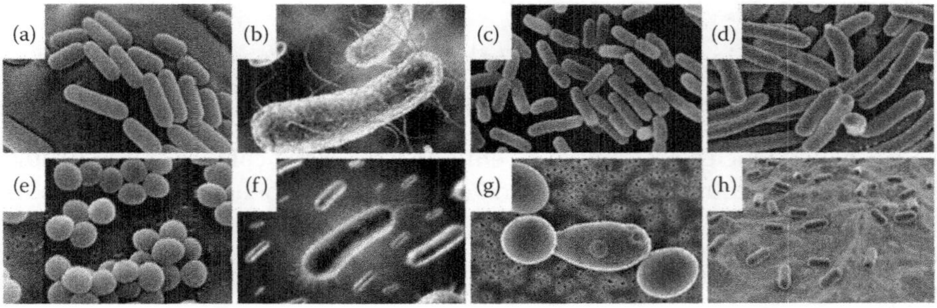

FIGURE 1.2
(See colour insert.) Image of bacteria used in the biosynthesis of AgNPs: (a) *Klebsiella pneumonia*, (b) *Bacillus licheniformis*, (c) *Bacillus subtilis*, (d) *Escherichia coli*, (e) *Staphylococcus aureus*, (f) *Bacillus cereus*, (g) *Saccharomyces boulardii*, (h) *Lactobacillus* strains. (Picture courtesy of Google images.)

TABLE 1.3
Various Bacterial Species Synthesising AgNPs

S. No.	Organism	Size (nm)	Reference
1	*Pseudomonas stutzeri* AG259	200	Klaus et al. 1999
2	*Lactobacillus* strains	500	Nair and Pradeep 2002
3	*Corynebacterium* sp.	10–15	Zhang et al. 2005
4	*Klebsiella pneumonia*	50	Kumar et al. 2007
5	*Bacillus licheniformis*	50	Kalishwaralal et al. 2008
6	*Bacillus subtilis*	5–60	Saifuddin et al. 2009
7	*Escherichia coli*	1–100	Gurunathan et al. 2009
8	*Staphylococcus aureus*	1–100	Nanda and Saravanan 2009
9	*Brevibacterium casei*	50	Kalishwaralal et al. 2010
10	*Morganella psychrotolerans*	350–530	Ramanathan et al. 2011
11	*Bacillus cereus*	62.8	Silambarasan and Abraham 2012
12	*Stenotrophomonas* sp.	40–60	Malhotra et al. 2013
13	*Saccharomyces boulardii*	3–10	Kaler et al. 2013
14	*Pseudomonas veronii* AS41G	5–50	Baker et al. 2015
15	*Streptomyces coelicolor* klmp33	28–50	Manikprabhu and Lingappa 2014
16	*Chryseobacterium artocarpi* CECT 8497	42	Venil et al. 2016
17	*Leuconostoc mesenteroides* T3	15–50	Davidovića et al. 2015
18	*Bacillus cereus* and *Escherichia fergusonii*	10–20	Pourali and Yahyaei 2016

1.3 Characterisation of Biosynthesised AgNPs

1.3.1 Visual Inspection and UV–Visible Spectroscopic Analysis

Metal nanoparticles are known to emit characteristic colours in the visible region of the electromagnetic spectrum owing to a phenomenon known as surface plasmon resonance (Bhaumik et al. 2014). Preliminary identification of nanoparticles was therefore performed by observing the change in colour of the reaction mixture in an aqueous solution before and after the reaction. Biosynthesised AgNPs show a characteristic yellowish brown to dark brown colour. The colour of the colloidal solution of nanoparticles is mostly dependent on their size and shape.

UV–visible spectroscopy is a universally used technique for the preliminary identification of nanoparticle formation. Different wavelengths in the range 300–800 nm are generally used for characterising various AgNPs in the size range of 2–100 nm. Spectrophotometric absorption measurements in the wavelength range of 400–450 is used in characterising the AgNPs (Figure 1.3) (Bhaumik et al. 2015).

1.3.2 Zeta-Size and Zeta Potential Analysis

Zeta-size analysis is essential to determine the average hydrodynamic particle size distribution and zeta potential of nanomaterials. Dynamic light scattering measurements are performed with a fixed wavelength of 532 nm at 35°C with a 90° detection angle. To estimate the particle size and zeta potential, a dilute suspension of AgNP is prepared in deionised water and sonicated in order to remove aggregation at 35°C for 30 min and subjected to zeta-size analysis. The AgNPs synthesised using *C. sinensis* (CS-AgNPs)

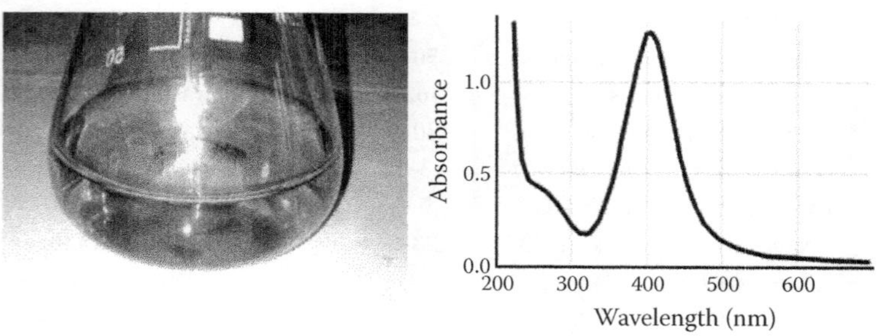

FIGURE 1.3
Visual inspection of colloidal solutions of AgNPs synthesised using medicinal plant (*C. sinensis*) extract and their corresponding UV–visible spectra. (Reprinted with permission from Bhaumik, Thakur et al. *ACS Biomat Sci Eng*, 1:382–392. Copyright 2015 American Chemical Society.)

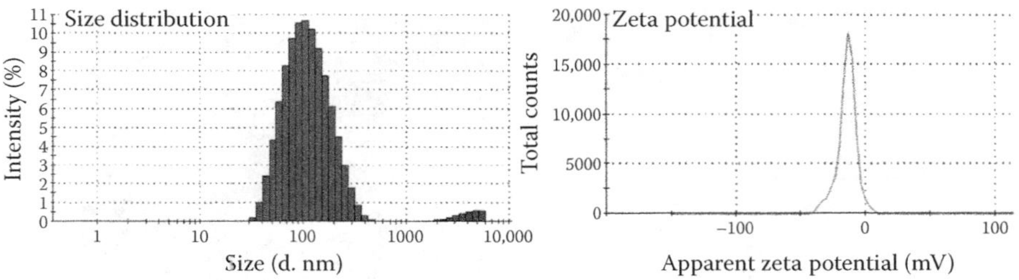

FIGURE 1.4
Size distribution and zeta potential graphs of CS-AgNPs. (Reprinted with permission from Bhaumik, Thakur et al. *ACS Biomat Sci Eng*, 1:382–392. Copyright 2015 American Chemical Society.)

exhibited a narrow size distribution range with an average zeta-size value of 96.98 nm, a zeta potential of −14.4 mV and a polydispersity index (PDI) of 0.216 (Figure 1.4). A PDI of 0.216 implies good monodispersity and a negative zeta potential assures the capping of nanoparticles by negatively charged groups (e.g. hydroxyl group) (Bhaumik et al. 2015).

1.3.3 Scanning Electron Microscopy

Scanning electron microscopy (SEM) provides details on the size and morphology of the nanoparticles (Goldstein et al. 1992). In SEM, an electron beam comes from a filament (tungsten) and is condensed by a condenser lens and then projected onto the sample by the objective lens. This beam scans over the surface of the sample, and various signals, including photons and electrons, are emitted from the sample surface. The interaction between the sample and the beam produces different types of signals, providing details on the surface structure and morphology of the nanomaterials. The resolution of the SEM is a few nanometres to micrometres, and it can operate at various magnifications, which can be easily adjusted.

1.3.4 Transmission Electron Microscopy

Transmission electron microscopy (TEM) is a powerful technique that is used for high-resolution imaging of a thin film on a solid sample for structural and compositional analysis of nanomaterials (Mittal et al. 2014). A TEM micrograph of AgNPs synthesised from *C. sinensis* extract confirmed that the AgNPs were spherical in shape with a size of ~100 nm and capped with plant constituents that prevented particle aggregation (Figure 1.5). Inherent capping offers the additional advantage of stabilising bioinspired nanoparticles. These stability characteristics of plant constituents are in agreement with reports of Ahmad et al (2011). They found that capping of plant constituents can reduce the aggregation of AgNPs.

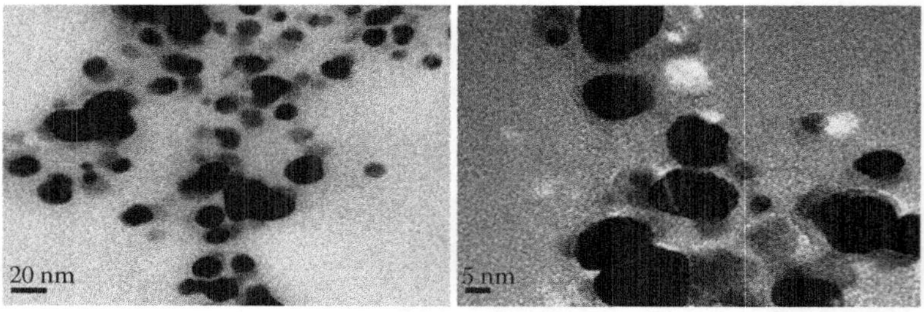

FIGURE 1.5
TEM images of biosynthesised AgNPs prepared from *C. sinensis* extract. (Reprinted with permission from Bhaumik, Thakur et al. *ACS Biomat Sci Eng*, 1:382–392. Copyright 2015 American Chemical Society.)

1.3.5 FTIR Spectroscopy

FTIR spectroscopic analysis is performed in order to identify the possible bioconstituents responsible for the reduction of silver ions to nanoparticles and their effective stabilisation and capping. Thus, FTIR data are collected for phytochemical capped metal nanoconstructs. Biosynthesised AgNPs prepared using *C. sinensis* showed peaks around 3400, 2900 and 1600 cm^{-1}, some of which were also found in the FTIR spectra of the corresponding plant extracts (Bhaumik et al. 2015). The peak at 3400 cm^{-1} indicates -OH structural polymeric association. Overall spectral pattern indicated the presence of catechin (flavonoid)-like molecules (from the phytochemical capping) in the plant extracts that might be responsible for the coating of hydroxyl groups on the nanoparticles (Bhaumik et al. 2015; Mittal et al. 2014). Therefore, it can be concluded that the nanoparticle surface is capped by polyphenolics and flavonoids. In can also be noted that the hydroxyl groups present on the nanoparticle surface can be functionalised by reacting with carboxylic acid groups present in drugs or imaging agents to construct nanotheranostic scaffolds.

1.3.6 Determination of Antioxidant Potential as a Measure of Therapeutic Potential

Antioxidant activity is the measure of inhibition of oxidation of molecules by which various life-threatening diseases including cancer can be suppressed. Through the inhibition of oxidation, nonreactive stable radicals are formed. Different bioingredients present in plants (e.g. flavonoids and polyphenols) have strong antioxidant properties, which help in reducing oxidative stress in cells. Thus, those plant constituents play a key role in treating cancer and inflammatory diseases (Mittal et al. 2014). Since AgNPs are coated with important bioingredients, determination of antioxidant properties is essential to estimate whether those properties are retained by the bioinspired nanoparticles. It is known that the synthesis and antioxidant activity of nanoparticles are mainly attributed to the flavonoid content, which can be calculated as quercetin dihydrate equivalent (QDE%) (quercetin standard) (Bhaumik et al. 2015; Mittal et al. 2014). The QDE values for CS-AgNPs (AgNPs synthesised from *C. sinensis*) were found to be 18%. Anti-oxidant activities were further confirmed by various assays (namely, ABTS and DPPH), which showed promising results owing to the presence of polyphenol and flavonoid capping agents on NPs (Bhaumik et al. 2015).

ABTS is a colorimetric assay, in which the oxidation of ABTS [2,2′-azinobis (3-ethylbenzothiazoline-6-sulfonic acid)] with potassium persulfate generates ABTS radical cation; hydrogen-donating antioxidants reduce these ABTS cation radicals and decolourise the solution, which is measured at 734 nm (Mittal et al. 2014). The antioxidant activities of bioinspired AgNPs synthesised using *C. sinensis* was found to be 39% with an IC_{50} value 1.3 μg/mL, while a standard ascorbic acid revealed 59% (IC_{50} = 0.85 μg/mL) scavenging at the same concentration (Bhaumik et al. 2015). In DPPH colorimetric assay, the antioxidant donates hydrogen atom to the stable DPPH (1,1-diphenyl-2-picrylhydrazyl) radical, for which the DPPH solution is decolourised (Mittal et al. 2014). The antioxidant activity of bioinspired AgNPs was calculated to be 49% with an IC_{50} value of 5.0 μg/mL, while ascorbic acid showed 52% (IC_{50} = 4.8 μg/mL) scavenging at the same concentration (Bhaumik et al. 2015). Biosynthesised AgNPs can be valuable in therapeutics because of their considerable amount of antioxidant potential.

1.4 Mechanism of AgNP Synthesis

1.4.1 Mechanism of AgNP Synthesis Using Plant Extract

Incubation of a silver salt in the presence of a particular plant extract at optimised reaction parameters results in the formation of a nanocluster (Bhaumik et al. 2015). However, the role of various organic molecules (such as bioreducing agents, flavonoids and peptides) present as plant ingredients can be held responsible for the reduction, stabilisation and capping of the resulting nanoparticle formation (Mittal et al. 2014). From different characterisation data (UV–vis spectroscopy, TEM, FTIR), it can be hypothesised that, initially, the metal ions present in metal salts are reduced by bioreducing agents, and then they are aggregated, capped and stabilised by bioingredients to grow nanostructures of defined size and shape (Figure 1.6, M = silver atom). The nature of bioreducing agents and reaction conditions (e.g. temperature, time, pH) plays major roles in controlling the morphology of the nanomaterials.

Our group has accomplished the synthesis of AgNPs using *S. cumini* fruit extract at room temperature (Mittal et al. 2014). Various techniques were used

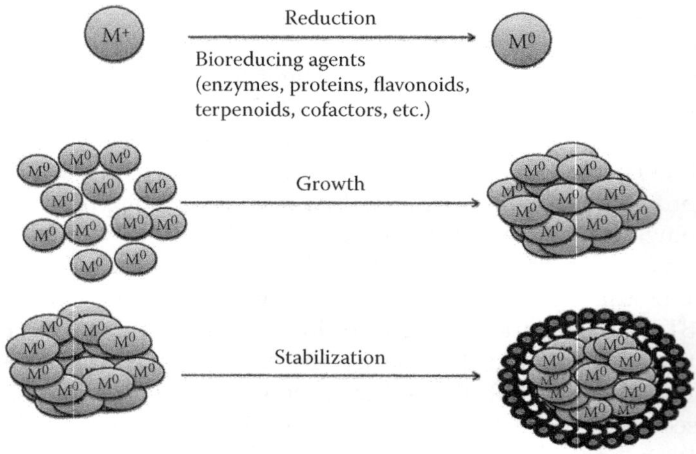

FIGURE 1.6
Mechanisms of nanoparticle synthesis (M+ silver cation). (Reprinted from *Biotech Adv* 31, Mittal et al., Synthesis of metallic nanoparticles using plant extracts, 346–356, Copyright 2013, with permission from Elsevier.)

to characterise the AgNPs, and their size was determined to be 10–15 nm. An important finding of this study was the identification of biomolecules responsible for the synthesis of AgNPs and for elucidating the mechanism of biosynthesis. Flavonoids present in *S. cumini* were mainly responsible for the reduction and the stabilisation of nanoparticles (Scheme 1.2). The antioxidant properties of AgNPs were evaluated using various assays. The nanoparticles were also found to destroy Dalton lymphoma cell lines under *in vitro* conditions.

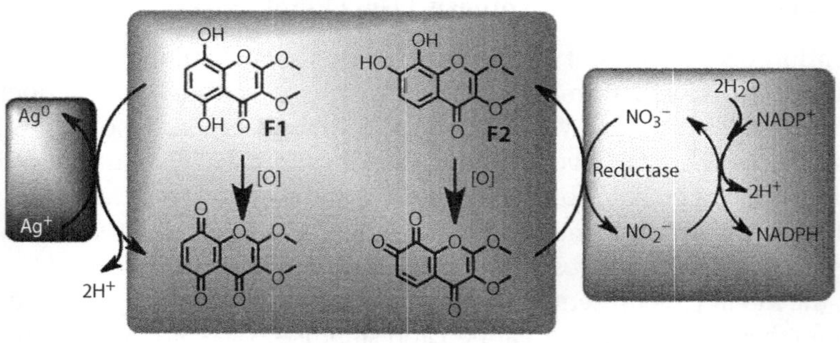

SCHEME 1.2
Prospective mechanism of silver nanoparticle biosynthesis (structures of isolated flavonoid molecules are shown) by the fruit extract of *S. cumini*. (Reprinted from *J Colloid Interface Sci*, 415, Mittal et al., Biosynthesis of silver nanoparticles: Elucidation of prospective mechanism and therapeutic potential, 39–47, Copyright 2014, with permission from Elsevier.)

1.4.2 Mechanism of AgNP Synthesis Using Fungi

In a preliminary study of *Fusarium oxysporum*–mediated synthesis of AgNPs, Ahmad et al. (2003) suggested that the NADH-dependent reductase protein had to be credited for the reduction of silver ions and the subsequent formation of AgNPs. Also, they demonstrated that this reductase perhaps is not present in all fungi because strains (i.e. *Fusarium moniliforme*) were not forming the AgNPs intra- or extracellularly. Durán et al. (2005) performed UV–vis spectroscopy, fluorescence spectroscopy and enzyme activity analysis and verified that the nitrate-dependent reductase and an extracellular shuttle quinone are responsible for reduction of the metal ions. The metal and N and S atom linked layer (1.6 nm) observed around the nanoparticles by TEM analysis indicates that the fungal proteins are also responsible for the stabilisation of synthesised nanoparticles (Durán et al. 2007). Ingle et al. (2008) used the commercial nitrate reductase discs to confirm the nitrate reductase in the fungal filtrate and further confirmed the findings of Durán et al. (2007) However, *F. moniliforme* also have nitrate reductase, but anthraquinone was absent in this fungal strain. This result showed that the reductase with an electron shuttle was essential for metal ion reduction (Durán et al. 2005). Kumar et al. (2007) extracted and purified the nitrate reductase from *F. oxysporum* and synthesised the AgNPs *in vitro* in the presence of 4-hydroxyquinoline and a cofactor (NADPH). They demonstrated that the absence of any one component (enzyme or 4-hydroxyquinolone or NADPH) from the reaction media affects the nanoparticle synthesis. These results show that all of these molecules participated in the mechanistic pathway of AgNP synthesis.

The FTIR spectra of AgNPs using *Coriolus versicolor* showed a changed band at 1735 cm^{-1}, owing to the oxidation of hydroxyl groups present in the fungal mycelium in silver ion reduction (Sanghi and Verma 2009). The presence of amine I and II (electrostatic attraction between the carboxyl group of enzymes with cysteine/free amine residues) indicated that the particles were stabilised by fungal proteins (Gole et al. 2001). The disappearing of S–H stretching (2526 cm^{-1}) in the AgNPs indicated the bond formation between S and silver particles (Sanghi and Verma 2009; Tan et al. 2002). Mukherjee et al. (2008) demonstrated that the decreased intensities of the amine II, O–H, S–H, carbonyl and carboxylic C=O stretching bands in the solution indicated the decreased peptide concentration after the formation of AgNPs. The N–H bond intensity was unchanged after nanoparticle formation. Moreover, a band of ~970 cm^{-1} that was observed in the medium only after nanoparticle formation indicated the formation of the C=C band after AgNP formation. This band referred to the mode of a trans-ethylenic moiety. These authors concluded that the amino acid with an S–H bond containing protein extract participates in the reduction mechanism of silver ion. The amino acid possibly involved in silver ion reduction is cysteine. Raman spectroscopic analysis of mycosynthesised AgNPs showed broadening of Ag–N and symmetric/

asymmetric C=O of CO_2^- ion bands owing to strain produced by AgNPs. The absence of Ag–S vibrations in FTIR and Raman spectroscopy demonstrated that thiolate or disulfide linkage was not responsible for stabilising the nanoparticles (Mukherjee et al. 2008).

1.4.3 Mechanism of AgNP Synthesis Using Bacteria

Only organisms that have 'silver resistance machinery' can synthesise AgNPs under the 'threshold limit' of silver ions. The resistance mechanism differs among organisms. The biological machinery of microorganisms may act both as a reducing and as a capping agent in AgNP synthesis. The reduction of Ag^+ ions by this biological machinery such as enzymes/proteins, vitamins, amino acids and polysaccharides is environmentally benign. Nitrate reductase, which is responsible for the reduction of a nitrate- to nitrite-mediated (Durán et al. 2005) mechanism, is widely accepted for the synthesis of AgNPs (Kalimuthu et al. 2008; Kumar et al. 2007). The homogenous catalysis using a bacterial system for the production of AgNPs requires complex downstream processing. This limitation can be overcome by the *in vitro* synthesis of nanoparticles using NADPH dependent nitrate reductase. This mechanism shows that *B. licheniformis* interceded AgNPs synthesis, and its enzymatic system might be responsible for the bioreduction of Ag^+ to Ag^0 and the subsequent formation of AgNPs. Figure 1.7 shows that the nitrate reductase present in the bacteria may aid the synthesis of AgNPs (Kalimuthu et al. 2008). Experimental proof for the role of nitrate reductase in Ag nanoparticles synthesis was reported by Anil Kumar et al. (2007). An experiment was conducted with the purified nitrate reductase obtained from *F. oxysporum*, silver nitrate and NADPH placed in a test tube. AgNP synthesis proves the major role of nitrate reductase. The defense mechanism of microorganisms against silver ions is mainly considered for AgNPs synthesis, which is popularly known as the 'potential' of the organism. An understanding of the silver ion antimicrobial activity mechanism elucidates details on AgNP synthesis (Silver et al. 2006). Silver ions bind with various vital components of the cell, which leads to programmed cell death (Figure 1.7).

Possible mechanism reported for the antimicrobial activity of silver ions include binding of silver ions to the negatively charged DNA and thiol-containing proteins and induction of reactive oxygen species synthesis, which leads to the formation of highly reactive radicals that destroy cells (Matsumura et al. 2003). This shows that the silver ions induce apoptosis in bacteria. Therefore, the bacterial cell tries to protect itself from the incoming silver ions, by converting them to the inactive Ag^0 form. Further, incoming silver ions were also shuttled with electrons, and this leads to the growth of the crystals. This defense mechanism is applicable to various metals, where the difference occurs only in the respective enzyme. Therefore, it can be regarded that in most of the organisms identified to synthesise AgNPs, nitrate reductase will be a crucial component of the organism. Moreover,

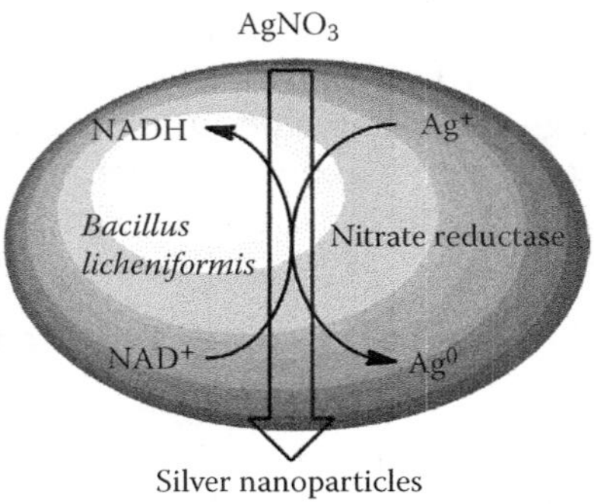

FIGURE 1.7
Nitrate reductase–mediated synthesis of AgNPs.

AgNP synthesis is faster under alkaline conditions than under acidic conditions. In other words, synthesis is enhanced as the pH increases (becoming more alkaline) and reaches the maximum at pH 10, after which the speed of the nanoparticle synthesis decreases. This shows that the synthesis of AgNPs favours an alkaline environment. Under alkaline conditions, there is no need for agitating the mixture for the formation of AgNPs, and all the silver ions supplied will be converted to AgNPs even within 30 min. The proteins involved in the synthesis may bind with silver at thiol regions (–SH) forming a –S–Ag bond, a clear indication of which is the conversion of Ag^+ to Ag^0. In addition, the alkaline ion (OH^-) is very much required for the reduction of metal ions. It takes approximately 4 days for the production of AgNPs under normal conditions, whereas it takes only less than an hour when the pH is made alkaline. Moreover, under alkaline conditions, the ability of the enzyme responsible (not only nitrate reductase) for the synthesis of AgNPs is enhanced.

1.5 Applications of Biosynthesised AgNPs

AgNPs are already used in numerous applications (Zinjarde and Varma 2011) including *in vitro* diagnostics, but their use in medicine is mostly on an experimental basis. Drugs bound to nanoparticles have been claimed to have advantages compared with conventional drugs (Wagner et al. 2006). AgNP-bound drugs have a prolonged half-life *in vivo*, have a longer circulation time and can convey a high concentration of a potent drug to where it is needed. The size of the drug nanoparticle and its surface characteristics can be modified to achieve the desired delivery characteristics (Bhaumik et al. 2015; Mohanraj and Chen 2006). As the nanoparticle-bound drug is not able to circulate broadly, its side effects are reduced and a highly localised concentration can be achieved where it is needed (Panyam and Labhasetwar 2003). In view of the large surface area per unit mass of nanoparticles, drug loading can be relatively high. Nanoparticle-bound drugs are easily suspended in liquids and are able to penetrate deep into organs and tissues.

1.5.1 Applications of Biosynthesised AgNPs Prepared from Plant Extracts

Biosynthesised AgNPs revealed a wide range of therapeutic properties including anticancer, antibacterial and antifungal (Arulkumar and Sabesan 2010; Kandasamy et al. 2012; Kim et al. 2007; Krishnaraj et al. 2010; Lara et al. 2011; MubarakAli et al. 2011; Patil et al. 2012a,b; Prasad and Elumalai 2011; Ravindra et al. 2010; Sathishkumar et al. 2009; Saxena et al. 2012; Seil and Webster 2012). The beneficial properties of biosynthesised AgNPs are summarised below.

Biosynthesised AgNPs using *M. piperita* (peppermint) developed by MubarakAli et al. (2011) demonstrated antibacterial activity against clinically isolated human pathogens such as *Escherichia coli* and *Staphylococcus aureus*. A leaf extract of *M. azedarach* was used by Sukirtha et al. (2012) to prepare AgNPs, which turned out to be active against the HeLa cervical cancer cell line, filariasis and malaria vectors (Rajakumar and Abdul Rahuman 2011). AgNPs generated from *M. paradisiaca* (peels of banana extract) displayed antifungal activity against the yeasts *Candida albicans* and *Candida lipolytica* and antibacterial activity against *E. coli, Shigella* sp., *Klebsiella* sp. and *Enterobacter aerogenes* (Bankar et al. 2010). Antibacterial activity was also present in the AgNPs formed using the peel extract of *C. sinensis* (Kaviya et al. 2011). AgNPs prepared by us using *S. cumini* destroyed Dalton lymphoma cell lines under *in vitro* conditions (Mittal et al. 2014). AgNPs (100 μg/mL) decreased the viability of Dalton lymphoma cell lines up to 50% (Figure 1.8).

AgNPs have been found to be active against plasmodial pathogens (Ponarulselvam et al. 2012) and cancer cells (Fortina et al. 2007; Ravindra et al. 2010; Sukirtha et al. 2012). The antifungal effects of AgNPs have been demonstrated (Vivek et al. 2011). Extensive literature exists on the mechanisms of antimicrobial action of AgNPs (Chaloupka et al. 2010; Li et al. 2010). Silver ion is highly toxic to most microorganisms (Jung et al. 2008) and at least one mode of antimicrobial action of nanoparticles is through a slow release of silver ions via oxidation within or outside the cell. AgNPs are known to affect the permeability of membranes of microbial and other cells (Li et al. 2010).

Silver nanoconstructs synthesised using plant extracts are promising candidates as delivery vehicles for therapeutic and diagnostic agents (Bhaumik et al. 2016). Upon conjugation of both drugs and imaging agents on a nanomaterial surface, theranostic nanoagents can be constructed for possible biomedical applications (Bhaumik et al. 2015). Bioinspired AgNPs are known to possess polyphenols and flavonoids as capping agents of their surface, which have multiple hydroxy functional groups. Choudhary et

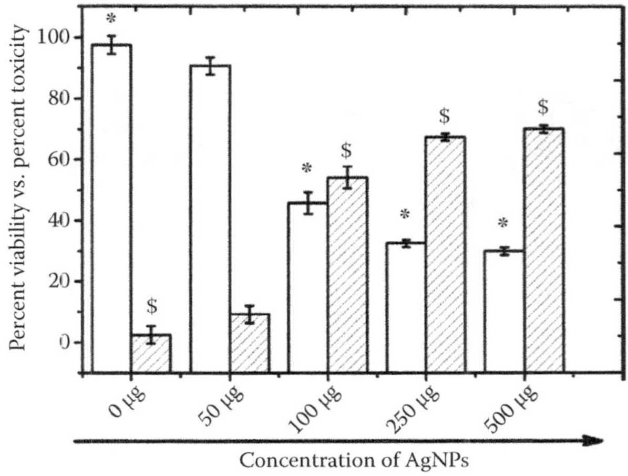

FIGURE 1.8
Effect of AgNPs on the viability of Dalton lymphoma (DL) cells in an *in vitro* experimental setting at increasing concentration of AgNPs [* and $ indicate $p = 0.05–0.001$ (control vs. experimental)]. (Reprinted from *J Colloid Interface Sci*, 415, Mittal et al., Biosynthesis of silver nanoparticles: Elucidation of prospective mechanism and therapeutic potential, 39–47, Copyright 2014, with permission from Elsevier.)

al. (2013) demonstrated that *Potentilla fulgens* is mainly composed of polar flavanols, including oligomeric flavan-3-ols as sources of –OH functional group. *C. sinensis* is also known to contain catechin and epicatechin moieties as sources for hydroxyl functionality (Bhaumik et al. 2015). A conjugatable moiety (either an imaging or a therapeutic agent) possessing carboxylic acid functionality can be attached to the nanoparticle surface via the formation of an ester bond (Figure 1.9). Carboxyl-containing therapeutic and imaging molecules (rose bengal, a commercial photosensitiser) and rhodamine B (an imaging agent) therefore reacted with the nanomaterials in the presence of a coupling agent (EDC) (Figure 1.9). The conjugated nanoparticles were further characterised by absorption spectroscopy (Figure 1.10), HPLC and FTIR analysis to confirm the conjugation.

1.5.2 Applications of AgNPs Synthesised Using Fungi

1.5.2.1 Applications in Medicine and Health Care

The antimicrobial activity of silver compounds is well known. The antibiotic resistance of pathogenic microorganisms has reintroduced interest in the biological effects of AgNPs (Mandal et al. 2006). Because of the antimicrobial activity of AgNPs against antibiotic-resistant strains and common pathogens, they have been successfully impregnated in textile fabrics and wound dressings (Rai et al. 2009, 2012). The concentration of AgNPs to prevent

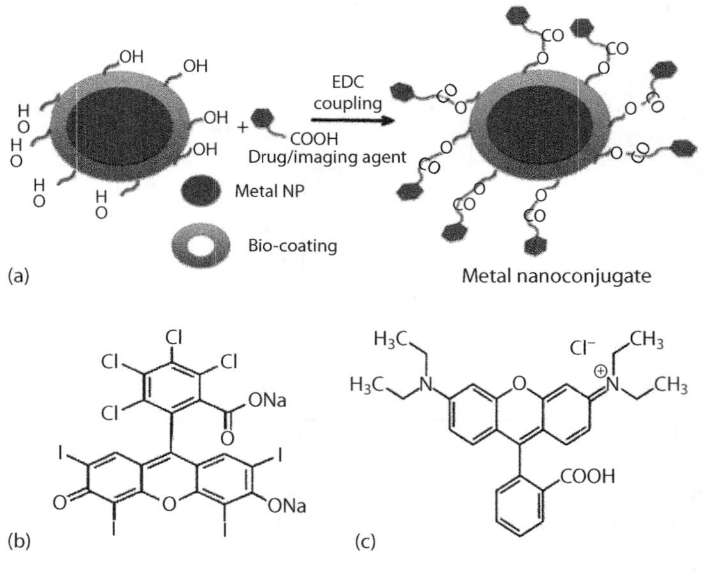

FIGURE 1.9
(a) Diagrammatic representation of drug/imaging agent conjugation on the nanoparticle surface. Chemical structures of a photosensitiser and an imaging agent used in the biofunctionalisation of nanoparticles: (b) rose bengal and (c) rhodamine B. (Reprinted with permission from Bhaumik, Thakur et al. *ACS Biomat Sci Eng*, 1:382–392. Copyright 2015 American Chemical Society.)

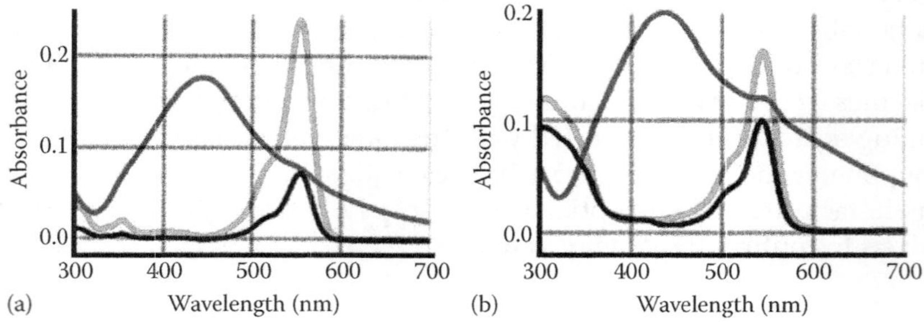

FIGURE 1.10
(a) Conjugation of rhodamine B with AgNPs. (b) Conjugation of rose bengal with AgNPs. Gray line: UV–vis spectra of rhodamine B or rose bengal before conjugation (control sample). Dark Gray line: UV–vis spectra after bioconjugation. Black line: UV–vis spectra of supernatant after NaOH treatment. (Reprinted with permission from Bhaumik, Thakur et al. *ACS Biomat Sci Eng*, 1:382–392. Copyright 2015 American Chemical Society.)

bacterial growth was different for each class/type of bacteria (i.e. higher for *Pseudomonas aeruginosa* and *Vibrio cholerae* than for *E. coli* and *Salmonella typhus*) (Ingle et al. 2008; Morones et al. 2005). It was also demonstrated that no significant growth of bacteria was observed in the environment of AgNPs (Rai et al. 2009).

It is well known that metal nanoparticles are good candidates to deliver drugs and diagnostics in the body. Antitumour and antifungal drugs using this simple delivery system are already presented in the market. Technically advanced stable, target-specific and controlled delivery of antitubercular drugs (hydrophilic and hydrophobic) has been reported (Gelperina et al. 2005). Pandey and Khuller (2007) determined that nanoparticles can be used as oral drug delivery systems for those drugs that are currently available as injectables.

The nanoparticle interaction with the microorganisms and biomolecules is a topic for advanced research. Elechiguerra et al. (2005) demonstrated the size-dependent interaction of AgNPs with HIV-1. They reported the AgNPs (1–10 nm) attached with HIV-1 and formed a regular spatial arrangement. The centre-to-centre distance between exposed sulfur-bearing residues of the glycoprotein knobs and the nanoparticles suggested that the AgNPs prevented the HIV-1 virus from binding to host cells through preferential binding.

1.5.2.2 Applications in Agriculture

Agriculture has a significant part in the economic development of most developing countries. Rickman et al. (2003) demonstrated the use of metal nanoparticles in precision farming to increase crop yield with minimal use of pesticides, herbicides and fertilisers. Nanopesticide and nanoherbicide formulations (100–250 nm) with higher water solubility were developed by several industries (Rickman et al. 2003).

1.5.2.3 Applications in Textile Industry

The large surface area to volume ratio and high surface energy of nanoparticles delivers high durability for treated fabrics. AgNPs have been used to produce 'self-cleaning' or 'anti-odour' clothes; furniture textiles or automotive interiors; household products such as kitchen cloth, sponges and towels; antibacterial wound dressings; patient dresses; bed linens; reusable surgical gloves and masks (Lee et al. 2007); protective face masks; biohazard suits; cosmetic products; toothbrushes; ultrahydrophobic fabrics with potential applications in the production of highly water-repellent materials; upholstery and sportswear (Ramaratnam et al. 2008). AgNPs have been used in the production of sterile materials. The incorporation of 2% of AgNPs (by *F. oxysporum*) in cotton fabrics has a high antibacterial effect against *S. aureus*, that is, a 99.9% bacterial reduction (Durán et al. 2007).

1.6 Concluding Remarks

The use of biomaterials (e.g. plant ectracts, fungi, bacteria) for the synthesis of AgNPs is economical, easily scalable and innocuous in nature. The biomaterial based synthesis can provide nanoparticles of a controlled size and morphology. It makes AgNPs free of toxic contaminants which is essential for their therapeutic applications. The physicochemical and optoelectronic properties of biosynthesized AgNPs have multiple application in various fields like electronics, aggriculture, textile and as medicinal agents (antimicrobial, anticancer etc.).

Acknowledgements

N.S.T. is grateful for the support of the INSPIRE fellowship Scheme, Department of Science and Technology, Government of India. B.P.D. was supported by a NIPER graduate research fellowship. J.B. was supported by the Department of Science and Technology [DST (WOS-A)], Government of India.

Conflict of Interest

The authors declare that they have no financial interest associated with this book chapter.

References

Ahamed, M., Khan, M.A.M., Siddiqui, M.K.J., AlSalhi, M.S. & Alrokayan, S.A., 2011. Green synthesis, characterization and evaluation of biocompatibility of silver nanoparticles. *Physica E: Low Dimensional Systems and Nanostructures*, 43:1266–1271.

Ahmad, A. et al., 2003. Extracellular biosynthesis of silver nanoparticles using the fungus *Fusarium oxysporum*. *Colloids and Surfaces B: Biointerfaces*, 28:313–318.

Ahmad, N. et al., 2011. Biosynthesis of silver nanoparticles from *Desmodium triflorum*: A novel approach towards weed utilization. *Biotechnology Research International*, 2011:1–8.

Alani, F., Moo-Young, M. & Anderson, W., 2012. Biosynthesis of silver nanoparticles by a new strain of *Streptomyces* sp. compared with *Aspergillus fumigatus*. *World Journal of Microbiology and Biotechnology*, 28:1081–1086.

Amerasan, D. et al., 2016. Myco-synthesis of silver nanoparticles using *Metarhizium anisopliae* against the rural malaria vector *Anopheles culicifacies* Giles (Diptera: Culicidae). *Journal of Pest Science*, 89(1):249–256.

Anil Kumar, S. et al., 2007. Nitrate reductase-mediated synthesis of silver nanoparticles from $AgNO_3$. *Biotechnology Letters*, 29:439–445.

Ankamwar, B. et al., 2005. Biosynthesis of gold and silver nanoparticles using *Emblica officinalis* fruit extract, their phase transfer and transmetallation in an organic solution. *Journal of Nanoscience and Nanotechnology*, 5:1665–1671.

Ankanna, S. et al., 2010. Production of biogenic silver nanoparticles using *Boswellia ovalifoliolata* stem bark. *Digest Journal of Nanomaterials and Biostructures*, 5:369–372.

Arulkumar, S. & Sabesan, M., 2010. Biosynthesis and characterization of gold nanoparticle using antiparkinsonian drug *Mucuna pruriens* plant extract. *International Journal of Research in Pharmaceutical Sciences*, 1:417–420.

Babu, S.A. & Prabu, H.G., 2011. Synthesis of AgNPs using the extract of *Calotropis procera* flower at room temperature. *Materials Letters*, 65:1675–1677.

Baker, S. et al., 2015. Extracellular synthesis of silver nanoparticles by novel *Pseudomonas veronii* AS 41G inhabiting *Annona squamosa* L. and their bactericidal activity. *Spectrochimica Acta Part A: Molecular and Biomolecular Spectroscopy*, 136:1434–1440.

Balaji, D.S. et al., 2009. Extracellular biosynthesis of functionalized silver nanoparticles by strains of *Cladosporium cladosporioides* fungus. *Colloids and Surfaces B: Biointerfaces*, 68:88–92.

Banerjee, J. & Narendhirakanan, R.T., 2011. Biosynthesis of silver nanoparticles from *Syzygium cumini* (L.) seed extract and evaluation of their in vitro antioxidant activities. *Digest Journal of Nanomaterials and Biostructures*, 6:961–968.

Bankar, A. et al., 2010. Banana peel extract mediated novel route for the synthesis of silver nanoparticles. *Colloids and Surfaces A: Physicochemical and Engineering Aspects*, 368:58–63.

Basavaraja, S. et al., 2008. Extracellular biosynthesis of silver nanoparticles using the fungus *Fusarium semitectum*. *Materials Research Bulletin*, 43:1164–1170.

Bawaskar, M. et al., 2010. A new report on mycosynthesis of silver nanoparticles by *Fusarium culmorum*. *Current Nanoscience*, 6:376–380.

Beveridge, J., 1976. Uptake and retention of metals by cell walls of *Bacillus subtilis*. *Journal of Bacteriology*, 127:1502–1518.

Beveridge, T.J. & Fyfe, W.S., 1985. Metal fixation by bacterial cell walls. *Canadian Journal of Earth Sciences*, 22:1893–1898.

Bhainsa, K.C. & D'Souza, S.F., 2006. Extracellular biosynthesis of silver nanoparticles using the fungus *Aspergillus fumigatus*. *Colloids and Surfaces B: Biointerfaces*, 47:160–164.

Bhaumik, J. et al., 2014. Applications of phototheranostic nanoagents in photodynamic therapy. *Nano Research*, 8:1373–1394.

Bhaumik, J., Gogia, G. et al., 2016. Bioinspired nanophotosensitizers: Synthesis and characterization of porphyrin–noble metal nanoparticle conjugates. *New Journal of Chemistry*, 40:724–731.

Bhaumik, J., Thakur, N.S. et al., 2015. Bioinspired nanotheranostic agents: Synthesis, surface functionalization, and antioxidant potential. *ACS Biomaterials Science & Engineering*, 1:382–392.

Birla, S.S. et al., 2013. Rapid synthesis of silver nanoparticles from *Fusarium oxysporum* by optimizing physicocultural conditions. *The Scientific World Journal*, 2013:796018.

Castro-Longoria, E., Vilchis-Nestor, A.R. & Avalos-Borja, M., 2011. Biosynthesis of silver, gold and bimetallic nanoparticles using the filamentous fungus *Neurospora crassa*. *Colloids and Surfaces B: Biointerfaces*, 83:42–48.

Chaloupka, K., Malam, Y. & Seifalian, A.M., 2010. Nanosilver as a new generation of nanoproduct in biomedical applications. *Trends in Biotechnology*, 28:580–588.

Chen, J.C., Lin, Z.H. & Ma, X.X., 2003. Evidence of the production of silver nanoparticles via pretreatment of *Phoma* sp. 3.2883 with silver nitrate. *Letters in Applied Microbiology*, 37:105–108.

Choudhary, A. et al., 2013. Two new stereoisomeric antioxidant triterpenes from *Potentilla fulgens*. *Fitoterapia*, 91:290–297.

Dar, M.A., Ingle, A. & Rai, M., 2013. Enhanced antimicrobial activity of silver nanoparticles synthesized by *Cryphonectria* sp. evaluated singly and in combination with antibiotics. *Nanomedicine: Nanotechnology, Biology, and Medicine*, 9:105–110.

Davidovića, S. et al., 2015. Impregnation of cotton fabric with silver nanoparticles synthesized by dextran isolated from bacterial species *Leuconostoc mesenteroides* T3. *Carbohydrate Polymers*, 131:331–336.

Devi, L.S., Bareh, D.A. & Joshi, S.R., 2014. Studies on biosynthesis of antimicrobial silver nanoparticles using endophytic fungi isolated from the ethno-medicinal plant *Gloriosa superba* L. *Proceedings of the National Academy of Sciences India Section B – Biological Sciences*, 84:1091–1099.

Dubey, M., Bhadauria, S. & Kushwah, B.S., 2009. Green synthesis of nanosilver particles from extract of *Eucalyptus hybrida* (Safeda) leaf. *Digest Journal of Nanomaterials and Biostructures*, 4:537–543.

Dubey, S., Lahtinen, M. & Sillanpää, M., 2010a. Green synthesis and characterizations of silver and gold nanoparticles using leaf extract of *Rosa rugosa*. *Colloids and Surfaces A: Physicochemical and Engineering Aspects*, 364:34–41.

Dubey, S., Lahtinen, M. & Sillanpää, M., 2010b. Tansy fruit mediated greener synthesis of silver and gold nanoparticles. *Process Biochemistry*, 45:1065–1071.

Durán, N. et al., 2005. Mechanistic aspects of biosynthesis of silver nanoparticles by several *Fusarium oxysporum* strains. *Journal of Nanobiotechnology*, 3:8.

Durán, N. et al., 2007. Antibacterial effect of silver nanoparticles produced by fungal process on textile fabrics and their effluent treatment. *Journal of Biomedical Nanotechnology*, 3:203–208.

Durán, N. et al., 2011. Mechanistic aspects in the biogenic synthesis of extracellular metal nanoparticles by peptides, bacteria, fungi, and plants. *Applied Microbiology and Biotechnology*, 90:1609–1624.

Dwivedi, A.D. & Gopal, K., 2010. Biosynthesis of silver and gold nanoparticles using *Chenopodium album* leaf extract. *Colloids and Surfaces A: Physicochemical and Engineering Aspects*, 369:27–33.

Elavazhagan, T. & Arunachalam, K.D., 2011. Memecylon edule leaf extract mediated green synthesis of silver and gold nanoparticles. *International Journal of Nanomedicine*, 6:1265–1278.

Elechiguerra, J.L. et al., 2005. Interaction of silver nanoparticles with HIV-1. *Journal of Nanobiotechnology*, 3:6.

El-Rafie, M.H. et al., 2010. Antimicrobial effect of silver nanoparticles produced by fungal process on cotton fabrics. *Carbohydrate Polymers*, 80:779–782.

Fayaz, A.M. et al., 2010a. Biogenic synthesis of silver nanoparticles and their synergistic effect with antibiotics: A study against gram-positive and gram-negative bacteria. *Nanomedicine: Nanotechnology, Biology, and Medicine*, 6:103–109.

Fayaz, M. et al., 2010b. Blue orange light emission from biogenic synthesized silver nanoparticles using *Trichoderma viride*. *Colloids and Surfaces B: Biointerfaces*, 75:175–178.

Fortina, P. et al., 2007. Applications of nanoparticles to diagnostics and therapeutics in colorectal cancer. *Trends in Biotechnology*, 25:145–152.

Gade, A. et al., 2010. Mycogenic metal nanoparticles: Progress and applications. *Biotechnology Letters*, 32:593–600.

Gade, A. et al., 2015. Synthesis of silver nanoparticles by *Phoma gardeniae* and in vitro evaluation of their efficacy against human disease-causing bacteria and fungi. *IET Nanobiotechnology*, 9:71–75.

Gajbhiye, M. et al., 2009. Fungus-mediated synthesis of silver nanoparticles and their activity against pathogenic fungi in combination with fluconazole. *Nanomedicine: Nanotechnology, Biology and Medicine*, 5:382–386.

Ganachari, S. V. et al., 2012. Extracellular biosynthesis of silver nanoparticles using fungi *Penicillium diversum* and their antimicrobial activity studies. *BioNanoScience*, 2:316–321.

Gelperina, S. et al., 2005. The potential advantages of nanoparticle drug delivery systems in chemotherapy of tuberculosis. *American Journal of Respiratory and Critical Care Medicine*, 172:1487–1490.

Gole, A. et al., 2001. Pepsin–gold colloid conjugates: Preparation, characterization, and enzymatic activity. *Langmuir*, 17:1674–1679.

Goldstein, J.I., Newbury, D.E., Echlin, P., Joy, D.C., Romig, A.D., Lyman, C.E., Fiori, C. & Lifshin, E., 1992. Scanning electron microscopy and X-ray microanalysis: A text for biologists, materials scientists, and geologists. 2nd edition, New York: Plenum Press.

Gurunathan, S. et al., 2009. Biomaterials antiangiogenic properties of silver nanoparticles. *Biomaterials*, 30:6341–6350.

Gurunathan, S. et al., 2013. Green synthesis of silver nanoparticles using *Ganoderma neo-japonicum* Imazeki: A potential cytotoxic agent against breast cancer cells. *International Journal of Nanomedicine*, 8:4399–4413.

Haefeli, C. et al., 1984. Plasmid-determined silver resistance in *Pseudomonas stutzeri* isolated from a silver mine. *Journal of Bacteriology*, 158:389–392.

Hemath Naveen, K.S. et al., 2010. Extracellular biosynthesis of silver nanoparticles using the filamentous fungus *Penicillium* sp. *Archives of Applied Science Research*, 2:161–167.

Honary, S. et al., 2013. Green synthesis of silver nanoparticles induced by the fungus *Penicillium citrinum*. *Tropical Journal of Pharmaceutical Research*, 12:7–11.

Huang, J. et al., 2007. Biosynthesis of silver and gold nanoparticles by novel sundried *Cinnamomum camphora* leaf. *Nanotechnology*, 18:105104.

Husseiny, M.I. et al., 2007. Biosynthesis of gold nanoparticles using *Pseudomonas aeruginosa*. *Spectrochimica Acta – Part A: Molecular and Biomolecular Spectroscopy*, 67:1003–1006.

Ingle, A. et al., 2008. Mycosynthesis of silver nanoparticles using the fungus *Fusarium acuminatum* and its activity against some human pathogenic bacteria. *Current Nanoscience*, 4:141–144.

Ingle, A. et al., 2009. *Fusarium solani*: A novel biological agent for the extracellular synthesis of silver nanoparticles. *Journal of Nanoparticle Research*, 11:2079–2085.

Jaidev, L.R. & Narasimha, G., 2010. Fungal mediated biosynthesis of silver nanoparticles, characterization and antimicrobial activity. *Colloids and Surfaces B: Biointerfaces*, 81:430–433.

Jain, D. et al., 2009. Synthesis of plant-mediated silver nanoparticles using papaya fruit extract and evaluation of their antimicrobial activities. *Digest Journal of Nanomaterials and Biostructures*, 4:557–563.

Jain, N. et al., 2011. Extracellular biosynthesis and characterization of silver nanoparticles using *Aspergillus flavus* NJP08: A mechanism perspective. *Nanoscale*, 3:635–641.

Jebali, A., Ramezani, F. & Kazemi, B., 2011. Biosynthesis of silver nanoparticles by *Geotricum* sp. *Journal of Cluster Science*, 22:225–232.

Jung, W.K. et al., 2008. Antibacterial activity and mechanism of action of the silver ion in *Staphylococcus aureus* and *Escherichia coli*. *Applied and Environmental Microbiology*, 74:2171–2178.

Kaler, A., Jain, S. & Banerjee, U.C., 2013. Green and rapid synthesis of anticancerous silver nanoparticles by *Saccharomyces boulardii* and insight into mechanism of nanoparticle synthesis. *BioMed Research International*, 2013:8, Article ID 872940.

Kalishwaralal, K. et al., 2010. Biosynthesis of silver and gold nanoparticles using *Brevibacterium casei*. *Colloids and Surfaces B: Biointerfaces*, 77:257–262.

Kalishwaralal, K. et al., 2008. Extracellular biosynthesis of silver nanoparticles by the culture supernatant of *Bacillus licheniformis*. *Materials Letters*, 62:4411–4413.

Kalimuthu, K., Suresh Babu, R., Venkataraman, D., Bilal, M. & Gurunathan, S., 2008. Biosynthesis of silver nanocrystals by *Bacillus licheniformis*. *Colloids and Surfaces B: Biointerfaces*, 65:150–153.

Kandasamy, K. et al., 2012. Synthesis of silver nanoparticles by coastal plant *Prosopis chilensis* (L.) and their efficacy in controlling vibriosis in shrimp *Penaeus monodon*. *Applied Nanoscience*, 3:65–73.

Kannan, N., Mukunthan, K.S. & Balaji, S., 2011. A comparative study of morphology, reactivity and stability of synthesized silver nanoparticles using *Bacillus subtilis* and *Catharanthus roseus* (L.) G. Don. *Colloids and Surfaces. B, Biointerfaces*, 86:378–383.

Kathiresan, K. et al., 2010. Analysis of antimicrobial silver nanoparticles synthesized by coastal strains of *Escherichia coli* and *Aspergillus niger*. *Canadian Journal of Microbiology*, 56:1050–1059.

Kathiresan, K. et al., 2009. Studies on silver nanoparticles synthesized by a marine fungus, *Penicillium fellutanum* isolated from coastal mangrove sediment. *Colloids and Surfaces B: Biointerfaces*, 71:133–137.

Kaviya, S. et al., 2011. Biosynthesis of silver nanoparticles using *Citrus sinensis* peel extract and its antibacterial activity. *Spectrochimica Acta – Part A: Molecular and Biomolecular Spectroscopy*, 79:594–598.

Kesharwani, J. et al., 2009. Phytofabrication of silver nanoparticles by leaf extract of *Datura metel*: Hypothetical mechanism involved in synthesis. *Journal of Bionanoscience*, 3:39–44.

Kim, J.S. et al., 2007. Antimicrobial effects of silver nanoparticles. *Nanomedicine: Nanotechnology, Biology, and Medicine*, 3:95–101.

Klaus, T., Joerger, R., Olsson, E. & Granqvist, C.G., 1999. Silver based crystalline nanoparticles, microbially fabricated. *Proceedings of the National Academy of Sciences of the United States of America*, 96:13611–13614.

Korbekandi, H. et al., 2013. Optimization of biological synthesis of silver nanoparticles using *Fusarium oxysporum*. *Iranian Journal of Pharmaceutical Research*, 12:289–298.

Kouvaris, P., Delimitis, A. & Zaspalis, V., 2012. Green synthesis and characterization of silver nanoparticles produced using *Arbutus unedo* leaf extract. *Materials Letters*, 76:18–20.

Krishnaraj, C. et al., 2010. Synthesis of silver nanoparticles using *Acalypha indica* leaf extracts and its antibacterial activity against water borne pathogens. *Colloids and Surfaces B: Biointerfaces*, 76:50–56.

Kumar, S., Abyaneh, M. & Gosavi, S., 2007. Nitrate reductase-mediated synthesis of silver nanoparticles from $AgNO_3$. *Biotechnology Letters*, 29:439–445.

Kumar, V., Yadav, S.C. & Yadav, S.K., 2010. *Syzygium cumini* leaf and seed extract mediated biosynthesis of silver nanoparticles and their characterization. *Journal of Chemical Technology & Biotechnology*, 85:1301–1309.

Lara, H.H. et al., 2011. Silver nanoparticles are broad-spectrum bactericidal and virucidal compounds. *Journal of Nanobiotechnology*, 9:30.

Lee, H.Y. et al., 2007. A practical procedure for producing silver nanocoated fabric and its antibacterial evaluation for biomedical applications. *Chemical Communications*, 28:2959–2961.

Li, G. et al., 2012. Fungus-mediated green synthesis of silver nanoparticles using *Aspergillus terreus*. *International Journal of Molecular Sciences*, 13:466–476.

Li, W.R. et al., 2010. Antibacterial activity and mechanism of silver nanoparticles on *Escherichia coli*. *Applied Microbiology and Biotechnology*, 85:1115–1122.

Malhotra, A. et al., 2013. Biosynthesis of gold and silver nanoparticles using a novel marine strain of *Stenotrophomonas*. *Bioresource Technology*, 142:727–731.

Mandal, D. et al., 2006. The use of microorganisms for the formation of metal nanoparticles and their application. *Applied Microbiology and Biotechnology*, 69:485–492.

Manikprabhu, D. & Lingappa, K., 2014. Synthesis of silver nanoparticles using the *Streptomyces coelicolor* klmp33 pigment: An antimicrobial agent against extended-spectrum beta-lactamase (ESBL) producing *Escherichia coli*. *Materials Science and Engineering C*, 45:434–437.

Matsumura, Y. et al., 2003. Mode of bactericidal action of silver zeolite and its comparison with that of silver nitrate mode of bactericidal action of silver zeolite and its comparison with that of silver nitrate. *Applied and Environmental Microbiology*, 69:4278–4281.

Mittal, A.K. et al., 2014. Biosynthesis of silver nanoparticles: Elucidation of prospective mechanism and therapeutic potential. *Journal of Colloid and Interface Science*, 415:39–47.

Mittal, A.K., Chisti, Y. & Banerjee, U.C., 2013. Synthesis of metallic nanoparticles using plant extracts. *Biotechnology Advances*, 31:346–356.

Mittal, A.K., Kaler, A. & Banerjee, U.C., 2012. Free radical scavenging and antioxidant activity of silver nanoparticles synthesized from flower extract of *Rhododendron dauricum*. *Nano Biomedicine & Engineering*, 4:118–124.

Mohanraj, V.J. & Chen, Y., 2006. Nanoparticles – A review. *Tropical Journal of Pharmaceutical Research*, 5:561–573.

Mondal, S. et al., 2011. Biogenic synthesis of Ag, Au and bimetallic Au/Ag alloy nanoparticles using aqueous extract of mahogany (*Swietenia mahogani* JACQ.) leaves. *Colloids and Surfaces B: Biointerfaces*, 82:497–504.

Morones, J.R. et al., 2005. The bactericidal effect of silver nanoparticles. *Nanotechnology*, 16:2346–2353.

MubarakAli, D. et al., 2011. Plant extract mediated synthesis of silver and gold nanoparticles and its antibacterial activity against clinically isolated pathogens. *Colloids and Surfaces B: Biointerfaces*, 85:360–365.

Mukherjee, P. et al., 2001. Fungus-mediated synthesis of silver nanoparticles and their immobilization in the mycelial matrix: A novel biological approach to nanoparticle synthesis. *Nano Letters*, 1:515–519.

Mukherjee, P. et al., 2008. Green synthesis of highly stabilized nanocrystalline silver particles by a non-pathogenic and agriculturally important fungus *T. asperellum*. *Nanotechnology*, 19:075103.

Musarrat, J. et al., 2010. Production of antimicrobial silver nanoparticles in water extracts of the fungus *Amylomyces rouxii* strain KSU-09. *Bioresource Technology*, 101:8772–8776.

Nabikhan, A. et al., 2010. Synthesis of antimicrobial silver nanoparticles by callus and leaf extracts from saltmarsh plant, *Sesuvium portulacastrum* L. *Colloids and Surfaces B: Biointerfaces*, 79:488–493.

Nair, B. & Pradeep, T., 2002. Coalescence of nanoclusters and formation of submicron crystallites assisted by *Lactobacillus* strains. *Crystal Growth & Design*, 2(4):293–298.

Nanda, A. & Saravanan, M., 2009. Biosynthesis of silver nanoparticles from *Staphylococcus aureus* and its antimicrobial activity against MRSA and MRSE. *Nanomedicine: Nanotechnology, Biology and Medicine*, 5:452–456.

Narayanan, K.B. & Sakthivel, N., 2010. Biological synthesis of metal nanoparticles by microbes. *Advances in Colloid and Interface Science*, 156:1–13.

Pandey, R. & Khuller, G.K., 2007. Nanoparticle-based oral drug delivery system for an injectable antibiotic – Streptomycin. Evaluation in a murine tuberculosis model. *Chemotherapy*, 53:437–441.

Pandian, S.R.K. et al. 2010. Mechanism of bactericidal activity of Silver Nitrate – A concentration dependent bi-functional molecule. *Brazilian Journal of Microbiology*, 41(3):805-809.

Panyam, J. & Labhasetwar, V., 2003. Biodegradable nanoparticles for drug and gene delivery to cells and tissue. *Advanced Drug Delivery Reviews*, 55:329–347.

Parashar, U., 2009. Bioinspired synthesis of silver nanoparticles. *Digest Journal of Nanomaterials & Biostructures*, 4:159–166.

Patil, R.S., Kokate, M.R. & Kolekar, S.S., 2012a. Bioinspired synthesis of highly stabilized silver nanoparticles using *Ocimum tenuiflorum* leaf extract and their antibacterial activity. *Spectrochimica Acta. Part A, Molecular and Biomolecular Spectroscopy*, 91:234–238.

Patil, S.V. et al., 2012b. Biosynthesis of silver nanoparticles using latex from few Euphorbian plants and their antimicrobial potential. *Applied Biochemistry and Biotechnology*, 167:776–790.

Pighi, L., Pmpel, T. & Schinner, F., 1989. Selective accumulation of silver by fungi. *Biotechnology Letters*, 11:275–280.

Ponarulselvam, S. et al., 2012. Synthesis of silver nanoparticles using leaves of *Catharanthus roseus* Linn. G. Don and their antiplasmodial activities. *Asian Pacific Journal of Tropical Biomedicine*, 2:574–580.

Poulose, S. et al., 2014. Biosynthesis of silver nanoparticles. *Journal of Nanoscience and Nanotechnology*, 14:2038–2049.

Pourali, P. & Yahyaei, B., 2016. Biological production of silver nanoparticles by soil isolated bacteria and preliminary study of their cytotoxicity and cutaneous wound healing efficiency in rat. *Journal of Trace Elements in Medicine and Biology*, 34:22–31.

Pradhan, N. et al., 2011. In situ synthesis of entrapped silver nanoparticles by a fungus – *Penicillium purpurogenum*. *Nanoscience and Nanotechnology Letters*, 3:659–665.

Prasad, T.N.V.K. V & Elumalai, E.K., 2011. Biofabrication of Ag nanoparticles using *Moringa oleifera* leaf extract and their antimicrobial activity. *Asian Pacific Journal of Tropical Biomedicine*, 1:439–442.

Qian, Y. et al., 2013. Biosynthesis of silver nanoparticles by the endophytic fungus *Epicoccum nigrum* and their activity against pathogenic fungi. *Bioprocess and Biosystems Engineering*, 36:1613–1619.

Raheman, F. et al., 2011. Silver nanoparticles: Novel antimicrobial agent synthesized from an endophytic fungus *Pestalotia* sp. isolated from leaves of *Syzygium cumini* (L). *Nano*, 3:174–178.

Rai, M., Yadav, A. & Gade, A., 2009. Silver nanoparticles as a new generation of antimicrobials. *Biotechnology Advances*, 27:76–83.

Rai, M.K. et al., 2012. Silver nanoparticles: The powerful nanoweapon against multidrug-resistant bacteria. *Journal of Applied Microbiology*, 112:841–852.

Rajakumar, G. & Abdul Rahuman, A., 2011. Larvicidal activity of synthesized silver nanoparticles using *Eclipta prostrata* leaf extract against filariasis and malaria vectors. *Acta Tropica*, 118:196–203.

Raliya, R. & Tarafdar, J.C., 2012. Novel approach for silver nanoparticle synthesis using *Aspergillus terreus* CZR-1: Mechanism perspective. *Journal of Bionanoscience*, 6:12–16.

Ramanathan, R. et al., 2011. Bacterial kinetics-controlled shape-directed biosynthesis of silver nanoplates using morganella psychrotolerans. *Langmuir*, 27:714–719.

Ramaratnam, K. et al., 2008. Ultrahydrophobic textiles: Lotus approach. *AATCC Review*, 8:42–48.

Ravindra, S. et al., 2010. Fabrication of antibacterial cotton fibres loaded with silver nanoparticles via 'Green Approach.' *Colloids and Surfaces A: Physicochemical and Engineering Aspects*, 367:31–40.

Ravindran, A., Chandran, P. & Khan, S.S., 2013. Biofunctionalized silver nanoparticles: Advances and prospects. *Colloids and Surfaces B: Biointerfaces*, 105:342–352.

Rickman, D. et al., 2003. Changing the face of farming. Geotimes. Available at: http://www.geotimes.org/nov03/feature_agric.html [Accessed February 22, 2016].

Rodrigues, A.G. et al., 2013. Biogenic antimicrobial silver nanoparticles produced by fungi. *Applied Microbiology and Biotechnology*, 97:775–782.

Roy, S., 2013. Biosynthesis, characterization & antifungal activity of silver nanoparticles synthesized by the fungus *Aspergillus foetidus* MTCC-8876. *Digest Journal of Nanomaterials and Biostructures*, 8:197–205.

Sadhasivam, S., Shanmugam, P. & Yun, K., 2010. Biosynthesis of silver nanoparticles by *Streptomyces hygroscopicus* and antimicrobial activity against medically important pathogenic microorganisms. *Colloids and Surfaces B: Biointerfaces*, 81:358–362.

Saha, S. et al., 2010. Production of silver nanoparticles by a phytopathogenic. *Digest Journal of Nanomaterials and Biostructures*, 5:887–895.

Saifuddin, N., Wong, C.W. & Yasumira, A.A., 2009. Rapid biosynthesis of silver nanoparticles using culture supernatant of bacteria with microwave irradiation. *Journal of Chemistry*, 6:61–70.

Salunkhe, R.B. et al., 2011. Larvicidal potential of silver nanoparticles synthesized using fungus *Cochliobolus lunatus* against *Aedes aegypti* (Linnaeus, 1762) and *Anopheles stephensi* Liston (Diptera; Culicidae). *Parasitology Research*, 109:823–831.

Sanghi, R. & Verma, P., 2009. Biomimetic synthesis and characterisation of protein capped silver nanoparticles. *Bioresource Technology*, 100:501–504.

Santhoshkumar, T. et al., 2011. Synthesis of silver nanoparticles using *Nelumbo nucifera* leaf extract and its larvicidal activity against malaria and filariasis vectors. *Parasitology Research*, 108:693–702.

Saravanan, M. & Nanda, A., 2010. Extracellular synthesis of silver bionanoparticles from *Aspergillus clavatus* and its antimicrobial activity against MRSA and MRSE. *Colloids and Surfaces B: Biointerfaces*, 77:214–218.

Sathishkumar, M. et al., 2009. *Cinnamon zeylanicum* bark extract and powder mediated green synthesis of nano-crystalline silver particles and its bactericidal activity. *Colloids and Surfaces. B, Biointerfaces*, 73:332–338.

Sathishkumar, M., Sneha, K. & Yun, Y.-S., 2010. Immobilization of silver nanoparticles synthesized using *Curcuma longa* tuber powder and extract on cotton cloth for bactericidal activity. *Bioresource Technology*, 101:7958–7965.

Saxena, A. et al., 2012. Green synthesis of silver nanoparticles using aqueous solution of *Ficus benghalensis* leaf extract and characterization of their antibacterial activity. *Materials Letters*, 67:91–94.

Seil, J.T. & Webster, T.J., 2012. Antimicrobial applications of nanotechnology: Methods and literature. *International Journal of Nanomedicine*, 7:2767–2781.

Shaligram, N.S. et al., 2009. Biosynthesis of silver nanoparticles using aqueous extract from the compactin producing fungal strain. *Process Biochemistry*, 44:939–943.

Silambarasan, S. & Abraham, J., 2012. Biosynthesis of silver nanoparticles using the bacteria *Bacillus cereus* and their antimicrobial property. *International Journal of Pharmacy and Pharmaceutical Sciences*, 4(SUPPL.1):536–540.

Silver, S., Phung, L.T. & Silver, G., 2006. Silver as biocides in burn and wound dressings and bacterial resistance to silver compounds. *Journal of Industrial Microbiology and Biotechnology*, 33:627–634.

Singh, D. et al., 2013. Biosynthesis of silver nanoparticle by endophytic fungi pencillium sp. Isolated from *Curcuma longa* (turmeric) and its antibacterial activity against pathogenic gram negative bacteria. *Journal of Pharmacy Research*, 7:448–453.

Soni, N. & Prakash, S., 2012. Efficacy of fungus mediated silver and gold nanoparticles against *Aedes aegypti* larvae. *Parasitology Research*, 110:175–184.

Soni, N. & Prakash, S., 2013. Possible mosquito control by silver nanoparticles synthesized by soil fungus (*Aspergillus niger* 2587). *Advances in Nanoparticles*, 02:125–132.

Subramanian, V., 2012. Green synthesis of silver nanoparticles using *Coleus amboinicus* lour, antioxitant activity and in vitro cytotoxicity against Ehrlich's Ascite carcinoma. *Journal of Pharmacy Research*, 5:126872.

Sukirtha, R. et al., 2012. Cytotoxic effect of Green synthesized silver nanoparticles using *Melia azedarach* against in vitro HeLa cell lines and lymphoma mice model. *Process Biochemistry*, 47:273–279.

Syed, A. et al., 2013. Biological synthesis of silver nanoparticles using the fungus *Humicola* sp. and evaluation of their cytoxicity using normal and cancer cell lines. *Spectrochimica Acta – Part A: Molecular and Biomolecular Spectroscopy*, 114:144–147.

Tan, Y. et al., 2002. Thiosalicylic acid-functionalized silver nanoparticles synthesized in one-phase system. *Journal of Colloid and Interface Science*, 249:336–345.

Thirumurugan, G. et al., 2011. Superior wound healing effect of topically delivered silver nanoparticle formulation using eco-friendly potato plant pathogenic fungus: Synthesis and characterization. *Journal of Biomedical Nanotechnology,* 7:659–666.

Tran, Q.H., Nguyen, V.Q. & Le, A.-T., 2013. Silver nanoparticles: Synthesis, properties, toxicology, applications and perspectives. *Advances in Natural Sciences: Nanoscience and Nanotechnology,* 4:033001.

Vahabi, K., Mansoori, G.A. & Karimi, S., 2011. Biosynthesis of silver nanoparticles by fungus *Trichoderma reesei* (a route for large-scale production of AgNPs). *Insciences Journal,* 1:65–79.

Vanaja, M. & Annadurai, G., 2012. *Coleus aromaticus* leaf extract mediated synthesis of silver nanoparticles and its bactericidal activity. *Applied Nanoscience,* 3:217–223.

Veerasamy, R. et al., 2011. Biosynthesis of silver nanoparticles using mangosteen leaf extract and evaluation of their antimicrobial activities. *Journal of Saudi Chemical Society,* 15(2):113–120.

Venil, C.K. et al., 2016. Synthesis of flexirubin-mediated silver nanoparticles using *Chryseobacterium artocarpi* CECT 8497 and investigation of its anticancer activity. *Materials Science and Engineering C,* 59:228–234.

Verma, V.C., Kharwar, R.N. & Gange, A.C., 2010. Biosynthesis of antimicrobial silver nanoparticles by the endophytic fungus *Aspergillus clavatus. Nanomedicine (London, England),* 5:33–40.

Vigneshwaran, N. et al., 2007. Biological synthesis of silver nanoparticles using the fungus *Aspergillus flavus. Materials Letters,* 61:1413–1418.

Vijayaraghavan, K. et al., 2012. One step green synthesis of silver nano/microparticles using extracts of *Trachyspermum ammi* and *Papaver somniferum. Colloids and Surfaces B: Biointerfaces,* 94:114–117.

Vilchis-Nestor, A.R. et al., 2008. Solventless synthesis and optical properties of Au and Ag nanoparticles using *Camellia sinensis* extract. *Materials Letters,* 62:3103–3105.

Vivek, M. et al., 2011. Biogenic silver nanoparticles by *Gelidiella acerosa* extract and their antifungal effects. *Avicenna Journal of Medical Biotechnology,* 3:143–148.

Wagner, V. et al., 2006. The emerging nanomedicine landscape. *Nature Biotechnology,* 24(10):1211–1217.

Zhang, H. et al., 2005. Biosorption and bioreduction of diamine silver complex by *Corynebacterium. Journal of Chemical Technology and Biotechnology,* 80:285–290.

Zinjarde, S. & Varma, R.S., 2011. Green synthesis of metal nanoparticles: Biodegradable polymers and enzymes in stabilization and surface functionalization. *Chemical Science,* 2:837–846.

2

Tuning the Properties of Silver Monolayers for Biological Applications

Magdalena Oćwieja

CONTENTS

2.1 Introduction

Thanks to numerous synthetic methods and developed preparation approaches, one can control not only the size, shape and surface properties of silver nanoparticles but also their porosity, dissolution ability and many other physicochemical properties. However, it is noteworthy that for various practical applications, in both science and industry, an effective and controlled deposition of silver nanoparticles on solid surfaces also plays a pivotal role. As is well known, the ability of efficient immobilisation of silver nanoparticles on colloidal carriers, textile fibres, surgical tools and devices is highly required in the case of biological and medical applications. Moreover, the surface concentration (coverage) of nanoparticles on modified materials as well as the homogeneity, structure and stability of obtained silver coatings contribute to the utility of antibacterial devices.

2.2 Methods of Silver Film and Monolayer Preparation

As in the case of a wide variety of methods of nanoparticle synthesis, many preparation routes have been developed in order to produce nanometric silver coatings of controlled and well-defined properties. Generally, among the methods of silver layer preparation, one can distinguish two groups of processes defined as *top-down* and *bottom-up* fabrication. The top-down process includes the methods of solid processing. This approach often uses the traditional methods where externally controlled tools are employed to cut, mill and shape materials into a desired structure (Zhang 2010). There is a range of top-down processes that can be used to produce nanostructured films. The most significant advances of these are physical methods (different lithographic techniques) and the combination of physical and chemical methods (e.g., stamp printing). On the other hand, the bottom-up approach uses the chemical properties of single molecules or small particles to arrange themselves into some functional conformations and coatings. Overall, the preparation of layers and films using this approach relies on chemical processes, performed in either liquid or gas phase (Zhang 2010). For this reason, the bottom-up processes can also be classified into two groups: *dry* and *wet processes*. The dry processes are traditionally used for numerous device applications, and have been expanded to nanostructure construction (Maenosono et al. 2003). For thin-film fabrication, the most common techniques are *chemical vapour deposition* and *physical vapour deposition* applied with various modifications (Zhang 2010). In these approaches, in order to produce silver monolayers and films, the fine crystalline powders of silver are deposited on selected substrates at high temperatures or sometimes at lower temperatures but under increased pressure. Among various positive aspects characterising these processes, one can also indicate few drawbacks connected with the high cost of specialised apparatus necessary for the production of films and the lack of opportunities to form such coatings on soft materials that are unstable under such specific conditions.

For comparison, the wet processes do not require sophisticated and expensive devices. Moreover, the bottom-up processes may be carried out in both aqueous and organic solvents. These processes allow one to produce films and coatings of controlled structure and functionalities by various approaches, including chemical precipitation, hydrothermal and solvothermal syntheses (Zhang 2010) as well as sol-gel coating processes based on the deposition of silver nanoparticles on solid surfaces from colloidal suspensions (Maenosono et al. 2003; Zhang 2010).

Chemical precipitation is a convenient, environmentally friendly and safe method that may be conducted at mild temperatures with the use of various substrates. It occurs when an insoluble product is formed on the selected substrates as a consequence of a chemical reaction. Chemical precipitation involves the mixing of the precipitating agent with metal ions (e.g. silver ions derived from the dissociation of soluble silver slats such as silver nitrate or silver acetate) in a liquid medium, hydrolysis–condensation of hydrated ions and complexes (inorganic polymerisation) and their heteronucleation onto substrates. The nucleation and growth of particles can be adjusted by the controlled release of anions and cations. In turn, the precipitation kinetics is influenced by the reactant concentration, temperature and pH of mixtures. By controlling these factors, high-quality nanostructured films with desired architecture can be produced (Zhang 2010).

It is also worth mentioning that the precisely controlled growth of silver films on selected surfaces can be achieved with the use of photodeposition, which is a simple modification of chemical precipitation. In the photodeposition, silver cations, because of attractive electrostatic interactions with negatively charged surfaces, deposit on them and afterwards they are reduced as a consequence of radiation with visible or ultraviolet light. In practice, the presence of chemical-reducing agents in the mixture is not necessary because silver ions are reduced by radicals generated from solvent molecules during irradiation (Huang et al. 1996). As was shown in various literature reports (Kéki et al. 2000; Lu et al. 2003; Piwoński et al. 2011; Sudeep and Kamat 2005), the chemical structure of solvents and additional compounds (stabilising agents) used in the liquid medium and the type of illumination source play a significant role in this method because they influence the structure and morphology of prepared silver coatings. In the literature, one can find numerous examples of the modification of cotton and polymer fibres (Hadad et al. 2007; Jiang et al. 2011), carbon nanotubes (Neelgund and Oki 2011) and silicon and titanium surfaces (Piwoński et al. 2011; Ye et al. 2007) by silver nanoparticles with the use of the chemical precipitation approach.

In the case of sol-gel processes, the sol (e.g. silver suspension) is the starting precursor that is deposited on a substrate to form a film or monolayer of desirable properties. This *wet chemical* approach is a cheap and low-temperature technique that allows fine control of the product composition and doping elements can be easily introduced (Zhang 2010). Moreover, it is worth emphasising that several efficient coating methods, based on the sol-gel approach, have been developed, among which *spin-coating* and *dip-coating* are frequently applied in practice (Hall et al. 1998; Zhang 2010).

Spin-coating is a procedure used for the preparation of uniform and thin films having a thickness in the range from a few nanometers to a few microns (Schubert and Dunkel 2003). The deposition process is carried out with the use of a rotating platform on which the flat substrate, which is modified by colloidal nanoparticles, is placed. An excess amount of a colloidal suspension is placed on the substrate, which is rotated at high speed in order to separate the fluid by centrifugal force (Zhang 2010). The structure and thickness of the prepared films and monolayers depend on the concentration of nanoparticles in the solutions as well as on the viscosity of solvents. Furthermore, the properties of prepared coatings can be modified by the speed of spinning. Generally, the higher angular speed of spinning, the thinner films can be obtained. In many literature reports, it was proven that spin-coating enables one to obtain silver nanoparticle coatings (He and Kunitake 2006; Schaefers et al. 2006). The nanostructures deposited on flat surfaces were produced using silver suspensions or combining this approach with chemical precipitation, where the preparation of the selected polymer films with silver precursors precedes the chemical reductions of delivered silver ions (He and Kunitake 2006). Despite many developed facilities and combinations in the spin-coating techniques, one can notice in the literature the lack of information related to the stability, homogeneity and other properties of silver coatings obtained hereby. Moreover, the uncontrolled aggregation of nanoparticles during the centrifugation of suspensions remains a serious disadvantage of this technique.

Dip-coating is another technique for producing film-coated materials. In this process, a selected substrate is dipped into a previously prepared suspension containing coating material in the form of nanoparticles. After a given period, the substrate is withdrawn from the colloidal solutions at controlled speed and finally the formed layer is left to dry (Kumar 2010; Zhang 2010). As was demonstrated in the literature reports, the thickness of the coatings obtained in this way increases with faster withdrawal speed. Additionally, the structure of such films strongly depends on fluid viscosity and density as well as on surface properties of nanoparticles and substrates (Zhang 2010). Although this approach is widely used for deposition of polymers or polyelectrolytes on solid surfaces, it has also been applied in the preparation of silver nanoparticle coatings (Malynych et al. 2002).

Discussing the preparation methods of silver coatings and films that are conducted with the use of wet processes, one should indicate other approaches in which colloidal suspensions are applied (Maenosono et al. 2003). It is also worth mentioning that, in some cases, the differences between the methods described by different names are subtle and difficult to explain unambiguously. For example, the differences between the driving forces in the dip-coating technique and *self-assembly processes* are particularly small and difficult to notice at first glance. Nevertheless, analyzing the literature data, one can observe countless articles and scientific reports devoted to the descriptions of film and monolayer preparation in self-assembly processes with the use of colloidal suspensions.

2.3 Self-Assembly Processes of Silver Nanoparticles

Self-assembly of nanoparticles is identified as an important process where the building blocks spontaneously organise into ordered structures. Therefore, the adsorption and deposition of molecules and colloidal particles at various interfaces without the additional external forces (e.g. centrifugal force) are referred to as *self-assembly processes*. In turn, the layers obtained in these processes are called *self-assembled layers*. The adsorption of molecules and particles usually occurs as a result of van der Waals and electrostatic interactions, although in some cases, chemisorptions can take place as well (Kumar 2010). In self-assembly processes, as in the case of the dip-coating technique, the substrate is dipped in the proper solutions containing molecules or particles, which are used for surface modification. However, in contrast to dip-coating, the monolayers are not formed during the withdrawal of the substrate from the solutions but directly during the storage of the substrates in these solutions.

Many researchers emphasise that self-assembly processes are one of the most reliable and efficient methods of producing silver nanoparticle monolayers and films of controlled properties (Michna et al. 2010). The following are among the advantages of these processes one can indicate:

(i) Precise control of the coating density by variation in the bulk concentration of the silver suspension, deposition time, temperature and transport conditions
(ii) Possibility of producing homogeneous monolayers over macroscopic areas with particle distribution and structure controlled by the ionic strength and pH of colloid suspension
(iii) Possibility of producing monolayers and multilayers of controlled architecture by applying the layer-by-layer (LBL) technique.

In the literature, one can find numerous reports describing preparation of self-assembled silver monolayers and multilayers (Oćwieja et al. 2015c). For practical applications, the issues related to the mechanisms of nanoparticle deposition, and their release from such coatings, have an important significance. For these reasons, basic researches are carried out in model systems. In many cases, such monolayers are deposited on glass, quartz, silicon and fibres. In a few recent studies, mica was also used as a model substrate, allowing one to precisely determine the deposition kinetics of silver nanoparticles and the stability of such monolayers. It is worth mentioning that before proper deposition of silver nanoparticles, most of the substrates are modified by adsorption of cationic polyelectrolytes, silanes or other positively charged compounds in order to promote an efficient deposition of negatively charged silver nanoparticles. Finally, after the deposition, which can be conducted in different periods, the obtained silver films are characterised with the use of scanning electron microscopy (SEM) or atomic force microscopy (AFM). Below, particular attention has been paid to the studies where deposition of silver nanoparticles was described in a quantitative manner.

In the work of Bar et al. (1996), deposition of silver and gold citrate-stabilised nanoparticles (size, 25 to 30 nm) on glass, silicon and indium tin oxide modified by dendrimers was studied under diffusion-controlled transport. The deposition time ranged from 5 min to 24 h. The coverage of particles was determined from AFM and SEM images by a direct counting procedure. The maximum surface concentration of silver particles obtained in this work was 22 (±2) × $10^9 \cdot cm^{-2}$ (220 μm^{-2}). This corresponds (for the 25-nm particles) to a dimensionless coverage of 10.8%. For 30-nm particles, the maximum coverage was 15.5%.

Using quartz crystal microbalance (QCM), Bandyopadhyay et al. (1997) measured the kinetics of silver particle deposition on aluminium surfaces modified by molecules of 4-carboxythiofenol. The particles with an average size of 10 nm were obtained in the reduction of silver sulfate (VI) by sodium borohydride. It was observed that the monolayer mass increased linearly with the deposition time and, after exceeding 5 min, attained a constant value of 730 ng cm^{-2}. This corresponds to the maximum coverage of the monolayer equal to 10.4%. It is worth mentioning that besides the QCM measurements, the monolayers were also characterised using microscopic methods (SEM).

The formation of silver nanoparticle monolayers on silanised surfaces of glass, carbon and gold was also described in the work of Bright et al. (1998). Citrate-stabilised nanoparticles with an average size of 22 and 55 nm and particles prepared by ethylenediaminetetraacetic acid (EDTA) reduction with size 14 and 15 nm were used in this study. The kinetics of deposition under diffusion-controlled transport was monitored using UV–vis spectroscopy for wavelengths of 408 and 410 nm. It was shown that the rate of nanoparticle deposition is proportional to the square root of deposition time. Unexpectedly, a significant difference in the deposition rate between citrate- and EDTA-stabilised nanoparticles was observed. This was attributed to the difference in the stabilising agents used in the synthesis. Additionally, in this work, particle deposition was monitored using QCM measurements. The experimental results were presented as the dependence of changes in the frequency on time upon exposure of the dendrimer-derivatised crystal to colloidal silver. Analogously as in the case of UV–vis measurements, the rate of monolayer formation was faster for EDTA-stabilised nanoparticles. The maximum mass of citrate-stabilised nanoparticles (55 nm in diameter) deposited on the substrate was equal to 10.5 $\mu g \cdot cm^{-2}$, which corresponds to a coverage of 15%. However, in the case of EDTA-stabilised nanoparticles (15 nm in diameter), the maximum mass of the monolayer was 17.2 $\mu g \cdot cm^{-2}$, which corresponds to a coverage of 163%, indicating formation of multilayer coverage (most probably silver mirror).

Analogous studies of the deposition kinetics of citrate-stabilised nanoparticles (50 and 60 nm in diameter) on glass modified with 3-aminopropyltrimethoxysilane (APTMS) or 3-mercaptopropyltrimethoxysilane (MPTMS) were carried out by Park et al. (1999). The UV–vis technique was used in order to monitor nanoparticle deposition. The maximum time of particle deposition was 48 h, but the experimental conditions, especially the suspension coverage, were not specified. Therefore, the coverage of particles cannot be quantitatively determined except for the maximum absorbance of 2.782.

Pallavicini et al. (2010) studied the deposition of 7-nm silver nanoparticles (citrate stabilised) on glass modified with APTMS or MPTMS at an elevated temperature of 303 K for 18 h. The coverage of particles was determined using AFM imaging analogously as in the work of Bar et al. (1996). The maximum surface concentration was 1.9×10^{10} cm^{-2}, which corresponds to a coverage of 7%.

Deposition of citrate-stabilised nanoparticles with a size of 24.9 nm on glass and silicon modified with poly(4-vinylpiridine) was studied using AFM and QCM by Kim et al. (2010). Sauerbrey's equation was used for calculating the mass of deposited particles and their surface concentration. In this way, the kinetics of the monolayer formation was achieved. The results obtained by QCM were in agreement with the experimental data derived from AFM. Although the plateau value of the monolayer coverage was not obtained, the QCM measurements indicated that the highest maximum coverage was 500 μm^{-2}, which corresponds to 24%.

An insightful analysis of the aforementioned results as well as other examples of deposition studies allows one to notice that, in many cases, the physicochemical characteristics of silver nanoparticles and surfaces used in the experiments were incomplete. As a consequence, it is not known if the nanoparticles were stable during the deposition. On the other hand, the lack of information related to the properties of precovered substrates prevents the quantitative descriptions of these processes. Similarly, nonspecified deposition parameters, such as pH, ionic strength, temperature and deposition time, may make the experiments nonreproducible. Recent literature evidence showed that the successful application of colloid self-assembly processes to produce silver particle monolayers and multilayers of controlled structure and functionality requires a thorough knowledge of the aforementioned parameters. In particular, the weight concentration of nanoparticles in the suspensions and the presence of other colloids, such as high-molecular-weight stabilising agent molecules, should be precisely determined (Michna et al. 2010; Oćwieja et al. 2012, 2013). In the case of nanoparticle properties, their size, shape and surface charge as well as stability under various external conditions should be carefully characterised.

The morphology and size distribution of silver nanoparticles are usually defined with the use of micrographs and images obtained from transmission electron microscopy and AFM. The electrokinetic properties of nanoparticles as well as their stability are routinely determined using dynamic light scattering (DLS) and microelectrophoretic mobility measurements (Michna et al. 2010; Oćwieja et al. 2012, 2013).

On the other hand, it should be remembered that the physicochemical properties of solid substrates also have an essential significance for the quantitative description of the mechanisms of silver nanoparticle deposition (Oćwieja et al. 2015b). As mentioned before, most substrates used in the described studies, for example, glass, indium tin oxide, quartz, silicon, titanium oxide and mica, exhibit negative surface charge analogous to usual silver nanoparticles. Therefore, in order to promote an efficient deposition of particles, these substrates are modified by adsorption of cationic high-molecular-weight compounds. This approach allows one to obtain positively charged layers, which are an appropriate platform for deposition of sliver nanoparticles (Bar et al. 1996; Morga and Adamczyk 2013).

For biological applications, silver nanoparticle coatings immobilised on monolayers of cationic polyelectrolytes seem to be the most promising. Polyelectrolytes are charged molecules consisting of ionisable groups, which release counterions when desolating in polar solvents such as water (Morga and Adamczyk 2013). Because of the growing applications of polyelectrolytes, especially in medicine, many techniques have been exploited to manufacture monolayer and multilayer films of desired coverage and structure. Thin polyelectrolyte films have been fabricated using various techniques such as Langmuir–Blodgett or self-assembly. One of the most promising approaches of surface modification using polyelectrolytes is the LBL assembly technique, which has become a powerful tool for fabricating thin materials with precise control of film composition and structure (Morga and Adamczyk 2013). It is worth mentioning that most cationic polyelectrolytes are building blocks used for the preparations of microcapsules applied in drug delivery systems (Antipov and Sukhorukov 2004).

Taking into account the biocompatibility of some polyelectrolytes (De Koker et al. 2007) as well as the bioactivity of silver nanoparticles (Kittler et al. 2010), one can predict that their multilayers and films should exhibit properties desirable in biological applications.

2.4 Silver Nanoparticle Coatings Deposited on Polyelectrolyte Supporting Layers

Usually, the process of preparation of silver nanoparticle coatings on polyelectrolyte layers consists of two stages. In the first step, the molecules of positively charged polyelectrolytes are adsorbed on negatively charged surfaces from their colloidal suspensions. Among cationic polyelectrolytes, poly(ethyleneimine), poly(allylamine hydrochloride) (PAH) and poly(diallyldimethylammonium chloride) are widely used to modify negatively charged solid surfaces (Chiarelli et al. 2002; Morga and Adamczyk 2013; Oćwieja et al. 2015b). The properties of polyelectrolyte films are precisely determined with the use of modern experimental techniques among which those working under *in situ* conditions (QCM, electrokinetic measurements) play a dominant role. Additionally, the control of ionic strength and pH of polyelectrolyte suspensions allows us to obtain films of desired structure, stability, thickness and other properties.

In the second step, the polyelectrolyte monolayers of well-defined properties are immersed in a silver suspension of controlled weight concentration of nanoparticles. The deposition of nanoparticles is carried out under a given temperature, pH and ionic strength. The surface concentration of deposited nanoparticles (N_s), obtained after a given period, is usually determined from AFM images and SEM micrographs (Morga et al. 2014; Oćwieja et al. 2011, 2013). Then, knowing the surface concentration and the size of nanoparticles, one can calculate the dimensionless coverage of obtained silver monolayers (θ) (Oćwieja et al. 2011, 2013). Furthermore, determining the coverage of silver nanoparticles for different periods, one can determine the kinetics of nanoparticle deposition.

Oćwieja et al. (2011) demonstrated that the diffusion-controlled transport condition, which is characteristic for self-assembly processes of nanoparticles, is appropriate to express the kinetic runs in terms of the square root of deposition time $t^{1/2}$, rather than the primary time variable t. This is so, because for a not too high nanoparticle coverage, where the surface blocking effects remain negligible, the kinetics of particle adsorption is described by the theoretical formula

$$\langle N_S \rangle = 2\left(\frac{D}{\pi}\right)^{1/2} t^{1/2} n_b, \qquad (2.1)$$

where D is the diffusion coefficient of nanoparticles, n_b is the bulk number concentration of nanoparticles connected with the weight concentration c_p (expressed in mg L^{-1}) via the linear dependence

$$n_b = \frac{6 \times 10^{-6}}{\pi d_p^3 \rho_p} c_p, \qquad (2.2)$$

where ρ_p is the specific density of silver and d_p is the diameter of nanoparticles.

As can be noticed from Equation 2.1, deposition kinetics is proportional to the bulk concentration of nanoparticles and to the square root of the diffusion coefficient. This means that in order to obtain dense silver nanoparticle monolayers in a shorter period, a higher concentration of nanoparticles should be used in the deposition experiment. Typical initial kinetic runs obtained for three various weight concentrations of nanoparticles (average size, 54 nm) are shown in Figure 2.1a.

Based on Equation 2.1, one can also predict that for a constant value of the bulk number concentration of nanoparticles, the formation of monolayers is faster for nanoparticles characterised by higher diffusion coefficients (smaller nanoparticles). In the work of Oćwieja et al. (2015c), it was proven that the characteristic monolayer formation time is proportional to the cube of particle size and inversely proportional to the square of the weight

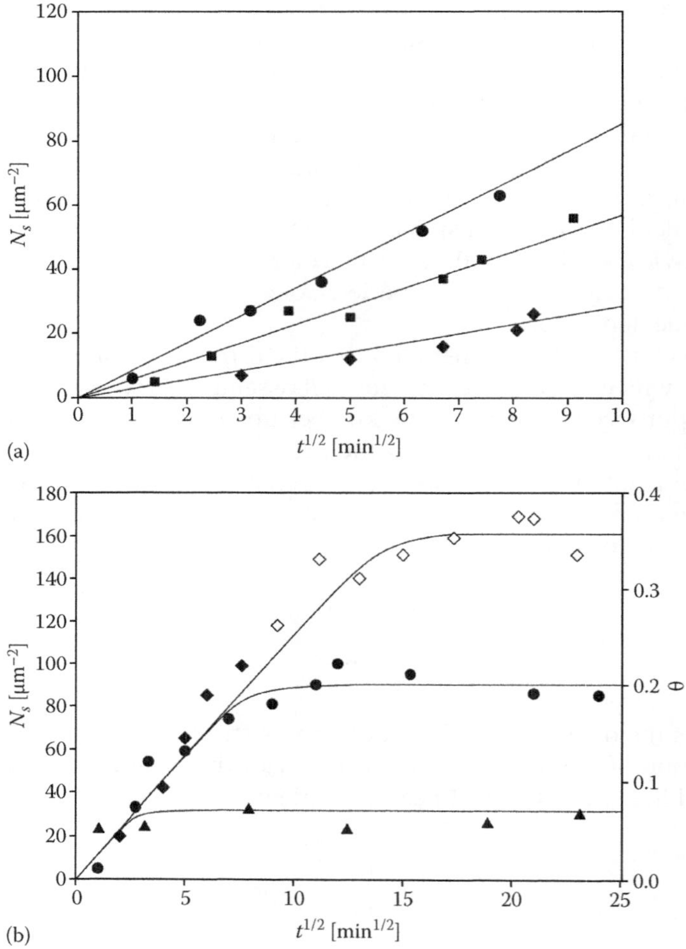

FIGURE 2.1
The kinetics of silver nanoparticle (54 nm) deposition on mica modified by the PAH monolayer, determined for pH 5.5, $T = 293$ K and for (a) various silver nanoparticle concentrations, (●) 300 mg L^{-1}, (■) 200 mg L^{-1}, (◆) 100 mg L^{-1} ($I = 10^{-2}$ M), and (b) various ionic strengths, (◆, ◇) $I = 10^{-2}$ M, (●) $I = 10^{-3}$ M, (▲) $I = 10^{-4}$ M, and fixed suspension concentration (500 mg L^{-1}). The points represent experimental results obtained from AFM (full points) and SEM (hollow points). The solid lines denote the theoretical results calculated from the RSA model.

concentration of nanoparticles in the suspensions. The comparison of deposition kinetics obtained for three types of citrate-stabilised nanoparticles, with an average size of 15, 28 and 54 nm, was also presented in the work of Oćwieja and Adamczyk (2013).

The kinetics measurements, performed for longer times, can be exploited for determining the maximum surface concentration of nanoparticles (maximum coverage), which is a parameter of major practical significance. The example of such long-lasting deposition kinetic runs is shown in Figure 2.1b. Characteristic features of these kinetic runs are a linear increase in N_s with $t^{1/2}$ and then, after reaching some critical time, an abrupt stabilisation of the surface concentration at a constant value. The maximum coverage (θ_{mx}) of silver nanoparticle monolayers is attained as a result of the surface blocking effect, which, in turn, is strongly connected with electrostatic interactions between deposited nanoparticles. For this reason, one can observe that the maximum surface concentration (coverage) of nanoparticles increases significantly with ionic strength (Figure 2.1b). In order to explain this effect in detail, the obtained experimental results are usually interpreted in terms of the random sequential adsorption (RSA) model (Adamczyk 2006). This is a universal approach allowing one to theoretically predict the maximum coverage of particles interacting via the screened Coulomb potential for various particle shapes and sizes. In the case of nearly spherical particles, the maximum coverage is only a function of the κd_p parameter (where $\kappa^{-1} = \left(\frac{\varepsilon kT}{2e^2 I}\right)^{1/2}$ is the thickness of the electric double layer, k is the Boltzmann constant, T is temperature and I is ionic strength) and can be approximated for $\kappa d_p > 1$ by the analytical formula

$$\theta_{mx} = \theta_\infty \frac{1}{(1 + 2h^*/d_p)^2} \tag{2.3}$$

where θ_∞ is the maximum coverage for hard (noninteracting) particles equal to 0.547 for spheres (Adamczyk 2006) and h^* is the effective interaction range characterising the repulsive double-layer interactions among particles, which can be calculated from the formula

$$2h^*/d_p = \frac{1}{\kappa d_p}\left\{\ln\frac{\phi_0}{2\phi_{ch}} - \ln\left[1 + \frac{1}{\kappa d_p}\ln\frac{\phi_0}{2\phi_{ch}}\right]\right\}, \tag{2.4}$$

where $\phi_0 = 16\pi\varepsilon d_p\left(\frac{kT}{e}\right)^2 \tanh^2\left(\frac{\zeta_p e}{4kT}\right)$ is the characteristic interaction energy of particles, ζ_p is the zeta potential of nanoparticles and ϕ_{ch} is the scaling interaction energy, close to the kT unit (Adamczyk 2006).

The results of studies broadly described in the literature, as well as those shown above, can be exploited as reference data for producing silver nanoparticle monolayers of a well-defined coverage that can be regulated by the deposition time, bulk suspension concentration and ionic strength. The optimum conditions, for fabricating the most dense monolayers (having the maximum coverage of 0.35), are ionic strength range from 0.01 to 0.03 M and nanoparticle size above 20 nm (Oćwieja et al. 2015c). For higher ionic strength, charge-stabilised silver nanoparticles are unstable and rapidly aggregate, which was observed with the use of DLS technique.

2.5 Release of Silver Nanoparticles from Monolayers Deposited on Polyelectrolyte Films

It should be emphasised that silver nanoparticles used to modify various materials can also desorb from surfaces, especially at elevated temperatures and in aqueous environments containing various salts.

Kong and Jang (2008) described silver nanoparticle release from poly(methyl methacrylate) nanofibre. The process was analysed using UV–vis spectrometry. As a consequence of continuous desorption of nanoparticles, the increase of intensity of maximum absorption peak was observed. The silver nanoparticle concentration in the aqueous solution was measured by inductively coupled atomic emission spectrometer.

Benn and Westerhoff (2008) measured silver nanoparticle release from commercially available sock fabrics into water. Similarly, Kulthong et al. (2010) carried out investigations of silver nanoparticle release from commercial and freshly prepared fabrics into artificial sweat. The silver content in materials before and after desorption was measured using a graphite furnace atomic absorption spectroscopy. The authors showed that the release of silver nanoparticles was dependent on the initial amount of silver coatings, the fabrics quality and pH of sweat.

It is worth mentioning that the uncontrolled nanoparticle release phenomenon affects not only fibres. Using inductively coupled plasma mass spectrometry, Kaegi et al. (2010) investigated the release of silver nanoparticles from paints used for outdoor applications. The results of the measurements showed a strong leaching of nanoparticles during the initial runoff events. After a period of 1 year, more than 30% of the nanoparticles from paints were released to the environment.

Additionally, in recent times, much effort of researchers was paid to the quantitative description of mechanisms of nanoparticle release, which are especially significant for various practical applications in medicine and biology. It is worth mentioning that the phenomenon of nanoparticle release is usually used in the disc diffusion method. This approach is applied in order to determine the biological activity of silver nanoparticles against various microorganisms (Kora et al. 2009; Rai et al. 2009). Although disc diffusion methods are widely used in practical applications, little is known about the role of external conditions on desorption of nanoparticles from the coatings. For this purpose, the kinetics of silver nanoparticle desorption from various polyelectrolyte films (Oćwieja et al. 2015b) were studied extensively under controlled conditions of temperature, ionic strength and pH (Morga et al. 2013; Oćwieja et al. 2013, 2015a). In the first step of these experiments, silver particle monolayers of a defined initial coverage were deposited on polyelectrolyte-modified mica sheets as described above. In the second step, the sheets were immersed in pure electrolyte solution of controlled ionic strength and pH. The silver nanoparticles were allowed to desorb under diffusion-controlled transport in a thermostated cell for a prescribed period. Their coverage was determined in a discontinuous way by *ex situ* SEM and AFM imaging followed by particle enumeration by an image analyzing software. In another version of the desorption experiments, monolayers were formed *in situ* in the streaming potential cell that allows one to precisely control their coverage. Afterwards, particle desorption was carried out under diffusion or flow conditions of controlled intensity. The change in particle coverage was followed *in situ* via the streaming potential measurements (Morga et al. 2013).

Typical desorption kinetics for an initial coverage of silver monolayers (deposited on PAH layers) equal to 0.05 and for nanoparticles with various average sizes are shown in Figure 2.2. As can be seen, for fixed external conditions (pH 6.2, I = 0.1 M, T = 298 K), the rate of desorption significantly decreases when the size of nanoparticle increases. Thus, for the smallest nanoparticles (15 nm), the residue coverage of the monolayer after a period of 166 h is only 30% of the initial value. In the case of nanoparticles with an average size of 54 nm, the residual coverage of monolayers, after the same period, remains at the level of 90%. Thus, one can conclude that stable silver

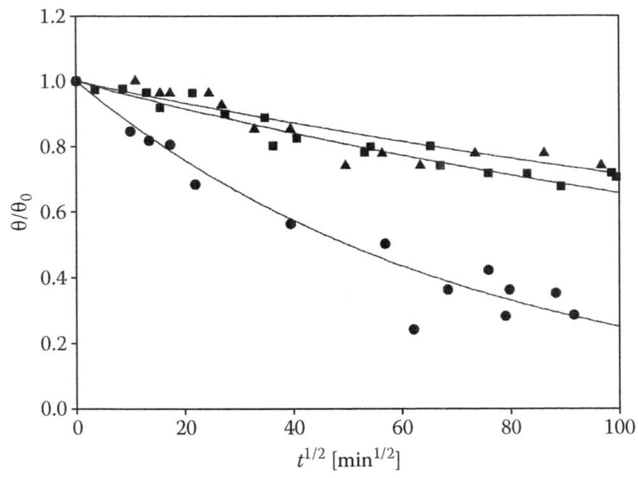

FIGURE 2.2
The kinetics of particle desorption expressed as the dependence of θ/θ_0 on $t^{1/2}$. The initial coverage of particles $\theta_0 = 0.05$. The points denote experimental data obtained by AFM for I = 0.1 M NaCl, pH 6.2, T = 298 K and particles: (▲) 54 nm, (■) 28 nm, (●) 15 nm. The solid lines denote the theoretical results calculated from the RSA model.

nanoparticle monolayers should be formed using nanoparticles of large sizes.

In order to get more insight into silver particle release mechanisms, extensive measurements were performed in recent work where the role of ionic strength, temperature and pH was systematically studied. It was found that independently on the silver nanoparticle size, the release rate increases when the ionic strength increases. The effect was more visible in the case of smaller nanoparticles (Oćwieja and Adamczyk 2013). Additional series of experiments were carried out for the silver monolayers formed from nanoparticles of various sizes (15, 28 and 54 nm) under controlled conditions of pH for fixed temperature and ionic strength (Oćwieja et al. 2015a). The results of studies revealed that in the case of nanoparticles deposited on PAH supporting layers, the silver coatings are particularly unstable at low pH. The fastest release of nanoparticles from monolayers of the same initial coverage was observed at pH 3.5. In the case of the nanoparticles of the same size, the differences between the desorption rate disappeared when pH increased to the highest values (7.4–9.0).

Additionally, the role of temperature in nanoparticle desorption from obtained monolayers was studied extensively (Oćwieja and Adamczyk 2013). As expected, the increase in temperature significantly enhanced the release of silver nanoparticles independently of their size, although similarly as in the previous experiments, this effect was greater in the case of smaller nanoparticles (Oćwieja and Adamczyk 2013).

The recently developed ion pair model was used (Oćwieja and Adamczyk 2013) in order to properly interpret the obtained experimental results. According to this approach, the electrostatic interactions are governed by the finite number of ion pairs formed as a result of penetration of silver nanoparticles into the PAH layers that is strictly related to the number of charges on silver particles in the interaction zone (Figure 2.3). It is assumed

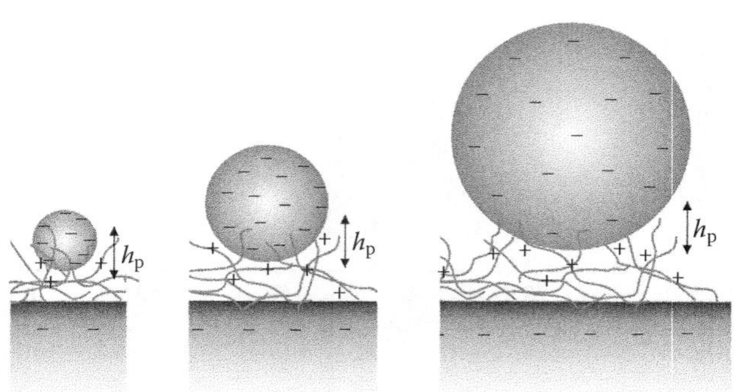

FIGURE 2.3
Schematic illustration of silver nanoparticle immobilisation on polyelectrolyte-covered mica.

(Oćwieja and Adamczyk 2013) that these interactions can be described by the unscreened Coulomb potential, that is,

$$\phi_{\mathrm{m}} = -N_{\mathrm{i}} \frac{e^2}{4\pi\varepsilon d_{\mathrm{im}}}, \tag{2.5}$$

where N_{i} is the number of ion pairs in the interaction zone and d_{im} is the minimum distance between ion pairs.

The number of charges involved in the interactions obviously depends on the size of particles, their surface charge and the penetration depth h_{p} (Figure 2.3). For the smallest particles, one can expect that the greater part of their surface is accessible for the ion pair formation. In the case of larger nanoparticles, it was found that the number of ion pairs involved in the interactions with PAH chains is lowest, which is related to the geometrical parameters (Oćwieja and Adamczyk 2013).

Based on the experimental results and using the abovementioned theoretical approach, the equilibrium adsorption constant and the energy minimum depth (binding energy of nanoparticles) were determined for various physicochemical conditions (Oćwieja and Adamczyk 2013; Oćwieja et al. 2015a). In contrast to predictions of the mean-field DLVO theory, the energy minima were little dependent on particle size, ionic strength and pH. Thus, for the typical desorption conditions of $I = 10^{-2}$ M, pH 6.2–5.8, energy varied between −16.9 and −19.1 kT for the particle size of 15 and 54 nm, respectively (Oćwieja and Adamczyk 2013; Oćwieja et al. 2015a). The decrease in energy minimum depth with the temperature was also observed, which contradicts the mean-field theory. These experimental evidences indicated that the role of van der Waals interactions in the silver nanoparticle release processes from polyelectrolyte-covered mica was negligible. The kinetics of these processes was governed by discrete electrostatic interactions among ion pairs and cannot be properly described by mean-field theories of the electrical double layer.

2.6 Conclusions

The above-described results of studies allow us to conclude that one can tune physicochemical properties of silver nanoparticle monolayers and films. The process of nanoparticle self-assembly can be modeled by temperature, ionic strength and pH. Controlling these parameters, one can obtain monolayers of desirable structure, the surface concentration of nanoparticles and stability.

References

Adamczyk Z. *Particles at Interfaces: Interactions, Deposition, Structure*. The Netherlands: Elsevier (2006).

Antipov A.A., Sukhorukov, G.B. Polyelectrolyte multilayer capsules as vehicles with tunable permeability. *Adv. Colloid Interface Sci.* 111 no. 1–2 (2004): 49–61.

Bandyopadhyay K., Patil V., Vijayamohanan K., Sastry M. Adsorption of silver colloidal particles through covalent linkage to self-assembled monolayers. *Langmuir* 13 no. 20 (1997): 5244–5248.

Bar G., Rubin S., Cutts R.W., Taylor T.N., Zawodzinski T.A. Dendrimer-modified silicon oxide surfaces as platforms for the deposition of gold and silver colloid monolayers: Preparation method, characterization and correlation between microstructure and optical properties. *Langmuir* 12 no. 5 (1996): 1172–1179.

Benn T.M., Westerhoff P. Nanoparticle silver released into water from commercially available sock fabrics. *Environ. Sci. Technol.* 42 no. 11 (2008): 4133–4139.

Bright R.M., Musick M.D., Natan M.J. Preparation and characterization of Ag colloid monolayers. *Langmuir* 14 no. 20 (1998): 5695–5701.

Chiarelli P.A., Johal M.S., Holmes D.J. et al. Polyelectrolyte spin-assembly. *Langmuir* 18 no. 1 (2002): 168–173.

De Koker S., De Geest B.G., Cuvelier C. et al. In vivo cellular uptake, degradation, and biocompatibility of polyelectrolyte microcapsules. *Adv. Funct. Mater.* 17 no. 18 (2007): 3754–3763.

Hadad L., Perkas N., Gofer Y. et al. Sonochemical deposition of silver nanoparticles on wool fibers. *J. Appl. Polym. Sci.* 104 no. 3 (2007): 1732–1737.

Hall D.B., Underhill P., Torkelson J.M. Spin coating of thin and ultrathin polymer films. *Poly. Eng. Sci.* 38 no. 12 (1998): 2039–2045.

He J., Kunitake T. Formation of silver nanoparticles and nanocraters on silicon wafers. *Langmuir* 22 no. 18 (2006): 7881–7884.

Huang H.H., Ni X.P., Loy G.L. et al. Photochemical formation of silver nanoparticles in poly(*N*-vinylpyrrolidone). *Langmuir* 12 no. 4 (1996): 909–912.

Jiang T., Liu L., Yao J. In situ deposition of silver nanoparticles on the cotton fabrics. *Fiber. Polym.* 12 no. 5 (2011): 620–625.

Kaegi R., Sinnet B., Zuleeg S. et al. Release of silver nanoparticles from outdoor facades. *Environ. Pollut.* 158 no. 9 (2010): 2900–2905.

Kéki S., Török J., Deák G. et al. Silver nanoparticles by PAMAM-assisted photochemical reduction of Ag^+. *J. Colloid Interface Sci.* 229 no. 2 (2000): 550–553.

Kim K., Ryoo H., Shin K.S. Adsorption and agreggation characteristics of silver nanoparticles onto a poly(4-vinylpyridine) film: A comparison with gold nanoparticles. *Langmuir* 26 no. 13 (2010): 10827–10832.

Kittler S., Greulich C., Gebauer J.S. et al. The influence of proteins on the dispersability and cell-biological activity of silver nanoparticles. *J. Mater. Chem.* 20 no. 3 (2010): 512–518.

Kong H., Jang, J. Antibacterial properties of novel poly(methyl methacrylate) nanofiber containing silver nanoparticles. *Langmuir* 25 no. 5 (2008): 2051–2056.

Kora A.J., Manjusha R., Arunachalam. Superior bacterial activity of SDS capped silver nanoparticles: Synthesis and characterization. *Mater. Sci. Eng.* C 29 no. 7 (2009): 2104–2109.

Kulthong K., Srisung S., Boonpavanitchakul K., Kangwansupamonkon W., Maniratanachote R. Determination of silver nanoparticle release from antibacterial fabrics into artificial sweat. *Part. Fibre Toxicol.* 7 no. 8 (2010): 1–9.

Kumar Ch. *Nanostructured Thin Films and Surfaces.* Weinheim: Wiley-VCH (2010).

Lu H.W., Liu S.H., Wang X.L. et al. Silver nanocrystals by hyperbranched polyurethane-assisted photochemical reduction of Ag^+. *Mater. Chem. Phys.* 81 no. 1 (2003): 104–107.

Maenosono S., Okubo T., Yamaguchi Y. Overview of nanoparticle array formation by wet coating. *J. Nanopart. Res.* 5 no. 1–2 (2003): 5–15.

Malynych S., Luzinov I., Chumanov G. Poly(vinyl pyridine) as a universal surface modifier for immobilization of nanoparticles. *J. Phys. Chem. B.* 106 no. 6 (2002): 1280–1285.

Michna A., Adamczyk Z., Siwek B., Oćwieja M. Silver nanoparticle monolayers on poly(ethylene imine) covered mica by colloidal self-assembly. *J. Colloid Interface Sci.* 345 no. 2 (2010): 187–193.

Morga M., Adamczyk Z. Monolayers of cationic polyelectrolytes on mica—Electrokinetic studies. *J. Colloid Interface Sci.* 407 (2013): 196–204.

Morga M., Adamczyk Z., Oćwieja M. Stability of silver nanoparticle monolayers determined in situ by streaming potential measurements. *J. Nanopart. Res.* 15 (2013): 2076.

Morga M., Adamczyk Z., Oćwieja M. Hematite/silver nanoparticle bilayers on mica—AFM, SEM and streaming potential studies. *J. Colloid Interface Sci.* 424 (2014): 75–83.

Neelgund Gururaj M., Oki A. Deposition of silver nanoparticles on dendrimer functionalized multiwalled carbon nanotubes: Synthesis, characterization and antimicrobial activity. *J. Nanosci. Nanotechnol.* 11 no. 4 (2011): 3621–3629.

Oćwieja M., Adamczyk Z. Controlled release of silver nanoparticles from monolayers deposited on PAH covered mica. *Langmuir* 29 no. 11 (2013): 3546–3555.

Oćwieja M., Adamczyk Z., Kubiak K. Tuning properties of silver particle monolayers via controlled adsorption–desorption processes. *J. Colloid Interface Sci.* 376 no. 1 (2012): 1–11.

Oćwieja M., Adamczyk Z., Morga M. pH-controlled desorption of silver nanoparticles from monolayers deposited on PAH-covered mica. *J. Nanopart. Res.* 17 (2015a): 235.

Oćwieja M., Adamczyk Z., Morga M., Kubiak K. Influence of supporting polyelectrolyte layers on the coverage and stability of silver nanoparticle coatings. *J. Colloid Interface Sci.* 445 (2015b): 205–212.

Oćwieja M., Adamczyk Z., Morga M., Kubiak K. Silver particle monolayers—Formation, stability, applications. *Adv. Colloid Interface Sci.* 222 (2015c): 530–563.

Oćwieja M., Adamczyk Z., Morga M., Michna A. High density silver nanoparticle monolayers produced by colloid self-assembly on polyelectrolyte supporting layers. *J. Colloid Interface Sci.* 363 no. 1 (2011): 39–48.

Oćwieja M., Morga M., Adamczyk Z. Self-assembled silver nanoparticles monolayers on mica—AFM, SEM, and electrokinetic characteristics. *J. Nanopart. Res.* 15 (2013): 1460.

Pallavicini P., Taglietti A., Dacarro G. et al. Self-assembled monolayers of silver nanoparticles firmly grafted on glass surfaces: Low Ag^+ release for an efficient antibacterial activity. *J. Colloid Interface. Sci.* 350 no. 1 (2010): 110–116.

Park S.H., Im J.H., Im J.W., Chun B.H., Kim J.H. Adsorption kinetics of Au and Ag nanoparticles on functionalized glass surfaces. *Microchem. J.*, 63 no. 1 (1999): 71–91.

Piwoński I., Kądziołka K., Kisielewska A. et al. The effect of the deposition parameters on size, distribution and antimicrobial properties of photoinduced silver nanoparticles on titania coatings. *Appl. Surf. Sci.* 257 no. 16 (2011): 7076–7082.

Rai M., Yadav A., Gade A. Silver nanoparticles as a new generation of antimicrobials. *Biotechnol. Adv.* 27 no. 1 (2009): 76–83.

Schaefers S., Rast L., Stanishevsky A. Electroless silver plating on spin-coated nanoparticle seed layers. *Mater. Lett.* 60 no. 5 (2006): 706–709.

Schubert D.W., Dunkel T. Spin coating from a molecular point of view: Its concentration regimes, influence of molar mass and distribution. *Mat. Res. Innovat.* 7 no. 5 (2003): 314–321.

Sudeep P.K., Kamat P.V. Photosensitized growth of silver nanoparticles under visible light irradiation: A mechanistic investigation. *Chem. Mater.* 17 no. 22 (2005): 5404–5410.

Ye X., Zhou Y., Chen J. et al. Deposition of silver nanoparticles on silica spheres via ultrasound irradiations. *Appl. Surf. Sci.* 252 no. 14 (2007): 6264–6267.

Zhang S. *Nanostructured Thin Films and Coatings Functional Properties*. Boca Raton, FL: CRC Press Taylor & Francis Group (2010).

3

Synergistic Antimicrobial Activity of Silver and Chitosan

Sulbha K. Sharma, Gitika Kharkwal, Ying-Ying Huang and Michael R. Hamblin

CONTENTS

3.1 Introduction

Bacterial infections are one of the most worrying problems at present owing to the development of resistance to traditional antibiotic drugs. The alarming rise in resistance can be attributed to the uncontrolled and unnecessary use of these drugs. The search for new therapeutic options that will be effective against resistant bacterial strains is a key challenge today (Ahamed et al. 2015). In recent times, combination materials based on silver nanoparticles coupled with biodegradable polymers have drawn much interest from researchers and clinicians for combating multidrug-resistant bacterial strains. The synergistic antibacterial mechanisms of chitosan and silver nanoparticles are expected to provide more efficient control of bacterial infections. In this chapter, we will cover the synergistic antimicrobial activity of silver and chitosan (Huang et al. 2011).

3.2 Antimicrobial Effects of Silver Alone

The use of silver as an antimicrobial agent dates back to the 18th century when silver nitrate was used in the treatment of nonhealing ulcers. Later, a preparation of colloidal silver solution was recognised as an effective agent in wound management and was approved by the Food and Drug Administration in the 1920s (Atiyeh et al. 2007). However, after the introduction of penicillin in the mid-20th century, there was a reduced use of silver as an antimicrobial. Some years later, silver was again used in the management of burns. With the problem of the development of antibiotic resistance, silver is again being widely considered and employed as an antimicrobial agent, and clinicians are now using silver-incorporated wound dressings. A greater range of silver dressings offering wider therapeutic options is being developed. Silver is also being used as an antiviral, an antifungal and an anti-inflammatory agent. Besides the silver ion–based antimicrobials, silver nanoparticles have also recently gained much interest. Silver nanoparticles are being applied in wound dressings and as antimicrobial coatings in nonliving systems such as refrigerators. Silver nanoparticles possess some particular properties that make them suitable materials such as a tunable size, variable shape, ease of surface modification and the ability to release silver ions. Some of the reports highlight the limitations of silver and its derivatives, owing to poor solubility and possible cytotoxicity (Dellera et al. 2014).

The mechanisms of the antimicrobial action of silver can be classified as those effects attributed to silver ions in solution and those effects attributed to silver present in nanoparticles (AgNP). Silver ions react with a number of functional groups that are electron rich and can act as electron donors: these are thiols, phosphates, hydroxyls, imidazoles and indoles (Franci et al. 2015). There is evidence that the biocidal activity of Ag is attributed to disruption of the bacterial electron transport chain. Silver ions cause proton leakage through the membrane by dissipating the chemiosmotic potential of the membrane. The damage to the cell membrane subsequently facilitates the further uptake of metal ions into the intracellular region where they generate reactive oxygen species (ROS) and disrupt DNA and protein structures (Park et al. 2011). The mechanism of antimicrobial action of silver is illustrated in Figure 3.1.

They key feature of silver nanoparticles is that they have a very large ratio of surface area to mass. Because of their large surface area, AgNPs are able to physically interact with the surface of various bacterial cells. Electrostatic forces that develop when AgNPs (with a positive zeta potential) encounter bacteria with a negative surface charge promote closer binding to bacteria. This binding is particularly important in the case of Gram-negative bacteria that have a more pronounced negative surface charge, where numerous studies have observed the adhesion to the bacterial surface and consequent accumulation in bacterial cells (Krishnaraj et al. 2015; Kujda et al. 2015).

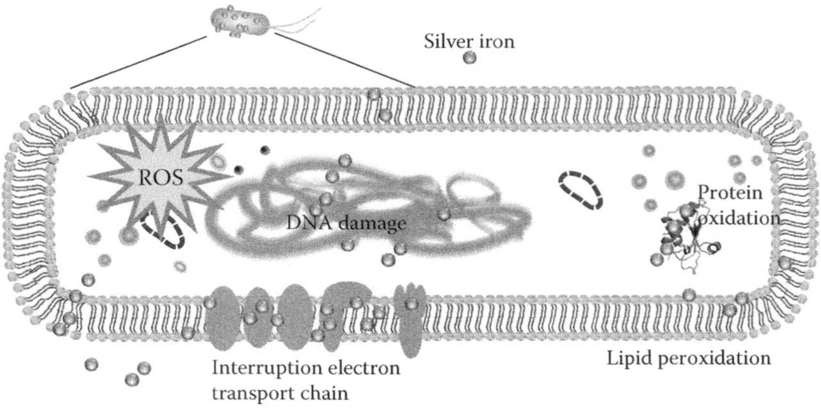

FIGURE 3.1
Mechanism of antibacterial effect of silver. Interruption of the bacterial electron transport chain. Dissipate cell membrane. The damage to the cell membrane subsequently generates ROS and disrupts DNA and protein structures.

Many studies have reported that AgNPs can damage cell membranes, leading to structural changes, which render bacteria more permeable, resulting in the leakage of cytoplasmic components (Chen et al. 2011). This effect is highly dependent on the size of the nanoparticles, with smaller AgNPs (<5 nm diameter) being more bactericidal than larger ones (Choi and Hu 2008).

However, it is clear that a certain number of silver ions are released from the AgNP both before and after they penetrate into bacterial cells. Therefore, AgNPs have a higher antibacterial activity than the same concentration of free silver ions because the antibacterial properties can be attributed to both the physical properties of the AgNP and the release of silver ions (Likus et al. 2013).

Bacterial resistance to elemental silver or silver ions is extremely rare, although not completely unknown. There was a report of a plasmid pMGH100 isolated from Salmonella containing nine genes in three transcription units that encoded for silver resistance (Silver 2003).

3.3 Antimicrobial Effects of Chitosan Alone

Chitosan is a biodegradable natural polymer and is derived from chitin, which is the second most abundant carbohydrate polymer in nature (after cellulose). Chitin is the ubiquitous structural material of the shells of crustaceans (shrimps, crabs and lobsters) and is also found in the cell walls of many species of fungi and mushrooms. Chemically, chitosan is a cationic polysaccharide based on poly-D-glucosamine with some remaining *N*-acetyl groups (Figure 3.2), obtained from partial alkaline hydrolysis of chitin, which is

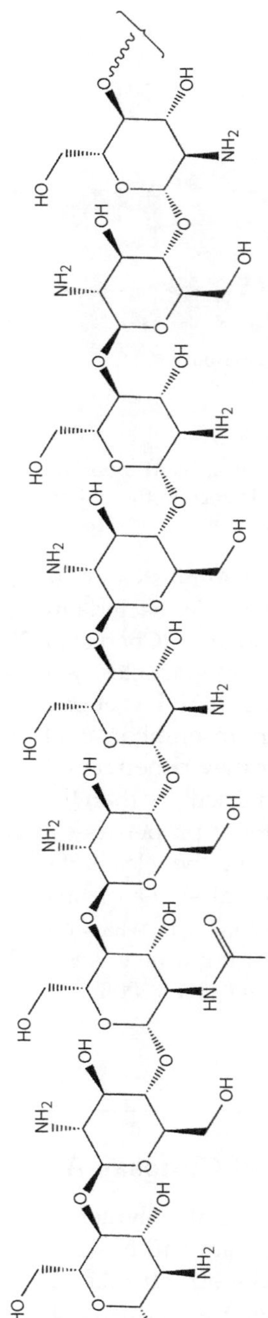

FIGURE 3.2
Molecular structure of chitosan. Molecular weight (chain length) and degree of deacetylation can vary between preparations.

poly-*N*-acetyl-D-glucosamine. Chitosan possesses many favorable properties such as biocompatibility, biodegradability and nontoxicity. Different types of chitosan are available depending on the conditions of the deacetylation, which decide the physicochemical properties of the polymer and its range of applications. Furthermore, chitosan is a polymer with a number of basic amino groups and hence possesses an overall cationic charge especially at acidic pH (Raafat and Sahl 2009). This is attributed to the presence of primary amine groups on the molecule that bind protons according to the equation:

$$\text{Chit-NH}_2 + \text{H}_3\text{O}^+ \Leftrightarrow \text{Chit-NH}_3^+ + \text{H}_2\text{O} \tag{3.1}$$

In common with many polycationic polymers such as polylysine (Hyldgaard et al. 2014) and polyethylenimine (Helander et al. 1997), chitosan has pronounced antimicrobial effects owing to destabilisation of the outer membrane of Gram-negative bacteria (Li et al. 2011b; Rabea et al. 2003) and pemeabilisation of the microbial plasma membrane (Rabea et al. 2003; Tang et al. 2010). Attachment of the other functional groups to the amino groups can further extend its properties and applications.

The protonated amino groups of chitosan displace divalent cations (Ca^{2+} and Mg^{2+}) from the outer membrane of Gram-negative bacteria. These divalent cations are instrumental in maintaining the complex outer membrane structure by anchoring the lipopolysaccharide (LPS) chains in place. When the divalent cations are displaced, the LPS chains detach and the outer membrane structure is substantially weakened. This is a progressive process and has been termed the 'self-promoted uptake pathway' (Hancock and Farmer 1993). The mechanism of antimicrobial action of chitosan is illustrated in Figure 3.3.

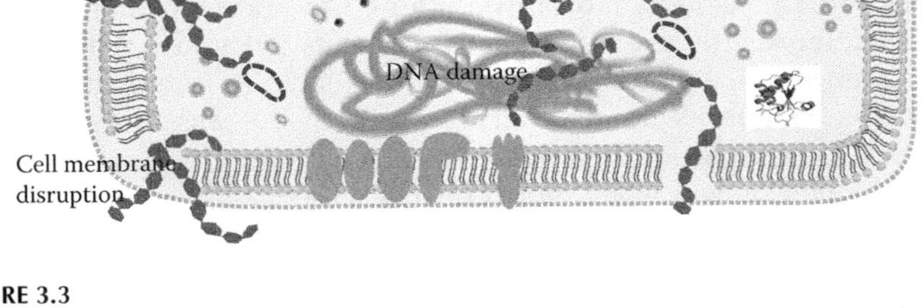

FIGURE 3.3
Mechanism of antibacterial effect of chitosan. Chitosan attached to the outer membrane of Gram-negative bacteria. The LPS chains detach and the outer membrane structure is substantially weakened. LPS, lipopolysaccharide.

Chitosan can also act to form coordination complexes or chelates with various metal ions. This metal ion complexation can deprive bacterial cells of essential trace metals they require as nutrients (Varma 2005). The molecular weight of chitosan is known to affect the degree of antimicrobial activity of chitosan preparation. Low-molecular-weight chitosans are known to enter the microbial cells more easily, while the higher-molecular-weight chitosans remain at the outer cell wall and act towards destabilising its barrier structure (Jarmila and Vavrikova 2011). The antimicrobial action of chitosan is also affected by the form in which it is used (solution, powder, membrane, etc.).

These distinctive characteristics taken together render chitosan a commercially applicable material that is widely employed in the fields of pharmaceutics, cosmetics, medicine, food industries and so on. The medical applications of chitosan are mainly in the areas of antimicrobial materials and wound healing properties.

The effective antimicrobial action of chitosan was illustrated by a study (Burkatovskaya et al. 2006) using an engineered chitosan acetate bandage preparation (HemCon) that was designed as a hemostatic dressing, and its chemical structure suggested that it would also be antimicrobial. Chitosan acetate bandages were applied to mice with excisional wounds that were infected by bioluminescent Gram-negative species *Pseudomonas aeruginosa* and *Proteus mirabilis* and the Gram-positive *Staphylococcus aureus* that had all been stably transduced with the entire bacterial lux operon to allow in vivo bioluminescence imaging. Figure 3.4a shows excellent in vitro bacterial killing, and interestingly, the effect against Gram-negative bacteria was even more pronounced that against Gram-positive *S. aureus*. An excisional wound in Balb/c mice was inoculated with 50–250 million cells followed after 30 min by application of HemCon bandage, alginate sponge bandage, silver sulfadiazine cream or no treatment as controls. HemCon was more adhesive to the wound and conformed well to the injury compared to alginate. Animal survival was followed over 15 days with observations of bioluminescence emission and animal activity daily. Chitosan acetate–treated mice infected with *P. aeruginosa* and *P. mirabilis* all survived while those receiving no treatment, alginate and silver sulfadiazine demonstrated 25%–100% mortality (Figure 3.4b and c). Chitosan acetate was much more effective than other treatments in rapidly reducing bioluminescence in the wound consistent with its rapid bactericidal activity in vitro as well as its light-scattering properties. *S. aureus* formed only nonlethal localised infections after temporary immunosuppression of the mice but HemCon was again more effective in reducing bioluminescence. The data suggest that chitosan acetate rapidly kills bacteria in the wound before systemic invasion can take place and is superior to alginate bandage and silver sulfadiazine that may both encourage bacterial growth in the short term.

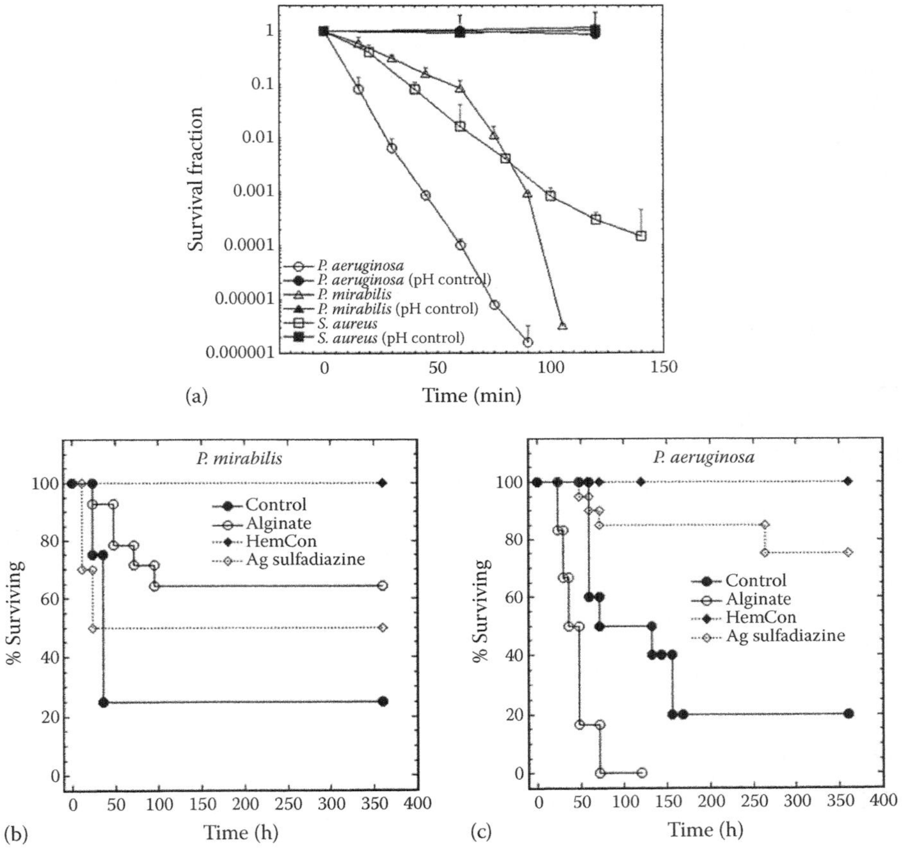

FIGURE 3.4
In vitro and in vivo antibacterial action of chitosan acetate bandage. (a) In vitro killing of three bacterial species by a solution of chitosan acetate in acetate buffer (1% wt/wt, pH 4.5). Kaplan–Meier survival curves for mice ($n = 6$ per group) with infected incisional wounds treated with chitosan bandage, alginate, AgSD or controls: (b) *P. mirabilis*; (c) *P. aeruginosa*.

3.4 Combinations of Silver and Chitosan

Combining different materials (or nanomaterials) that have individual antibacterial activity but operate via different mechanisms of action is not easy, but is possible and is now an area of growing interest. It has been observed that most substances are highly toxic to bacterial cells and are, to some extent, toxic to human cells as well. Therefore, antimicrobial substances to be used inside the human body to treat or prevent infections should possess appropriate properties or be delivered by methods of application that reduce their toxicity towards human cells. There have been several innovative approaches to create combination biomaterials with superior antimicrobial applications to either individual component alone. One of these approaches has been to combine silver ions or silver nanoparticles with chitosan. Several in vitro studies have shown that synergistic effects of such combinations are better than the antimicrobial activity of each component (chitosan or silver) alone. Chitosan–silver nanocomposites have proven to be a good option for these types of chitosan–silver combinations. The combined action of chitosan and silver nanoparticles can be either additive or synergistic since the individual mechanisms of action of chitosan and silver are fundamentally different (see above). There are three broad reasons for investigating the combinations of chitosan and nanosilver. First, there is the two different synergistic mechanisms of antimicrobial action whereby chitosan destabilises the outer membrane of the bacteria, increasing its permeability, and allowing the silver nanoparticles to penetrate better into the interior of the microbial cells where they carry out their killing action. Second, there is the ability of chitosan to act as a biological reducing agent for silver ions that can be taken advantage of in the preparation of silver nanoparticles, and chitosan could also stabilise them once prepared and prevent aggregation. Third, there is the possibility that chitosan could reduce the toxicity of silver nanoparticles towards host mammalian cells (Sondi and Salopek-Sondi 2004; Varma 2005).

3.4.1 Preparation and Analysis of Silver–Chitosan Combinations

Chitosan is produced commercially by deacetylation of chitin, which is the structural element in the exoskeleton of crustaceans (such as crabs and shrimp) and cell walls of fungi. The degree of deacetylation (% DD) can be determined by NMR spectroscopy, and the % DD in commercial chitosans ranges from 60% to 100%. On average, the molecular weight of commercially produced chitosan is between 3800 and 20,000 Da. A common method for the synthesis of chitosan is the deacetylation of chitin by heating it with an aqueous solution of sodium hydroxide. The reaction occurs in two stages under first-order kinetic control. The activation energy for the first step is higher than the second; its value is an estimated 48.76 kJ/mol at 25°C–120°C (Ahlafi et al. 2013). This reaction pathway, when allowed to go to completion (complete deacetylation), yields up to 98% product.

The amino group in chitosan has a pK_a value of ~6.5, which leads to protonation in mildy acidic solutions with a charge density dependent on both the solvent pH and on the % DD value. These basic amino groups make chitosan water soluble in acid and also makes it a particularly effective bioadhesive substance that readily binds to negatively charged surfaces (Lee et al. 2013) such as blood (Szatmari 2015), tissue (Altinel et al. 2012) and mucosal membranes (Islam et al. 2015). Chitosan enhances the transport of polar drugs across epithelial surfaces, and is biocompatible and biodegradable.

A variety of techniques has been used for analysing and characterising chitosan films and other chitosan preparations including scanning electron microscopy (Ebrahimiasl et al. 2015), Fourier transform infrared spectroscopy (Marei et al. 2016), x-ray diffraction (Archana et al. 2015), thermogravimetric analysis (Lewandowska 2015) and electrical conductivity measurements (Ebrahimiasl et al. 2015).

The methods that have been used for the synthesis of silver nanoparticles can be classified into three broad categories: wet chemistry (the most common), ion implantation (Haug et al. 2009) or physical vapour deposition (Cohen et al. 2007). Wet chemical methods for creating silver nanoparticles typically involve the reduction of a silver salt such as silver nitrate with a reducing agent like sodium borohydride ($NaBH_4$) in the presence of a colloidal stabiliser (Iravani et al. 2014). Polyvinyl alcohol, poly(vinylpyrrolidone), bovine serum albumin (BSA), citrate and cellulose have all been used as stabilising agents. In the case of BSA, the sulfur atom–, oxygen atom– and nitrogen atom–containing groups mitigate the high surface energy of the nanoparticles to allow the reduction to proceed better. The hydroxyl groups on the cellulose also help stabilise the particles. Natural products such as cellulose and sugars have been used to create silver nanoparticles without addition of an extra reducing agent (Shervani et al. 2011). These types of synthetic routes to silver nanoparticles have become widely known as 'green chemistry' because they avoid the use of reagents like $NaBH_4$, which is perceived to be harmful to the environment (Raveendran et al. 2003; Sharma et al. 2009). Many plant products and plant extracts have been used to prepare AgNP by green synthesis routes (Dinesh et al. 2015; Nayak et al. 2015). A green sonochemical synthesis route for silver nanoparticles was developed using κ-carrageenan (Elsupikhe et al. 2015).

A further step along this road has been the use of living organisms to biosynthesise silver nanoparticles, a procedure that is also called 'biogenic synthesis' (Duran et al. 2015). The advantages of using bacterial and fungal cells and cultures to synthesise AgNP are that bacteria and fungi are relatively easy to handle and can be genetically modified with ease. This flexibility may provide a means to develop systems that can synthesise AgNPs with different desired shapes and sizes in high yields, which is a current challenge in AgNP synthesis. Fungal species such as *Fusarium oxysporum* (Duran et al. 2005) and bacterial strains such as *Klebsiella pneumoniae* and *Bacillus* spp. (Gopinath and Velusamy 2013) can be used in the synthesis of AgNP. When the fungus/bacteria are added to silver nitrate solution, protein biomass is released from the cells. Electron-donating residues such as tryptophan and tyrosine reduce silver ions in the silver nitrate solution. This causes colloid crystallisation and thus the formation of nanoparticles similar to the previous methods. Figure 3.5 shows the preparation of Ag–chitosan composite nanoparticles, films, fibres and textiles.

The following techniques have been used to characterise silver nanoparticles. Hollow-fibre flow field-flow fractionation and multi-angle light scattering (Marassi et al. 2015); Auger nano-probe spectroscopy, micro-x-ray

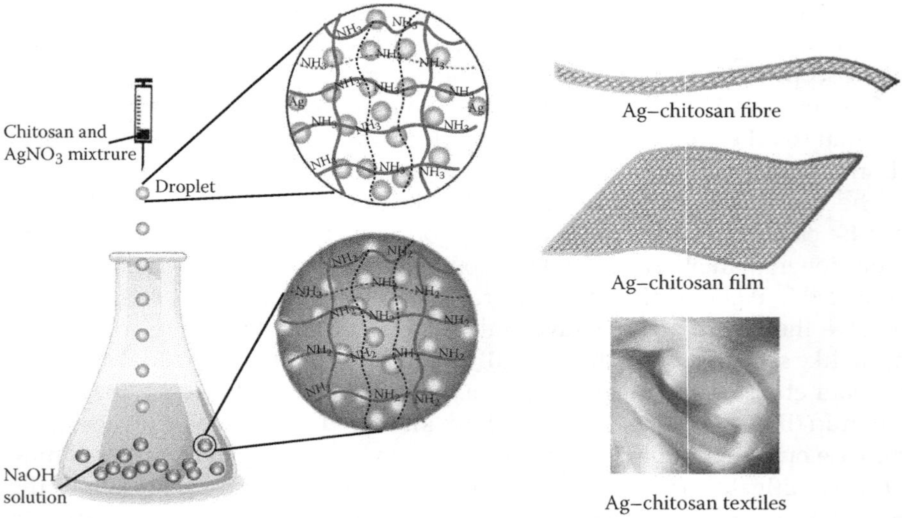

FIGURE 3.5
Schematic drawing of preparation of Ag–chitosan composite nanoparticles, films, fibres and textiles. The silver nanoparticles–chitosan composite spheres were synthesised by pumping droplets of chitosan and silver nitrate ($AgNO_3$) into a sodium hydroxide (NaOH) solution.

photoelectron spectroscopy and scanning electron microscopy (Ledeuil et al. 2014); and UV-visible spectrometry and transmission electron microscopy (Khan et al. 2013).

Chitosan preparations with varying degrees of deacetylation (DDAc < 30%) and chitosan powders and sheets (DDAc > 75%) with varying surface structure properties have been evaluated as carriers of AgNP. Chitin/chitosan–AgNP composites in powder or sheet form can be prepared by mixing AgNP suspensions with each of the chitin/chitosan-based material at pH 7.3, leading to homogeneous dispersion and stable adsorption of AgNPs onto chitin carriers with nanoscale fibre-like surface structures, and chitosan carriers with nanoscale porous surface structures (Ishihara et al. 2015).

Silver–chitosan nanocomposites can also be prepared by a one-pot method (Yadollahi et al. 2015). We will describe this method in some detail as an example. A series of chitosan/AgNP nanocomposite hydrogel beads (CH/Ag) were prepared according to a previously reported technique (Shu and Zhu 2000) using sodium tripolyphosphate (STPP) as the crosslinking agent and sodium borohydride ($NaBH_4$) as the AgNP-forming reducing agent. Typically, 1 g of chitosan and the desired amount of $AgNO_3$ (0.5–1.5 mmol) were added to 35 mL of distilled water. Then, 2.5 mL of acetic acid was added to the abovementioned mixture and stirred until a clear homogeneous viscous solution was obtained. The solution was extruded from a syringe to form droplets, into an aqueous solution (400 mL) containing STPP (4 g) and $NaBH_4$ (2.0 g). The beads were left in the solution for 24 h in order to crosslink the chitosan with STPP and to convert Ag^+ ions into AgNPs. The formation of AgNPs was confirmed by a change in the colour of the beads from pale brown to black. After that, the beads were filtered, washed several times with distilled water and dried under vacuum for 24 h.

3.4.2 Films, Fibres and Textiles

Chitosan films combined with silver have demonstrated a very efficient antibacterial activity in a variety of different studies. Formation of chitosan/silver nanoparticle films has proved to be an excellent 'green approach' for the synthesis of metal nanoparticle composites. These films can be used as antimicrobial packaging materials and wound dressings and can also be grafted or coated onto various implants to form antimicrobial surfaces (Thomas et al. 2009). One study examined four different types of chitosan-based nanocomposite films and compared their level of antimicrobial activity (Rhim et al. 2006). They found that chitosan films that contained silver showed a promising level of antimicrobial activity. The mechanism of antimicrobial action of the synergistic combination of chitosan and silver is graphically illustrated in Figure 3.6.

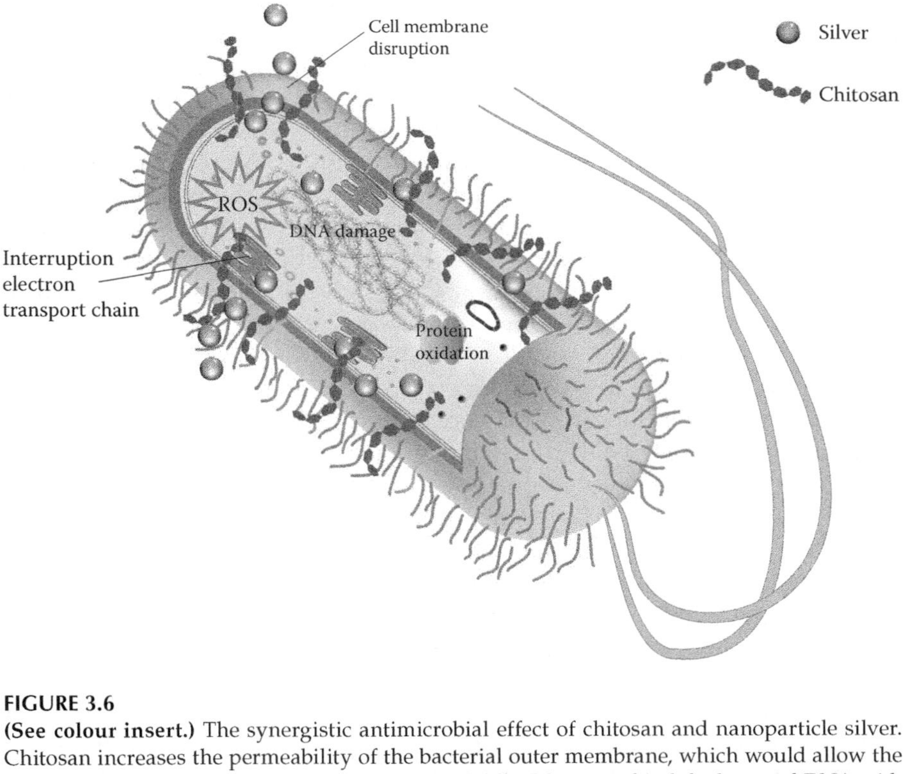

FIGURE 3.6
(See colour insert.) The synergistic antimicrobial effect of chitosan and nanoparticle silver. Chitosan increases the permeability of the bacterial outer membrane, which would allow the silver nanoparticles to penetrate into the bacterial cells. Silver ions bind the bacterial DNA with subsequent DNA damage, protein oxidation and interruption of the electron transport chain.

Silver-impregnated chitosan films were formed by combining initial separate materials composed of silver nitrate and chitosan through a thermal treatment. Compared with pure chitosan films, chitosan films with silver showed both fast and long-lasting antibacterial effectiveness against *Escherichia coli* (Gram-negative bacteria). The silver-containing antibacterial materials prepared in this study promised to be a good candidate for a broad range of biomedical and general applications (Lopez-Carballo et al. 2013; Wei et al. 2009). In another study, composite films were prepared from chitosan (Ch) and sago starch (SG) impregnated with silver nanoparticles (AgNP) with and without the antibiotic gentamicin (G). They showed that increasing the chitosan content in the composite material resulted in a decrease in its water absorption capacity (Arockianathan et al. 2012). Antibacterial activity of optically transparent nanocomposite films based on chitosan provided a basis for the evaluation of chitosan–silver composites in applications requiring flexible films with tuned optical properties and antimicrobial activity (Pinto et al. 2012).

Enhanced physical properties were achieved by incorporating CNC/ZnO–AgNPs into films, which could be useful in various applications (Azizi et al. 2014). The preparation, characterisation and antibacterial activity of a chitosan-g-poly-acrylonitrile/silver nanocomposite was described (Hebeish et al. 2014). The Cs-g-PAN/Ag nanocomposite showed excellent antimicrobial activity towards *E. coli* and *S. aureus* (Gram-positive bacteria). The results presented in this work indicated that silver sulfadiazine (AgSD)–loaded chitosan/chondroitin sulfate films exhibited the potential to be applied as a wound dressing material (Fajardo et al. 2013). Porous chitosan–silver nanocomposite films were prepared with applications in wound dressing, antibacterial application and water purification because of their excellent antimicrobial activity (Vimala et al. 2010). The lethal effect of chitosan–Ag (I) films on *S. aureus* was evaluated by electron microscopy, which clearly showed that chitosan–Ag (I) films displayed a notable anti-staphylococcal activity (Diaz-Visurraga et al. 2010).

Multilayering of the films provides a greater benefit in wound dressing applications. Antibacterial multilayered films containing nanosilver were prepared via a layer-by-layer fashion. Multilayered chitosan films containing nanosilver may have good potentials for surface modification of medical devices, especially for cardiovascular implants (Fu et al. 2006). Chitosan and heparin multilayered films were successfully constructed via layer-by-layer self-assembly. These films were used as a polymeric template to synthesise silver nanoparticles, which might provide great potential to design biofunctional nanocomposite films (Fu et al. 2006).

Fibres have proved to be very useful in the fabrication of wound dressings because of their high surface area, good ability to absorb liquids and a variety of product forms available. Fibres used in wound care products can be classified as either biodegradable or nonbiodegradable. A wide variety of different fibres and textiles (as well as films) has been applied for the treatment of wounds and other infections. Chitosan is a bioactive and biodegradable material that can be loaded with silver to make fibres, which are excellent materials to be used in wound dressings (Rennukka et al. 2014).

A material with enhanced antimicrobial activity was fabricated as a poly(3-hydroxybutyrate-co-44%-4-hydroxybutyrate) [P(3HB-co-44%4HB)]/chitosan-based silver nanocomposite material using different proportions of silver nanoparticles (Rennukka et al. 2014). A green fabrication process was used to prepare quaternised chitosan/rectorite/AgNP nanocomposites with antimicrobial activity. This study revealed that the obtained QCRAg nanocomposites had great potential for biomedical applications (Luo et al. 2014). Gamma irradiation of cotton fabrics in $AgNO_3$ solution was employed for preparation of antibacterial fabrics. The antibacterial activity against *S. aureus* and *E. coli* was found to be 99.99%. In addition, the AgNPs fabrics were not harmful to the skin of rabbits (Hanh et al. 2014).

Antimicrobial wound dressing nanofibre mats were prepared by assembly of multiple components (chitosan/silver-NPs/polyvinyl alcohol). These materials showed superior properties and synergistic antibacterial effects by combining chitosan with AgNPs (Abdelgawad et al. 2014). Chitosan combined with cellulose fibres was used to prepare sponge-like structures (membranes, foams) for the binding of silver ions. The composite material had very promising antibacterial properties against *P. aeruginosa* Gram(−) ≫ *E. coli* Gram(−) > *Staphylococcus hominis* Gram(+) ≫ *S. aureus* Gram(+) (Guibal et al. 2013). Antibacterial cotton fabrics were prepared containing core–shell Ag nanoparticles (Abdel-Mohsen et al. 2012). A multi-finishing treatment of cotton fabrics was carried out using core-shell nanoparticles that consisted of silver nanoparticles (Ag(0)) as the core and chitosan-O-methoxy polyethylene glycol (CTS-O-MPEG) as the shell. These NPs showed excellent antibacterial activity against Gram-negative *E. coli* and Gram-positive *S. aureus*. Electronic textiles and other smart textiles offer new possibilities in health care and risk management but bear their own risks for causing problems such as allergies (Wollina et al. 2006).

3.4.3 In Vitro Antimicrobial Effects of Silver–Chitosan Combinations

The antibacterial activity of chitosan films containing silver ions Ag(+1), against *Staphylococci* was studied using the broth dilution method and agar diffusion test. Incubation of bacteria with the film for 3, 6, 12 and 16 h affected the cell structure of *S. aureus*, causing elongation of the cells, disaggregation of the grape-like clusters, contraction of the bacterial cytoplasm, thickening of cell wall, increase in the cell wall roughness, cell disruption with loss of intracellular material, filamentation and finally bacteriolysis as revealed by transmission and scanning electron microscopy (TEM and SEM) techniques (Diaz-Visurraga et al. 2010). Films prepared by loading silver sulfadiazine onto chitosan/chondroitin sulfate had activity against *P. aeruginosa* and *S. aureus* bacteria but they were not toxic to mammalian Vero cells (Fajardo et al. 2013).

The advantage of Ag nanoparticles over larger particles is that they can dissolve faster in a given solution volume, thereby releasing higher amounts of metal ions (Palza 2015). Researchers are trying various approaches to improve the antimicrobial applications of metals by incorporating metal nanoparticles into polymer matrices and have reported better antimicrobial activity for such composites as compared to larger particles or polymer individually (Sanpui et al. 2008). Sanpul et al. found that AgNP–chitosan composites had significantly higher antimicrobial activity than components at their respective concentrations (Sanpui et al. 2008). Recombinant green fluorescent protein expressing *E. coli* was used and it was found that only a small percentage of (2.15% w/w) of metal nanoparticles in the composite was enough to significantly enhance inactivation of *E. coli* as compared with unaltered chitosan. The fluorescence spectroscopy showed release of cellular green fluorescent protein into the medium at a faster rate than with chitosan, indicating that *E. coli* growth stopped after exposure to the composite. This was further corroborated by results of fluorescence confocal laser scanning and SEM that revealed attachment of the bacteria to the composite and their subsequent fragmentation. The composite had no effect on the bacterial proteins as indicated by native protein gel electrophoresis experiments. Mori et al. (2013) reported that chitosan alone did not show any antiviral activity against H1N1 influenza A virus, while AgNP (having 3.5, 6.5 and 12.9 nm average diameter)/Ch composites showed antiviral activity that was concentration dependent as well as size dependent. The antiviral activity was measured by comparing the TC ID_{50} ratio of viral suspension treated with composites to those of untreated suspensions and showed an increase in viral inactivation with an increase in concentration of AgNPs. Furthermore, smaller-sized AgNP in the composites had stronger antiviral activity in general. Another study showed that the synergistic effects of Ch with AgNPs (25 nm diameter) were better than nanofibre mats not loaded with AgNPs in halting growth of aerobic bacteria (Abdelgawad et al. 2014). The antimicrobial activity of carboxymethyl chitosan/polyethylene nanofibres embedded with AgNPs against *S. aureus* ATCC 25923, *P. aeruginosa* ATCC 27853 and *E. coli* ATCC 25922 and *Candida albicans* ATCC 10231 was better than the antimicrobial activity of nanofibres without AgNPs, and better than AgNPs alone (Fouda et al. 2013).

Huang et al. showed that the synergistic combination of chitosan acetate with AgNPs inhibited the in vitro growth of Gram-positive methicillin-resistant *S. aureus* (MRSA) and the Gram-negative bacteria (*P. aeruginosa, P. mirabilis* and *Acinetobacter baumannii*), as judged by bioluminescence monitoring and isobolographic analysis of MIC data, and also produced synergistic killing after 30 min of incubation, as measured by a CFU assay. The synergistic effect was hypothesised to be caused by chitosan-mediated permeabilisation of bacterial cells, allowing better penetration of silver ions into the cell (Huang et al. 2011). Figure 3.7 shows the isobolographic analysis demonstrating true synergy.

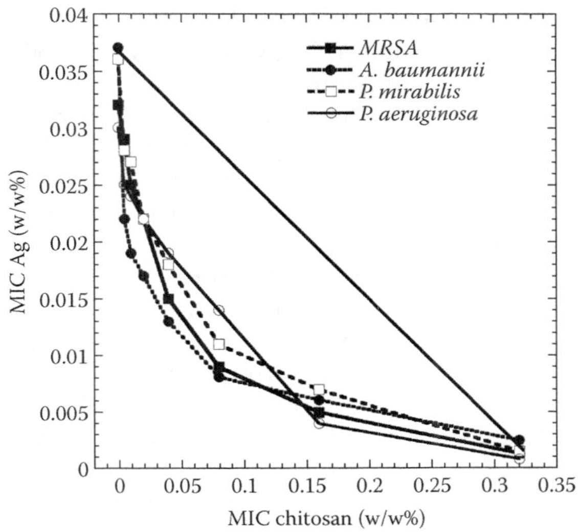

FIGURE 3.7
Synergy between nanoparticle silver and chitosan in vitro against four different bacterial species determined by isobolographic analysis of MIC values.

Chitosan films loaded with AgNPs showed faster and longer-lasting antibacterial activity against *E. coli* compared to chitosan films alone (Wei et al. 2009). The antimicrobial activity of chitosan–AgNP against *Candida glabrata, Saccharomyces cerevisiae, E. coli, K. pneumoniae, Salmonella* spp., *S. aureus* and *Bacillus cereus* was found to be more effective than $AgNO_3$, as the MIC values of the nanocomposites were lower than that for $AgNO_3$ (Rodriguez-Arguelles et al. 2011). Chitosan was reported to be a better stabilising carbohydrate as compared to potato starch when used to stabilise AgNPs for inhibition of growth of two clinical/medical relevant bacterial strains (*E. coli* and *S. aureus*). This difference was mainly attributed to the known antibacterial properties of chitosan, combined with the overall positive charge of the nanoparticles that were coated with this polymer. The nanoparticles that were obtained in the presence of starch showed lesser bactericidal effects, since the starch-capping agent was not able to contribute to the inhibition of bacteria growth, and also conferred a quasi-neutral charge to the nanoparticles (Oliveira et al. 2013). Antimicrobial activity studies with hybrid nanofibrous yarns based on *N*-carboxyethylchitosan and containing 5 wt% or 10 wt% AgNPs revealed that at an AgNP content of 5 wt%, the mats had a bacteriostatic effect, while at an AgNP content of 10 wt%, they had clear bactericidal activity (Penchev et al. 2010). AgNPs were incorporated into chitosan/polyethylene oxide electrospun nanofibres to create a nanofibre mat that showed excellent antibacterial activity against *E. coli* and *S. aureus* bacteria, and the release of silver nanoparticles from fibres continued for longer than 72 h (Wang et al. 2015). Wang et al. created nanocomposite films of chitosan/polyvinylpyrrolidone (PVP) with spherical AgNPs (diameters of 10–50 nm) stabilised after being immersed in PBS for 35 days. These films could eliminate *S. aureus* (ATCC 6538) and *E. coli* (ATCC 8739) in 5 min and had good long-lasting antibacterial activity. The anti-adhesion activity of the nanocomposite film was enhanced with an increase of the amount of PVP (Wang et al. 2012). A green approach was used by Thomas et al. to develop chitosan–nano-Ag films that demonstrated excellent antibacterial action against model bacteria, *E. coli* and *Bacillus* spp. (Thomas et al. 2009). Rhim et al. (2006) showed that Ag-containing chitosan-based nanocomposite films showed a promising range of antimicrobial activity. The system was found to have high antibacterial activity against Gram-positive bacteria (i.e. *S. aureus* and MRSA) and Gram-negative bacteria (i.e. *E. coli* O157:H7 and *P. aeruginosa*) as tested by the disc diffusion method (Shameli et al. 2011). A preparation of β-cyclodextrin (β-CD)–stabilised silver–chitosan nanocomposites showed promising activity against *E. coli* and *S. aureus* bacteria (Punitha et al. 2014).

A new series of composite nanoparticles was developed by El-Sherbiny et al. by incorporating AgNPs into interpenetrating polymeric networks based on a cationic trimethyl chitosan (TMCS) and anionic poly(acrylamide-co-sodium acrylate) copolymer. Promising bactericidal activity was shown by both simple AgNPs and the prepared composite nanoparticles as compared with the controls, and the antibacterial activity of the composite nanoparticles increased along with increasing the concentrations of AgNPs and the TMCS (El-Sherbiny et al. 2015). The embedding of AgNP into a dopamine-modified alginate/chitosan multilayer polyelectrolyte nanocomposite material inhibited growth of both *E. coli* and *S. aureus* (Chen et al. 2013). In yet another approach, Zain et al. tested the antibacterial activities of Ag, Cu, mixtures of Ag and Cu and Ag/Cu bimetallic nanoparticles in the presence of chitosan using *B. subtilis* and *E. coli*. *B. subtilis* was found to be more susceptible compared to *E. coli* under all conditions investigated. AgNPs were more toxic than copper nanoparticles and mixtures of both nanoparticles of the same mean particle size. However, when compared on an equal concentration basis, Cu nanoparticles proved more lethal to the bacteria because of a higher surface area (Zain et al. 2014). A triple-component approach was also used by Banerjee et al, wherein they prepared chitosan–AgNP composites in the presence of molecular iodine. Their study showed significantly higher bactericidal activity of the nanocomposite in the presence of iodine, compared to any single component alone (chitosan, AgNP or iodine). The bacteria became attached to the composite as detected by TEM, and there was cell wall damage of the bacteria that had been treated with the composite in the presence of iodine, as indicated by the results of flow cytometry. Further, the nanocomposite and iodine combination was found to produce ROS that could generate oxidative stress in the cytoplasm of bacterial cells, leading to cell death. Elucidation of the mechanism of synergy owing to three potential antibacterial components suggested that the surface of AgNPs interacted with molecular iodine to generate iodine atoms (iodine radicals), thus contributing toward free radical–induced oxidative stress, whereas chitosan and AgNPs facilitated the process of cell killing and thus synergistically enhanced the potency of the overall antimicrobial effect at the lowest concentrations of individual components (Banerjee et al. 2010).

AgNPs have more potent antimicrobial effects as compared to free silver ions, but one of the most important applications of these nanoparticles is in animals or human patients as an effective bactericidal agent. There are concerns that these nanoparticles could have some toxicity to eukaryotic cells. Some in vitro toxicity studies of AgNP have looked at cell viability, inflammation, developmental toxicity and genotoxicity in eukaryotic cell lines (such as L929 fibroblasts and RAW 264.7 macrophages). These studies have shown that 20-nm AgNPs are more toxic than silver ions (Park et al. 2011). AgNPs impregnated into an alginate–chitosan-blended nanocomposite material was found to induce apoptotic cell death in refractory U87MG (human glioblastoma cells), which involved extensive DNA damage, oxidative stress and mitochondrial dysfunction (Sharma et al. 2014). Anisha et al. showed that chitosan–hyaluronic acid/AgNPs composite sponges had potent antimicrobial activity against *E. coli*, *S. aureus*, MRSA, *P. aeruginosa* and *K. pneumoniae* (Anisha et al. 2013). Although sponges containing a higher proportion of AgNPs (0.005%, 0.01% and 0.02%) showed higher antibacterial activity against MRSA, the cytotoxicity and cell attachment studies done using human dermal fibroblast cells showed that there was also an AgNP concentration-dependent toxicity towards human cells. There is an urgent need for more studies that focus on the preparation of composites with an overall particle size that has potent antimicrobial activity but at the same time does not elicit toxic reactions towards the host eukaryotic cells. Toxicity and nanotoxicity concerns have been addressed by some groups. Travan et al. prepared AgNPs in a 3D hydrogel structure, provided by mixing chitosan with the polysaccharide alginate; the particles showed an effective bactericidal activity towards both Gram-positive and Gram-negative bacteria without any cytotoxic effect towards three different eukaryotic cell lines. These results were due to the fact that the nanoparticles that were immobilised in the gel matrix exerted their antimicrobial activity by simple contact with the bacterial membrane but were not taken up and internalised by the eukaryotic cells (Travan et al. 2009). This group also showed that nanocomposite materials based on lactose-modified chitosan and AgNPs were effective in killing both Gram-negative and Gram-positive bacterial strains without exerting any significant cytotoxic effect towards osteoblast-like cell lines. Moreover, these osteoblast cells were able to firmly attach and even able to proliferate on the surface of the coating (Travan et al. 2011). Chitosan-stabilised AgNPs were tested for antimicrobial activity as well as toxicity against macrophage cells. Ch-AgNPs exhibited potent antibacterial activity against different human pathogens and also impeded bacterial biofilm formation as revealed by CFU assays and SEM. SEM analysis indicated that the nanocomposite killed bacteria by disrupting the cell membrane. At the same time, the Ch-AgNPs did not harm the host cells since no significant cytotoxicity or DNA damage was seen in the macrophages (Jena et al. 2012). Another study with AgNPs stabilised by lactose-modified chitosan showed that the synergistic activity of chitosan and AgNPs was able to inhibit the growth of *S. aureus, E. coli, Staphylococcus epidermidis* and *P. aeruginosa* strains and to break apart mature biofilms. The biocompatibility assays further revealed that there were no harmful effects on the viability of keratinocytes and fibroblasts (Sacco et al. 2015). The clay mineral montmorillonite (MMT) can form nanocomposites with chitosan that can then be loaded with silver sulfadiazine (AgSD) using an intercalation solution technique (Aguzzi et al. 2014). Structure and morphology of loaded nanocomposites were studied and compared with pure components and unloaded nanocomposites using x-ray diffraction, Fourier transformed infrared spectroscopy, high-resolution transmission electron microscopy coupled with energy-dispersion x-ray analysis and thermal and elemental analysis. MMT/CS nanocomposites loaded with AgSD prepared using 100 mg of MMT were studied for in vitro wound healing using normal human dermal fibroblasts. The nanocomposite showed good in vitro biocompatibility and hastened the closure of gaps created in fibroblast monolayers in tissue culture, while maintaining the antimicrobial properties expected of AgSD (especially against *P. aeruginosa*). Fu et al. prepared multilayered films containing nano-Ag that were effective not only as antibacterial agents but also as anticoagulant coatings. Moreover, evaluation of the eukaryotic cell toxicity showed that these films did not exert any cytotoxicity (Fu et al. 2006).

3.4.4 In Vivo Studies of Silver–Chitosan Combinations

Employment of nanoparticles is a growing antimicrobial approach to overcoming drug resistance developed by microbes against antibiotics. By increasing the amount of drug uptake and by inhibiting the efflux of drugs from the microbial cells, nanoparticles can fight against biofilm development and could also conceivably combat intracellular bacteria. Moreover, nanoparticles may be able to guide antimicrobial agents to the spot of infection and improve aspects of drug delivery and controlled release, so that effective doses of drug are administered at the infected site, while reducing the overall doses necessary to the patient and thus mitigating the development of drug resistance (Pelgrift and Friedman 2013). Chitosan and silver nanoparticles have proved their effectiveness by studies carried out in vivo (Gaafar et al. 2014). A nanocomposite coating formed by attaching the polysaccharide 1-deoxylactit-1-yl chitosan (Chitlac) and AgNPs onto methacrylate thermosets was studied, and this system showed good antibacterial and antibiofilm activity (Marsich et al. 2013). CS/nHAp/nAg biocomposite scaffolds showed potential in controlling implant-associated bacterial infection during reconstructive surgery of bones (Saravanan et al. 2011).

3.4.5 In Vivo Effects on Protecting and Treating Wounds

Wounds are often considered to be difficult to treat in certain circumstances, such as when excessive bleeding occurs, and when infections develop due to microbial contamination that can easily occur in their initial stages. Bleeding remains a leading cause of early death after trauma, and infectious complications that can arise if the initial trauma is survived are also a challenge. Moreover, burn wounds and wounds in diabetic patients have their own different set of complications, which render the wounds very challenging to treat. Thus, proper management of 'difficult to heal' wounds can considerably reduce the time required for tissue repair, promote the healing process and minimise the risk of infection. Silver compounds have been reported to be effective antimicrobial agents against almost all known bacteria, fungi and some viruses. Conversely, the clinically employed AgSD has been revealed to be cytotoxic towards fibroblasts and keratinocytes in vitro and as a result has been hypothesised to retard wound healing in patients in vivo. These drawbacks of silver and AgSD can be overcome by methods such as the loading of AgSD in MMT/CS nanocomposites as mentioned above (Aguzzi et al. 2014). Another study evaluated the antimicrobial properties of this AgSD-MMT/CS against four reference bacterial strains and showed excellent in vitro biocompatibility, with good gap closure properties in fibroblasts, and maintained the antimicrobial properties of AgSD against skin pathogens (particularly against *P. aeruginosa*) (Sandri et al. 2014). Nanofibres prepared with AgNP/chitosan oligosaccharide/poly(vinyl alcohol) for wound dressings significantly inhibited growth of *E. coli* and *S. aureus* bacteria. Moreover, PVA/COS-AgNP nanofibres accelerated the rate of wound healing compared to that found with a control dressing (gauze) (Li et al. 2013). In case of diabetic wounds infected with drug-resistant bacteria, a chitosan–hyaluronic acid/nanosilver composite showed potent antimicrobial properties against the tested organisms, at the optimal concentration of nano-Ag (best antibacterial action with least toxicity towards mammalian cells) that was identified (Anisha et al. 2013).

Wound dressings made from either hydroxypropylmethyl cellulose or chitosan glutamate (CS-glu) containing silver sulfadiazine encapsulated in solid lipid nanoparticles were investigated for applications in tissue repair (Sandri et al. 2013). These polymers were chosen to obtain a sponge matrix with suitable elasticity and softness and, moreover, with good bioadhesive properties to skin lesions, and moreover, platelet lysate (a source of growth factors) was added to stimulate healing. Dressings based on chitosan glutamate showed the best antimicrobial activity both with and without platelet lysate. Nanoparticle-based materials are often used as coatings applied to biomaterial devices on order to enhance sterility against a variety of microbes. In one study, silk fibres (SF) were coated with chitosan impregnated with AgNP (Ag-C-SF). The modified fibres also showed good antimicrobial activity and improved thermal stability (Karthikeyan et al. 2011). Fabrication of new chitosan-based composite sponges containing AgNP for wound dressings showed that the new AgNP-loaded chitosan-based composite sponges possessed not only bacteriostatic but also bactericidal activity against these tested bacteria (Li et al. 2011a).

Chitosan microspheres (CSM) loaded with AgSD were developed using a novel water-in-oil emulsion technique to address the problem of infection in wounds (Seetharaman et al. 2011). This material showed extended release of an antimicrobial drug from a matrix that may provide an excellent cellular environment for revascularisation of infected wounds. The AgSD-loaded microspheres were porous with needle-like structures (attributed to AgSD) that were evenly distributed over the spheres. The average particle size of the AgSD-CSM was 125–180 μm with 76.50% ± 2.8% drug entrapment. As a potential new wound dressing with pro-angiogenic activity, AgSD-CSM particles were impregnated in polyethylene glycol (PEGylated) fibrin gels. In vitro drug release studies showed that a burst release of 27.02% in 6 h was achieved, with controlled release for 72 h, with an equilibrium concentration of 27.7% (70 μg). AgSD-CSM-PEGylated fibrin gels showed good microbicidal activity at 125 and 100 μg/mL against *S. aureus* and *P. aeruginosa*, respectively. The in vitro vasculogenic activity of this composite dressing was shown by seeding adipose-derived stem cells (ASC) in SSD-CSM-PEGylated fibrin gels. The ASC spontaneously formed microvascular tube-like structures without the addition of any exogenous factors.

Membranes of chitosan and alginate were prepared via a casting/solvent evaporation technique (Meng et al. 2010). Membranes of chitosan and alginate with SSD as a model drug incorporated in different concentrations and different membrane compositions were obtained. The polyblend solution viscosity reached its highest at a polyblend composition of 1:1. Chitosan/alginate membranes showed pH- and ionic strength–dependent water uptake properties and had the WVTR range from 442 to 618 g/m^2/day. The maximum value of the breaking strength of the dry membrane was 52.16 MPa, and the maximum value of the wet membrane breaking elongation was 46.28%. The results of controlled-release studies showed that the silver sulfadiazine release rate was the fastest when the alginate content was 50%. On the basis of the requisite physical properties, the chitosan–alginate PEC membrane can be considered for potential wound dressing or controlled release application.

As mentioned above, the engineered freeze-dried chitosan acetate bandage preparation (HemCon) is used as a hemostatic dressing, and a previous report showed that it could be effectively antimicrobial in a mouse model of heavily contaminated wounds (Burkatovskaya et al. 2006). In an attempt to further improve its antimicrobial activity, a dressing composed of HemCon chitosan acetate incorporating nanoparticle silver was compared with a dressing of chitosan acetate alone in an in vivo burn model infected with bioluminescent *P. aeruginosa* (Huang et al. 2011). The survival rates of mice treated with silver–chitosan or regular chitosan or left untreated were 64.3% ($P = 0.0082$ vs. regular chitosan and $P = 0.0003$ vs. the control), 21.4% and 0%,

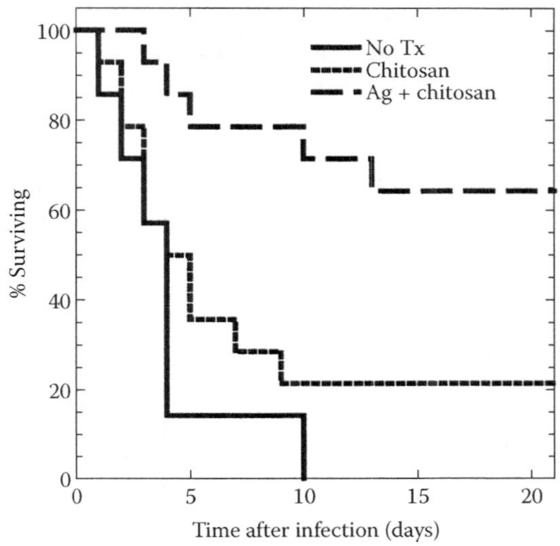

FIGURE 3.8
Chitosan bandage incorporating silver nanoparticles as a treatment for mice with third-degree burns infected with *P. aeruginosa*. Kaplan–Meier survival curves for no treatment ($n = 7$), chitosan alone ($n = 14$) and AgNP–chitosan ($n = 14$).

respectively (Figure 3.8). Most of the fatalities occurred between 2 and 5 days postinfection. Silver–chitosan dressings effectively controlled the development of systemic sepsis, as shown by blood culture. These data suggest that a dressing combining chitosan acetate with silver leads to improved antimicrobial efficacy against fatal burn infections.

Another study investigated the feasibility of a novel nanocomposite (GC/Ag) formed from a genipin-crosslinked chitosan (GC) film in which AgNPs were embedded in various amounts for wound-dressing applications. The results showed that silver ions had dual functions – structural reinforcement and provision of antimicrobial properties to a biocompatible polymer (Liu and Huang 2008). Although chitosan dressings have been developed to address the problems of wound healing, they are not always effective in controlling bleeding or killing bacteria. Refining a chitosan dressing by incorporating a procoagulant (polyphosphate) and an antimicrobial (silver) improved hemostatic and antimicrobial properties (Ong et al. 2008).

3.5 Conclusions and Future Directions

The discovery of the synergistic effects of the combination of chitosan and silver nanoparticles has opened new horizons in the fabrication of antimicrobial materials. These two approaches have different mechanisms of action in that the polycationic chitosan can increase the permeability of the bacterial outer membranes and allow the silver nanoparticles to penetrate further into the bacterial cells, where they can exert antibacterial effects by increasing the production of ROS and releasing silver ions to bind to and inactivate essential bacterial proteins. Nanosilver–chitosan composite materials have been fabricated into fibres, films and textiles. The flexible nature of these materials has primarily encouraged their development as dressings for wounds and burns, where it is well established that a prolonged antimicrobial effect is beneficial in prevention of infections and stimulation of wound healing. In future directions, we believe that nanosilver–chitosan hybrid materials may have wider applications in biomedical fields. Chitosan is well established as a hemostatic agent, and the addition of nanosilver could add a desirable anti-infective component into these materials. There may be applications in dentistry where nanotechnology is rapidly contributing to technological advances. New antimicrobial coatings for implantable medical devices such as catheters, prosthetic joints, orthopedic implants and reconstructive meshes are a rapidly growing area of research and nanosilver–chitosan hybrid materials may have a role to play. Tissue engineering is another field where these composites may have applications.

Acknowledgement

M.R.H. was supported by US National Institutes of Health grant AI050875.

References

Abdelgawad, A.M., Hudson, S.M., Rojas, O.J. Antimicrobial wound dressing nanofiber mats from multicomponent (chitosan/silver-NPs/polyvinyl alcohol) systems. *Carbohydr Polym* 100 (2014) 166–178.

Abdel-Mohsen, A.M., Abdel-Rahman, R.M., Hrdina, R., Imramovsky, A., Burgert, L., Aly, A.S. Antibacterial cotton fabrics treated with core–shell nanoparticles. *Int J Biol Macromol* 50 (2012) 1245–1253.

Aguzzi, C., Sandri, G., Bonferoni, C., Cerezo, P., Rossi, S., Ferrari, F., Caramella, C., Viseras, C. Solid state characterisation of silver sulfadiazine loaded on montmorillonite/chitosan nanocomposite for wound healing. *Colloids Surf B Biointerfaces* 113 (2014) 152–157.

Ahamed, M.I., Sankar, S., Kashif, P.M., Basha, S.K., Sastry, T.P. Evaluation of biomaterial containing regenerated cellulose and chitosan incorporated with silver nanoparticles. *Int J Biol Macromol* 72 (2015) 680–686.

Ahlafi, H., Moussout, H., Boukhlifi, F., Echetna, M., Bennani, M.N., Slimane, M.S. Kinetics of *N*-deacetylation of chitin extracted from shrimp shells collected from coastal area of Morocco. *Mediterranean J Chem* 2 (2013) 503–513.

Altinel, Y., Ozturk, E., Ozkaya, G., Akyildiz, E.U., Ulcay, Y., Ozguc, H. The effect of a chitosan coating on the adhesive potential and tensile strength of polypropylene meshes. *Hernia* 16 (2012) 709–714.

Anisha, B.S., Biswas, R., Chennazhi, K.P., Jayakumar, R. Chitosan–hyaluronic acid/nano silver composite sponges for drug resistant bacteria infected diabetic wounds. *Int J Biol Macromol* 62 (2013) 310–320.

Archana, D., Singh, B.K., Dutta, J., Dutta, P.K. Chitosan–PVP–nano silver oxide wound dressing: In vitro and in vivo evaluation. *Int J Biol Macromol* 73 (2015) 49–57.

Arockianathan, P.M., Sekar, S., Kumaran, B., Sastry, T.P. Preparation, characterization and evaluation of biocomposite films containing chitosan and sago starch impregnated with silver nanoparticles. *Int J Biol Macromol* 50 (2012) 939–946.

Atiyeh, B.S., Costagliola, M., Hayek, S.N., Dibo, S.A. Effect of silver on burn wound infection control and healing: Review of the literature. *Burns* 33 (2007) 139–148.

Azizi, S., Ahmad, M.B., Hussein, M.Z., Ibrahim, N.A., Namvar, F. Preparation and properties of poly(vinyl alcohol)/chitosan blend bionanocomposites reinforced with cellulose nanocrystals/ZnO–Ag multifunctional nanosized filler. *Int J Nanomedicine* 9 (2014) 1909–1917.

Banerjee, M., Mallick, S., Paul, A., Chattopadhyay, A., Ghosh, S.S. Heightened reactive oxygen species generation in the antimicrobial activity of a three component iodinated chitosan-silver nanoparticle composite. *Langmuir* 26 (2010) 5901–5908.

Burkatovskaya, M., Tegos, G.P., Swietlik, E., Demidova, T.N., P. Castano, A., Hamblin, M.R. Use of chitosan bandage to prevent fatal infections developing from highly contaminated wounds in mice. *Biomaterials* 27 (2006) 4157–4164.

Chen, M., Yang, Z., Wu, H., Pan, X., Xie, X., Wu, C. Antimicrobial activity and the mechanism of silver nanoparticle thermosensitive gel. *Int J Nanomedicine* 6 (2011) 2873–2877.

Chen, Z., Zhang, X., Cao, H., Huang, Y. Chitosan-capped silver nanoparticles as a highly selective colorimetric probe for visual detection of aromatic ortho-trihydroxy phenols. *Analyst* 138 (2013) 2343–2349.

Choi, O., Hu, Z. Size dependent and reactive oxygen species related nanosilver toxicity to nitrifying bacteria. *Environ Sci Technol* 42 (2008) 4583–4588.

Cohen, M.S., Stern, J.M., Vanni, A.J., Kelley, R.S., Baumgart, E., Field, D., Libertino, J.A., Summerhayes, I.C. In vitro analysis of a nanocrystalline silver-coated surgical mesh. *Surg Infect (Larchmt)* 8 (2007) 397–403.

Dellera, E., Bonferoni, M.C., Sandri, G., Rossi S., F. Ferrari, Fante, Del, C., Perotti, C., Grisoli, P., Caramella, C. Development of chitosan oleate ionic micelles loaded with silver sulfadiazine to be associated with platelet lysate for application in wound healing. *Eur J Pharm Biopharm* 88 (2014) 643–650.

Diaz-Visurraga, J., Garcia, A., Cardenas, G. Lethal effect of chitosan–Ag (I) films on *Staphylococcus aureus* as evaluated by electron microscopy. *J Appl Microbiol* 108 (2010) 633–646.

Dinesh, D., Murugan, K., Madhiyazhagan, P., Panneerselvam, C., Kumar, P.M., Nicoletti, M., Jiang, W., Benelli, G., Chandramohan, B., Suresh, U. Mosquitocidal and antibacterial activity of green-synthesized silver nanoparticles from Aloe vera extracts: Towards an effective tool against the malaria vector *Anopheles stephensi*? *Parasitol Res* 114 (2015) 1519–1529.

Duran, M., Silveira, C.P., Duran, N. Catalytic role of traditional enzymes for biosynthesis of biogenic metallic nanoparticles: A mini-review. *IET Nanobiotechnol* 9 (2015) 314–323.

Duran, N., Marcato, P.D., Alves, O.L., Souza, G.I., Esposito, E. Mechanistic aspects of biosynthesis of silver nanoparticles by several *Fusarium oxysporum* strains. *J Nanobiotechnology* 3 (2005) 8.

Ebrahimiasl, S., Zakaria, A., Kassim, A., Basri, S.N. Novel conductive polypyrrole/zinc oxide/chitosan bionanocomposite: Synthesis, characterization, antioxidant, and antibacterial activities. *Int J Nanomedicine* 10 (2015) 217–227.

El-Sherbiny, I., Salih, E., Reicha, F. New trimethyl chitosan-based composite nanoparticles as promising antibacterial agents. *Drug Dev Ind Pharm* (2015) 1–10.

Elsupikhe, R.F., Shameli, K., Ahmad, M.B., Ibrahim, N.A., Zainudin, N. Green sonochemical synthesis of silver nanoparticles at varying concentrations of kappa-carrageenan. *Nanoscale Res Lett* 10 (2015) 916.

Fajardo, A.R., Lopes, L.C., Caleare, A.O., Britta, E.A., Nakamura, C.V., Rubira, A.F., Muniz, E.C. Silver sulfadiazine loaded chitosan/chondroitin sulfate films for a potential wound dressing application. *Mater Sci Eng C Mater Biol Appl* 33 (2013) 588–595.

Fouda, M.M., El-Aassar, M.R., Al-Deyab, S.S. Antimicrobial activity of carboxymethyl chitosan/polyethylene oxide nanofibers embedded silver nanoparticles. *Carbohydr Polym* 92 (2013) 1012–1017.

Franci, G., Falanga, A., Galdiero, S., Palomba, L., Rai, M., Morelli, G., Galdiero, M. Silver nanoparticles as potential antibacterial agents. *Molecules* 20 (2015) 8856–8874.

Fu, J., Ji, J., Fan, D., Shen, J. Construction of antibacterial multilayer films containing nanosilver via layer-by-layer assembly of heparin and chitosan–silver ions complex. *J Biomed Mater Res A* 79 (2006) 665–674.

Gaafar, M.R., Mady, R.F., Diab, R.G., Shalaby, T.I. Chitosan and silver nanoparticles: Promising anti-toxoplasma agents. *Exp Parasitol* 143 (2014) 30–38.

Gopinath, V., Velusamy, P. Extracellular biosynthesis of silver nanoparticles using *Bacillus* sp. GP-23 and evaluation of their antifungal activity towards *Fusarium oxysporum*. *Spectrochim Acta A Mol Biomol Spectrosc* 106 (2013) 170–174.

Guibal, E., Cambe, S., Bayle, S., Taulemesse, J.M., Vincent, T. Silver/chitosan/cellulose fibers foam composites: From synthesis to antibacterial properties. *J Colloid Interface Sci* 393 (2013) 411–420.

Hancock, R.E., Farmer, S.W. Mechanism of uptake of deglucoteicoplanin amide derivatives across outer membranes of *Escherichia coli* and *Pseudomonas aeruginosa*. *Antimicrob Agents Chemother* 37 (1993) 453–456.

Hanh, T.T., Van Phu, D., Thu, N.T., Quoc le, A., Duyen do, N.B., Hien, N.Q. Gamma irradiation of cotton fabrics in AgNO(3) solution for preparation of antibacterial fabrics. *Carbohydr Polym* 101 (2014) 1243–1248.

Haug, J., Kruth, H., Dubiel, M., Hofmeister, H., Haas, S., Tatchev, D., Hoell, A. ASAXS study on the formation of core–shell Ag/Au nanoparticles in glass. *Nanotechnology* 20 (2009) 505705.

Hebeish, A.A., Ramadan, M.A., Montaser, A.S., Farag, A.M. Preparation, characterization and antibacterial activity of chitosan-g-poly acrylonitrile/silver nanocomposite. *Int J Biol Macromol* 68 (2014) 178–184.

Helander, I.M., Alakomi, H.L., Latva-Kala, K., Koski, P. Polyethyleneimine is an effective permeabilizer of gram-negative bacteria. *Microbiology* 143 (Pt 10) (1997) 3193–3199.

Huang, L., Dai, T., Xuan, Y., Tegos, G.P., Hamblin, M.R. Synergistic combination of chitosan acetate with nanoparticle silver as a topical antimicrobial: Efficacy against bacterial burn infections. *Antimicrob Agents Chemother* 55 (2011) 3432–3438.

Hyldgaard, M., Mygind, T., Vad, B.S., Stenvang, M., Otzen, D.E., Meyer, R.L. The antimicrobial mechanism of action of epsilon-poly-L-lysine. *Appl Environ Microbiol* 80 (2014) 7758–7770.

Iravani, S., Korbekandi, H., Mirmohammadi, S.V., Zolfaghari, B. Synthesis of silver nanoparticles: Chemical, physical and biological methods. *Res Pharm Sci* 9 (2014) 385–406.

Ishihara, M., Nguyen, V.Q., Mori, Y., Nakamura, S., Hattori, H. Adsorption of silver nanoparticles onto different surface structures of chitin/chitosan and correlations with antimicrobial activities. *Int J Mol Sci* 16 (2015) 13973–13988.

Islam, M.A., Park, T.E., Reesor, E., Cherukula, K., Hasan, A., Firdous, J., Singh, B., Kang, S.K., Choi, Y.J., Park, I.K., Cho, C.S. Mucoadhesive chitosan derivatives as novel drug carriers. *Curr Pharm Des* 21 (2015) 4285–4309.

Jarmila, V., Vavrikova, E. Chitosan derivatives with antimicrobial, antitumour and antioxidant activities – A review. *Curr Pharm Des* 17 (2011) 3596–3607.

Jena, P., Mohanty, S., Mallick, R., Jacob, B., Sonawane, A. Toxicity and antibacterial assessment of chitosan-coated silver nanoparticles on human pathogens and macrophage cells. *Int J Nanomedicine* 7 (2012) 1805–1818.

Karthikeyan, K., Sekar, S., Devi, M.P., Inbasekaran, S., Lakshminarasaiah, C.H., Sastry, T.P. Fabrication of novel biofibers by coating silk fibroin with chitosan impregnated with silver nanoparticles. *J Mater Sci Mater Med* 22 (2011) 2721–2726.

Khan, Z., Singh, T., Hussain, J.I., Obaid, A.Y., Al-Thabaiti, S.A., El-Mossalamy, E.H. Starch-directed green synthesis, characterization and morphology of silver nanoparticles. *Colloids Surf B Biointerfaces* 102 (2013) 578–584.

Krishnaraj, C., Harper, S.L., Choe, H. S., Kim, K. P., Yun, S.I. Mechanistic aspects of biologically synthesized silver nanoparticles against food- and water-borne microbes. *Bioprocess Biosyst Eng* 38 (2015) 1943–1958.

Kujda, M., Ocwieja, M., Adamczyk, Z., Bochenska, O., Bras, G., Kozik, A., Bielanska, E., Barbasz, J. Charge stabilized silver nanoparticles applied as antibacterial agents. *J Nanosci Nanotechnol* 15 (2015) 3574–3583.

Ledeuil, J.B., Uhart, A., Soule, S., Allouche, J., Dupin, J.C., Martinez, H. New insights into micro/nanoscale combined probes (nanoAuger, muXPS) to characterize Ag/Au@SiO_2 core–shell assemblies. *Nanoscale* 6 (2014) 11130–11140.

Lee, D.W., Lim, C., Israelachvili, J.N., Hwang, D.S. Strong adhesion and cohesion of chitosan in aqueous solutions. *Langmuir* 29 (2013) 14222–14229.

Lewandowska, K. Characterization of chitosan composites with synthetic polymers and inorganic additives. *Int J Biol Macromol* 81 (2015) 159–164.

Li, C., Fu, R., Yu, C., Li, Z., Guan, H., Hu, D., Zhao, D., Lu, L. Silver nanoparticle/chitosan oligosaccharide/poly(vinyl alcohol) nanofibers as wound dressings: A preclinical study. *Int J Nanomedicine* 8 (2013) 4131–4145.

Li, D., Diao, J., Zhang, J., Liu, J. Fabrication of new chitosan-based composite sponge containing silver nanoparticles and its antibacterial properties for wound dressing. *J Nanosci Nanotechnol* 11 (2011a) 4733–4738.

Li, P., Poon, Y.F., Li, W., Zhu, H.Y., Yeap, S.H., Cao, Y., Qi, X., Zhou, C., Lamrani, M., Beuerman, R.W., Kang, E.T., Mu, Y., Li, C.M., Chang, M.W., Leong, S.S., Chan-Park, M.B. A polycationic antimicrobial and biocompatible hydrogel with microbe membrane suctioning ability. *Nat Mater* 10 (2011b) 149–156.

Likus, W., Bajor, G., Siemianowicz, K. Nanosilver – Does it have only one face? *Acta Biochim Pol* 60 (2013) 495–501.

Liu, B.S., Huang, T.B. Nanocomposites of genipin-crosslinked chitosan/silver nanoparticles – Structural reinforcement and antimicrobial properties. *Macromol Biosci* 8 (2008) 932–941.

Lopez-Carballo, G., Higueras, L., Gavara, R., Hernandez-Munoz, P. Silver ions release from antibacterial chitosan films containing in situ generated silver nanoparticles. *J Agric Food Chem* 61 (2013) 260–267.

Luo, J., Xie, M., Wang, X. Green fabrication of quaternized chitosan/rectorite/Ag NP nanocomposites with antimicrobial activity. *Biomed Mater* 9 (2014) 011001.

Marassi, V., Casolari, S., Roda, B., Zattoni, A., Reschiglian, P., Panzavolta, S., Tofail, S.A., Ortelli, S., Delpivo, C., Blosi, M., Costa, A.L. Hollow-fiber flow field-flow fractionation and multi-angle light scattering investigation of the size, shape and metal-release of silver nanoparticles in aqueous medium for nano-risk assessment. *J Pharm Biomed Anal* 106 (2015) 92–99.

Marei, N.H., Samiee, E.A., Salah, T., Saad, G.R., Elwahy, A.H. Isolation and characterization of chitosan from different local insects in Egypt. *Int J Biol Macromol* 82 (2016) 871–877.

Marsich, E., Travan, A., Donati, I., Turco, G., Kulkova, J., Moritz, N., Aro, H.T., Crosera, M., Paoletti, S. Biological responses of silver-coated thermosets: An in vitro and in vivo study. *Acta Biomater* 9 (2013) 5088–5099.

Meng, X., Tian, F., Yang, J., He, C.N., Xing, N., Li, F. Chitosan and alginate polyelectrolyte complex membranes and their properties for wound dressing application. *J Mater Sci Mater Med* 21 (2010) 1751–1759.

Mori, Y., Ono, T., Miyahira, Y., Nguyen, V.Q., Matsui, T., Ishihara, M. Antiviral activity of silver nanoparticle/chitosan composites against H1N1 influenza A virus. *Nanoscale Res Lett* 8 (2013) 93.

Nayak, D., Ashe, S., Rauta, P.R., Nayak, B. Biosynthesis, characterisation and antimicrobial activity of silver nanoparticles using *Hibiscus rosa-sinensis* petals extracts. *IET Nanobiotechnol* 9 (2015) 288–293.

Oliveira, de L.F., Goncalves, Jde, O., Goncalves, Kde, A., Kobarg, J., Cardoso, M.B. Sweeter but deadlier: Decoupling size, charge and capping effects in carbohydrate coated bactericidal silver nanoparticles. *J Biomed Nanotechnol* 9 (2013) 1817–1826.

Ong, S.Y., Wu, J., Moochhala, S.M., Tan, M.H., Lu, J. Development of a chitosan-based wound dressing with improved hemostatic and antimicrobial properties. *Biomaterials* 29 (2008) 4323–4332.

Palza, H. Antimicrobial polymers with metal nanoparticles. *Int J Mol Sci* 16 (2015) 2099–2116.

Park, M.V., Neigh, A.M., Vermeulen, J.P., de la Fonteyne, L.J., Verharen, H.W., Briede, J.J., van Loveren, H., de Jong, W.H. The effect of particle size on the cytotoxicity, inflammation, developmental toxicity and genotoxicity of silver nanoparticles. *Biomaterials* 32 (2011) 9810–9817.

Pelgrift, R.Y., Friedman, A.J. Nanotechnology as a therapeutic tool to combat microbial resistance. *Adv Drug Deliv Rev* 65 (2013) 1803–1815.

Penchev, H., Paneva, D., Manolova, N., Rashkov, I. Hybrid nanofibrous yarns based on *N*-carboxyethylchitosan and silver nanoparticles with antibacterial activity prepared by self-bundling electrospinning. *Carbohydr Res* 345 (2010) 2374–2380.

Pinto, R.J., Fernandes, S.C., Freire, C.S., Sadocco, P., Causio, J., Neto, C.P., Trindade, T. Antibacterial activity of optically transparent nanocomposite films based on chitosan or its derivatives and silver nanoparticles. *Carbohydr Res* 348 (2012) 77–83.

Punitha, N., Ramesh, P.S., Geetha, D. Spectral, morphological and antibacterial studies of beta-cyclodextrin stabilized silver – Chitosan nanocomposites. *Spectrochim Acta A Mol Biomol Spectrosc* 136PC (2014) 1710–1717.

Raafat, D., Sahl, H.G. Chitosan and its antimicrobial potential – A critical literature survey. *Microb Biotechnol* 2 (2009) 186–201.

Rabea, E.I., Badawy, M.E., Stevens, C.V., Smagghe, G., Steurbaut, W. Chitosan as antimicrobial agent: Applications and mode of action. *Biomacromolecules* 4 (2003) 1457–1465.

Raveendran, P., Fu, J., Wallen, S.L. Completely 'green' synthesis and stabilization of metal nanoparticles. *J Am Chem Soc* 125 (2003) 13940–13941.

Rennukka, M., Sipaut, C.S., Amirul, A.A. Synthesis of poly(3-hydroxybutyrate-co-4-hydroxybutyrate)/chitosan/silver nanocomposite material with enhanced antimicrobial activity. *Biotechnol Prog* 30 (2014) 1469–1479.

Rhim, J.W., Hong, S.I., Park, H.M., Ng, P.K. Preparation and characterization of chitosan-based nanocomposite films with antimicrobial activity. *J Agric Food Chem* 54 (2006) 5814–5822.

Rodriguez-Arguelles, M.C., Sieiro, C., Cao, R., Nasi, L. Chitosan and silver nanoparticles as pudding with raisins with antimicrobial properties. *J Colloid Interface Sci* 364 (2011) 80–84.

Sacco, P., Travan, A., Borgogna, M., Paoletti, S., Marsich, E. Silver-containing antimicrobial membrane based on chitosan-TPP hydrogel for the treatment of wounds. *J Mater Sci Mater Med* 26 (2015) 128.

Sandri G., Bonferoni, M.C., D'Autilia, F., Rossi, S., Ferrari, F., Grisoli, P., Sorrenti, M., Catenacci, L., Fante, Del, C., Perotti, C., Caramella, C. Wound dressings based on silver sulfadiazine solid lipid nanoparticles for tissue repairing. *Eur J Pharm Biopharm* 84 (2013) 84–90.

Sandri, G., Bonferon, M.C., Ferrari, F., Rossi, S., Aguzzi, C., Mori, M., Grisoli, P., Cerezo, P., Tenci, M., Viseras, C., Caramella, C. Montmorillonite–chitosan–silver sulfadiazine nanocomposites for topical treatment of chronic skin lesions: In vitro biocompatibility, antibacterial efficacy and gap closure cell motility properties. *Carbohydr Polym* 102 (2014) 970–977.

Sanpui, P., Murugadoss, A., Prasad, P.V., Ghosh, S.S., Chattopadhyay, A. The antibacterial properties of a novel chitosan–Ag–nanoparticle composite. *Int J Food Microbiol* 124 (2008) 142–146.

Saravanan, S., Nethala, S., Pattnaik, S., Tripathi, A., Moorthi, A., Selvamurugan, N. Preparation, characterization and antimicrobial activity of a bio-composite scaffold containing chitosan/nano-hydroxyapatite/nano-silver for bone tissue engineering. *Int J Biol Macromol* 49 (2011) 188–193.

Seetharaman, S., Natesan, S., Stowers, R.S., Mullens, C., Baer, D.G., Suggs, L.J., Christy, R.J. A PEGylated fibrin-based wound dressing with antimicrobial and angiogenic activity. *Acta Biomater* 7 (2011) 2787–2796.

Shameli, K., Bin, Ahmad, M., Zargar, M., Yunus, W.M., Ibrahim, N.A., Shabanzadeh, P., Moghaddam, M.G. Synthesis and characterization of silver/montmorillonite/chitosan bionanocomposites by chemical reduction method and their antibacterial activity. *Int J Nanomedicine* 6 (2011) 271–284.

Sharma, S., Chockalingam, S., Sanpui, P., Chattopadhyay, A., Ghosh, S.S. Silver nanoparticles impregnated alginate–chitosan-blended nanocarrier induces apoptosis in human glioblastoma cells. *Adv Healthc Mater* 3 (2014) 106–114.

Sharma, V.K., Yngard, R.A., Lin, Y. Silver nanoparticles: Green synthesis and their antimicrobial activities. *Adv Colloid Interface Sci* 145 (2009) 83–96.

Shervani, Z., Yamamoto, Y. Carbohydrate-directed synthesis of silver and gold nanoparticles: Effect of the structure of carbohydrates and reducing agents on the size and morphology of the composites. *Carbohydr Res* 346 (2011) 651–658.

Shu, X.Z., Zhu, K.J. A novel approach to prepare tripolyphosphate/chitosan complex beads for controlled release drug delivery. *Int J Pharm* 201 (2000) 51–58.

Silver, S. Bacterial silver resistance: Molecular biology and uses and misuses of silver compounds. *FEMS Microbiol Rev* 27 (2003) 341–353.

Sondi, I., Salopek-Sondi, B. Silver nanoparticles as antimicrobial agent: A case study on *E. coli* as a model for Gram-negative bacteria. *J Colloid Interface Sci* 275 (2004) 177–182.

Szatmari, V. Chitosan hemostatic dressing in controlling hemorrhage from femoral arterial puncture site in dogs. *J Vet Sci* 16 (2015) 517–523.

Tang, H., Zhang, P., Kieft, T.L., Ryan, S.J., Baker, S.M., Wiesmann, W.P., Rogelj, S. Antibacterial action of a novel functionalized chitosan-arginine against Gram-negative bacteria. *Acta Biomater* 6 (2010) 2562–2571.

Thomas, V., Yallapu, M.M., Sreedhar, B., Bajpai, S.K. Fabrication, characterization of chitosan/nanosilver film and its potential antibacterial application. *J Biomater Sci Polym Ed* 20 (2009) 2129–2144.

Travan, A., Marsich, E., Donati, I., Benincasa, M., Giazzon, M., Felisari, L., Paoletti, S. Silver-polysaccharide nanocomposite antimicrobial coatings for methacrylic thermosets. *Acta Biomater* 7 (2011) 337–346.

Travan, A., Pelillo, C., Donati, I., Marsich, E., Benincasa, M., Scarpa, T., Semeraro, S., Turco, G., Gennaro, R., Paoletti, S. Non-cytotoxic silver nanoparticle-polysaccharide nanocomposites with antimicrobial activity. *Biomacromolecules* 10 (2009) 1429–1435.

Varma, A.J. Biodegradable polymers from sugars. In *Biodegradable Polymers for Industrial Applications*. Cambridge, UK: Woodhead Publishing (2005).

Vimala, K., Mohan, Y.M., Sivudu, K.S., Varaprasad, K., Ravindra, S., Reddy, N.N., Padma, Y., Sreedhar, B., MohanaRaju, K. Fabrication of porous chitosan films impregnated with silver nanoparticles: A facile approach for superior antibacterial application. *Colloids Surf B Biointerfaces* 76 (2010) 248–258.

Wang, B.L., Liu, X.S., Ji, Y., Ren, K.F., Ji, J. Fast and long-acting antibacterial properties of chitosan–Ag/polyvinylpyrrolidone nanocomposite films. *Carbohydr Polym* 90 (2012) 8–15.

Wang, X., Cheng, F., Gao, J., Wang, L. Antibacterial wound dressing from chitosan/polyethylene oxide nanofibers mats embedded with silver nanoparticles. *J Biomater Appl* 29 (2015) 1086–1095.

Wei, D., Sun, W., Qian, W., Ye, Y., Ma, X. The synthesis of chitosan-based silver nanoparticles and their antibacterial activity. *Carbohydr Res* 344 (2009) 2375–2382.

Wollina, U., Abdel-Naser, M.B., Verma, S. Skin physiology and textiles – Consideration of basic interactions. *Curr Probl Dermatol* 33 (2006) 1–16.

Yadollahi, M., Farhoudian, S., Namazi, H. One-pot synthesis of antibacterial chitosan/ silver bio-nanocomposite hydrogel beads as drug delivery systems. *Int J Biol Macromol* 79 (2015) 37–43.

Zain, N.M., Stapley, A.G., Shama, G. Green synthesis of silver and copper nanoparticles using ascorbic acid and chitosan for antimicrobial applications. *Carbohydr Polym* 112 (2014) 195–202.

4

Titania Nanotubes as Silver Nanoparticle Carriers to Prevent Implant-Associated Infection

Ruiqiang Hang, Ang Gao, Long Bai and Paul K. Chu

CONTENTS

4.1 Introduction

Titanium (Ti) and its alloys are widely used in the orthopedic and dental fields because of their good mechanical properties, corrosion resistance and biocompatibility (Chu et al. 2002; Geetha et al. 2009; Liu et al. 2004). However, implant-associated infection remains one of the most prevalent and catastrophic postoperative complications (Zhao et al. 2009). Although the infection rate has been reduced to less than 5% on account of more thorough disinfection, strict aseptic surgical protocols and intraoperative systemic prophylactic treatment (Lee and Murphy 2013), the total number of people infected continues to increase because of growing medical demand for prosthetic replacements by the increasing aging population and prevalence of joint degenerative and periodontal diseases (Kurtz et al. 2012). Exogenously virulent bacteria such as *Staphylococcus aureus* and *Escherichia coli* and endogenously low-virulent ones such as *coagulase-negative Staphylococci* (CoNS) and *Propionibacterium acnes* (*P. acnes*) may serve as pathogens. The infection is mainly ascribed to bacteria adhesion, colonisation and finally formation of biofilms on the implant surface. Accurate diagnosis of the infection is sophisticated and time consuming, and it is difficult to treat such infection because bacteria in the biofilms are highly resistant to antibiotics (Mah and O'Toole 2001). Usually, extraction of the contaminated implant is the only viable option to eliminate the infection.

Owing to the large resistance of biofilms to systemic antibiotic therapy, endowing the implant surface with the ability to resist bacteria adhesion, colonisation and formation of biofilms through active release of antibacterial agents is a promising strategy. To this end, various surface modification techniques such as ion implantation, physical vapor deposition, micro-arc oxidation and anodisation have been utilised (Liu et al. 2004). In addition, construction of size-adjustable titania (TiO_2) nanotubes (NTs) on Ti-based implants by anodisation has drawn tremendous attention since the first report in 1999 (Zwilling et al. 1999). TiO_2 NT can not only improve osteoblast functions *in vitro* and osseointegration ability *in vivo* compared with pure Ti but also serve as drug carriers to prevent implant-associated infection (Popat et al. 2007a; von Wilmowsky et al. 2009; Yu et al. 2010). Silver (Ag) possesses excellent broad-spectrum antibacterial properties, good long-term stability, low effective concentration and satisfactory cytocompatibility for a proper dose and thus is considered an ideal bactericide (Chernousova and Epple 2013). Compared to metallic Ag, Ag nanoparticles (NPs) possess more effective antibacterial activity because of their extremely large specific surface area, which provides more contact with aqueous solutions to release more Ag^+. Therefore, loading Ag NPs into TiO_2 NTs and controlling the Ag^+ release profiles constitute an effective strategy to prevent infection of Ti-based implants.

In this chapter, we briefly review the synthesis method and biological properties of TiO_2 NTs and focus on recent progress on TiO_2 NTs loaded with Ag NPs as anti-infective coatings. Finally, some critical concerns on this topic are highlighted.

4.2 Electrochemical Synthesis of TiO_2 NTs

In 1999, Zwilling and co-authors first reported the synthesis of TiO_2 NTs on Ti and Ti6Al4V alloy by electrochemical anodisation in an aqueous electrolyte containing chromic acid and hydrofluoric acid, and they observed that the presence of fluoride ions (F^-) was essential to the formation of nanotubular

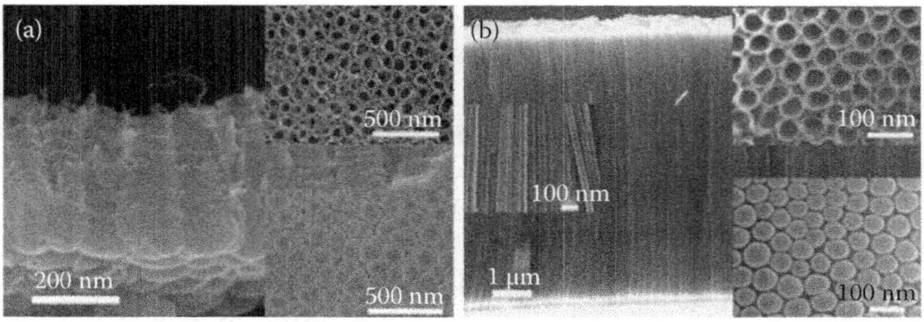

FIGURE 4.1
SEM images of TiO_2 NT layers prepared by different anodisation processes of Ti: (a) morphology obtained in the HF electrolytes; and (b) morphology obtained in the glycerol/F electrolytes. (Reprinted with permission from Macak, JM, H Tsuchiya, A Ghicov, K Yasuda, R Hahn, S Bauer, and P Schmuki. 2007. TiO_2 nanotubes: Self-organized electrochemical formation, properties and applications. *Current Opinion in Solid State and Materials Science* 11 (1):3–18.)

structure (Zwilling et al. 1999). Early follow-up works showed that by tailoring anodic parameters, TiO_2 NTs with different diameters (15 nm to 120 nm) and lengths (20 nm to 1000 nm) could be successfully fabricated (Bauer et al. 2006; Ghicov et al. 2005). However, the NTs synthesised in aqueous electrolytes possessed limited lengths and inhomogeneous sidewalls because of rapid field-assisted chemical dissolution and current fluctuations during anodisation (Roy et al. 2011). Later works showed that organic electrolytes with high viscosity such as ethylene glycol and glycerol could overcome these limitations by retarding dissolution of NTs and restraining local current fluctuations (Macak et al. 2005). By using various organic electrolytes and tailoring the electrochemical parameters, TiO_2 NTs with diameters ranging from 15 to 800 nm and lengths ranging from less than 1 to 1000 μm have been produced (Lee et al. 2014; Paulose et al. 2007; Roy et al. 2011) and the typical SEM images of TiO_2 NTs fabricated in aqueous and nonaqueous electrolytes are depicted in Figure 4.1. The growth mechanism of TiO_2 NTs in the F-containing electrolyte is mainly ascribed to the attack by F^- of newly formed TiO_2 under an electric field to form water-soluble $[TiF_6]^{2-}$. For more information on this topic, readers are referred to some recent reviews (Lee et al. 2014; Regonini et al. 2013; Roy et al. 2011).

4.3 Biological Properties of TiO_2 NTs

It is well established that surface characteristics, especially morphology, are crucial to the clinical success of biomedical implants and many studies have aimed at constructing various morphologies on biomaterials to improve the biological properties (Geetha et al. 2009; Liu et al. 2004, 2010). In the past decade, the possibility of using TiO_2 NTs on implant coatings has been extensively explored. A significant finding is the strong dependence of cell functions on the NT diameter. Oh and co-authors reported that human mesenchymal stem cells with multiple differentiation potential maintained their undifferentiated phenotype on TiO_2 NTs with a small diameter (<30 nm), while NTs with a large diameter (>70 nm) could selectively induce them to differentiate into osteoblasts (Oh et al. 2009). Moreover, almost all of the osteoblast functions including cell proliferation, alkaline phosphatase (ALP) activity, secretion of type I collagen and extracellular matrix mineralisation were reported to be promoted on TiO_2 NTs with a large diameter (Brammer et al. 2009; Zhao et al. 2010). These enhanced *in vitro* osteoblast functions were further evidenced by some *in vivo* experiments (Bjursten et al. 2010; von Wilmowsky et al. 2009, 2012). Overall, these results clearly indicate that TiO_2 NTs are promising coatings on Ti-based implant materials.

Although TiO_2 NTs possess good osseointegration ability, they have poor antibacterial activity and so cannot combat implant-associated infection. However, the open hollow structure of NTs suggests that they may serve as reservoirs for anti-infective drugs. Popat and co-authors loaded gentamicin into NTs and good antibacterial effect was observed (Popat et al. 2007a); similar results were observed by loading antimicrobial peptides (Ma et al. 2012). Nevertheless, the poor long-term stability and fast release rate of these organic antibacterial agents cannot meet clinical requirements. In contrast, inorganic antibacterial agents such as silver (Ag), copper (Cu) and zinc (Zn) are relatively stable at low concentrations and loading them into NTs and controlling their release profiles may generate effective and long-term antibacterial activity. The following two sections will focus on TiO_2 NTs decorated with Ag NPs because of their merits mentioned in Section 4.1.

4.4 TiO_2 NTs Loaded with Silver NPs

4.4.1 Preparation Methods

Ag NPs can be incorporated into TiO_2 NTs by physical and chemical methods, and the typical loading techniques are compared in Table 4.1. The physical methods are mainly vacuum-based technology. Magnetron sputtering, an industrial technique to deposit structural and functional coatings on various substrates, has been utilised to introduce Ag NP into TiO_2 NTs (Roguska et al. 2012a,b). During the process, Ag atoms or their clusters that are sputtered from a silver target by bombardment of energetic Ar^+ are deposited onto the NTs to form Ag NPs via spontaneous nucleation and island growth. Because of the line-of-sight motion of sputtered atoms, the Ag NPs are located mainly on the top edges of the NTs (Figure 4.2a). Excessive supply of Ag atoms leads

TABLE 4.1

Loading Methods of Ag NPs into TiO_2 NTs

Loading Methods		Characterisations	References
Physical	Magnetron sputtering	Diameter varies from 2 to 50 nm; located mainly on the top edges of the NTs.	Roguska et al. 2012a
	Electron beam evaporation	Diameter varies from 5 to 20 nm; increased NT diameter leads to decreased aggregation of Ag NPs near the NT surface.	Lan et al. 2013
	Plasma immersion ion implantation (PIII)	~20 nm in diameter; the distribution of Ag NPs can be tailored by varying PIII voltage.	Mei et al. 2014
	Electrophoretic deposition (EPD)	The initial diameter is the same as that in the Ag NP colloids (~6 nm) but increases with EPD time (even larger than 100 nm).	Jiang et al. 2013
Chemical	Photocatalytical reduction	Diameter of 10 to 20 nm; distributed mainly near the top of the NT surface.	Zhao et al. 2011
	Chemical reduction	~20 nm in diameter; distributed along the entire NT length but the content decreases with depth.	Liang et al. 2011
	Electrodeposition	~10 nm in diameter.	Ma et al. 2011
	Thermal decomposition	~40 nm in diameter.	Chen et al. 2013

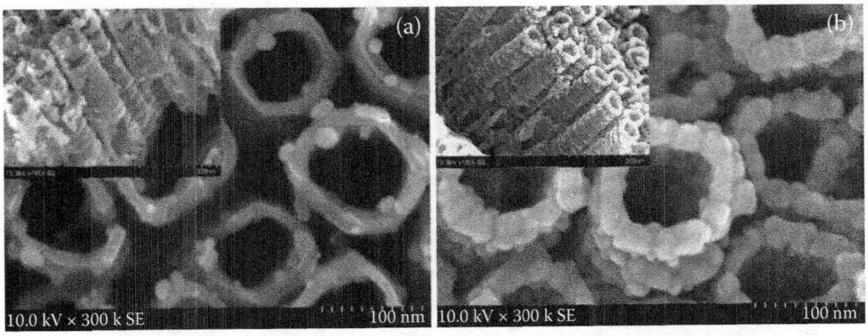

FIGURE 4.2

Typical SEM images of TiO_2 NT layers with different Ag contents: (a) 0.01 mg/cm^2; (b) 0.04 mg/cm^2. Insets show the cross-sectional views. (Reprinted with permission from Roguska, Agata, Anna Belcarz, Tomasz Piersiak, Marcin Pisarek, Grażyna Ginalska, and Małgorzata Lewandowska. 2012. Evaluation of the antibacterial activity of Ag-loaded TiO_2 nanotubes. *European Journal of Inorganic Chemistry* 2012 (32):5199–5206; and Roguska, Agata, Marcin Pisarek, Mariusz Andrzejczuk, Malgorzata Lewandowska, Krzysztof J Kurzydlowski, and Maria Janik-Czachor. 2012. Surface characterization of Ca-P/Ag/TiO_2 nanotube composite layers on Ti intended for biomedical applications. *Journal of Biomedical Materials Research Part A* 100 (8):1954–1962.)

to NP aggregation (Figure 4.2b), thus decreasing the specific surface area and compromising the antibacterial activity. Electron beam evaporation, an ideal technique to deposit materials with high melting point such as oxides, is also used to achieve this purpose (Lan et al. 2013; Uhm et al. 2013). Ag atoms in the target are transformed into the gaseous phase by electron beam bombardment, followed by transferring to substrate, nucleation and precipitation forming Ag NPs. After Ag deposition, the surface morphology of the TiO_2 NTs changes depending on the diameter (Figure 4.3). Another physical method used to introduce Ag NPs into TiO_2 NTs is plasma immersion ion implantation (PIII) in conjunction with filtered cathodic arc (Mei et al. 2014). An outstanding advantage of this technique compared to the previous two is its non–line-of-sight nature, rendering it particularly suitable for biomedical implants with a complex shape. Because energetic ion bombardment may destroy the nanotubular structure, a low implantation voltage (typically less than 1 kV) is desirable. Mei et al. (2014) found that Ag NPs aggregated near the top surface of NTs at a PIII voltage of 0.5 kV, while 1.0 kV led to penetration of the Ag NPs into the NTs. Besides these vacuum-based techniques, liquid-based ones such as electrophoretic deposition (EPD) have also been reported (Jiang et al. 2013). During EPD, negatively charged Ag NPs

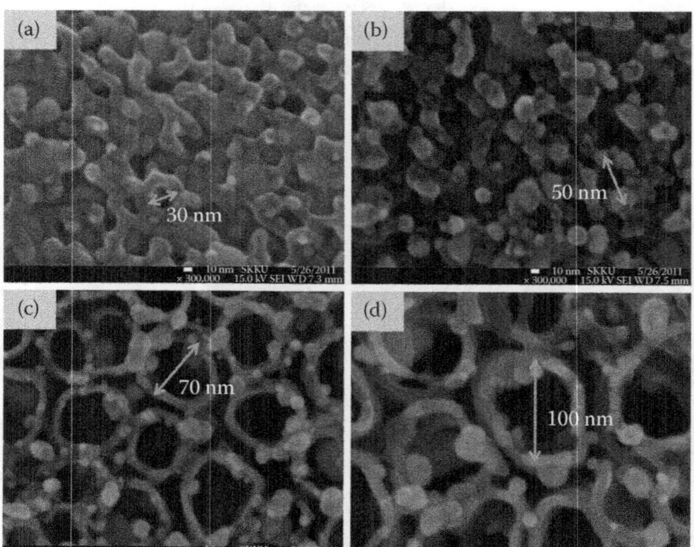

FIGURE 4.3
SEM images of the Ag NPs precipitated on the TiO_2 NTs with diameters of (a) 30 nm, (b) 50 nm, (c) 70 nm, and (d) 100 nm prepared by electron beam evaporation. (Reprinted with permission from Uhm, Soo-Hyuk, Doo-Hoon Song, Jae-Sung Kwon, Sang-Bae Lee, Jeon-Geon Han, Kwang-Mahn Kim, and Kyoung-Nam Kim. 2013. E-beam fabrication of antibacterial silver nanoparticles on diameter-controlled TiO_2 nanotubes for bio-implants. *Surface and Coatings Technology* 228:S360–S366.)

suspended in the colloidal solution are attracted to the anode and deposited onto TiO_2 NTs. Increasing the deposition time is beneficial to the dosage but leads to aggregation and growth of Ag NPs under the electric field.

Chemical methods used to load Ag NPs into TiO_2 NTs are mainly based on the reduction of Ag^+, and photocatalytic reduction is a widely used approach to achieve this purpose. Typically, TiO_2 NTs are first immersed in the $AgNO_3$ solution to adsorb $AgNO_3$ and then illuminated by UV light. During irradiation, Ag^+ is reduced to Ag^0 by the following reaction (Ohtani and Nishimoto 1993):

$$4Ag^+ + 2H_2O \rightarrow 4Ag + O_2 + 4H^+. \quad (4.1)$$

The loaded amount can be adjusted by varying the $AgNO_3$ concentration, soaking time, irradiation intensity and duration (Bian et al. 2013; Zhao et al. 2011). The same as vacuum-based methods, the photocatalytic reaction occurs near the top surface of the NTs because of the line-of-sight property of light. In contrast, liquid-based chemical reduction can produce uniformly distributed Ag NPs on TiO_2 NTs (Figure 4.4). The reaction using $NaBH_4$ as a reducing agent is expressed as follows (Wang et al. 2012):

$$4Ag^+ + BH_4^- + 3H_2O \rightarrow 4Ag + B(OH)_3 + 2H_2 + 3H^+. \quad (4.2)$$

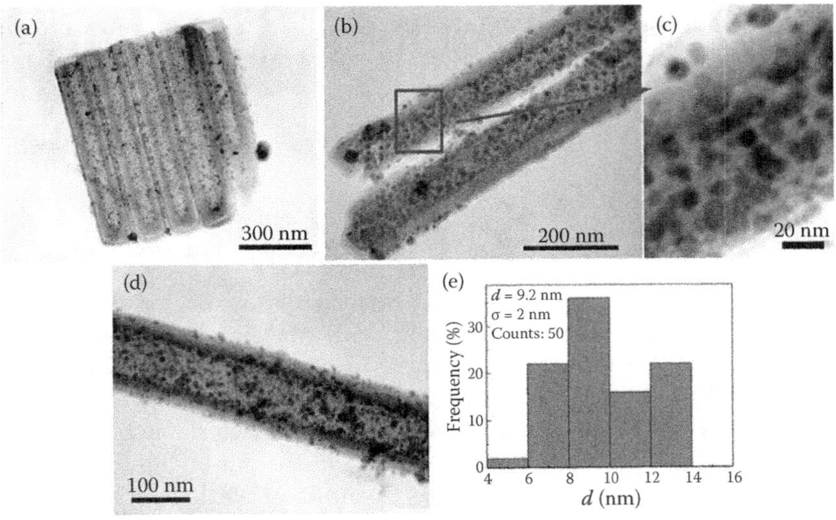

FIGURE 4.4
TEM images of Ag/TiO_2 NTs: (a) overall, (b) front side and (d) middle region; (c) HR-TEM image of Ag/TiO_2 NTs and (e) size distribution of the Ag nanoparticles. (Reprinted with permission from Wang, Qingyao, Xiuchun Yang, Dan Liu, and Jianfu Zhao. 2012. Fabrication, characterization and photocatalytic properties of Ag nanoparticles modified TiO_2 NTs. *Journal of Alloys and Compounds* 527:106–111.)

Another liquid-based technique is electrodeposition in which the TiO_2 NTs act as the cathode and Ag^+ is attracted and reduced to Ag^0 on the surface. The reduced Ag atoms evolve into Ag NPs by field-assistant nucleation and growth. A prominent advantage of this technique is the short deposition time (typically less than 60 s) (Ma et al. 2011; Zhang et al. 2011). Thermal decomposition has also been reported to introduce Ag NPs into TiO_2 NTs (Chen et al. 2013; He et al. 2010). Briefly, the samples are soaked in the $AgNO_3$ solution to adsorb $AgNO_3$ and then annealed under nitrogen or argon. The decomposition reaction is shown in the following (Lin et al. 2009):

$$2AgNO_3 \rightarrow 2Ag + 2NO_2 + O_2. \tag{4.3}$$

Since there is no line-of-sight limitation, Ag NPs can distribute evenly across the entire length of the NTs.

4.4.2 Antibacterial Activity of the Ag NP–Loaded NTs

Ag NPs are widely used as antibacterial agents in the biomedical and consumer products industry. However, the mechanism in which they interact with biological systems remains controversial. It has been shown that compared to their 'nano effects', release of Ag^+ plays a decisive role (Xiu et al. 2012). In aqueous solutions with dissolved oxygen, Ag^0 on the surface of Ag NPs can be oxidised to Ag_2O (Equation 4.4), leading to the release of Ag^+ under acidic conditions (Equation 4.5) (Liu and Hurt 2010):

$$4Ag + O_2 \rightarrow 2Ag_2O \tag{4.4}$$

$$2Ag_2O + 4H^+ \rightarrow 4Ag^+ + 2H_2O. \tag{4.5}$$

The released Ag^+ may induce toxicity by deactivating bacterial synthetase, disturbing cell membranes, interfering with nucleic acid replication and destroying intracellular respiratory and transport systems (Chernousova and Epple 2013; Lee and Murphy 2013). Accordingly, with regard to Ag NP–loaded TiO_2 NTs, the Ag^+ release profiles and antibacterial activity are primarily determined by the total surface area of the Ag NPs in contact with H_2O, regardless of the loading methods. As implant coatings, Ag NP–loaded TiO_2 NTs have two major advantages. One is that the loaded amount can be easily adjusted by varying the preparation parameters, for instance, the dimensions of TiO_2 NTs, deposition time in physical methods and $AgNO_3$ concentrations in chemical ones. The other is that the release profiles can meet clinical requirements. In general, Ag NP–loaded TiO_2 NTs release a large amount of Ag^+ during the early days and the rate decreases gradually thereafter. The initial phase after implantation is more susceptible to infection because of the compromised host defense after surgery. Hence, the early potent antibacterial ability derived from a large amount of Ag^+ can kill planktonic bacteria to prevent postoperation infection. After this stage, mild antibacterial ability through sustained and low-dose release of Ag^+ is sufficient to inhibit bacterial adhesion and formation of biofilms on the implants. Typical results concerning this topic reported by Zhao et al. are summarised in Figure 4.5.

Although the powerful bactericidal capability of Ag NP–loaded TiO_2 NTs has been demonstrated, the longest experimental period only covers the early stage of infection (<2 months after implantation) and whether the strategy can combat delayed (2–24 months after implantation) and late (>24 months) infection is

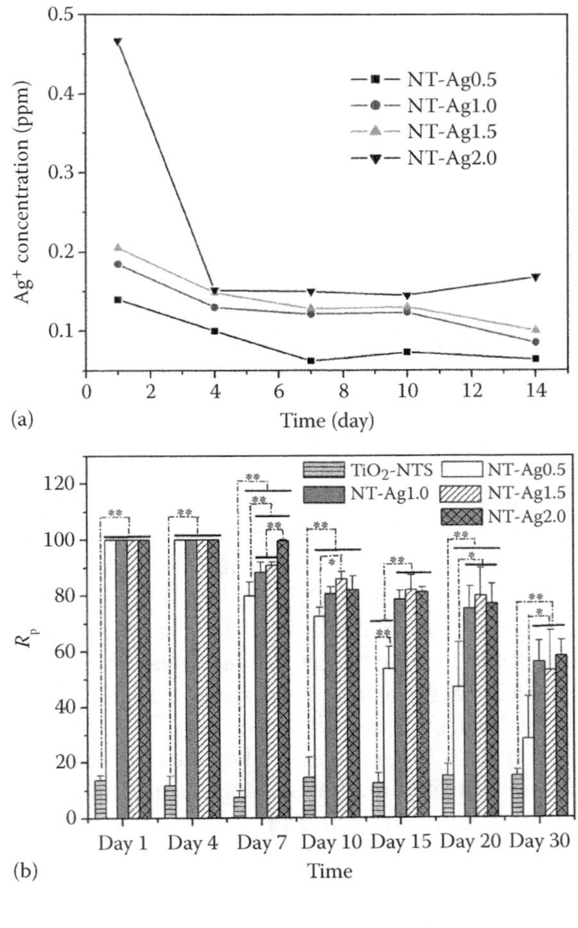

FIGURE 4.5
(a) Noncumulative Ag^+ release profiles from Ag NP–loaded TiO_2 NTs into PBS, (b) antibacterial rates against planktonic bacteria in the medium (R_p). *(Continued)*

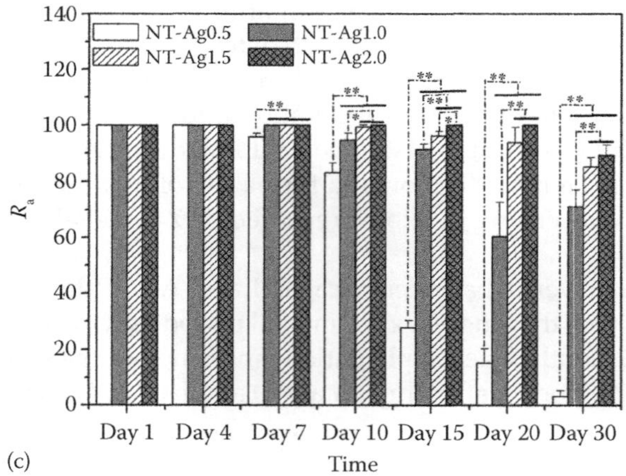

(c)

FIGURE 4.5 (CONTINUED)
(c) Antibacterial rates against adherent bacteria on the specimen (R_a). The antibacterial assay data are expressed as means ± standard deviations (n = 3). The one-way ANOVA followed by SNK post hoc test is utilised to determine the level of significance (*$p < 0.05$ and **$p < 0.01$). (Reprinted with permission from Zhao, Lingzhou, Hairong Wang, Kaifu Huo, Lingyun Cui, Wenrui Zhang, Hongwei Ni, Yumei Zhang, Zhifen Wu, and Paul K Chu. 2011. Antibacterial nano-structured titania coating incorporated with silver nanoparticles. *Biomaterials* 32 (24): 5706–5716.)

still unclear. Similar to other drugs, release of Ag^+ is too rapid in the early stage and too slow in the later stage. From the chemical viewpoint, in order to achieve sustained release of a moderate amount of Ag^+, controlling the rates of the chemical reactions (Equations 4.4 and 4.5) by regulating the supply of O_2 and H^+ may be effective. However, this strategy is difficult to implement *in vivo*. A proposed alternative is illustrated in Figure 4.6. The NTs doped with small Ag NPs release Ag^+ swiftly in the initial stage because of the large specific surface area. The consumption is relatively fast, and after a short period, the released Ag^+ concentration may be lower than the minimum inhibitory concentration (MIC). In contrast, for small + big Ag NP–loaded TiO_2 NTs with the same dose, the small ones contribute to initial fast release of Ag^+ to ensure that the implant survives the susceptible stage, whereas the big ones provide sustained release of Ag^+ above the MIC to achieve long-term antibacterial ability.

Alternatively, Ag NPs may detach from the NT walls and contribute to the antibacterial ability in several ways (Chernousova and Epple 2013; Rai et al. 2009). The first is that they may attach to sulfur-containing cell walls and membranes to disturb functions and properties such as permeability and respiration. In addition, they may penetrate into the bacteria binding to and inactivating phosphorus-containing DNA. Ag NPs lead to the formation of reactive oxygen species (ROS), which may induce oxidative damage of proteins and DNA. Nevertheless, detachment and direct release of Ag NPs from TiO_2 NTs may compromise the long-term antibacterial activity and should be avoided.

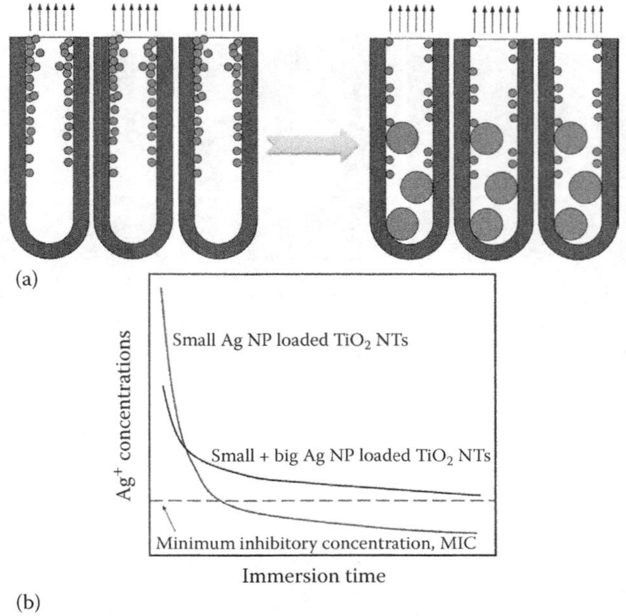

FIGURE 4.6
Schematic diagrams showing incorporation of small and big Ag NPs instead of only small ones into the TiO_2 NTs (a) to achieve long-term release of Ag^+ above MIC (b).

4.4.3 Biocompatibility of the Ag NP–Loaded NTs

The use of Ag as a bactericide may raise safety concerns and so the biocompatibility of Ag NP–loaded TiO_2 NTs should be fully understood before clinical use. Recent research has shown that the cytotoxicity of this structure is closely related to the amount of released Ag^+ (Zhao et al. 2011). Excessive release of Ag^+ leads to elevated lactate dehydrogenase activity as well as suppressed proliferation, intracellular total protein synthesis and ALP activity of osteoblasts, while insufficient supply compromises the antibacterial activity. Therefore, considering the safety window of Ag^+ concentrations to balance the antibacterial activity and biocompatibility is of importance. Much research has been devoted to the exploration of this window, and it has been shown that the MIC of Ag^+ is between 0.1 and 20 mg/L, and for mammalian cells, the toxic concentration is 1–10 mg/L (Chernousova and Epple 2013). Although a definite conclusion has not yet been drawn because of different experimental conditions and bacteria/cell types, the safe range of Ag^+ concentration for treatment of implant-associated infection is expected to be between 0.1 and 1 mg/L. It has been shown that by tailoring the NT dimensions and loading manners of Ag NPs, good antibacterial ability (Figure 4.7) and biocompatibility (Figure 4.8) can be simultaneously achieved (Lan et al. 2013). However, good biocompatibility is usually linked to a small

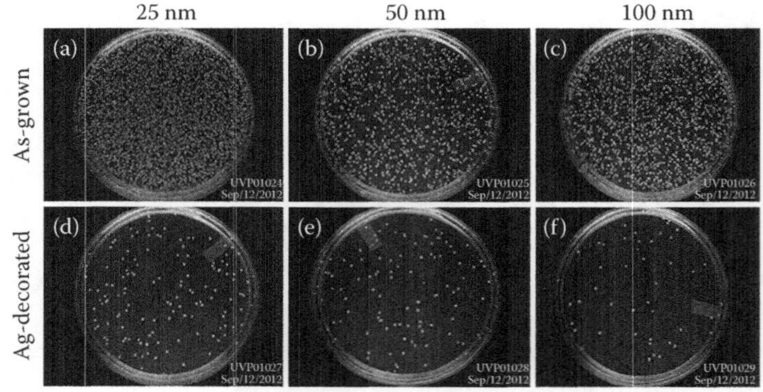

FIGURE 4.7
Photographs of bacteria cultures. Plates with *S. aureus* were grown in the presence of as-grown (a through c) and Ag-decorated (d through f) TiO_2 NTs with different diameters.

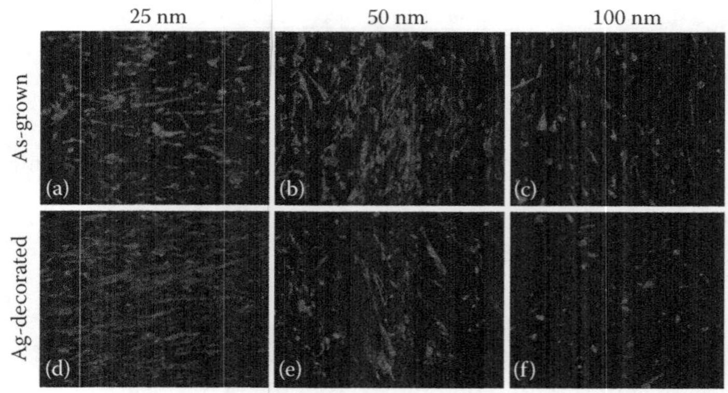

FIGURE 4.8
(See colour insert.) Fluorescence microscopy images of human fibroblasts attached to the as-grown (a through c) and Ag-decorated (d through f) TiO_2 NTs with different diameters. The red fluorescence indicates cytoskeletal actin and the blue fluorescence indicates cell nuclei. For both as-grown and Ag-decorated TiO_2 NTs, longer and better-defined actin cytoskeleton and a higher density of fibroblasts are observed from NTs with a smaller diameter.

concentration of Ag NPs, which may compromise the long-term antibacterial ability. Accordingly, TiO_2 NTs with a large concentration of Ag NPs that can continuously release Ag^+ within the safety window is highly desirable. To this end, several approaches can be adopted, for instance, increasing the ratio of length to diameter (Peng et al. 2009) and narrowing the openings of the NTs by depositing biocompatible species (Tsuchiya et al. 2006). Ideally, the NTs should release a moderate amount of Ag^+ only when bacteria invasion occurs in order to minimise the side effects of sustained Ag^+ release and guarantee long-term antibacterial activity. Since the occurrence of infection leads to variations in the local microenvironment in the vicinity of the implant, coating the NTs with environmentally sensitive materials to control the release of Ag^+ may be promising (Qiu and Park 2012; Winter et al. 2007).

Besides Ag^+, Ag NPs may detach from the NT walls and be taken up readily by cells through receptor-mediated endocytosis and micropinocytosis. It is deemed that the size, shape, solubility, surface area and physicochemical and structural properties of the NPs influence their biokinetics, which may in turn determine the toxicity. AshaRani et al. (2008) have shown that exposure of mammalian cells to Ag NPs with a small size (6–20 nm in diameter) can result in mitochondrial dysfunction, DNA damage, chromosomal aberrations and cell cycle arrest. In contrast, as shown by some recent papers (Carlson et al. 2008; Kim et al. 2012; Park et al. 2011), large Ag NPs are more biocompatible than small ones. Therefore, TiO_2 NTs loaded with relatively big Ag NPs may reduce cytotoxicity. It is necessary to explore novel approaches to avoid detachment of Ag NPs from the NT walls to overcome the side effects.

4.5 TiO_2 NTs Embedded with Silver Oxide NPs

4.5.1 Preparation Method

As aforementioned, Ag NPs can be readily loaded into TiO_2 NTs by various techniques to improve the antibacterial capability. However, the Ag NPs introduced by these methods adsorb physically onto the NT walls and there are concerns about either the failure of delivering sustained antibacterial effects or serious cytotoxicity attributed to the detachment of loose Ag NPs in conjunction with burst release of Ag^+ (schematically shown in Figure 4.9a). It is thus necessary to develop new Ag doping strategies to achieve

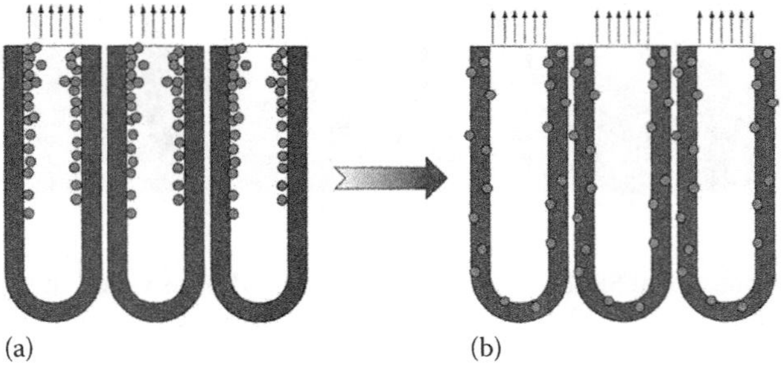

FIGURE 4.9
Schematic illustration of the difference between (a) physically adsorbed Ag NPs and (b) embedded Ag_2O NPs in the TiO_2 NTs.

the antibacterial capability without compromising the benefits in promoting osteoblast functions. Our recent work has confirmed the feasibility to dope Ag during the formation of TiO_2 NTs by anodising the TiAg composite coatings deposited by magnetron sputtering (Gao et al. 2014). Using the 'deposition–anodisation' technique, Ag can be *in situ* incorporated into the TiO_2 nanotubular walls and released in a sustained and controllable manner (schematically shown in Figure 4.9b).

The fabrication flow chart of silver oxide (Ag_2O) NP–embedded TiO_2 NTs (denoted as NT-Ag_2O) is schematically illustrated in Figure 4.10. Succinctly speaking, the TiAg coating is deposited on the Ti substrate by pulsed DC magnetron sputtering and then the coating is anodised in an F-containing electrolyte to fabricate the NTs. The SEM images of anodised samples in Figure 4.11 confirm the fabrication of self-organised homogeneous and

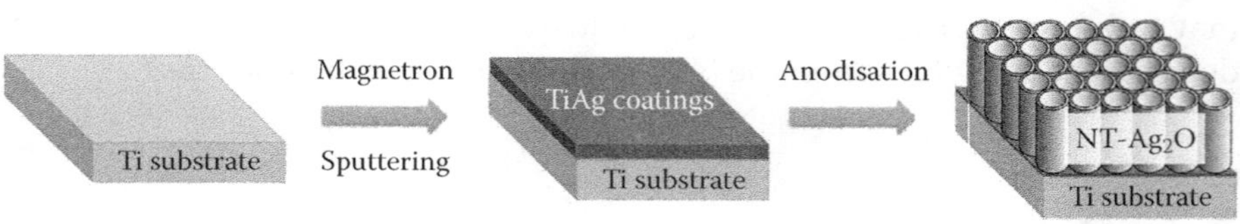

FIGURE 4.10
Schematic diagram of the preparation process of Ag_2O NP–embedded TiO_2 NTs.

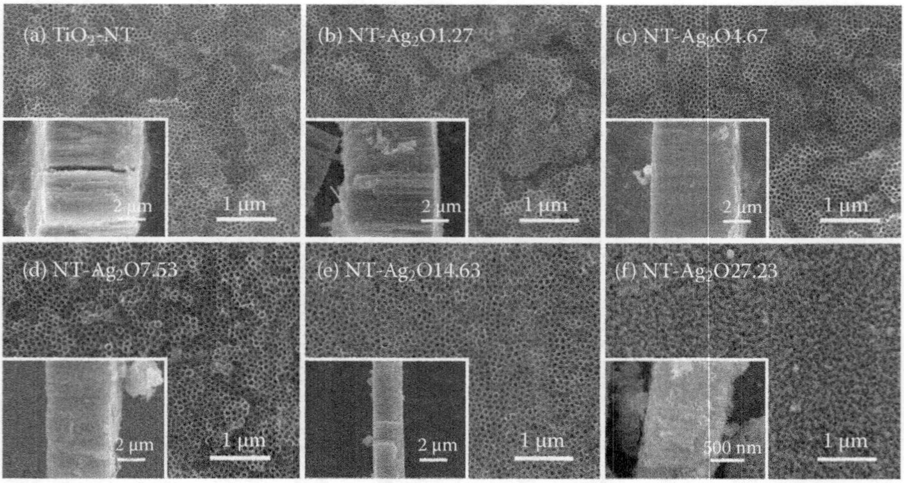

FIGURE 4.11
Surface and cross-sectional SEM images of the (a) anodised pure Ti and (b–f) TiAg coatings. The numbers behind NT-Ag_2O labels represent the atomic concentration of Ag in the corresponding TiAg coatings. The samples are anodised at 30 V and 30°C in an ethylene glycol solution containing 0.3 wt% NH_4F and 2.0 vol% H_2O for 4 h. (Reprinted with permission from Gao, Ang, Ruiqiang Hang, Xiaobo Huang, Lingzhou Zhao, Xiangyu Zhang, Lin Wang, Bin Tang, Shengli Ma, and Paul K Chu. 2014. The effects of titania nanotubes with embedded silver oxide nanoparticles on bacteria and osteoblasts. *Biomaterials* 35 (13):4223–4235.)

uniform NTs by anodising the TiAg coating. However, excessive Ag in the TiAg coating gives rise to a nonuniform nanoporous structure under the given anodic conditions (Figure 4.11f). To fabricate a well-defined nanotubular structure on the coating with a large Ag concentration, optimisation of the anodic parameters is necessary.

The TEM images in Figure 4.12 reveal that after anodisation, the crystallised NPs are uniformly distributed along the amorphous nanotubular wall. While some are totally enwrapped by the tubular wall, others are partially embedded. If the Ag concentration in the TiAg coating is large, the density of NPs after anodisation increases as expected. The high-resolution TEM

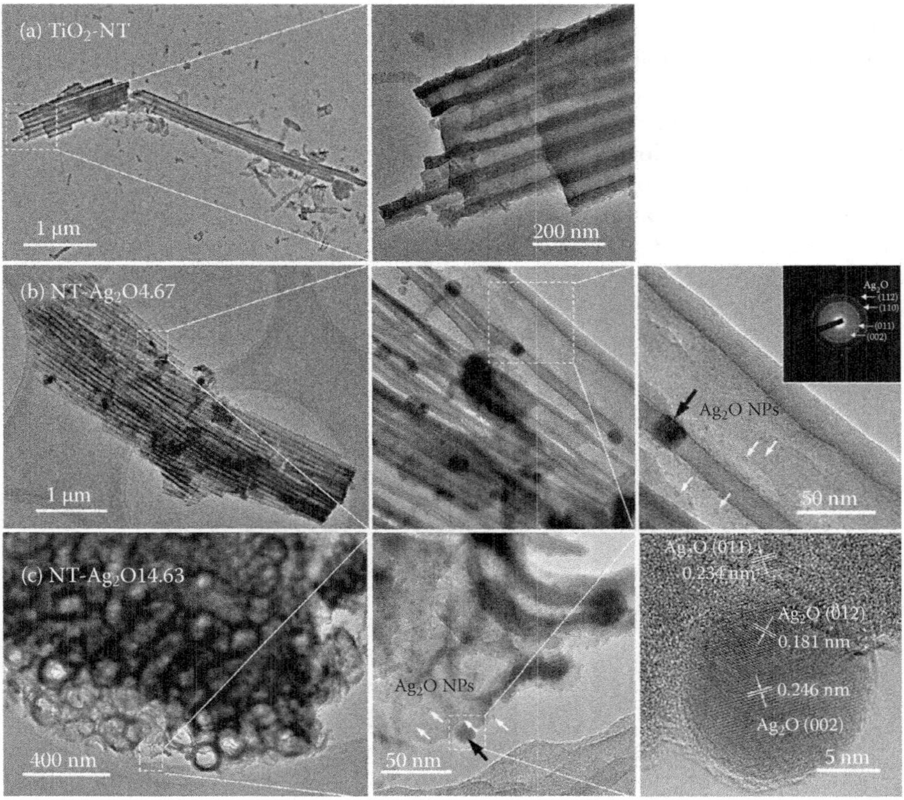

FIGURE 4.12
Typical TEM images of (a) as-anodised TiO_2 NTs, (b) NT-Ag_2O4.67, and (c) NT-Ag_2O14.63 together with the corresponding high magnification or HR-TEM images taken from the area enclosed by a square. The number after NT-Ag_2O represents the atomic concentration of Ag in the corresponding TiAg coatings. The inset in (b) is the SAED pattern obtained from the corresponding region. (Reprinted with permission from Gao, Ang, Ruiqiang Hang, Xiaobo Huang, Lingzhou Zhao, Xiangyu Zhang, Lin Wang, Bin Tang, Shengli Ma, and Paul K Chu. 2014. The effects of titania nanotubes with embedded silver oxide nanoparticles on bacteria and osteoblasts. *Biomaterials* 35 (13):4223–4235.)

images disclose lattice spacings of 1.81, 2.34 and 2.46 Å, corresponding to the (012), (011) and (002) crystallographic planes of hexagonal Ag_2O, respectively. The selected-area electron diffraction (SAED) shows four diffraction rings representative of the (002), (011), (110) and (112) crystallographic planes of Ag_2O as well. The results show that during anodisation of the TiAg coatings, Ag is oxidised to Ag_2O NPs and embedded into the TiO_2 NTs during growth.

As aforementioned, growth of TiO_2 NTs is the result of the competition between electrochemical anodisation and chemical dissolution of the oxide layer in the F-containing electrolyte. The similarity in the current density versus time plots obtained during anodisation of pure Ti and TiAg4.67 coating (Figure 4.13) indicates that the presence of Ag has little influence on the formation of the NTs. Four stages are illustrated in the insets in Figure 4.13. Addition of Ag accelerates dissolution of the NTs (manifested as a large current density), presumably because of the high solubility of Ag–F compounds in the electrolyte.

Magnetron sputtering is a well-developed and low-cost industrial technique for the deposition of uniform and adherent coatings (Kelly and Arnell 2000). Because of the low processing temperature, the Ag intrinsically doped TiO_2 NTs can be fabricated on a variety of substrate materials such as ceramics, polymers, metals and natural products. This technique can also be extended to introduce other elements such as silicon, strontium, zinc and copper to yield more diverse biofunctionalities. The amount of incorporated agents

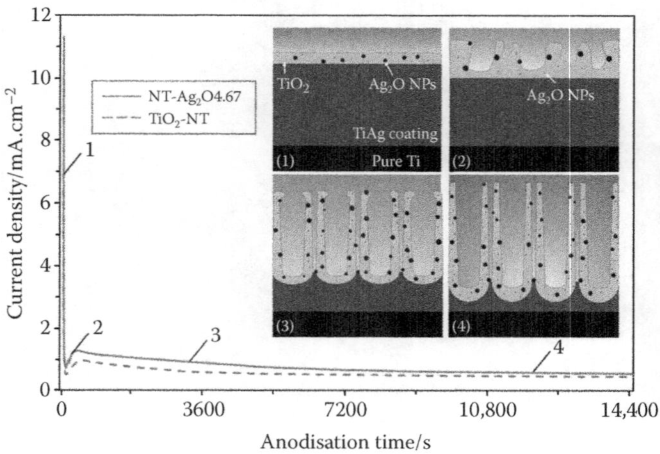

FIGURE 4.13
Typical current density–time curves during anodisation of the as-deposited pure Ti and TiAg4.67 film with the inset showing the formation mechanism of NT-Ag_2O. (Reprinted with permission from Gao, Ang, Ruiqiang Hang, Xiaobo Huang, Lingzhou Zhao, Xiangyu Zhang, Lin Wang, Bin Tang, Shengli Ma, and Paul K Chu. 2014. The effects of titania nanotubes with embedded silver oxide nanoparticles on bacteria and osteoblasts. *Biomaterials* 35 (13):4223–4235.)

and subsequent release patterns can be controlled by varying the dopant concentration in the coatings and morphology of the NTs. This 'deposition–anodisation' technique provides a versatile and effective approach to prepare biomedical coatings with different functions.

4.5.2 Antibacterial Activity of Ag_2O NP–Embedded NTs

The antibacterial activities against Gram-positive *S. aureus* and Gram-negative *E. coli* have been accessed for as long as 28 days under conditions that are harsher than those *in vivo*. Figure 4.14b and c indicates that during the first 14 days, NT-Ag_2O inactivates almost all the bacteria. Despite a slight decrease after repeating for 28 days, high antibacterial rates higher than 97% against both types of bacteria are maintained, thus indicating excellent long-term, broad-spectrum antibacterial activity of NT-Ag_2O.

Since Ag_2O NPs are embedded in the NTs, the contribution of detached particles to the bactericidal effect may be excluded. Therefore, the structure may exert its long-term antibacterial activity through sustained and controllable release of Ag^+. The noncumulative Ag^+ release profiles (Figure 4.14a) acquired from the NT-Ag_2O show initial rapid release followed by the sustained slower release believed to be beneficial to clinical applications (Zhao et al. 2011). During the 28 days, the amounts of released Ag^+ drop from approximately 40 parts per billion (ppb) to less than 10 ppb, but the antibacterial rate is maintained at greater than 97%, indicating that released Ag^+ may not be the only reason for the good antibacterial ability of NT-Ag_2O. It has been indicated that direct contact between bacteria and Ag NPs can induce structural changes and functional damage of the plasma membranes of bacteria (Chernousova and Epple 2013; Marambio-Jones and Hoek 2010; Morones et al. 2005). The SEM images in Figure 4.14d show the morphology of *S. aureus* cultured on NT-Ag_2O. They have a cracked and ruptured morphology and are surrounded by cell fragments indicating leakage of cytoplasmic contents. It may be concluded that the good long-term antibacterial activity of the NT-Ag_2O is ascribed to the synergistic effects of released Ag^+ and direct contact between the bacteria and Ag_2O NPs. Since the two antibacterial mechanisms complement each other, NT-Ag_2O may create a sustained antibacterial environment adjacent to the implant surface.

4.5.3 Biocompatibility of Ag_2O NP–Embedded NTs

Ag_2O NPs themselves and Ag^+ released together may exert toxicity to cells in a similar mechanism to bacteria. The loosely adhered NPs diffuse and are taken up by cells to impair cellular functions by generating ROS, by releasing Ag^+ and by other mechanisms (Greulich et al. 2011). However, the Ag_2O NPs are immobilised on the nanotubular wall in NT-Ag_2O, thus minimising the risk of cell uptake. Moreover, Ag^+ can show cytotoxicity in a dose-dependent manner (Chen and Schluesener 2008; Park et al. 2010). Release of

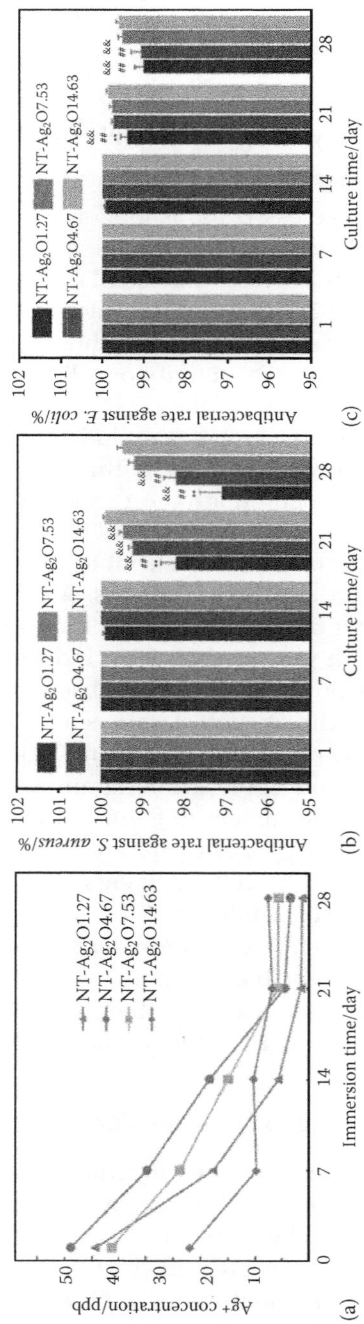

FIGURE 4.14
(a) Noncumulative Ag^{+} release profiles of NT-Ag_2O; (b) antibacterial ability of NT-Ag_2O against *S. aureus*; (c) antibacterial ability of NT-Ag_2O against *E. coli*.
(Continued)

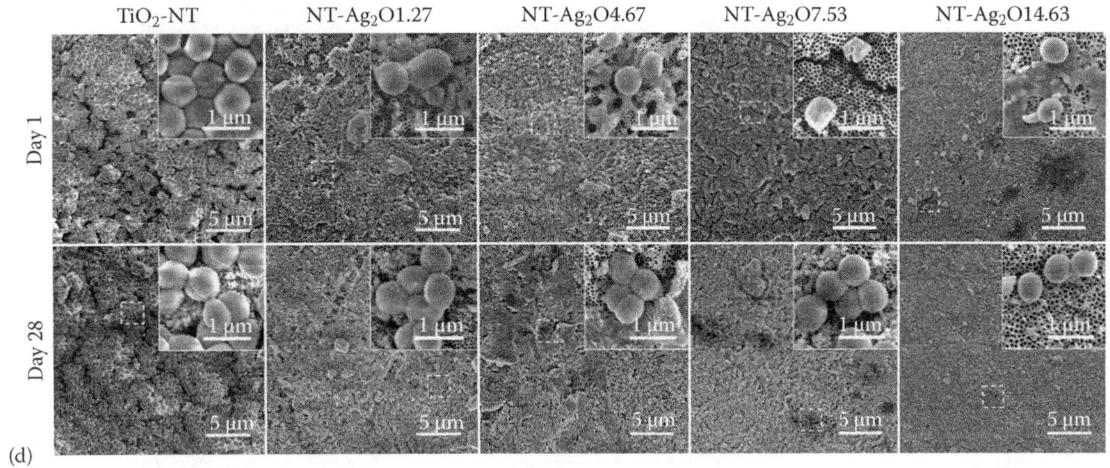

FIGURE 4.14 (CONTINUED)
(d) SEM images of *S. aureus* incubated on the TiO_2 NTAs and NT-Ag_2O, which have been immersed in PBS for 1 and 28 days. $^{**}p < 0.01$ compared to the NT-Ag_2O4.67, $^{\#\#}p < 0.01$ compared to the NT-Ag_2O7.53, $^{\&\&}p < 0.01$ compared to the NT-Ag_2O14.63. (Reprinted with permission from Gao, Ang, Ruiqiang Hang, Xiaobo Huang, Lingzhou Zhao, Xiangyu Zhang, Lin Wang, Bin Tang, Shengli Ma, and Paul K Chu. 2014. The effects of titania nanotubes with embedded silver oxide nanoparticles on bacteria and osteoblasts. *Biomaterials* 35 (13):4223–4235.)

Ag^+ from the Ag_2O NPs is related to the local acidic environment (Equation 4.5). However, as for NT-Ag_2O, because of the barrier effect of the surrounding TiO_2, noncumulative Ag^+ release from NT-Ag_2O is maximum of approximately 50 ppb, which contributes to the antibacterial activity but is lower than the generally accepted threshold of toxic concentrations for human cells (Chernousova and Epple 2013; Lewinski et al. 2008). This can explain the results obtained from cell proliferation and viability assay that no appreciable deleterious effects are detected on cells cultured on NT-Ag_2O.

TiO_2 NTs are known for their effectiveness in promoting osteoblast functions (Popat et al. 2007b; von Wilmowsky et al. 2009; Wang et al. 2011b). After incorporation with Ag_2O NPs, no obvious side effects are observed concerning the activity of ALP (Figure 4.15a), which is the early differentiation marker of osteoblasts. Although excessive Ag in the NTs show some hindering effects on collagen synthesis and extracellular matrix mineralisation

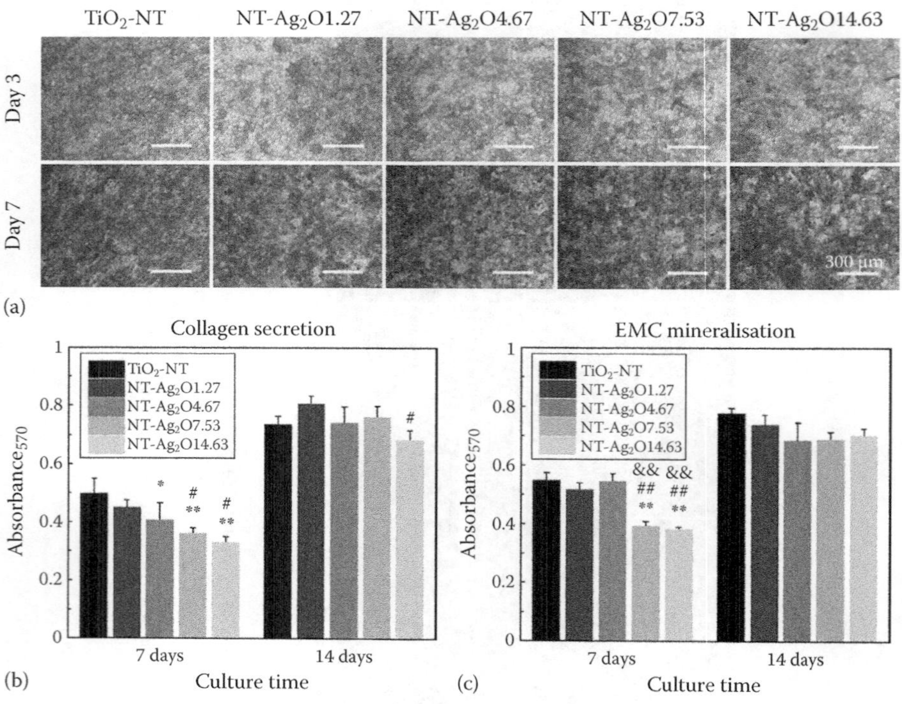

FIGURE 4.15
(a) Microscopic images of ALP product; (b) collagen secretion and (c) extracellular matrix mineralisation by MC3T3-E1 cells cultured on TiO_2 NTAs and NT-Ag_2O after osteogenic induction for 7 and 14 days. $^*p < 0.05$ and $^{**}p < 0.01$ compared to the TiO_2 NTAs, $^{\#}p < 0.05$ and $^{\#\#}p < 0.01$ compared to the NT-Ag_2O1.27, $^{\&\&}p < 0.01$ compared to the NT-Ag_2O4.67. (Reprinted with permission from Gao, Ang, Ruiqiang Hang, Xiaobo Huang, Lingzhou Zhao, Xiangyu Zhang, Lin Wang, Bin Tang, Shengli Ma, and Paul K Chu. 2014. The effects of titania nanotubes with embedded silver oxide nanoparticles on bacteria and osteoblasts. *Biomaterials* 35 (13):4223–4235.)

compared to TiO_2 NTs during the early stage of culture, nearly no influence can be observed from prolonged culturing (Figure 4.15b and c) and the initial side effects may be easily eliminated by depositing a thin coating such as hydroxyapatite or chitosan. Generally, Ag_2O NP–embedded TiO_2 NTs have excellent long-term antibacterial capability without appreciable cytotoxicity and can accelerate osseointegration.

4.6 Critical Concerns

The biological properties of TiO_2 NTs have been extensively studied in the past several years. However, their mechanical and chemical stability is frequently overlooked although it is crucial to clinical applications. In particular, their poor adhesion on metallic substrates because of the presence of an F-rich layer (FRL) is a concern. Annealing has been reported to alter the interfacial chemistry and improve adhesion (Schmidt-Stein et al. 2010; Xiong et al. 2011). As previously reported, burying the FRL by additional anodisation in an F-free electrolyte may be promising (Yu et al. 2014; Zhang et al. 2012). Another concern is the poor mechanical strength that may manifest as brittle fracture of the tube apexes during storage, transportation or surgical operation. There is still no good solution to overcome the hurdle. Wang et al. (2011a) have reported that after the as-anodised amorphous TiO_2 NTs are immersed in water at room temperature, they spontaneously transform to anatase mesoporous nanowires. Since the human body is a water-rich environment, the use of amorphous TiO_2 NTs as implant coatings should be carefully considered. Nevertheless, another study has shown that the amorphous TiO_2 NTs can preserve the geometry even after long-term *in vivo* implantation (von Wilmowsky et al. 2009), suggesting that organic and inorganic species in the aqueous medium may affect the transformation.

4.7 Conclusion

TiO_2 NTs can serve as Ag NP carriers to prevent implant-associated infection via active release of Ag^+. By tailoring the NT dimensions, loading methods and incorporated amounts, the antibacterial activity and biocompatibility can be balanced. Compared to TiO_2 NTs loaded with Ag NPs, Ag_2O NP–embedded TiO_2 NTs may be a safer choice because of the controllable release of Ag^+ and small risk of NP detachment. Although the structure is very promising as implant coatings, their long-term effectiveness and mechanical and chemical stability need more in-depth studies before clinical use.

Acknowledgements

The work was jointly supported by the National Natural Science Foundation of China (31400815), by Hong Kong Research Grants Council General Research Funds Nos. CityU 112212 and 11301215 and by City University of Hong Kong Donation Research Grant No. 9220061.

References

AshaRani, PV, Grace Low Kah Mun, Manoor Prakash Hande, and Suresh Valiyaveettil. 2008. Cytotoxicity and genotoxicity of silver nanoparticles in human cells. *ACS Nano* 3 (2):279–290.

Bauer, Sebastian, Sebastian Kleber, and Patrik Schmuki. 2006. TiO_2 nanotubes: Tailoring the geometry in H_3PO_4/HF electrolytes. *Electrochemistry Communications* 8 (8):1321–1325.

Bian, Haidong, Xia Shu, Jianfang Zhang, Bao Yuan, Yan Wang, Lingjuan Liu, Guangqing Xu, Zhong Chen, and Yucheng Wu. 2013. Uniformly dispersed and controllable ligand-free silver-nanoparticle-decorated TiO_2 nanotube arrays with enhanced photoelectrochemical behaviors. *Chemistry, an Asian Journal* 8 (11):2746–2754.

Bjursten, Lars M, Lars Rasmusson, Seunghan Oh, Garrett C Smith, Karla S Brammer, and Sungho Jin. 2010. Titanium dioxide nanotubes enhance bone bonding in vivo. *Journal of Biomedical Materials Research Part A* 92 (3):1218–1224.

Brammer, Karla S, Seunghan Oh, Christine J Cobb, Lars M Bjursten, Henri van der Heyde, and Sungho Jin. 2009. Improved bone-forming functionality on diameter-controlled TiO_2 nanotube surface. *Acta Biomaterialia* 5 (8):3215–3223.

Carlson, Cataleya, Saber M Hussain, Amanda M Schrand, Laura K. Braydich-Stolle, Krista L Hess, Richard L Jones, and John J Schlager. 2008. Unique cellular interaction of silver nanoparticles: Size-dependent generation of reactive oxygen species. *The Journal of Physical Chemistry B* 112 (43):13608–13619.

Chen, Xiao, and Hermann J Schluesener. 2008. Nanosilver: A nanoproduct in medical application. *Toxicology Letters* 176 (1):1–12.

Chen, Xiuyong, Kaiyong Cai, Jiajia Fang, Min Lai, Jinghua Li, Yanhua Hou, Zhong Luo, Yan Hu, and Liling Tang. 2013. Dual action antibacterial TiO_2 nanotubes incorporated with silver nanoparticles and coated with a quaternary ammonium salt (QAS). *Surface and Coatings Technology* 216:158–165.

Chernousova, Svitlana, and Matthias Epple. 2013. Silver as antibacterial agent: Ion, nanoparticle, and metal. *Angewandte Chemie International Edition* 52 (6):1636–1653.

Chu, Paul K, Junying Chen, Langping Wang, and Nan Huang. 2002. Plasma-surface modification of biomaterials. *Materials Science and Engineering: R: Reports* 36 (5):143–206.

Gao, Ang, Ruiqiang Hang, Xiaobo Huang, Lingzhou Zhao, Xiangyu Zhang, Lin Wang, Bin Tang, Shengli Ma, and Paul K Chu. 2014. The effects of titania nanotubes with embedded silver oxide nanoparticles on bacteria and osteoblasts. *Biomaterials* 35 (13):4223–4235.

Geetha Manivasagam, Ashok K Singh, Rajamanickam Asokamani, and Ashok K Gogia. 2009. Ti based biomaterials, the ultimate choice for orthopaedic implants – A review. *Progress in Materials Science* 54 (3):397–425.

Ghicov, Andrei, Hiroaki Tsuchiya, Jan M Macak, and Patrik Schmuki. 2005. Titanium oxide nanotubes prepared in phosphate electrolytes. *Electrochemistry Communications* 7 (5):505–509.

Greulich, Christina, Jörg Diendorf, Tobias Simon, Gunther Eggeler, Matthias Epple, and Manfred Köller. 2011. Uptake and intracellular distribution of silver nanoparticles in human mesenchymal stem cells. *Acta Biomaterialia* 7 (1):347–354.

He, Xingliang, Yunyu Cai, Hemin Zhang, and Changhao Liang. 2010. Photocatalytic degradation of organic pollutants with Ag decorated free-standing TiO_2 nanotube arrays and interface electrochemical response. *Journal of Materials Chemistry* 21 (2):475–480.

Jiang, Yanshu, Baozhan Zheng, Juan Du, Guangyue Liu, Yong Guo, and Dan Xiao. 2013. Electrophoresis deposition of Ag nanoparticles on TiO_2 nanotube arrays electrode for hydrogen peroxide sensing. *Talanta* 112:129–135.

Kelly, Peter J, and R Derek Arnell. 2000. Magnetron sputtering: A review of recent developments and applications. *Vacuum* 56 (3):159–172.

Kim, Tae Hyun, Meeju Kim, Hyung Seok Park, Ueon Sang Shin, Myoung Seon Gong, and Hae Won Kim. 2012. Size-dependent cellular toxicity of silver nanoparticles. *Journal of Biomedical Materials Research Part A* 100 (4):1033–1043.

Kurtz, Steven M, Edmund Lau, Heather Watson, Jordana K Schmier, and Javad Parvizi. 2012. Economic burden of periprosthetic joint infection in the United States. *The Journal of Arthroplasty* 27 (8):61–65.e1.

Lan, Ming-Ying, Chia-Pei Liu, Her-Hsiung Huang, and Sheng-Wei Lee. 2013. Both enhanced biocompatibility and antibacterial activity in Ag-decorated TiO_2 nanotubes. *PLoS One* 8:e75364.

Lee, Jae Sung, and William L Murphy. 2013. Functionalizing calcium phosphate biomaterials with antibacterial silver particles. *Advanced Materials* 25 (8):1173–1179.

Lee, Kiyoung, Anca Mazare, and Patrik Schmuki. 2014. One-dimensional titanium dioxide nanomaterials: Nanotubes. *Chemical Reviews* 114 (19):9385–9454.

Lewinski, Nastassja, Vicki Colvin, and Rebekah Drezek. 2008. Cytotoxicity of nanoparticles. *Small* 4 (1):26–49.

Liang, Yanqin, Zhenduo Cui, Shengli Zhu, Yunde Liu, and Xianjin Yang. 2011. Silver nanoparticles supported on TiO_2 nanotubes as active catalysts for ethanol oxidation. *Journal of Catalysis* 278 (2):276–287.

Lin, Dandan, Hui Wu, Xiaolu Qin, and Wei Pan. 2009. Electrical behavior of electrospun heterostructured Ag–ZnO nanofibers. *Applied Physics Letters* 95 (11):112104.

Liu, Jingyu, and Robert H Hurt. 2010. Ion release kinetics and particle persistence in aqueous nano-silver colloids. *Environmental Science & Technology* 44 (6):2169–2175.

Liu, Xuanyong, Paul K Chu, and Chuanxian Ding. 2004. Surface modification of titanium, titanium alloys, and related materials for biomedical applications. *Materials Science and Engineering: R: Reports* 47 (3):49–121.

Liu, Xuanyong, Paul K Chu, and Chuanxian Ding. 2010. Surface nano-functionalization of biomaterials. *Materials Science and Engineering: R: Reports* 70 (3):275–302.

Ma, Menghan, Mehdi Kazemzadeh Narbat, Yu Hui, Shanshan Lu, Chuanfan Ding, David DY Chen, Robert EW Hancock, and Rizhi Wang. 2012. Local delivery of antimicrobial peptides using self-organized TiO_2 nanotube arrays for peri-implant infections. *Journal of Biomedical Materials Research Part A* 100 (2):278–285.

Ma, Qianli, Shenglin Mei, Kun Ji, Yumei Zhang, and Paul K Chu. 2011. Immobilization of Ag nanoparticles/FGF-2 on a modified titanium implant surface and improved human gingival fibroblasts behavior. *Journal of Biomedical Materials Research Part A* 98 (2):274–286.

Macak, Jan M, Hiroaki Tsuchiya, Luciano Taveira, Saule Aldabergerova, and Patrik Schmuki. 2005. Smooth anodic TiO_2 nanotubes. *Angewandte Chemie International Edition* 44 (45):7463–7465.

Macak, Jan M, Hiroaki Tsuchiya, Andrei Ghicov, Kouji Yasuda, Robert Hahn, Sebastian Bauer, and Patrik Schmuki. 2007. TiO_2 nanotubes: Self-organized electrochemical formation, properties and applications. *Current Opinion in Solid State and Materials Science* 11 (1):3–18.

Mah, Thien-Fah C, and George A O'Toole. 2001. Mechanisms of biofilm resistance to antimicrobial agents. *Trends in Microbiology* 9 (1):34–39.

Marambio-Jones, Catalina, and Eric MV Hoek. 2010. A review of the antibacterial effects of silver nanomaterials and potential implications for human health and the environment. *Journal of Nanoparticle Research* 12 (5):1531–1551.

Mei, Shenglin, Huaiyu Wang, Wei Wang, Liping Tong, Haobo Pan, Changshun Ruan, Qianli Ma, Mengyuan Liu, Huiling Yang, and Liang Zhang. 2014. Antibacterial effects and biocompatibility of titanium surfaces with graded silver incorporation in titania nanotubes. *Biomaterials* 35 (14):4255–4265.

Morones, Jose Ruben, Jose Luis Elechiguerra, Alejandra Camacho, Katherine Holt, Juan B Kouri, Jose Tapia Ramírez, and Miguel Jose Yacaman. 2005. The bactericidal effect of silver nanoparticles. *Nanotechnology* 16 (10):2346.

Oh, Seunghan, Karla S Brammer, Yi-Shuan Julie Li, Dayu Teng, Adam J Engler, Shu Chien, and Sungho Jin. 2009. Stem cell fate dictated solely by altered nanotube dimension. *Proceedings of the National Academy of Sciences* 106 (7):2130–2135.

Ohtani, Bunsho, and Seiichi Nishimoto. 1993. Effect of surface adsorptions of aliphatic alcohols and silver ion on the photocatalytic activity of titania suspended in aqueous solutions. *The Journal of Physical Chemistry* 97 (4):920–926.

Park, Eun-Jung, Jongheop Yi, Younghun Kim, Kyunghee Choi, and Kwangsik Park. 2010. Silver nanoparticles induce cytotoxicity by a Trojan-horse type mechanism. *Toxicology in Vitro* 24 (3):872–878.

Park, Margriet VDZ, Arianne M Neigh, Jolanda P Vermeulen, Liset JJ de la Fonteyne, Henny W Verharen, Jacob J Briedé, Henk van Loveren, and Wim H de Jong. 2011. The effect of particle size on the cytotoxicity, inflammation, developmental toxicity and genotoxicity of silver nanoparticles. *Biomaterials* 32 (36):9810–9817.

Paulose, Maggie, Haripriya E Prakasam, Oomman K Varghese, Lily Peng, Ketul C Popat, Gopal K Mor, Tejal A Desai, and Craig A Grimes. 2007. TiO_2 nanotube arrays of 1000 μm length by anodization of titanium foil: Phenol red diffusion. *The Journal of Physical Chemistry C* 111 (41):14992–14997.

Peng, Lily, Adam D Mendelsohn, Thomas J LaTempa, Sorachon Yoriya, Craig A Grimes, and Tejal A Desai. 2009. Long-term small molecule and protein elution from TiO_2 nanotubes. *Nano Letters* 9 (5):1932–1936.

Popat, Ketul C, Lara Leoni, Craig A Grimes, and Tejal A Desai. 2007b. Influence of engineered titania nanotubular surfaces on bone cells. *Biomaterials* 28 (21):3188–3197.

Popat, Ketul C, Matthew Eltgroth, Thomas J LaTempa, Craig A Grimes, and Tejal A Desai. 2007a. Decreased *Staphylococcus* epidermis adhesion and increased osteoblast functionality on antibiotic-loaded titania nanotubes. *Biomaterials* 28 (32):4880–4888.

Qiu, Yong, and Kinam Park. 2012. Environment-sensitive hydrogels for drug delivery. *Advanced Drug Delivery Reviews* 64:49–60.

Rai, Mahendra, Alka Yadav, and Aniket Gade. 2009. Silver nanoparticles as a new generation of antimicrobials. *Biotechnology Advances* 27 (1):76–83.

Regonini, Domenico, Chris R Bowen, Angkhana Jaroenworaluck, and Ron Stevens. 2013. A review of growth mechanism, structure and crystallinity of anodized TiO_2 nanotubes. *Materials Science and Engineering: R: Reports* 74 (12):377–406.

Roguska, Agata, Anna Belcarz, Tomasz Piersiak, Marcin Pisarek, Grażyna Ginalska, and Małgorzata Lewandowska. 2012a. Evaluation of the antibacterial activity of Ag-loaded TiO_2 nanotubes. *European Journal of Inorganic Chemistry* 2012 (32):5199–5206.

Roguska, Agata, Marcin Pisarek, Mariusz Andrzejczuk, Malgorzata Lewandowska, Krzysztof J Kurzydlowski, and Maria Janik-Czachor. 2012b. Surface characterization of Ca-P/Ag/TiO_2 nanotube composite layers on Ti intended for biomedical applications. *Journal of Biomedical Materials Research Part A* 100 (8):1954–1962.

Roy, Poulomi, Steffen Berger, and Patrik Schmuki. 2011. TiO_2 nanotubes: Synthesis and applications. *Angewandte Chemie International Edition* 50 (13):2904–2939.

Schmidt-Stein, Felix, Stefan Thiemann, Steffen Berger, Robert Hahn, and Patrik Schmuki. 2010. Mechanical properties of anatase and semi-metallic TiO_2 nanotubes. *Acta Materialia* 58 (19):6317–6323.

Tsuchiya, Hiroaki, Jan M Macak, Lenka Müller, Julia Kunze, Frank Müller, Peter Greil, Sannakaisa Virtanen, and Patrik Schmuki. 2006. Hydroxyapatite growth on anodic TiO_2 nanotubes. *Journal of Biomedical Materials Research Part A* 77 (3):534–541.

Uhm, Soo-Hyuk, Doo-Hoon Song, Jae-Sung Kwon, Sang-Bae Lee, Jeon-Geon Han, Kwang-Mahn Kim, and Kyoung-Nam Kim. 2013. E-beam fabrication of antibacterial silver nanoparticles on diameter-controlled TiO_2 nanotubes for bioimplants. *Surface and Coatings Technology* 228:S360–S366.

von Wilmowsky, Cornelius, Sebastian Bauer, Rainer Lutz, Mark Meisel, Friedrich Wilhelm Neukam, Takeshi Toyoshima, Patrik Schmuki, Emeka Nkenke, and Karl Andreas Schlegel. 2009. In vivo evaluation of anodic TiO_2 nanotubes: An experimental study in the pig. *Journal of Biomedical Materials Research Part B: Applied Biomaterials* 89 (1):165–171.

von Wilmowsky, Cornelius, Sebastian Bauer, Stefanie Roedl, Friedrich Wilhelm Neukam, Patrik Schmuki, and Karl Andreas Schlegel. 2012. The diameter of anodic TiO_2 nanotubes affects bone formation and correlates with the bone morphogenetic protein-2 expression in vivo. *Clinical Oral Implants Research* 23 (3):359–366.

Wang, Daoai, Lifeng Liu, Fuxiang Zhang, Kun Tao, Eckhard Pippel, and Kazunari Domen. 2011a. Spontaneous phase and morphology transformations of anodized titania nanotubes induced by water at room temperature. *Nano Letters* 11 (9):3649–3655.

Wang, Na, Hongyi Li, Wulong Lu, Jinghui Li, Jinshu Wang, Zhenting Zhang, and Yiran Liu. 2011b. Effects of TiO_2 nanotubes with different diameters on gene expression and osseointegration of implants in minipigs. *Biomaterials* 32 (29):6900–6911.

Wang, Qingyao, Xiuchun Yang, Dan Liu, and Jianfu Zhao. 2012. Fabrication, characterization and photocatalytic properties of Ag nanoparticles modified TiO_2 NTs. *Journal of Alloys and Compounds* 527:106–111.

Winter, Jessica O, Stuart F Cogan, and Joseph F Rizzo. 2007. Neurotrophin-eluting hydrogel coatings for neural stimulating electrodes. *Journal of Biomedical Materials Research Part B: Applied Biomaterials* 81 (2):551–563.

Xiong, Jianyu, Xiaojian Wang, Yuncang Li, and Peter D Hodgson. 2011. Interfacial chemistry and adhesion between titanium dioxide nanotube layers and titanium substrates. *The Journal of Physical Chemistry C* 115 (11):4768–4772.

Xiu, Zong-ming, Qing-bo Zhang, Hema L Puppala, Vicki L Colvin, and Pedro JJ Alvarez. 2012. Negligible particle-specific antibacterial activity of silver nanoparticles. *Nano Letters* 12 (8):4271–4275.

Yu, Dongliang, Xufei Zhu, Zhen Xu, Xiaomin Zhong, Qunfang Gui, Ye Song, Shaoyu Zhang, Xiaoyuan Chen, and Dongdong Li. 2014. Facile method to enhance the adhesion of TiO_2 nanotube arrays to Ti substrate. *ACS Applied Materials & Interfaces* 6 (11):8001–8005.

Yu, Wei-qiang, Xing-quan Jiang, Fu-qiang Zhang, and Ling Xu. 2010. The effect of anatase TiO_2 nanotube layers on MC3T3-E1 preosteoblast adhesion, proliferation, and differentiation. *Journal of Biomedical Materials Research Part A* 94 (4):1012–1022.

Zhang, Lan, Shaobo Wang, and Yong Han. 2012. Interfacial structure and enhanced adhesion between anodized ZrO_2 nanotube films and Zr substrates by sedimentation of fluoride ions. *Surface and Coatings Technology* 212:192–198.

Zhang, Shengsen, Feng Peng, Hongjuan Wang, Hao Yu, Shanqing Zhang, Jian Yang, and Huijun Zhao. 2011. Electrodeposition preparation of Ag loaded N-doped TiO_2 nanotube arrays with enhanced visible light photocatalytic performance. *Catalysis Communications* 12 (8):689–693.

Zhao, Lingzhou, Paul K Chu, Yumei Zhang, and Zhifen Wu. 2009. Antibacterial coatings on titanium implants. *Journal of Biomedical Materials Research Part B: Applied Biomaterials* 91 (1):470–480.

Zhao, Lingzhou, Shenglin Mei, Paul K Chu, Yumei Zhang, and Zhifen Wu. 2010. The influence of hierarchical hybrid micro/nano-textured titanium surface with titania nanotubes on osteoblast functions. *Biomaterials* 31 (19):5072–5082.

Zhao, Lingzhou, Hairong Wang, Kaifu Huo, Lingyun Cui, Wenrui Zhang, Hongwei Ni, Yumei Zhang, Zhifen Wu, and Paul K Chu. 2011. Antibacterial nanostructured titania coating incorporated with silver nanoparticles. *Biomaterials* 32 (24):5706–5716.

Zwilling, Valérie, Evelyne Darque-Ceretti, Annick Boutry-Forveille, Daniel David, Michel-Yves Perrin, and Marc Aucouturier. 1999. Structure and physicochemistry of anodic oxide films on titanium and TA6V alloy. *Surface and Interface Analysis* 27 (7):629–637.

5

Polymer–Silver Nanocomposites: Preparation, Characterisation and Antibacterial Mechanism

Lin Mei and Xinge Zhang

CONTENTS

5.1 Introduction

Infections by pathogenic microorganisms are of great concern in many fields, particularly in medical devices, hospital surfaces/furniture and surgery equipment. Approximately 64% of hospital-acquired infections worldwide are attributed to the attachment of bacteria to medical implants, and they are associated with an annual mortality of 100,000 persons in the United States as well as an increase in healthcare costs (Costerton et al. 1999). To solve the problem of increasing resistance of bacteria towards antibiotics, much attention has been focused on developing new antimicrobial systems in the biomedical industry. Metal nanoparticles have been considered to be highly promising antibacterial agents because of their outstanding physical, chemical and biological properties, which are provided by their large active surface area (Dobrovolskaia and McNeil 2007; Hirano 2009), and studies on metal nanoparticles have been followed by recent advances in the field of nanotechnology (Cioffi and Rai 2012). These advances include the development of silver nanoparticles (Ag NPs) that release silver ions and show broad antibacterial activity against both Gram-positive and Gram-negative bacteria, including highly multiresistant strains such as methicillin-resistant *Staphylococcus aureus* (Monteiro et al. 2009; Panacek et al. 2006). In addition, various surface functionalisation methods for immobilisation of Ag NPs have also been studied to ensure appropriate levels of biological safety as well as antibacterial activity (Li et al. 2006; Taglietti et al. 2014). Thus, biomedical materials incorporating Ag NPs have been devised, including catheters, dental materials and medical devices using a chemical or physical method (Liao et al. 2010; Oloffs et al. 1994). However, the synthesis of Ag NPs by a chemical or physical method needs a surfactant and a stabiliser to prevent unwanted agglomeration (Vaidyanathan et al. 2009).

Among the stabilisers, polymers are the preferred choice because of their special configuration, physicochemical properties and structural characteristics for grafting onto metal nanoparticles with good dispersion. In addition, the functional groups on polymers can be used as the binding sites of targeting reaction to control the oriented synthesis of the nanocomposites (Chen et al. 2005; Ijeri et al. 2010; Zhang et al. 2006). To obtain polymer–metal nanocomposites with excellent antibacterial activity, the polymers, such as polyethylene glycols (Popa et al. 2007), poly(vinylalcohols) (Chou et al. 2000), poly(vinylpyrrolidons) (Choi et al. 2008; Greulich et al. 2012; Heckel et al. 2009; Huang et al. 1996), poly(acrylamides) (Chen et al. 2006, 2013), polyurethanes (Chou et al. 2006), poly(methyl methacrylate) (Kong and Jang 2008), poly(bisphosphonate-*b*-2-vinylpyridine) (Zhang et al. 2014), poly(D,L-lactide-*co*-glycolide) (Fortunati et al. 2013), poly(styrene–divinylbenzene) (Kumar et al. 2013), polysaccharide (Cheng et al. 2013; Lu et al. 2015), protein (Fei et al. 2013; Zimoch-Korzycka and Jarmoluk 2015) and peptide (Liu et al. 2013; Regiel-Futyra et al. 2015), have been commonly employed as substrates for Ag NPs. The aim of this chapter is to offer a rather comprehensive survey of the well-established and newly developed polymer–Ag nanocomposites having anti-infective activity.

5.2 Preparation Methods

Polymer–Ag nanocomposites are typically surface modified with polymer grafts during nanoparticle synthesis, in a postsynthetic ligand exchange step or the solvent evaporation.

5.2.1 Modification *In Situ*

Surface functionalisation is performed by introducing the desired polymer into the reaction mixture during the synthetic process of Ag NPs (Figure 5.1). The polymer can be used as both a shape-directing molecule and a surface passivating agent. For example, the process of hydroxylation, which means metal reduction in a diol solvent, is a common method for the synthesis of Ag NPs (Sun and Xia 2002; Tao et al. 2006). During the reduction of silver ion, poly(vinyl pyrrolidone) (PVP) is generally added as a stabiliser to minimise energy crystal faces of Ag and prompt the formation of polyhedral nanoparticles. PVP chains are grafted to the metal surface through interaction with their pyrrolidone functional groups for protecting the obtained polyhedral nanoparticles. In this reaction, PVP with a molecular weight of 29–200 kDa is used in the synthesis for avoiding poor control to polymer grafting density (Panacek et al. 2009; Sun and Xia 2002; Tao et al. 2006; Xia et al. 2012). Ag NP synthesis protocols are also developed using soluble starch as a capping agent with individual reducing agents dextrose and arabinose with microwave technology (Kahrilas et al. 2014).

Similarly, Ag NPs are synthesized in the presence of cationic polyelectrolytes to obtain a crystalline structure with a narrow size distribution (Mayer et al. 2000). The cationic polyelectrolyte–Ag nanocomposites are prepared by rapidly adding the reducing agent (such as $NaBH_4$) into a mixed aqueous solution of inorganic metal salt (such as $AgNO_3$) and excess polyelectrolyte. Modification *in situ* is mainly dependent on the complexing capability of the polyelectrolyte with silver ion, and various chloride-based cationic polyelectrolytes, such as poly(diallyldimethylammonium chloride) and poly(2-hydroxy-3-methacryloxypropyltrimethyl ammonium chloride) and chitosan, are mainly used (Katz and Willner 2004). The polymer grafted layers that are subjected to *in situ* modification with a polyelectrolyte on the Ag NP surface incline to form a sub-monolayer shell for nucleation and growth of nanoparticles. The thinner polymer layers can be obtained by grafting Ag NPs with cross-linked amphiphilic (or functional) copolymers and can be controlled via monitoring the ratio of nanoparticles and copolymers in the solution (Kang and Taton 2005). In addition, Ag NPs can be incorporated in hydrogel coatings (Fischer et al. 2015; Guan et al. 2015), glass substrates

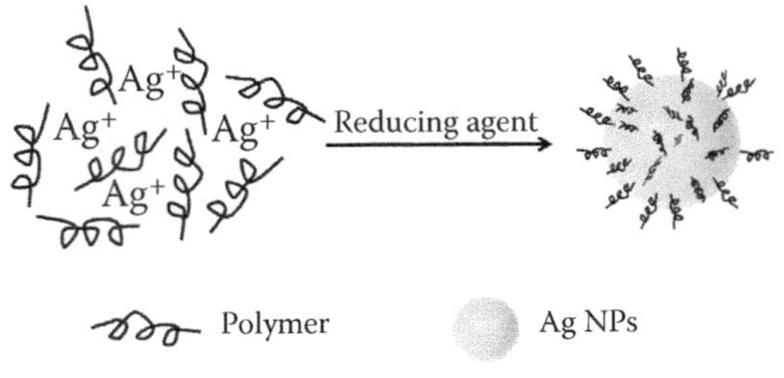

FIGURE 5.1
Schematic illustration of polymer grafting strategy on Ag NPs surfaces (modification *in situ*).

(Lorenzini et al. 2015), polymer nanofibres (Kong and Jang 2008; Song et al. 2012) and proteins (Jo et al. 2014) for obtaining extraordinary antimicrobial activities against Gram-negative and Gram-positive bacteria.

5.2.2 Grafting-To Approach

After the preparation of Ag NPs, the nanoparticles can be modified via ligand exchange reactions wherein the capping molecules of the obtained nanoparticle surface are instead of a polymer, or via chemical alteration of the capping molecule. Sodium citrate and various cationic surfactants, such as cetyltrimethylammonium bromide (Jana et al. 2001), benzyldimethyl hexadecylammonium chloride (Nikoobakht and El-Sayed 2003; Park et al. 2010) and cetylpyridinium chloride monohydrate (Bronstein et al. 2000; Setua et al. 2010), are commonly used as capping molecules. However, these capping molecules are labile with weakly chemisorption to the nanoparticle surface. As a result, ligand exchange reactions become a general strategy for surface modification of nanoparticles with polymer grafts (Figure 5.2). The capping molecules are substituted through covalent binding of the graft to the nanoparticle surface or physisorption of the polymer graft. The effectiveness of this displacement depends on the affinity of the polymer graft with the nanoparticle surface. Therefore, postsynthetic modification of Ag NPs is a typical method for polymer grafts that display strong binding affinity to the nanoparticle surface. For example, thiol-functionalised polymer grafts are widely used in the surface modification of plasmonic nanoparticles, because the high affinity of the thiol to Ag makes the terminus of the polymer easily graft to the Ag NPs surface (Love et al. 2006; Rucareanu et al. 2008).

5.2.3 Grafting-From Approach

In order to modify the compound of the chemical grafts on the nanoparticle surface *in situ*, in this approach, the polymers can be grown from the nanoparticle surface via polymerisation reactions (Figure 5.3). This method can obtain brush-like or cross-linked ligand shells with thickness on order structure or a larger diameter than naked nanoparticles. Responsive polymers can be

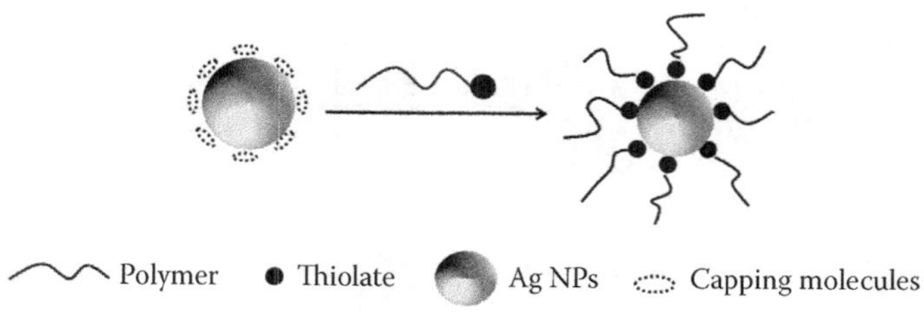

FIGURE 5.2
Schematic illustration of polymer grafting strategy on Ag NPs surfaces (grafting-to approach).

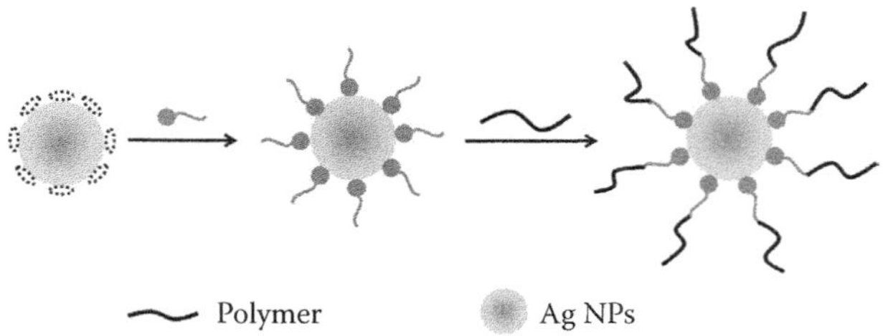

FIGURE 5.3
Schematic illustration of polymer grafting strategy on Ag NPs surfaces (grafting-from approach).

employed in this method to create smart core–shell nanoparticles and microgels that respond to the external stimulation by shrinking or swelling. For example, polystyrene (Khanal and Zubarev 2007; Zhang et al. 2008), poly(vinyl alcohol) (Pérez-Juste et al. 2005), polystyrene-*block*-poly(acrylic acid) (Wang et al. 2012; Yang et al. 2009), polypyrrole (Munoz-Rojas et al. 2008) and phenol formaldehyde resin (Guo et al. 2008) have also been adopted to successfully graft on the nanoparticle surface by this method.

5.2.4 The Solvent Evaporation

To control silver release rate, multifunctional nanocomposites based on biodegradable polymer matrix and Ag NPs were fabricated via solvent evaporation. A specific round-like poly(D,L-lactide-*co*-glycolide) nanocomposite based on Ag NPs was fabricated by the chloroform evaporation in the presence of Ag NPs and demonstrated the role of the microstructure nanocomposite surface on bacteria adhesion properties (Fortunati et al. 2011, 2013). Moreover, the silver-containing poly-(3-hydroxybutyric acid-*co*-3-hydroxyvaleric acid) nanofibrous scaffolds as tissue engineering scaffolds were prepared by electrospinning and showed good antibacterial activity and good *in vitro* cell compatibility (Xing et al. 2010). Ag NPs coated with poly(4-vinylpyridine) shells were also synthesised by dissolving poly(4-vinylpyridine) in ethanol with poly(diallyldimethylammonium chloride) and subsequently adding to Ag NP aqueous solution at elevated temperatures. The polymer shells imparted affinity on the Ag NP surface, which allowed them to spontaneously self-assemble with unmodified Ag NPs (Heckel et al. 2009).

5.3 Characterisation of Antimicrobial Activity

Susceptibility tests are most often indicated when the causative organism is thought to belong to a species capable of exhibiting resistance to commonly used antimicrobial agents. A variety of laboratory methods can be used to characterise the *in vitro* susceptibility of bacteria to antimicrobial agents. This department describes some standard test techniques, and it includes a series of procedures through which the tests are performed.

5.3.1 Minimum Inhibitory Concentration

The minimum inhibitory concentration (MIC) of the antimicrobial agent is the lowest concentration that inhibited visible growth of the microorganism in a susceptibility test, and it is determined according to the guidelines of the Clinical and Laboratory Standards Institute (2006).

The first step is the inoculum preparation. Select at least three to five well-isolated colonies of the same morphologic type from an agar plate culture. Touch the top of each colony with a sterile swab and transfer the growth into a tube containing 4 to 5 mL of a suitable broth medium. Incubate the broth culture at 35°C until it achieves or exceeds the turbidity of the 0.5 McFarland standard (usually 2 to 6 h). Adjust the turbidity of the actively growing broth culture with sterile broth to achieve a turbidity equivalent to that of a 0.5 McFarland standard.

The actively growing broth culture is mixed with an equal volume of two-fold diluted antimicrobial agent solution and incubates for 8 h at 35°C. The visible growth of the bacterial cells is assessed by measuring their turbidity. The lowest concentration is the one at which there is no turbidity greater than the faint turbidity (Figure 5.4).

In addition, the agar dilution method for determining antimicrobial susceptibility is also a well-established technique. The antimicrobial agent is incorporated into the agar medium, with each plate containing certain concentration of the agent. The inocula can be applied rapidly and simultaneously to the agar surfaces using a sterile swab capable of transferring 32 to 36 inocula to each plate. Record the MIC as the lowest concentration of antimicrobial agent that completely inhibits growth, disregarding a single colony or a faint haze caused by the inoculum. Table 5.1 shows the toxicity of Ag

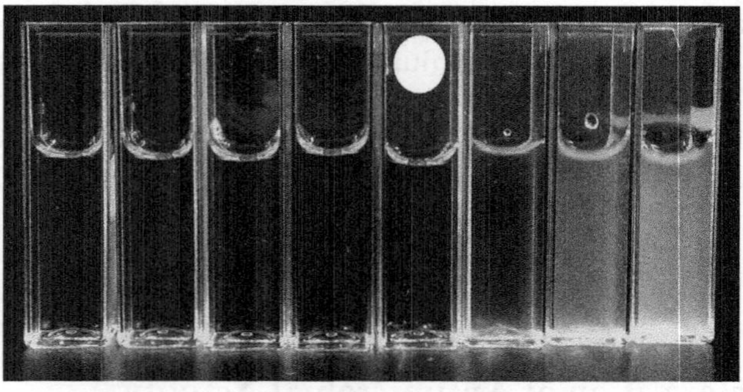

FIGURE 5.4
Photo of antibacterial testing results for the nanocomposites against *S. aureus*. The concentrations are reduced from left to right and these in the test tubes with white dots are MIC of complexes.

TABLE 5.1

The Biological Effect of Silver on Single-Celled Organisms (Bacteria, Fungi and Algae)

Organism	Silver Species	Particle Diameter	Functionalisation	Effect	Source
Escherichia coli DH5a	Ag NPs	75–20 nm	PVP	MBC = 12.5–20 mg/L for 103 cells at cultivation in RPMI/FCS	Greulich et al. 2012
E. coli PHL628-gfp	Ag NPs	14–16 nm	PVP	0.5 mg/L inhibits bacterial growth by 55% ± 8%	Greulich et al. 2012
Nitrifying bacteria	Ag NPs	14–16 nm	PVP	1 mg/L inhibits respiratory activity by 86% ± 3%	Choi et al. 2008
Staphylococcus aureus	Ag NPs	75–20 nm	PVP	MBC = 20 mg/L for 103 cells at cultivation in RPMI/FCS	Greulich et al. 2012
E. coli	Ag NPs	4–12 nm	PS–DVB	Complete inactivation in 0.5 h for 100 mg of resin	Kumar et al. 2013
E. coli	Ag NPs	–	PMMA	Complete inactivation at the concentration of Ag in the Ag/polymer (770 ng/mL)	Chou et al. 2006
S. aureus	Ag NPs	–	PMMA	Complete inactivation at the concentration of Ag in the Ag/polymer (770 ng/mL)	Chou et al. 2006
E. coli	Ag NPs	–	PDMAA	Complete inactivation at the concentration of 10 mg/mL MIC = 10 mg/mL	Chen et al. 2013
Stenotrophomonas maltophilia	Ag NPs	–	Aminocellulose	MIC = 1.64 μg/mL	Cheng et al. 2013
E. coli	Ag NPs	–	Aminocellulose	MIC = 3.25 μg/mL	Cheng et al. 2013
Acinetobacter baumannii	Ag NPs	–	Aminocellulose	MIC = 6.5 μg/mL	Cheng et al. 2013
Methicillin-resistant *S. aureus*	Ag NPs	12.0 nm	Silk fibroin	MIC = 19.2 mg/L	Fei et al. 2013
Bacillus subtilis	Ag NPs	–	Peptide	MIC = 0.01 nM	Liu et al. 2013
Candida albicans I	Ag NPs	25 nm	PVP	MIC = 0.1 mg/L	Panacek et al. 2009
Candida albicans II	Ag NPs	25 nm	PVP	MIC = 0.21 mg/L	Panacek et al. 2009
Candida parapsilosis	Ag NPs	25 nm	PVP	MIC = 0.84 mg/L	Panacek et al. 2009

(Continued)

TABLE 5.1 (CONTINUED)

The Biological Effect of Silver on Single-Celled Organisms (Bacteria, Fungi and Algae)

Organism	Silver Species	Particle Diameter	Functionalisation	Effect	Source
Candida tropicalis	Ag NPs	25 nm	PVP	MIC = 0.42 mg/L	Panacek et al. 2009
S. aureus	Ag NPs	5–13 nm	PHBV	Complete inactivation in the nanofibre containing 1.0 wt% of silver	Heckel et al. 2009
Klebsiella pneumoniae	Ag NPs	5–13 nm	PHBV	Complete inactivation in the nanofibre containing 1.0 wt% of silver	Heckel et al. 2009
S. aureus	Ag NPs	5–13 nm	PHBV	Complete inactivation in the nanofibre containing 1.0 wt% of silver	Heckel et al. 2009

Note: Inhibitory and lethal concentrations are on the order of 0.1–20 mg/L. If the particle morphology is not explicitly stated, particles with either spherical or unspecified morphology were applied. FCS, foetal calf serum; MIC, minimum inhibitory concentration; MBC, minimum bactericidal concentration;RPMI,RPMI-1640(cellculturemedium);PDMAA,poly(N,N-dimethylacrylamide);PHBV,poly(3-hydroxybutyrate-co-3-hydroxyvalerate); PMMA, poly(methyl methacrylate); PS–DVB, poly(styrene-divinylbenzene); PS, polystyrene.

NPs as a function of particle size. It is not possible to extract a clear trend because of the variation of the nanoparticles used with respect to functionalisation and charge and the variation of the biological systems used.

5.3.2 Zone of Inhibition Test

The zone of inhibition test (or agar diffusion test) is a test that uses antimicrobial agent–impregnated filter papers to test whether bacteria are affected by antimicrobial agents. In this case, filter papers containing an antimicrobial agent are placed on the surface of the agar plate where bacteria have been placed, and the plate is left to incubate. The antimicrobial agent diffuses from the filter paper into the agar. The concentration of the compound will be highest next to the disk and will decrease as the distance from the disk increases. If the antimicrobial agent inhibits the bacteria growth or kills the bacteria, there will be an area around the filter paper where the bacteria have not grown enough to be visible. This is called a zone of inhibition (Figure 5.5). The size of this zone depends on how effective the antimicrobial agent is at stopping the growth of the bacterium. A stronger antimicrobial agent will create a larger zone at a lower concentration. In general, larger zones correlate with smaller MIC values of the antimicrobial agent for the bacteria.

5.3.3 LIVE/DEAD Bacterial Viability Assay

The LIVE/DEAD bacterial viability assay is a convenient method to distinguish between living cell mass and dead cell mass through two colours. Acridine orange (AO) and ethidium bromide (EB) are common fluorescent dyes in this experiment. After staining, the bacterial cells are imaged by fluorescence microscope. AO is a vital dye and will stain both live and dead cells. EB will stain only cells that have lost membrane integrity. Under the

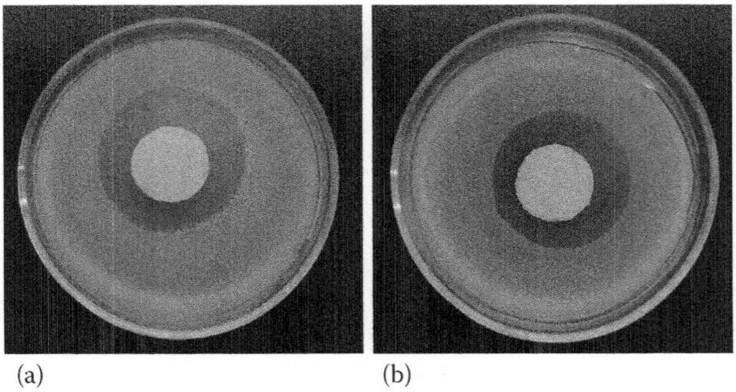

(a) (b)

FIGURE 5.5
Inhibition zones of the nanocomposites against *S. aureus* (a) and *P. aeruginosa* (b), respectively. (Reprinted with permission from Mei, L., Lu, Z. T., Zhang, X. G., Li, C. X., Jia, Y. X. Polymer–Ag nanocomposites with enhanced antimicrobial activity against bacterial infection. *ACS Appl Mater Inter* 6(2014): 15813–15821. Copyright 2014 American Chemical Society.)

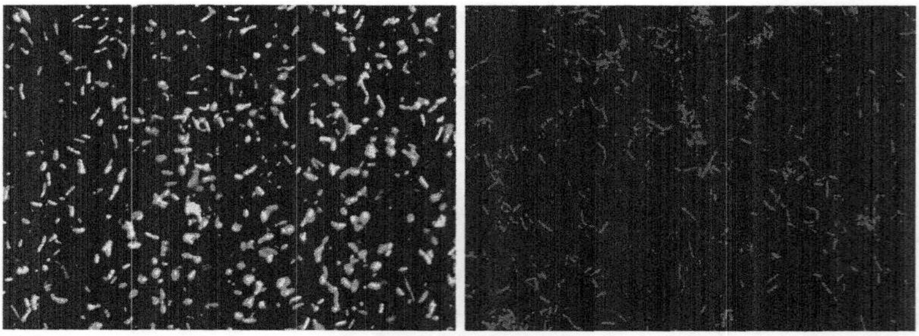

(a) (b)

FIGURE 5.6
(See colour insert.) Fluorescence micrograph of *P. aeruginosa* after being treated with the nanocomposites for 0 (a) and 20 min (b), respectively. (Reprinted with permission from Mei, L., Lu, Z. T., Zhang, X. G., Li, C. X., Jia, Y. X. Polymer–Ag nanocomposites with enhanced antimicrobial activity against bacterial infection. *ACS Appl Mater Inter* 6(2014): 15813–15821. Copyright 2014 American Chemical Society.)

fluorescence microscope, the living cells appear as diffuse green splotches, as the dye is taken into the entire cell membrane. Also, the dead cells appear as sharp red points, as this dye binds itself with the nuclei of ruptured cells (Figure 5.6).

Besides, the LIVE/DEAD BacLight bacterial kit is also used to examine bacterial cell viability under a fluorescence microscope. The kit consists of two stains, SYTO 9 and propidium iodide (PI), which both stained nucleic acids. These dyes have different cell penetration properties as well as different spectral characteristics. SYTO 9 binds to the nucleic acid of both living and dead cells, while PI can only bind to the nucleic acid of dead cells. Consequently, all live cells show green fluorescence, and dead cells with compromised cell membrane appear red under the fluorescence microscope. Therefore, microscopic assessment of LIVE/DEAD-stained bacterial cells is usually simplified to either 'green'-labeled (live) or 'red'-labeled (dead) cells.

5.3.4 Dynamic Contact Antimicrobial Assay

This test is designed to evaluate the resistance of nonleaching antimicrobial agents to the growth of microbes under dynamic contact conditions. Immobilised antimicrobial agents on the substrate surface are not free to diffuse into their environment under normal conditions. The antimicrobial activity of a substrate-bound antimicrobial is dependent on direct contact of microbes with the active chemical agent. This test determines the antimicrobial activity of the treated specimen by shaking samples of surface-bound materials in a concentrated bacterial suspension for a 1-h contact time or other contact times as specified by the investigator. The suspension is serially diluted both before and after contact and cultured. The number of viable organisms in the suspension is determined and the percent reduction is calculated based on initial counts or on retrievals from appropriate untreated controls.

5.4 Antibacterial Mechanism

5.4.1 The Permeability of the Outer Membrane

The outer membrane of Gram-negative bacteria provides the cell with an effective permeability barrier against external noxious agents, including cationic polymer–functionalised Ag NPs, but is itself a target for antibacterial agents. Both groups of agents weaken the molecular interactions of the lipopolysaccharide constituent of the outer membrane (Hancock 1984; Nikaido 1989, 2003; Nikaido and Vaara 1985; Vaara 1992). The molecular basis of the integrity of the outer membrane relies on its lipopolysaccharide. The lipopolysaccharide binds cations, since it is polyanionic because of a number of negative charges in its lipid A and inner-core parts. Adjacent polyanionic lipopolysaccharide molecules are apparently linked electrostatically by divalent cations (Mg^{2+}, Ca^{2+}), inherent in the outer membrane, to each other to form a stable envelope on the surface of the outer membrane. However, cationic polymers of nanocomposite surfaces that possess a high number of positive charges bind to the negatively charged bacterial surface lipopolysaccharide via electrostatic interactions. Thus, cationic polymers replace these divalent cations from their binding sites in lipopolysaccharide, resulting in damage to the outer membrane.

The outer-membrane permeabilisation activity of antibacterial agents was determined by the hydrophobic fluorescent probe 1-*N*-phenylnaphthylamine (NPN) assay (Loh 1984). For this assay, samples of the bacteria mixed with NPN were monitored with a fluorescence spectrophotometer (excitation wavelength, 350 nm; emission wavelength, 420 nm), and fluorescence intensity was recorded before and after the addition of desired concentrations of test agents. Increased fluorescence indicates uptake of NPN by the bacterial membrane, as partitioning of NPN into the outer membrane was measured by the addition of various concentrations of test agents.

5.4.2 The Permeability of the Inner Membrane

The inner membrane (cytoplasmic membrane) will be threatened where the outer membrane has been damaged. The enzyme β-galactosidase is present in the cytoplasm of *Enterobacteriaceae* (e.g. *Escherichia coli*). When β-galactosidase was released into the medium after cytoplasmic membrane disruptions, it can catalyse the hydrolysis of extracellular ortho-nitrophenyl-β-D-galactopyranoside (ONPG) to produce ortho-nitrophenol (ONP), which is determined by measuring the optical density value at 420 nm using UV–vis spectroscopy (Je and Kim 2006; Koepsel and Russell 2003; Vestro et al. 2000; Wu et al. 1999). Therefore, inner-membrane permeabilisation can be assayed by determining the release of β-galactosidase from the cytoplasm of *E. coli* into the culture medium using ONPG as the substrate. In this assay, the bacterial suspension is treated with ONPG and polymer–Ag nanocomposites in order and analysed. If the release of cytoplasmic β-galactosidase increases with an increase in nanocomposite concentration and reaction time, it indicates that the integrality of the inner membrane has been damaged, leading to leakage of the cytoplasm.

5.4.3 The Fluidity of the Cytoplasmic Membrane

A fluorescent membrane probe, 1,6-diphenyl-1,3,5-hexatriene, which is hydrophobic and easily associates with lipophilic tails of phospholipids in the cytoplasmic membrane without disrupting their structure, offers a means of quantitatively measuring the relative changes in fluidity of the bacterial cytoplasmic membrane under different growth conditions (Mykytczuk et al. 2007; Vincent et al. 2004). Membrane polarisation values can be estimated as the averages of total cells, whereby a small change reflects significant alterations in the membrane structure (Chen and Bowman 1965). A high polarisation value indicates low membrane fluidity with disruption of the bacterial cytoplasmic membrane (Trevors 2003). We have studied the effect of cationic polymer quaternised poly(2-(dimethylamino)ethyl methacrylate)-functionalised Ag NPs on the cytoplasmic membrane of *P. aeruginosa* and *S. aureus*. It is found that bacterial cells grown in the absence of nanoparticles exhibit lower values than those grown in the presence of nanoparticles. Moreover, polarisation values increase with increasing nanoparticle concentrations in both *P. aeruginosa* and *S. aureus*. These results indicate that the nanocomposites can hinder bacterial modulation of membrane composition to maintain fluidity for cell growth and division, leading to a decrease in fluidity and disruption of the bacterial cytoplasmic membrane.

5.4.4 Microscopic Study of Cell Morphological Change

Transmission electron microscopy (TEM) images of ultrathin sections are used to observe the ultrastructural damage in bacterial cells. The ultrathin sections of bacterial samples for TEM are prepared via the following steps: washing, fixing, dehydrating, filling resin, polymerising, cutting and staining. The bacterial cell microscopic change (e.g. the change of membrane morphology and the leakage of the cytoplasm) can be directly visualised by TEM images. As shown in Figure 5.7a (Mei et al. 2013), the cell surface of *S. aureus* without any treatment appears smooth. After addition of the nanocomposites (Ag NPs functionalised with both bacitracin A and polymyxin E), the nanoparticles are found on the surface of the bacterial cell wall at multiple

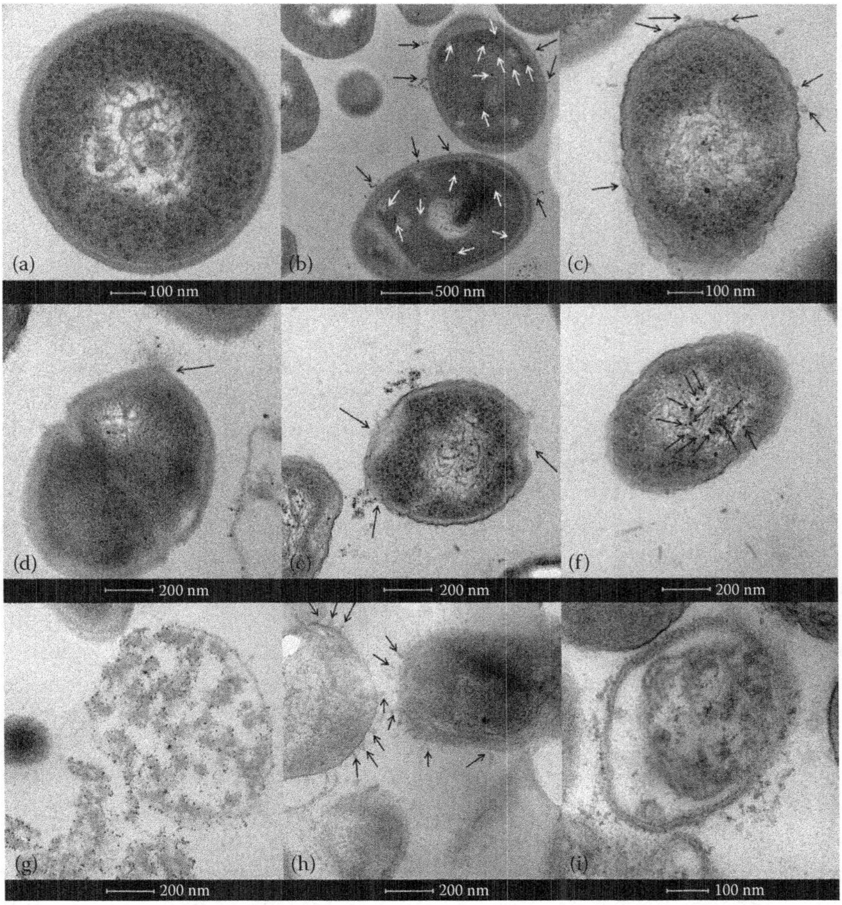

FIGURE 5.7
TEM images of a thin section of *S. aureus* (a through g) and *P. aeruginosa* (h and i) before (a) and after (b through i) incubation with the nanocomposites for 1 h. (Reprinted from *Biomaterials*, 34, Mei, L., Lu, Z., Zhang, W., Wu, Z. M., Zhang, X. G., Wang, Y. N., Luo, Y. T., Li, C. X., Jia, Y. X., Bioconjugated nanoparticles for attachment and penetration into pathogenic bacteria, 10328–10337, copyright 2013, with permission from Elsevier.)

sites (Figure 5.7b, black arrows), and some of them have penetrated the cell wall into the cytoplasm (Figure 5.7b, white arrows). The bacterial cell is seriously damaged with obvious undulating appearance on a disorganised cell surface (Figure 5.7c) and few vesicles emanating from the cell wall (Figure 5.7c, arrows). The damage was evident with the cytoplasmic release (Figure 5.7d, arrow) and disorganised cell wall (Figure 5.7e, arrows). Furthermore, the nanoparticles not only are present in the cytoplasm but are also detected in the bacterial nucleoid (Figure 5.7f, arrows). In addition, in the disintegrated bacteria, there are no aggregated nanoparticles inside the bacteria and the nanoparticles maintain their original size and spherical shape (Figure 5.7g). Similar results are obtained from the TEM images of *P. aeruginosa* treated with nanoparticles. The *P. aeruginosa* cell surface is severely damaged with numerous blebs (Figure 5.7h), and after the disorganisation of the bacterial cytomembrane, the intracellular content leaked out (Figure 5.7i).

5.5 Applications

Silver-based compounds (ions, salts and nanoparticles) have been used in a wide range of antibacterial and antifungal applications from clothing and fabrics, washing machines, water purification, toothpaste, fabrics, deodorants, filters, kitchen utensils, toys and humidifiers, to a range of wound dressings (Varner et al. 2010). However, existing silver dressings contain high loadings of silver and typically lead to the delivery of a large excess of silver to wounds and surrounding tissue, causing tissue toxicity and impaired wound healing (Asharani et al. 2010; Kristiansen et al. 2008; Van Den Plas et al. 2008). To address the challenge of nontoxicity to tissue but antibacterial to wound beds, the functional materials of polymer–Ag nanocomposites are designed as an important alternative for the application of wound healing. Recently, a cationic polymer–functionalised Ag NP was synthesised against bacterial infection, displaying good cytocompatibility and strong antimicrobial activity in healthy and diabetic rats (Figure 5.8). After administration to the infected wounds for 24 days, the wounds can be healed with epithelialisation, formation of granulation tissue and contraction of underlying wound connective tissues. The nanocomposites have a promising future in treatment of other infectious diseases (Mei et al. 2014).

Similarly, polyelectrolyte multilayers are impregnated with a range of loadings of Ag NPs and stamp onto the dermis of human cadaver skin that was subsequently incubated with bacterial cultures. Skin dermis stamped with polyelectrolyte multilayers can release silver ions, which kill *S. epidermidis* and *P. aeruginosa* within 12 h. Significantly, the level of silver release is below that which is cytotoxic to NIH 3T3 mouse fibroblast cells (Agarwal et al. 2011).

Infections arising from bacterial adhesion and colonisation on medical device surfaces are a significant healthcare problem. Silver-based antibacterial coatings have attracted a great deal of attention as a potential solution. These coatings have excellent antibacterial efficacy against clinically significant pathogenic bacteria and noncytotoxic to primary mammalian cells. The Ag NP–generating antibacterial coatings have great potential to be used for the prevention of bacterial infection in diverse biomedical fields (Agarwal et al. 2010; Jo et al. 2014; Taheri et al. 2014).

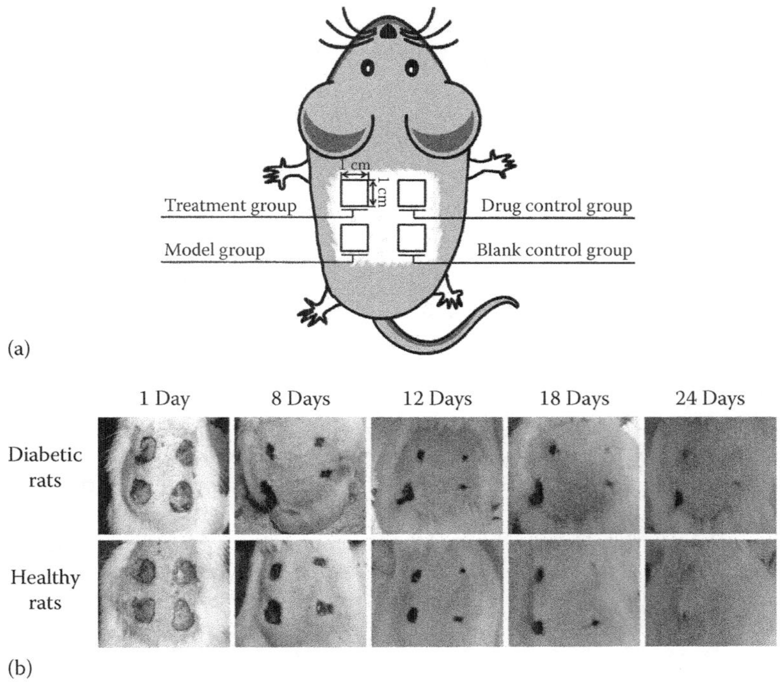

FIGURE 5.8
In vivo study on the effects of treatment of bacteria-induced wound infections for diabetic and healthy rats with the nanocomposites. Diagrammatic sketch of four wounds with different treatments in a rat (a). Wound photographs of the rats (b). (Reprinted with permission from Mei, L., Lu, Z. T., Zhang, X. G., Li, C. X., Jia, Y. X. Polymer–Ag nanocomposites with enhanced antimicrobial activity against bacterial infection. *ACS Appl Mater Inter* 6(2014): 15813–15821. Copyright 2014 American Chemical Society.)

5.6 Conclusions and Future Perspectives

Polymer–Ag nanocomposites are promising agents for recognising and killing the pathogen. These antibacterial agents have also demonstrated their capabilities as therapeutic agents for the treatment of infectious disease. These agents to date have been successful in catering to the requirements of the antibacterial research community by providing better efficiency, specificity and sensitivity. Recent research in this field has primarily been focused on the development of antibacterial agents for drug-resistant bacteria. Early preclinical trials have also been successful and promising. Future research investigations must now be directed at the translation of these technologies to clinical applications. In parallel, the continued evolution of more polymer–Ag nanoparticle–based agents for imaging and therapy is anticipated in the future. Given the prevalence and impact of infectious disease, bacterial detection, imaging and therapy are expected to be the earliest applications for these polymer–Ag composite antibacterial agents.

References

Agarwal, A., Guthrie, K. M., Czuprynski, C. J., Schurr, M. J., McAnulty, J. F., Murphy, C. J., Abbott, N. L. Polymeric multilayers that contain silver nanoparticles can be stamped onto biological tissues to provide antibacterial activity. *Adv Funct Mater* 21(2011): 1863–1873.

Agarwal, A., Weis, T. L., Schurr, M. J., Faith, N. G., Czuprynskic, C. J., McAnultyd, J. F., Murphyd, C. J., Abbot, N. L. Surfaces modified with nanometer-thick silver-impregnated polymeric films that kill bacteria but support growth of mammalian cells. *Biomaterials* 31(2010): 680–690.

Asharani, P. V., Sethu, S., Vadukumpully, S., Zhong, S. P., Lim, C. T., Hande, M. P., Valiyaveettil, S. Investigations on the structural damage in human erythrocytes exposed to silver, gold, and platinum nanoparticles. *Adv Funct Mater* 20(2010): 1233–1242.

Bronstein, L. M., Chernyshov, D. M., Timofeeva, G. I., Dubrovina, L. V., Valetsky, P. M., Obolonkova, E. S., Khokhlov, A. R. Interaction of polystyrene-block-poly(ethylene oxide) micelles with cationic surfactant in aqueous solutions. Metal colloid formation in hybrid systems. *Langmuir* 16(2000): 3626–3632.

Chen, A., Wang, H., Li, X. One-step process to fabricate Ag–polypyrrole coaxial nanocables. *Chem Commun* 14(2005):1863–1864.

Chen, M., Wang, L. Y., Han, J. T., Zhang, J. Y., Li, Z. Y., Qian, D. J. Preparation and study of polyacryamide-stabilized silver nanoparticles through a one-pot process. *J Phys Chem B* 110(2006): 11224–11231.

Chen, M., Zhao, Y., Yang, W., Yin, M. UV-irradiation-induced templated/in-situ formation of ultrafine silver/polymer hybrid nanoparticles as antibacterial. *Langmuir* 29(2013):16018–16024.

Chen, R. F., Bowman, R. L. Fluorescence polarization: Measurement with ultraviolet-polarizing filters in a spectrophotofluorometer. *Science* 147(1965): 729–732.

Cheng, F., Betts, J. W., Kelly, S. M., Schaller, J., Heinze, T. Synthesis and antibacterial effects of aqueous colloidal solutions of silver nanoparticles using aminocellulose as a combined reducing and capping reagent. *Green Chem* 15(2013): 989.

Choi, O., Deng, K. K., Kim, N. J., Ross, J. L., Surampalli, R. Y., Hu, Z. The inhibitory effects of silver nanoparticles, silver ions, and silver chloride colloids on microbial growth. *Water Res* 42(2008): 3066–3074.

Chou, C. W., Hsu, S., Chang, H., Tseng, S. M., Lin, H. R. Enhanced thermal and mechanical properties and biostability of polyurethane containing silver nanoparticles. *Polym Degrad Stab* 91(2006): 1017–1024.

Chou, K. S., Ren, C. Y. Synthesis of nanosized silver particles by chemical reduction method. *Mater Chem Phys* 64(2000): 241–246.

Cioffi, N., Rai, M. Progress and prospects. In *Nano-antimicrobials,* 504. Berlin, Heidelberg: Springer-Verlag Publisher (2012).

Clinical and Laboratory Standards Institute. Methods for dilution antimicrobial susceptibility tests for bacteria that grow aerobically; Approved standard – seventh edition. Clinical and Laboratory Standards Institute document M7-A7 [ISBN 1-56238-587-9]. Clinical and Laboratory Standards Institute, 940 West Valley Road, Suite 1400, Wayne, Pennsylvania 19087-1898 USA (2006).

Costerton, J. W., Stewart, P. S., Greenberg, E. P. Bacterial biofilms: A common cause of persistent infections. *Science* 284(1999): 1318–1322.

Dobrovolskaia, M. A., McNeil, S. E. Immunological properties of engineered nanomaterials. *Nat Nanotechnol* 2(2007): 469–478.

Fei, X., Jia, M., Du, X., Yang, Y., Zhang, R., Shao, Z., Zhao, X., Chen, X. Green synthesis of silk fibroin–silver nanoparticle composites with effective antibacterial and biofilm-disrupting properties. *Biomacromolecules* 14(2013): 4483–4488.

Fischer, M., Vahdatzadeh, M., Konradi, R., Friedrichs, J., Maitz, M. F., Freudenberg, U., Werner, C. Multilayer hydrogel coatings to combine hemocompatibility and antimicrobial activity. *Biomaterials* 56(2015): 198–205.

Fortunati, E., Latterini, L., Rinaldi, S., Kenny, J. M., Armentano, I. PLGA/Ag nanocomposites: In vitro degradation study and silver ion release. *J Mater Sci: Mater Med* 22(2011): 2735–2744.

Fortunati, E., Mattioli, S., Visai, L., Imbriani, M., Fierro, J. L. G., Kenny, J. M., Armentano, I. Combined effects of Ag nanoparticles and oxygen plasma treatment on PLGA morphological, chemical, and antibacterial properties. *Biomacromolecules* 14(2013): 626–636.

Greulich, C., Braun, D., Peetsch, A., Diendorf, J., Siebers, B., Epple, M., Köller, M. The toxic effect of silver ions and silver nanoparticles towards bacteria and human cells occurs in the same concentration range. *RSC Adv* 2(2012): 6981–6987.

Guan, Y., Chen, J., Qi, X., Chen, G., Peng, F., Sun, R. Fabrication of biopolymer hydrogel containing Ag nanoparticles for antibacterial property. *Ind Eng Chem Res* 54(2015): 7393–7400.

Guo, S. R., Gong, J. Y., Jiang, P., Wu, M., Lu, Y., Yu, S. H. Biocompatible, luminescent silver@phenol formaldehyde resin core/shell nanospheres: Large-scale synthesis and application for in vivo bioimaging. *Adv Funct Mater* 18(2008): 872–879.

Hancock, R. E. W. Alterations in outer membrane permeability. *Annu Rev Microbiol* 38(1984): 237–264.

Heckel, J. C., Kisley, L. M., Mannion, J. M., Chumanov, G. Synthesis and self-assembly of polymer and polymer-coated Ag nanoparticles by the reprecipitation of binary mixtures of polymers. *Langmuir* 25(2009):9671–9676.

Hirano, S. A current overview of health effect research on nanoparticles. *Environ Health Prev Med* 14(2009): 223–225.

Huang, H. H., Ni, X. P., Loy, G. L., Chew. C. H., Tan. K. L., Loh, F. C., Deng, J. F., Xu, G. Q. Photochemical formation of silver nanoparticles in poly(*N*-vinylpyrrolidone). *Langmuir* 12(1996): 909–912.

Ijeri, V. S., Nair, J. R., Gerbaldi, C., Bongiovanni, R. M., Penazzi, N. Metallopolymer capacitor in "one pot" by self-directed UV-assisted process. *ACS Appl Mater Interfaces* 2(2010): 3192–3200.

Jana, N. R., Gearheart, L., Murphy, C. J. Seed-mediated growth approach for shape-controlled synthesis of spheroidal and rod-like gold nanoparticles using a surfactant template. *Adv Mater* 13(2001): 1389–1393.

Je, J. Y., Kim, S. K. Chitosan derivatives killed bacteria by disrupting the outer and inner membrane. *J Agric Food Chem* 54(2006): 6629–6633.

Jo, Y. K., Seo, J. H., Choi, B. H., Kim, B. J., Shin, H. H., Hwang, B. H., Cha, H. J. Surface-independent antibacterial coating using silver nanoparticle-generating engineered mussel glue. *ACS Appl Mater Interfaces* 6(2014): 20242–20253.

Kahrilas, G. A., Haggren, W., Read, R. L., Wally, L. M., Fredrick, S. J., Hiskey, M., Prieto, A. L., Owens, J. E. Investigation of antibacterial activity by silver nanoparticles prepared by microwave-assisted green syntheses with soluble starch, dextrose, and arabinose. *ACS Sustainable Chem Eng* 2(2014): 590–598.

Kang, Y., Taton, T. A. Controlling shell thickness in core–shell gold nanoparticles via surface-templated adsorption of block copolymer surfactants. *Macromolecules* 38(2005): 6115–6121.

Katz, E., Willner, I. Integrated nanoparticle–biomolecule hybrid systems: Synthesis, properties, and applications. *Angew Chem Int Ed* 43(2004): 6042–6108.

Khanal, B. P., Zubarev, E. R. Rings of nanorods. *Angew Chem Int Ed* 46(2007): 2195–2198.

Koepsel, R. R., Russell, A. J. Directed capture of enzymes and bacteria on bioplastic films. *Biomacromolecules* 4(2003): 850–855.

Kong, H., Jang, J. Antibacterial properties of novel poly(methyl methacrylate) nanofiber containing silver nanoparticles. *Langmuir* 24(2008): 2051–2056.

Kristiansen, S., Ifversen, P., Danscher, G. Ultrastructural localization and chemical binding of silver ions in human organotypic skin cultures. *Histochem Cell Biol* 130(2008): 177–184.

Kumar, P., Ansari, K. B., Koli, A. C., Gaikar, V. G. Sorption behavior of thiourea-grafted polymeric resin toward silver ion, reduction to silver nanoparticles, and their antibacterial properties. *Ind Eng Chem Res* 52(2013): 6438–6445.

Li, Z., Lee, D., Sheng, X., Cohen, R. E., Rubner, M. F. Two-level antibacterial coating with both release-killing and contact-killing capabilities. *Langmuir* 22(2006): 9820–9823.

Liao, Y., Wang, Y., Feng, X., Wang, W., Xu, F., Zhang, L. Antibacterial surfaces through dopamine functionalization and silver nanoparticle immobilization. *Mater Chem Phys* 121(2010): 534–540.

Liu, L., Yang, J., Xie, J., Luo, Z., Jiang, J., Yang, Y. Y., Liu, S. The potent antimicrobial properties of cell penetrating peptide-conjugated silver nanoparticles with excellent selectivity for Gram-positive bacteria over erythrocytes. *Nanoscale* 5(2013): 3834–3840.

Loh, B., Grant, C., Hancock, R. E. W. Use of the fluorescent probe 1-*N*-phenylnaphthylamine to study the interactions of the aminoglycoside antibiotics with the outer membrane of *Pseudomonas aeruginosa*. *Antimicrob Agents Chemother* 26(1984): 546–551.

Lorenzini, C., Haider, A., Kang, I. et al. Photoinduced development of antibacterial materials derived from isosorbide moiety. *Biomacromolecules* 16(2015): 683–694.

Love, J. C., Estroff, L. A., Kriebel, J. K. et al. Theoretical study on self-assembly in organic materials. *Chem Rev* 105(2006): 1103–1170.

Lu, Z. T., Zhang, X. G., Li, Z. Y., Wu, Z. M., Song, J., Li, C. X. Composite copolymer hybrid silver nanoparticles: Preparation and characterization of antibacterial activity and cytotoxicity. *Polym Chem* 6(2015): 772–779.

Mayer, A. B. R., Hausner, S. H., Mark, J. E. Colloidal silver nanoparticles generated in the presence of protective cationic polyelectrolytes. *Polym J* 32(2000): 15–22.

Mei, L., Lu, Z. T., Zhang, X. G., Li, C. X., Jia, Y. X. Polymer–Ag nanocomposites with enhanced antimicrobial activity against bacterial infection. *ACS Appl Mater Inter* 6(2014): 15813–15821.

Mei, L., Lu, Z., Zhang, W., Wu, Z. M., Zhang, X. G., Wang, Y. N., Luo, Y. T., Li, C. X., Jia, Y. X. Bioconjugated nanoparticles for attachment and penetration into pathogenic bacteria. *Biomaterials* 34(2013): 10328–10337.

Monteiro, D. R., Gorup, L. F., Takamiya, A. S., Ruvollo-Filho, A. C., de Camargo, E. R., Barbosa, D. B. The growing importance of materials that prevent microbial adhesion: Antimicrobial effect of medical devices containing silver. *Int J Antimicrob Agents* 34(2009): 103–110.

Munoz-Rojas, D., Oro-Sole, J., Ayyad, O., Gómez-Romero, P. Facile one-pot synthesis of self-assembled silver@polypyrrole core/shell nanosnakes. *Small* 4(2008): 1301–1306.

Mykytczuk, N. C. S., Trevors, J. T., Leduc, L. G., Ferroni, G. D. Fluorescence polarization in studies of bacterial cytoplasmic membrane fluidity under environmental stress. *Prog Biophys Mol Biol* 95(2007): 60–82.

Nikaido, H. Molecular basis of bacterial outer membrane permeability revisited. *Microbiol Mol Biol Rev* 67(2003): 593–656.

Nikaido, H. Outer membrane barrier as a mechanism of antimicrobial resistance. *Antimicrob Agents Chemother* 33(1989): 1831–1836.

Nikaido, H., Vaara, M. Molecular basis of bacterial outer membrane permeability. *Microbiol Rev* 49(1985): 1–32.

Nikoobakht, B., El-Sayed, M. A. Preparation and growth mechanism of gold nanorods (NRs) using seed-mediated growth method. *Chem Mater* 15(2003): 1957–1962.

Oloffs, A., Grosse-Siestrup, C., Bisson, S., Rinck, M., Rudolph, R., Gross, U. Biocompatibility of silver-coated polyurethane catheters and silver-coated dacron material. *Biomaterials* 15(1994): 753–758.

Panacek, A., Kolar, M., Vecerova, R., Prucek, R., Soukupova, J., Krystof, V., Hamal, P., Zboril, R., Kvıtek, L. Antifungal activity of silver nanoparticles against *Candida* spp. *Biomaterials* 30(2009): 6333–6340.

Panacek, A., Kvitek, L., Prucek, R., Kolar, M., Vecerova, R., Pizurova, N., Sharma, V. K., Nevecna, T., Zboril, R. Silver colloid nanoparticles: Synthesis, characterization, and their antibacterial activity. *J Phys Chem B* 110(2006): 16248–16253.

Park, K., Koerner, H., Vaia, R. A. Depletion-induced shape and size selection of gold nanoparticles. *Nano Lett* 10(2010): 1433–1439.

Pérez-Juste, J., Rodríguez-González, B., Mulvaney, P., Liz-Marzµn, L. M. Optical control and patterning of gold-nanorod–poly(vinyl alcohol) nanocomposite films. *Adv Funct Mater* 15(2005): 1065–1071.

Popa, M., Pradell, T., Crespo, D., Calderon-Moreno, J. M. Stable silver colloidal dispersions using short chain polyethylene glycol. *Colloids Surf A Physicochem Eng Asp* 303(2007): 184–190.

Regiel-Futyra, A., Kus-Liśkiewicz, M., Sebastian, V., Irusta, S., Arruebo, M., Stochel, G., Kyziol, A. Development of noncytotoxic chitosan-gold nanocomposites as efficient antibacterial materials. *ACS Appl Mater Interfaces* 7(2015): 1087–1099.

Rucareanu, S., Maccarini, M., Shepherd, J. L., Lennox, R. B. Polymer-capped gold nanoparticles by ligand-exchange reactions. *J Mater Chem* 18(2008): 5830–5834.

Setua, P., Pramanik, R., Sarkar, S., Ghatak, C., Das, S. K., Sarkar, N. Synthesis of silver nanoparticle inside the nonaqueous ethylene glycol reverse micelle and a comparative study to show the effect of the nanoparticle on the reverse micellar aggregates through solvation dynamics and rotational relaxation measurements. *J Phys Chem B* 114(2010): 7557–7564.

Song, J., Kang, H., Lee, C., Hwang, S. H., Jang, J. Aqueous synthesis of silver nanoparticle embedded cationic polymer nanofibers and their antibacterial activity. *ACS Appl Mater Interfaces* 4(2012): 460–465.

Sun, Y., Xia, Y. Shape-controlled synthesis of gold and silver nanoparticles. *Science* 298(2002): 2176–2179.

Taglietti, A., Arciola, C. R., D'Agostino, A., Dacarro, G., Montanaro, L., Campoccia, D., Cucca, L., Vercellino, M., Poggi, A., Pallavicini, P., Visai, L. Antibiofilm activity of a monolayer of silver nanoparticles anchored to an amino-silanized glass surface. *Biomaterials* 35(2014): 1779–1788.

Taheri, S., Cavallaro, A., Christo, S. N., Smith, L. E., Majewski, P., Barton, M., Hayball, J. D., Vasile, K. Substrate independent silver nanoparticle based antibacterial coatings. *Biomaterials* 35(2014): 4601–4609.

Tao, A., Sinsermsuksakul, P., Yang, P. Polyhedral silver nanocrystals with distinct scattering signatures. *Angew Chem Int Ed* 45(2006): 4597–4601.

Trevors, J. T. Fluorescent probes for bacterial cytoplasmic membrane research. *J Biochem Biophys Methods* 57(2003): 87–103.

Vaara, M. Agents that increase the permeability of the outer membrane. *Microbiol Rev* 56(1992): 395–411.

Vaidyanathan, R., Kalishwaralal, K., Gopalram, S., Gurunathan, S. Nanosilver – The burgeoning therapeutic molecule and its green synthesis. *Biotechnol Adv* 27(2009): 924–937.

Van Den Plas, D., De Smet, K., Lens, D. Differential cell death programmes induced by silver dressings in vitro. *Eur J Dermat* 18(2008): 416–421.

Varner, K. E., El-Badawy, A., Feldhake, D., Venkatapathy, R. *State-of-the-Science Review: Everything Nanosilver and More*. Washington, DC: U.S. Environmental Protection Agency (2010).

Vestro, L. S., Weiser, J. N., Axelsen, P. H. Antibacterial and antimembrane activities of Cecropin A in *Escherichia coli*. *Antimicrob Agents Chemother* 44(2000): 602–607.

Vincent, M., England, L. S., Trevors, J. T. Cytoplasmic membrane polarization in gram-positive and gram-negative bacteria grown in the absence and presence of tetracycline. *Biochim Biophys Acta* 1672(2004): 131–134.

Wang, H., Chen, L. Y., Shen, X. S., Zhu, L., He, J., Chen, H. Unconventional chain-growth mode in the assembly of colloidal gold nanoparticles. *Angew Chem Int Ed* 51(2012): 8021–8025.

Wu, M. H., Maier, E., Benz, R., Hancock, R. E. W. Mechanism of interaction of different classes of cationic antimicrobial peptides with planar bilayers and with the cytoplasmic membrane of *Escherichia coli*. *Biochemistry* 38(1999): 7235–7242.

Xia, X., Zeng, J., Oetjen, L., Li, Q., Xia, Y. Quantitative analysis of the role played by poly(vinylpyrrolidone) in seed-mediated growth of Ag nanocrystals. *J Am Chem Soc* 134(2012): 1793–1801.

Xing, Z. C., Chae, W. P., Baek, J. Y., Choi, M. J., Jung, Y., Kang, I. K. In vitro assessment of antibacterial activity and cytocompatibility of silver-containing PHBV nanofibrous scaffolds for tissue engineering. *Biomacromolecules* 11(2010): 1248–1253.

Yang, M., Chen, T., Lau, W. S., Wang, Y., Tang, Q., Yang, Y., Chen, H. Development of polymer-encapsulated metal nanoparticles as surface-enhanced Raman scattering probes. *Small* 5(2009): 198–202.

Zhang, L., Shen, Y., Xie, A., Li, S., Jin, B., Zhang, Q. One-step synthesis of monodisperse silver nanoparticles beneath vitamin E Langmuir monolayers. *J Phys Chem B* 110(2006): 6615–6620.

Zhang, Q. M., Serpe, M. J. Synthesis, characterization, and antibacterial properties of a hydroxyapatite adhesive block copolymer. *Macromolecules* 47(2014): 8018–8025.
Zhang, X. W., Liu, L., Tian, J., Zhang, J., Zhao, H. Copolymers of styrene and gold nanoparticles. *Chem Commun* 48(2008): 6549–6551.
Zimoch-Korzycka, A., Jarmoluk, A. The use of chitosan, lysozyme, and the nano-silver as antimicrobial ingredients of edible protective hydrosols applied into the surface of meat. *J Food Sci Technol* 52(2015): 5996–6002.

Section II

The Risk of Silver

6

Dissolution of Silver Nanoparticles

Erchao Meng, Qingbo Zhang, Feng Li and Tanya S. Peretyazhko

CONTENTS

6.1 Introduction

The development of nanotechnology in the last decades has led to a rapid proliferation and application of nanomaterials (Navarro et al. 2008). The materials in nanoscale, which exhibit unique properties distinct from those of their counterpart in bulk, have been widely used in a variety of commercial products. Silver (Ag) nanoparticles are among of the most used nanomaterials with the estimated production between 500 and 1200 tons each year (Mueller et al. 2008; Maurer-Jones et al. 2013). Silver nanoparticles have excellent antibacterial properties and, therefore, have been widely applied in an increasing number of medical and consumer products such as clothing, toys, housing materials, disinfecting medical devices and water treatment (Lok et al. 2007; Marambio-Jones et al. 2010; Sotiriou et al. 2010).

The cause of the antimicrobial properties of Ag nanoparticles and their toxicity is a subject of intense debate. The antimicrobial activity of Ag nanoparticles is likely attributed to both release of silver ions (Ag^+) during Ag nanoparticle dissolution (Xiu et al. 2011, 2012) and the Ag nanoparticle itself (Asghari et al. 2012; Shen et al. 2015). Silver nanoparticles can act as a Trojan horse, entering a cell by bypassing typical barriers because of their small size and then dissolving Ag^+. The released Ag^+ harms cell functioning, leading to damage of deoxyribonucleic acid and cell death (Arora et al. 2008, 2009; Foldbjerg et al. 2009; Laban et al. 2010; Lubick 2008).

Dissolution is one of the principal processes that controls the release of Ag^+ from Ag nanoparticles and consequently antimicrobial properties of the nanoparticles (Batchelor-McAuley et al. 2014; Kittler et al. 2010; Loza et al. 2014; Maurer-Jones et al. 2013; Peretyazhko et al. 2014). Dissolution of Ag nanoparticles occurs through oxidation of metallic Ag to Ag(I) oxide and release of Ag^+ into solution (Peretyazhko et al. 2014). The combination of intrinsic physicochemical properties (surface coating, shape and size) and solution properties (ionic strength, pH, dissolved oxygen concentration, temperature and dissolved complexing ligands) controls dissolution (Levard et al. 2012; Misra et al. 2012; Peretyazhko et al. 2014).

An understanding of Ag nanoparticle dissolution mechanisms is a key factor to evaluate nanoparticle antimicrobial properties and their potential impact on human health. The chapter summarises recent progress in investigating dissolution of Ag nanoparticles in aquatic systems and covers an overview of Ag nanoparticle synthesis and mechanisms, thermodynamics and kinetics of Ag nanoparticle dissolution. We discuss how intrinsic properties of Ag nanoparticles and solution composition control dissolution. We conclude the chapter with a discussion of how dissolution affects antimicrobial properties of the nanoparticles.

6.2 Fundamentals of Ag Nanoparticle Dissolution

6.2.1 Brief Overview of Synthesis of Ag Nanoparticles

Recent advances in the field of colloidal synthesis of nanoparticles have enabled generation of a large library of silver nanoparticles with various shape, size and surface chemistry. The large silver nanoparticle library allows us to tailor the dissolution profile and antibacterial activity of silver nanoparticles and to optimise their performance in a broad range of applications.

Silver nanoparticles are usually produced by reduction of a silver salt in solvents in the presence of a capping agent (Dastjerdi et al. 2010; Iravani et al.

2014; Kumar et al. 2017; Ponnaian et al. 2015; Qin et al. 2012; Rodriguez-Sanchez et al. 2000; Singh et al. 2015; Tolaymat et al. 2010; Wiley et al. 2007; Zhang et al. 2009, 2010). The dissolution-controlling parameters such as size, shape and surface chemistry of nanoparticles can be varied by the selection of initial reaction systems and changes in reaction conditions (Albanese et al. 2012; Callegari et al. 2003; Grass et al. 2008; He et al. 2004; Ma et al. 2011; Pillai and Kamat 2004; Yang et al. 2011; Zeng et al. 2010; Zhu et al. 2000). Generally, the size of nanoparticles is determined by the kinetics of nucleation and growth. The shape of silver nanoparticles is usually determined by the number and distribution of twins within the particle and the growth kinetics of nanoparticles along different crystallographic directions. The shape control of silver nanoparticles will be discussed in detail in Section 6.4.2. The surface chemistry of silver nanoparticles is usually determined by the capping agent used in the synthesis process. The surface chemistry of silver nanoparticles can also be modified through chemical substitution after the synthesis of silver nanoparticles. In addition to chemical synthesis, biological synthesis is used to prepare silver nanoparticles. In a typical biological synthesis, silver nanoparticles are produced by mixing a silver salt with an extract of living system, for example, plants. Biomolecules in the plant extracts can serve as reducing agents and capping agents to produce silver nanoparticles. This method was discussed in detail in Chapter 5.

6.2.2 Dissolution Mechanism of Ag Nanoparticles

Oxidative dissolution of Ag nanoparticles is proposed to occur through oxidation of metallic Ag ($Ag_{(s)}$) to Ag(I) oxide (Ag_2O) and release of Ag^+ into solution (Liu et al. 2010). The dissolution is initiated by oxidation of $Ag_{(s)}$ on the surface of Ag nanoparticles by an oxidising agent present in solution [for instance, dissolved oxygen (O_2) or hydrogen peroxide (H_2O_2)], leading to the formation of a core–shell structure with metallic silver as the core and the surface Ag_2O layer as the outer shell (Figure 6.1) (AshaRani et al. 2008; Geranio et al. 2009; Ho et al. 2010; Kuzma et al. 2012; Levard et al. 2012; Sotiriou et al. 2012). Initially, one to two atomic layers of Ag_2O form on the surface, then Ag_2O dissolves, releasing Ag^+ into solution and exposing the nonoxidised metallic Ag that might undergo further oxidation (Figure 6.1). This formation and dissolution of the Ag_2O cycle occur concurrently, resulting in a continuous dissolution process (Li et al. 2010; Peretyazhko et al. 2014). The described oxidative dissolution mechanism with O_2 as an oxidant can be summarised by the following reactions (Damm et al. 2008; Henglein 1998; Henglein et al. 1991; Li et al. 2010; Liu and Hurt 2010; Peretyazhko et al. 2014):

$$4Ag_{(s)} + O_2 \rightarrow 2Ag_2O_{(s)} \quad (6.1)$$

$$(Ag^0)_n + H_2O_2 \xrightarrow{K_a} (Ag^0)_{n-2} + 2Ag^+ + 2OH^- \quad (6.2)$$

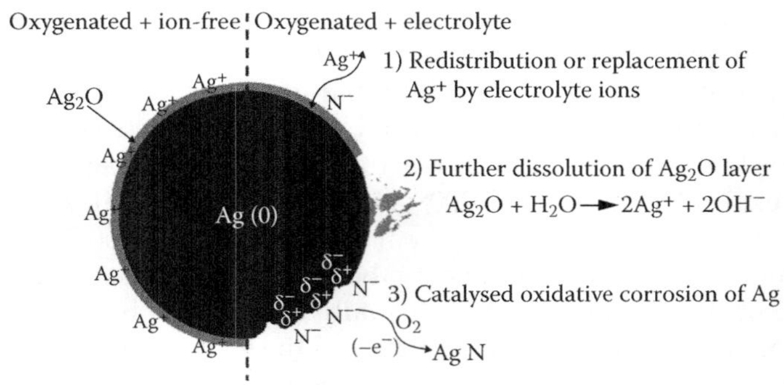

FIGURE 6.1
Schematic illustration of oxidative dissolution of Ag nanoparticles through formation of the surface layer of Ag_2O with and without electrolyte (N) addition. (From Li, X. et al., *Langmuir* 28(2) (2011): 1095–1104.)

In terms of oxidant reactivity, H_2O_2 is a more powerful oxidant than O_2 and consequently is more reactive with Ag nanoparticles (Geranio et al. 2009; Ho et al. 2010). Moreover, some living organisms, such as algae and macrophages, can release H_2O_2 as a metabolic product into a natural aquatic environment, leading to more intensive dissolution of Ag nanoparticles (Ho et al. 2010; Navarro et al. 2008).

The proposed mechanism of Ag nanoparticle dissolution through the formation of intermediate Ag_2O was supported by dissolution studies and by direct analysis. Dissolution studies demonstrated that formation of the oxidised layer of presumably Ag_2O on the surface of Ag nanoparticles was required for dissolution to occur (Liu and Hurt 2010; Loza et al. 2014; Sotiriou et al. 2012). Liu and Hurt (2010) investigated the dissolution of Ag nanoparticles in O_2-containing and deoxygenated water. The authors found that dissolution of Ag nanoparticles was inhibited in deoxygenated solution while it occurred in the presence of O_2. Moreover, the authors also found that dissolution was enhanced at acidic over neutral or basic pH since Ag_2O dissolution was a proton-consuming process (Equation 6.2; Liu and Hurt 2010). Dissolution of Ag nanoparticles before and after reduction by H_2 revealed a striking difference in the amount of released Ag^+ (Sotiriou et al. 2012). Nonreduced Ag nanoparticles had one to two layers of oxidised Ag and, as a result, approximately 50% of the total Ag was dissolved. H_2-reduced Ag nanoparticles did not have an oxide surface layer and consequently dissolution did not exceed 5% of the total Ag (Sotiriou et al. 2012). The results, therefore, showed an important role of surface oxidation for Ag nanoparticle dissolution. Formation of Ag_2O on the surface of the Ag nanoparticle was confirmed by x-ray diffraction (XRD), x-ray photoelectron and Raman spectroscopies. XRD analysis of Ag nanoparticles revealed the presence of diffraction peaks for both Ag and Ag_2O (Kuzma et al. 2012; Wiesinger et al. 2013). Kuzma et al. (2012) performed simulation of the surface plasmon resonance wavelength as a function of Ag_2O thickness and proposed the thickness of the forming oxide to be around 1.2 nm. The presence of Ag_2O (1.5 ± 0.4 nm thick) was revealed by x-ray photoelectron spectroscopy after exposure of Ag nanoparticles to O_3-containing atmosphere (Han et al. 2011). Raman spectroscopy analysis could also identify Ag_2O forming during Ag nanoparticle oxidation (Wiesinger et al. 2013).

6.2.3 Thermodynamics and Kinetics of Ag Nanoparticle Oxidative Dissolution

Oxidative dissolution of Ag nanoparticles (Equations 6.1 and 6.2) is a thermodynamically favored process with a Gibbs free energy of reaction of −91.3 kJ/mol at 25°C (Levard et al. 2012; Liu and Hurt 2010). The amount of Ag^+ released into solution at equilibrium depends on nanoparticle solubility. The solubility of Ag nanoparticle is size dependent and is defined by a modified Kelvin equation:

$$\ln(S_{NP}/S_b) = 2\gamma V_m / rRT \tag{6.3}$$

where S_{NP} is the solubility of the Ag nanoparticle with a radius r, S_b is the solubility of silver with a flat surface, γ is the surface tension of the particle, V_m is the molar volume of the particle, R is the gas constant and T is the temperature (Liu et al. 2009; Ma et al. 2011). The modified Kelvin equation (Equation 6.3) predicts that dissolution of small particles is more thermodynamically favourable with respect to bulk material. Studies of size-dependent Ag nanoparticle dissolution revealed that small nanoparticles are energetically unstable and, as a result, more soluble, because of higher surface-to-volume ratio (Borm et al. 2006). Moreover, small nanoparticles have a larger fraction of atoms at edges and corners than large particles, which makes the surface more reactive (Liu et al. 2009).

In general, the dissolution kinetics of silver nanoparticles is described by the first-order kinetics:

$$[Ag^+]_{released} = [Ag]_{initial}\,[1 - \exp(-kt)] \tag{6.4}$$

where $[Ag^+]_{released}$ is a concentration of Ag^+ at time t, $[Ag]_{initial}$ is a total initial concentration of the Ag nanoparticle and k is a pseudo–first-order reaction constant (Kittler et al. 2010; Peretyazhko et al. 2014; Zhang et al. 2011). The reaction constant is affected by solution properties (dissolved O_2, pH, temperature, salinity and presence of complexing agents) and by the intrinsic nanoparticle properties (size, shape, surface coating and aggregation) (Liu and Hurt 2010; Navarro et al. 2008). Below, we summarise a few examples of Ag nanoparticle dissolution kinetic studies demonstrating how kinetics changes with intrinsic and solution properties.

Peretyazhko et al. (2014), for instance, investigated the dissolution kinetics of silver nanoparticles with different sizes in ultrapure deionised water (pH 7) and acetic acid (pH 3). The authors revealed that dissolution kinetics followed the first order at both pH values. The reaction constants depended on the particle sizes with the smallest particles dissolved faster than the larger ones (Table 6.1) (Peretyazhko et al. 2014).

Zhang et al. (2011) applied hard sphere collision theory to describe kinetics of Ag nanoparticle dissolution in aqueous environments. The theory approximated molecules and atoms as hard spheres and chemical reaction as a collision between the hard spheres. Dissolution kinetics was described by the first order (Equation 6.4), and experimental and fitting results are shown in Figure 6.2. Modelling revealed that dissolution depended on the nanoparticle size and increased with the decrease in size (Figure 6.2).

TABLE 6.1

Pseudo–First-Order Rate Constants (*k*) for Dissolution of Ag Nanoparticles in Ultrapure Deionised water (pH 7) and Acetic Acid (pH 3)

Size (nm)	*k* (pH 7), day^{-1}	*k* (pH 3), day^{-1}
6.2 ± 1.6	1.24	1.65
9.2 ± 3.0	0.43	0.65
12.9 ± 3.5	0.15	0.29
70.5 ± 12.0		0.25

Source: Peretyazhko, T. S. et al., *Environmental Science & Technology* 48(20) (2014): 11954–11961.

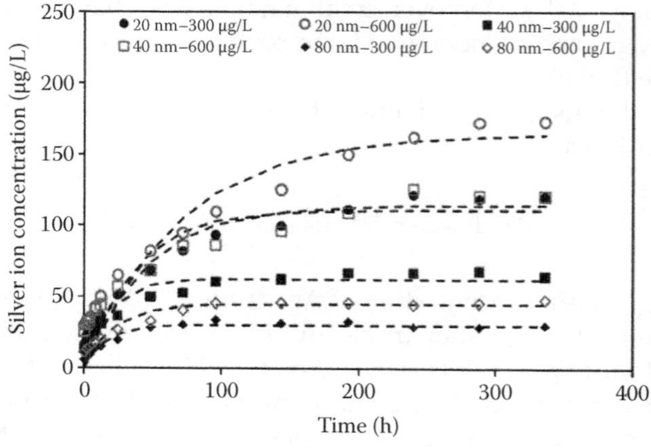

FIGURE 6.2
(See colour insert.) Kinetics of Ag^+ release from Ag nanoparticles in Hoagland medium; the model fits by Equation 6.4 are shown by the dashed lines. (From Zhang, W. et al., *Environmental Science & Technology* 45(10) (2011): 4422–4428.)

Ho et al. (2010) investigated the mechanism and kinetics of Ag nanoparticle oxidative dissolution by H_2O_2 in aqueous solutions. The authors described the oxidative dissolution of Ag nanoparticles by the following reactions (Equations 6.5 through 6.7):

$$H_2O_2 \xleftrightarrow{K_a} HO_2^- + H^+ \tag{6.5}$$

$$(Ag^0)_n + H_2O_2 \xrightarrow{K_a} (Ag^0)_{n-2} + 2Ag^+ + 2OH^- \tag{6.6}$$

$$(Ag^0)_n + HO_2^- + H_2O \xrightarrow{K_b} (Ag^0)_{n-2} + 2Ag^+ + 3OH^- \tag{6.7}$$

Oxidative dissolution kinetics followed the first order for Ag^+ (Equation 6.4) and oxidation of Ag by H_2O_2 and HO_2^- were the rate-determining steps (Ho et al. 2010).

The above-described examples of Ag nanoparticle dissolution kinetics studied relatively simple systems with one or two variables (e.g. size, pH, oxidising agent). Introducing more variables into systems makes it more difficult to fit the experimental data. For instance, Liu and Hurt (2010) investigated the effects of dissolved O_2, pH, temperature, ocean salts and natural organic matter (NOM) on the dissolution of citrate-stabilised Ag nanoparticles. The authors could fit dissolution data using the following empirical kinetic law (Equation 6.8):

$$-\frac{1}{m}\frac{dm}{dt} = Ae^{-E/RT}\left(\frac{[H^+]}{10^{-7}M}\right)^{0.18} e^{-a[NOM]} \tag{6.8}$$

where [NOM] is the concentration of NOM and E = 77 kJ/mol, $A = 2.5 \times 10^{13}$ day^{-1} and a = 0.083 L/mg are the constants. The obtained kinetic equation worked well to estimate Ag^+ release rates in the low concentration regime (~0.05 mg/L total added Ag nanoparticles) but not at high concentrations (Liu and Hurt 2010).

6.3 Influence of Solution Physicochemical Parameters on Silver Nanoparticle Dissolution

6.3.1 Effect of Temperature

Temperature is one of the factors controlling the dissolution of metallic Ag (Özmetin et al. 2000). Laboratory studies reveal that the dissolution rate of Ag

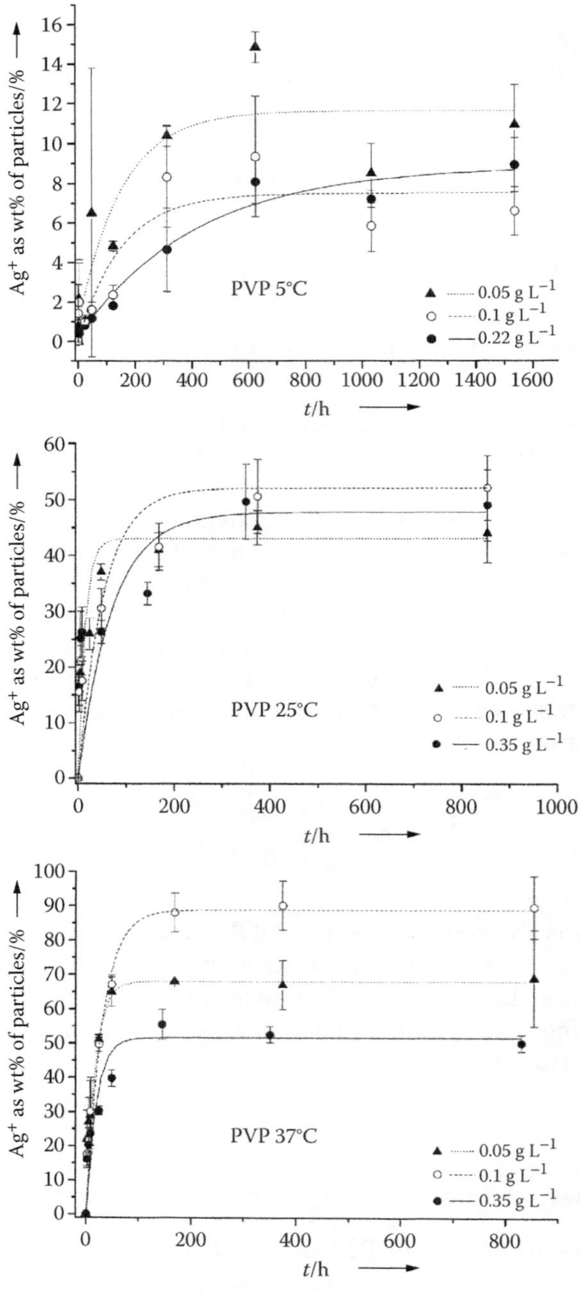

FIGURE 6.3
Concentration of Ag^+ released during dissolution of PVP-stabilised silver nanoparticles at 5°C, 25°C and 37°C. (From Kittler, S. et al., *Chemistry of Materials* 22(16) (2010): 4548–4554.)

nanoparticles increases with temperature increase (Ho et al. 2010; Kittler et al. 2010; Liu and Hurt 2010). Kittler et al. (2010) studied the dissolution of 50 ± 20 nm Ag nanoparticles stabilised by citrate and polyvinylpyrrolidone (PVP) at 5°C, 25°C and 37°C (Figures 6.3 and 6.4). The authors revealed that during a period of 200 h, the dissolution of 0.1 g/L PVP-stabilised Ag nanoparticles led to Ag^+ releases of ~5% at 5°C, ~50% at 25°C and ~90% at 37°C (Figure 6.3). A similar temperature trend was observed for citrate-coated Ag nanoparticles (Figure 6.4). Liu and Hurt (2010) also found a similar increase in dissolution of 4.8 ± 1.6 nm citrate-stabilised Ag nanoparticles when temperature increased from 4°C to 37°C (Figure 6.5). During the 5-day experiment ~40% and ~97% of total added Ag nanoparticles dissolved at 4°C and 37°C, respectively, as shown in Figure 6.5. A kinetic study of dissolution of 10.6 ± 2.8 nm

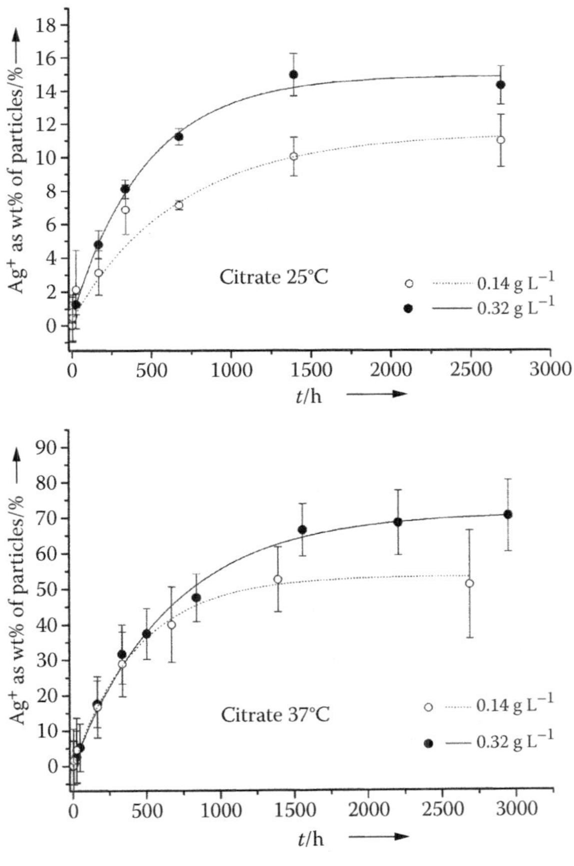

FIGURE 6.4
Concentration of Ag^+ released during dissolution of citrate-stabilised silver nanoparticles at 25°C and 37°C. (From Kittler, S. et al., *Chemistry of Materials* 22(16) (2010): 4548–4554.)

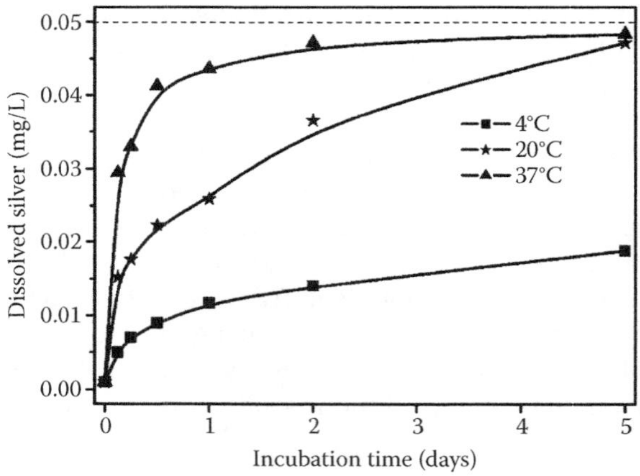

FIGURE 6.5
Concentration of Ag^+ released during dissolution of silver nanoparticles in air saturated deionised water at 4°C, 20°C and 37°C. (From Liu, J. and R. H. Hurt, *Environmental Science & Technology* 44(6) (2010): 2169–2175.)

Ag nanoparticles in the presence of H_2O_2 at pH 7.4 and at a temperature range of 15°C–45°C showed that dissolution obeyed the Arrhenius equation (Ho et al. 2010):

$$\kappa = Ae^{-E_a/RT} \tag{6.9}$$

where κ is the rate constant, R is the gas constant, T is the temperature, A is a pre-exponential factor and E_a is the activation energy (Stumm and Morgan 2012). The obtained E_a was determined to be 35.1 ± 0.9 kJ/mol (Ho et al. 2010).

6.3.2 Effect of Solution Composition

The solution composition and the presence of Ag^+ complexing species in particular (e.g. sulfide [S^{2-}], chloride [Cl^-] and organic matter) can substantially influence dissolution of Ag nanoparticles (Levard et al. 2011, 2012, 2013; Liu et al. 2010). The presence of Cl^- in natural waters and biological growth media has been shown to either decrease dissolution owing to precipitation of Ag chloride [$AgCl_{(s)}$] or enhance it because of the formation of soluble complexes (Ho et al. 2010; Levard et al. 2013; Li et al. 2010). Levard et al. (2013) performed detailed kinetic and thermodynamic studies of dissolution of 32.9 ± 4.9 nm Ag nanoparticles at a Cl/Ag molar ratio from 5 to 26,750. Kinetic studies revealed that the rate of Ag nanoparticle dissolution depended on aqueous Cl^- content and increased with increase of the Cl/Ag ratio (Table 6.2). The addition of NaCl at Cl/Ag = 5 resulted in little Ag^+ release with respect to

TABLE 6.2

Dissolution Rates of Ag Nanoparticles as a Function of Cl/Ag Molar Ratio

Cl/Ag	Dissolution Rate (%/h)
5	0.012 ± 0.001
54	0.056 ± 0.004
267	0.068 ± 0.011
535	0.107 ± 0.020
2675	0.240 ± 0.013
26750	0.850 ± 0.036

Source: Levard, C. et al., *Environ Sci Technol* 47(11) (2013): 5738–5745.

Cl^- free control (Figure 6.6). An increase in Cl/Ag ratio from 5 to 2675 leads to an increase in dissolution; however, dissolved Ag^+ concentration was still lower than in the Cl^- free control (Figure 6.6). Once the Cl/Ag ratio reached 26,750, dissolution of Ag nanoparticles becomes more intense than without Cl^- addition (Figure 6.6). Thermodynamic calculations showed that for Cl/Ag = 26,750, $AgCl^0$, $AgCl^{2-}$, $AgCl^{3-}$ and $AgCl^{4-}$ soluble species dominated over solid $AgCl_{(s)}$ while for Cl/Ag < 26,750, $AgCl_{(s)}$ was expected to be the dominant phase (Levard et al. 2013). Formation of $AgCl_{(s)}$ was directly confirmed by XRD analysis of Ag nanoparticles incubated in the presence of NaCl (Badawy et al. 2010). Precipitation of $AgCl_{(s)}$ during dissolution of Ag nanoparticles in the presence of NaCl was also observed by transmission

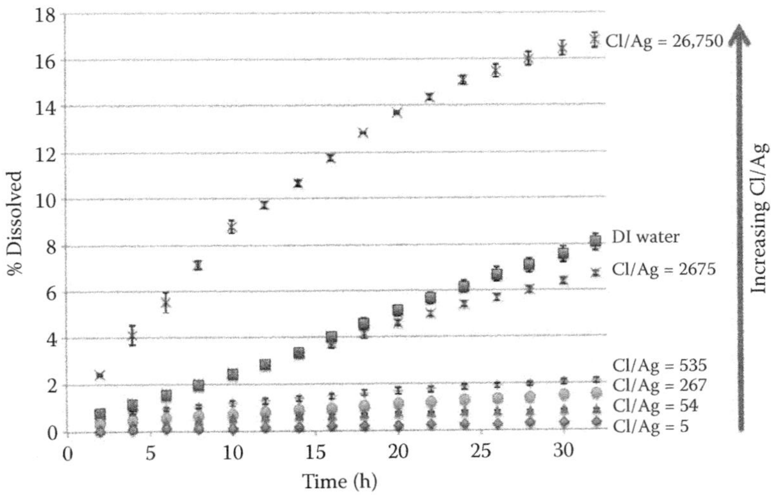

FIGURE 6.6
Dissolution of silver nanoparticles with and without addition NaCl at different Cl/Ag molar ratio. (From Levard C., S. Mitra, T. Yang et al. Effect of chloride on the dissolution rate of silver nanoparticles and toxicity to *E. coli*. *Environ Sci Technol* 47(11) (2013): 5738–5745.)

electron microscopy (TEM) (Li et al. 2010). The authors found substantial changes in nanoparticle morphology at the end of the dissolution experiment owing to deposition or formation of $AgCl_{(s)}$ on the surface of Ag nanoparticles (Li et al. 2010).

The presence of S^{2-}-containing species in aqueous phase substantially affects the dissolution behaviour of Ag nanoparticles (Levard et al. 2011; Liu et al. 2010). Studies of Ag nanoparticle dissolution at an S/Ag molar ratio from 0 to 1 revealed that dissolution of the Ag nanoparticles decreased upon addition of Na_2S (Figure 6.6; Levard et al. 2011). An increase of the S/Ag ratio to 0.019 led to a decrease of dissolved Ag^+ species by a factor of 7 with respect to S^{2-}-free solution (Figure 6.7). As the S/Ag ratio further increased, the dissolution decreased and finally Ag^+ could not be detected at S/Ag > 0.432 (Figure 6.7). The observed decline in dissolution was attributed to precipitation of Ag sulfide (Ag_2S). Application of synchrotron-based XRD and extended x-ray absorption fine structure spectroscopy demonstrated the increasing formation of Ag_2S with an increasing S/Ag ratio (Levard et al. 2011). TEM observations allowed the determination of the morphology of the forming Ag_2S and its distribution around Ag nanoparticles. The authors showed that Ag_2S formed nanobridges between the Ag nanoparticles resulting in formation of chain-like structures (Levard et al. 2011).

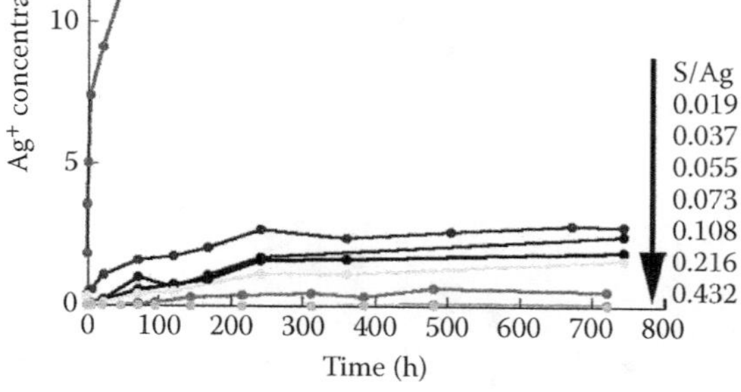

FIGURE 6.7
Dissolved Ag^+ concentration released from silver nanoparticles with and without addition of Na_2S at different S/Ag molar ratio. (From Levard, C. et al., *Environmental Science & Technology* 45(12) (2011): 5260–5266.)

The presence of organic sulfur-containing compounds and NOM suppresses dissolution of Ag nanoparticles (Liu and Hurt 2010; Liu et al. 2010; Loza et al. 2014). A comparative study of Ag nanoparticle dissolution with cysteine [α-amino acid containing thiol (SH) group $HO_2\,CCH(NH_2)CH_2SH$] and with a reducing sugar glucose [$C_6H_{12}O_6$] revealed different dissolution behaviours of the nanoparticles (Figure 6.8). Cysteine adsorption on the surface of nanoparticles through Ag complexation with the thiol group led to complete suppression of oxidative dissolution (Loza et al. 2014). In contrast, glucose slowed down the dissolution of silver nanoparticles in comparison to pure water but did not prevent dissolution on a longer time scale (Loza et al. 2014). The decelerating effect could be attributed to the ability of glucose to partially reduce Ag^+ to Ag^0 on the surface of Ag nanoparticles. Suppression of dissolution by SH-containing organic compounds was also reported by Liu et al. (2010) who studied dissolution in the presence of 11-mercaptoundecanoic (MUA) acid. The authors showed that MUA addition reduced the dissolution to undetectable dissolved Ag^+ as a result of Ag complexation with SH (Liu et al. 2010). The addition of NOM, such as Suwannee River humic and fulvic acids, led to the suppression of Ag nanoparticle dissolution (Liu and Hurt 2010). The decrease of Ag nanoparticle dissolution in the presence of NOM could be the result of several effects including blocking of Ag nanoparticle oxidation sites through NOM adsorption and reduction of the released Ag^+ to Ag^0 by NOM (Liu and Hurt 2010).

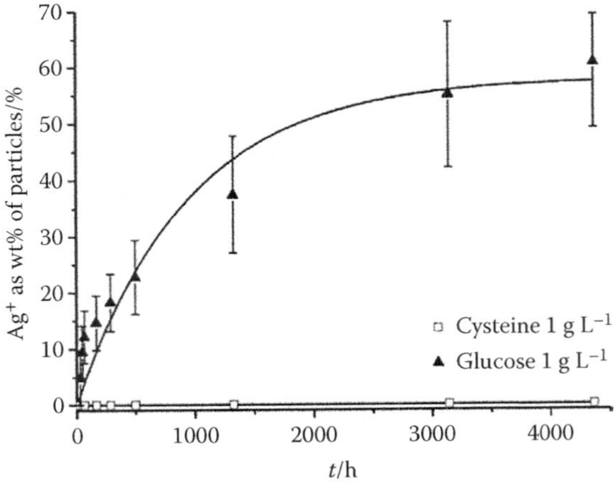

FIGURE 6.8
Concentration of dissolved Ag^+ released during dissolution of silver nanoparticles in the presence of cysteine or glucose. (Provided by Dr. Loza.)

6.3.3 Effect of pH

The oxidative dissolution of Ag nanoparticles involves reactions with protons (H^+) and dissolved O_2 (Equations 6.1 and 6.2). Dissolution of Ag is favourable under acidic pH (Equation 6.2), and experimental and theoretical studies showed that pH decrease, in general, leads to faster dissolution kinetics (Liu and Hurt 2010; Molleman and Hiemstra, 2015; Peretyazhko et al. 2014). For instance, Liu and Hurt (2010) studied dissolution of Ag nanoparticles in buffered solutions (acetate and borate buffer) in a pH range from 4 to 9 as well as in natural lake and river waters (pH 7.9–8.4). The authors observed that increasing pH from 4 to 9 resulted in 10 times less Ag^+ release. Dissolution of Ag nanoparticles in slightly alkaline natural waters was also slower in comparison to pH 4 behaviour.

Faster dissolution of Ag nanoparticles under acidic conditions could be attributed to surface protonation and decrease in Ag nanoparticle aggregation (Elzey and Grassian 2010; Peretyazhko et al. 2014). Peretyazhko et al. investigated dissolution of Ag nanoparticles in ultrapure deionised water (pH 7) and acetic acid (pH 3). The experimental results showed that the extent of the dissolution of silver nanoparticles in acetic acid was higher than that in water, as shown in Figure 6.9 (Peretyazhko et al. 2014). The authors proposed that dissolution of the surface layers of Ag_2O was facilitated at low pH owing to protonation of Ag nanoparticle surface (Peretyazhko et al. 2014). The surface of the Ag_2O layer is covered with hydroxyl groups (Ag–OH) at neutral pH. Hydroxyl groups undergoes protonation to form $Ag–OH^{2+}$ under acidic conditions. As a result, surface Ag–O bonds become weaker and break, leading to the larger release of Ag^+ into solution at pH 4 than at pH 7 (Peretyazhko et al. 2014). Alternatively, Elzey and Grassian (2010) proposed that a decrease in pH led to a decrease in Ag nanoparticle aggregation, which facilitated dissolution. Studies of Ag dissolution in water and nitric acid revealed that Ag nanoparticles existed as large aggregates between pH 6.5 and 3. However, when pH values ranged between 2.5 and 1, Ag nanoparticles were present as isolated particles, and at pH 0.5, Ag nanoparticles dissolved completely (Elzey and Grassian 2010).

The pH-dependent behaviour of Ag nanoparticles towards dissolution might be affected by the nature of the oxidising agent. For instance, in the presence of H_2O_2, an opposite dissolution trend was observed. Ho et al. (2010) found that dissolution of Ag nanoparticles increased with increasing pH in H_2O_2-containing solution. The increase in pH leads to H_2O_2 dissociation and formation of the hydroperoxide anion $\left(HO_2^-\right)$, which is a stronger Ag oxidising agent than H_2O_2 (He et al. 2012a; Hocking et al. 1982).

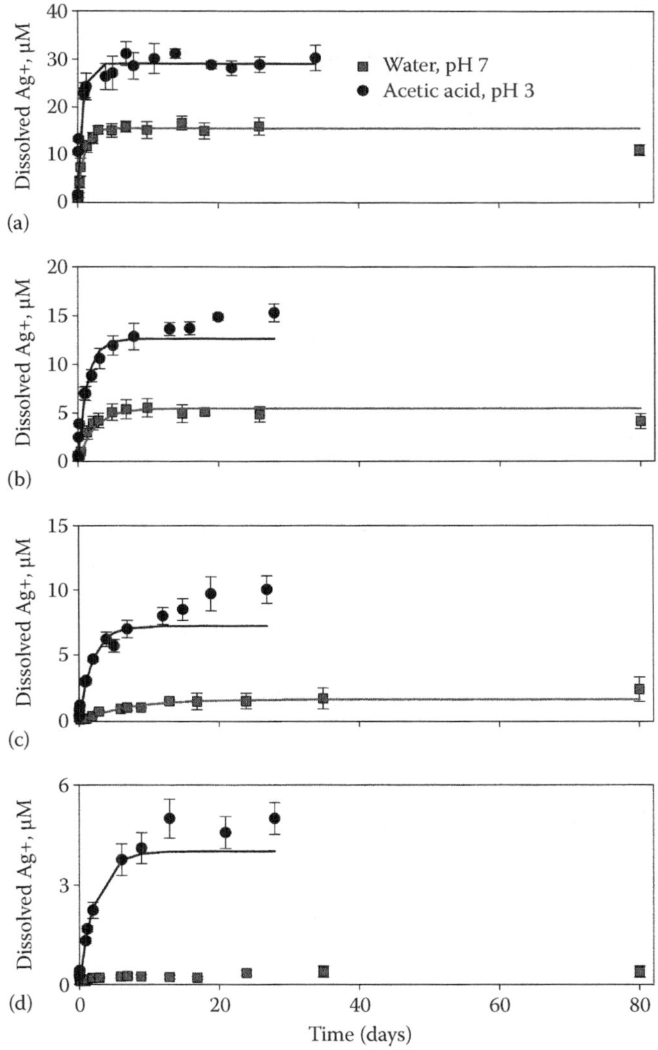

FIGURE 6.9
Release of dissolved Ag^+ in PEGSH-coated silver nanoparticles suspensions of different size in water (pH 7) and 0.05 M acetic acid (pH 3); (a) 6 nm, (b) 9 nm, (c) 13 nm and (d) 70 nm. First-order kinetic fits (Equation 6.4) are shown as solid lines. (Provided by Dr. Peretyazhko.)

6.4 Influence of Intrinsic Parameters on Dissolution

6.4.1 Effect of Nanoparticle Size

Studies of silver nanoparticle behaviour in aqueous media demonstrated that size is one of the main physicochemical parameters controlling nanoparticle dissolution (Dobias and Bernier-Latmani 2013; Levard et al. 2011; Liu et al. 2009; Peretyazhko et al. 2014). Size-dependent solubility of silver nanoparticles has been intensively studied. Laboratory studies of dissolution of silver nanoparticles in aqueous media are discussed below. Liu et al. (2010) studied dissolution of citrate-coated silver nanoparticles and Ag foil in pH 4 acetate buffer. The authors demonstrated that dissolved Ag^+ release followed the order of 4.8 nm > 60 nm >> Ag foil. However, dissolved Ag^+ normalised by surface was the same order of magnitude for both silver nanoparticle samples, demonstrating that silver nanoparticle dissolution was controlled by size (Liu et al. 2010). Three different sizes of citrate-coated silver nanoparticles mixed with Hoagland medium followed the similar dissolution order of 20 nm > 60 nm > 80 nm (Navarro et al. 2008). Release of Ag^+ in natural waters from silver nanoparticles coated with PVP, tannic acid or citric acid also revealed size dependence behaviour (Dobias and Bernier-Latmani 2013). The 5-nm silver nanoparticles were the most reactive, followed by the 10-nm ones, while the 50-nm nanoparticles were more resistant towards dissolution during 4 months of field experiment. Dissolution studies of 5- to 80-nm silver nanoparticles coated with PVP or gum arabic in $NaHCO_3$ solution (pH 8) demonstrated that silver nanoparticle solubility was controlled by size (Ma et al. 2011). Peretyazhko et al. (2014) investigated the dissolution behaviour of silver nanoparticles coated with thiol functionalised methoxyl polyethylene glycol (PEGSH). Solubility of nanoparticles with an average diameter of 6, 9, 13 and 70 nm was investigated at pH 3 and 7 (Figure 6.9 and Tables 6.1 and 6.3). Dissolved Ag^+ increased over time at both pH values (except silver nanoparticles of 70 nm, which did not dissolve in water) and followed the order 6 nm > 9 nm > 13 nm > 70 nm (Figure 6.9).

In addition to the size-dependent release of Ag^+, dissolution of silver nanoparticles leads to changes in nanoparticle size and shape, which could consequently affect silver nanoparticle long-term stability and toxicity (shape changes are discussed in Section 6.4.2). Peretyazhko et al. (2014) compared average diameters and size distributions of silver nanoparticles before and after 80 days of dissolution in water (Figures 6.8 and 6.9 and Table 6.3). The results of TEM analysis revealed that the average diameter of 6-, 9- and 13-nm silver nanoparticles became larger than the initial diameters while the size of nondissolving 70-nm silver nanoparticles remained the same after 80 days (Table 6.3). Size distributions of 6-, 9- and 13-nm silver nanoparticles after dissolution broadened and shifted to larger particle sizes than

TABLE 6.3

Average Diameters of Silver Nanoparticles before and after Dissolution in pH 7 Water

Diameter before Dissolution (nm)	Diameter after Dissolution (nm)
6.2 ± 1.6	10.4 ± 3.5
9.2 ± 3.0	13.3 ± 4.1
12.9 ± 3.5	16.0 ± 3.3
70.5 ± 12.0	72.0 ± 13.4

Source: Peretyazhko, T. S. et al., *Environmental Science & Technology* 48(20) (2014): 11954–11961.

before dissolution. Furthermore, the 80-day dissolved silver nanoparticles contained nanoparticles of the size not present in the initial silver nanoparticle suspensions (Figure 6.10). In contrast, size distribution of nondissolving 70-nm silver nanoparticles remained unchanged during dissolution in water. Based on observation of the size distribution broadening as well as size increase, Peretyazhko et al. (2014) suggested that Oswald ripening led to nanoparticle growth (Iggland and Mazzotti 2012; Jang et al. 2011). According to Oswald ripening, large particles are more stable than smaller ones because of their small surface-to-volume ratio, resulting in dissolution of small particles and precipitation of dissolved atoms on more stable larger particles. Oswald ripening of silver nanoparticles occurs through an oxidation–reduction mechanism, involving oxidation of smaller silver nanoparticles by O_2, release of Ag^+ into solution, followed by simultaneous Ag^+ reduction and deposition of Ag atoms on larger silver nanoparticles, resulting in further size increase. Peretyazhko et al. (2014) suggested that the H_2O_2 formed during silver nanoparticle dissolution was responsible for Ag^+ reduction. Formation of H_2O_2 during silver nanoparticle dissolution and Ag^+ reduction by H_2O_2 has been previously reported. For instance, production of ~0.4 μM H_2O_2 was detected during dissolution of silver nanoparticles coated with citrate in pH 8 air-saturated water (Ma et al. 2011). Hydrogen peroxide has been shown to reduce silver nanoparticles at pH >5.5, and the size of final silver nanoparticles increased (He et al. 2012b). An increase in silver nanoparticle size might have an important consequence for silver nanoparticle behaviour in aqueous systems. Larger nanoparticles become more stable, leading to prolonged exposure to toxic silver compounds (Peretyazhko et al. 2014).

6.4.2 Effect of Nanoparticle Shape

A limited number of studies on the shape influence on dissolution of silver nanoparticles has been reported to date. The suggested general trend is that silver nanoparticles with shapes containing numerous sharp edges and corners release silver ions more rapidly than smoother particles (Kent and Vikesland 2012; Zhang et al. 2005). During dissolution, nanoparticles tend to change their shape into spherical. Kent and Vikesland (2012) investigated

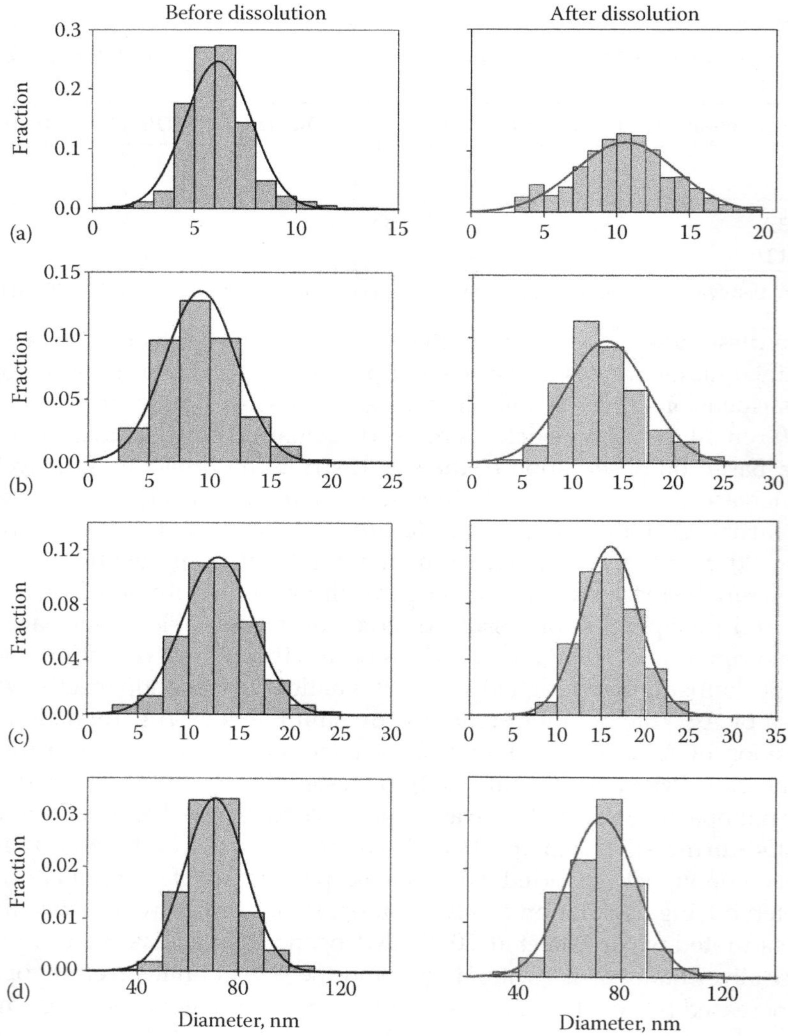

FIGURE 6.10
Normalised size distributions of PEGSH-coated silver nanoparticles before and after 80 days of dissolution in water (pH 7): (a) 6 nm, (b) 9 nm, (c) 13 nm and (d) 70 nm. (Provided by Dr. Peretyazhko.)

dissolution and changes in morphology of ~53-nm Ag nanoparticles of truncated tetrahedral shape in NaCl-containing phosphate buffer at pH 7 (Figure 6.11). The authors observed that Ag nanoparticles dissolved preferentially at locations with a small radius of curvature (tetrahedron tips), and within 1 day of dissolution, the nanoparticle shape changed from triangular to circular (Figure 6.11b). Zhang et al. (2005) also reported similar results. The authors

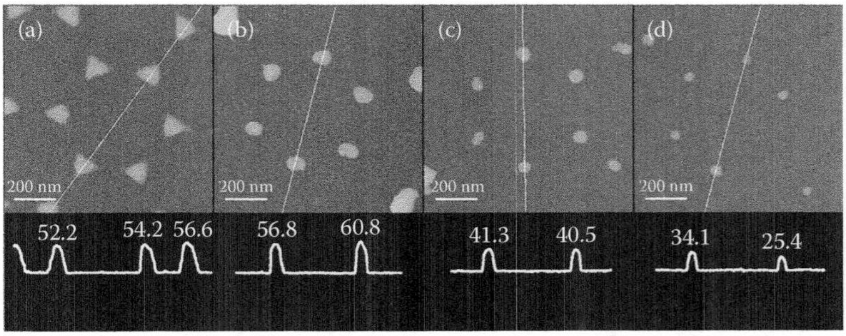

FIGURE 6.11
Deconvoluted atomic force microscopy (AFM) micrographs and height profiles for silver nanoparticles (a) before dissolution and after (b) 1 day, (c) 7 days and (d) 15 days of dissolution in 550 mM NaCl phosphate buffer at pH 7 and 25°C. (From Kent, R. D. and P. J. Vikesland, *Environmental Science & Technology* 46(13) (2012): 6977–6984.)

synthesised Ag nanotriangles and monitored changes in size and morphology during Ag nanoparticle dissolution in 0.1 M $NaClO_4$ solution. Zhang et al. reported that Ag nanoparticles changed shape during dissolution as was evident from the plasmon peak shifts toward shorter wavelengths from 896 to 803 nm (Figure 6.12a). Analysis by AFM further confirmed that dissolution was accompanied by the change in nanoparticle geometry. First, the bottom edges were dissolved and then the triangular corners and finally the out-of-plane height (Figure 6.12b through d). Such dissolution behaviour is likely because the regions of a nanoparticle surface with sharp radii of curvature have lower redox potentials than the regions with large radii of curvature, creating a redox potential gradient between the regions. As a result, oxidation of Ag to Ag^+ takes place at the bottom edges and corners of Ag nanotriangles while reduction of Ag^+ to Ag occurs at their tops (Kent and Vikesland 2012; Zhang et al. 2005). The proposed oxidation–reduction mechanism could lead to the formation of Ag^+ concentration gradient and a net flow of silver from the bottom of a nanoparticle to the top and shape change from triangular to circular (Kent and Vikesland 2012).

In addition, it is worth mentioning that the polycrystalline silver nanoparticles dissolve more rapidly than the single crystalline ones (Wiley et al. 2004; Yang et al. 2007). The polycrystalline nanoparticles contain high-energy defects at grain boundaries and the defects provide active sites for oxidation and dissolution (Wiley et al. 2004; Yang et al. 2007).

6.4.3 Effect of Surface Coating

Dissolution of Ag nanoparticles is affected by the nature of capping agents and their surface coordination (Levard et al. 2012). In an aqueous environment, nanoparticle coatings can provide electrostatic or steric repulsion, increasing the stability of the nanoparticles against aggregation and

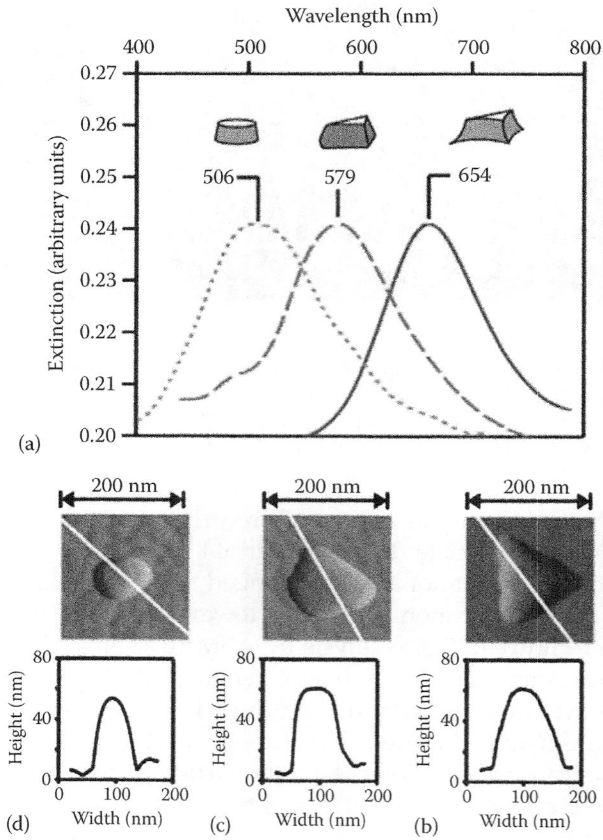

FIGURE 6.12
(a) The localised surface plasmon resonance (LSPR) spectra before and after dissolution and (b through d) the AFM images of silver nanoparticles fabricated on indium tin oxide electrode surface. (From Zhang, X. et al., *Nano Letters* 5(7) (2005): 1503–1507.)

consequently enhancing dissolution (Levard et al. 2012; Li et al. 2011). Coating of Ag nanoparticles with citrate (Huynh and Chen 2011), branched polyethyleneimine (Badawy et al. 2010) and sodium borohydride ($NaBH_4$) (Badawy et al. 2010) is usually used to enhance electrostatic repulsion, while coating of Ag nanoparticles with PVP (Badawy et al. 2010; Huynh and Chen 2011), ethylene glycol (Bonet et al. 2000), polyethylene glycol (PEG) (Shkilnyy et al. 2009) and sorbitan monooleate ethoxylate (Tween) (Li and Lenhart 2012) leads to an increase in steric repulsion.

Dissolution studies reveal that Ag nanoparticles coated with steric capping agents are more stable against aggregation and dissolve more readily. For instance, PVP- and citrate-capped Ag nanoparticles behave differently towards dissolution. Kittler et al. (2010) demonstrated that dissolution of

PVP-stabilised Ag was more intensive than dissolution of citrate-stabilised Ag nanoparticles of the same size. Contrasting dissolution behaviour is explained by aggregation of citrate-coated Ag nanoparticles, resulting in decrease of sites available for dissolution and slow mass transfer (Levard et al. 2012; Vikesland et al. 2007). Li and Lenhart (2012) investigated the effect of aggregation on dissolution behaviour of noncoated, citrate-coated and Tween-coated Ag nanoparticles in natural water (Li and Lenhart 2012). The results revealed that hydrodynamic diameters of noncoated and citrate-coated Ag nanoparticles increased from 82 to 500–800 nm within 6 h (Figure 6.13). The particles continued to grow, forming aggregates of a few to tens of micrometers within 24 h (Figure 6.13a). In opposite, Tween-coated Ag nanoparticles did not aggregate, and the nanoparticle diameter progressively decreased

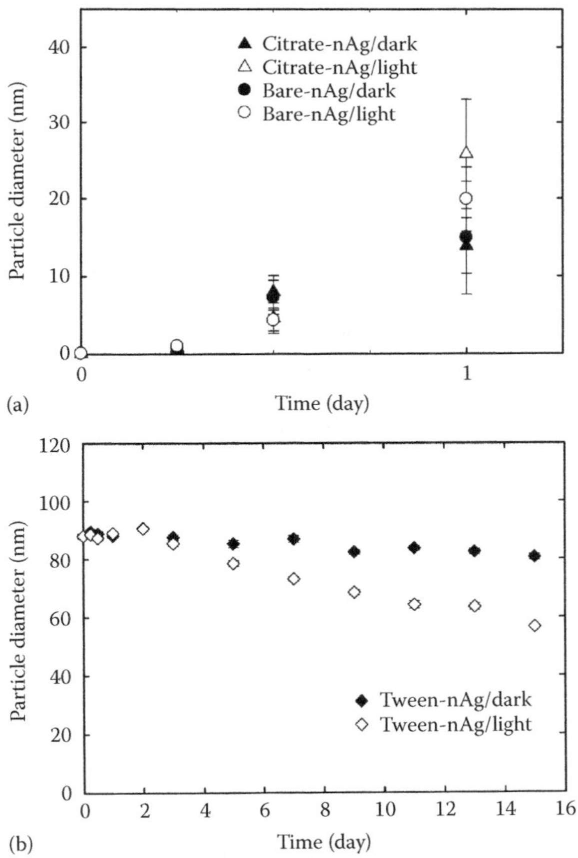

FIGURE 6.13
Change in hydrodynamic radius over time for the (a) citrate and noncoated silver nanoparticles and (b) Tween-coated silver nanoparticles dispersed in river water. (From Li, X. and J. J. Lenhart, *Environmental Science & Technology* 46(10) (2012): 5378–5386.)

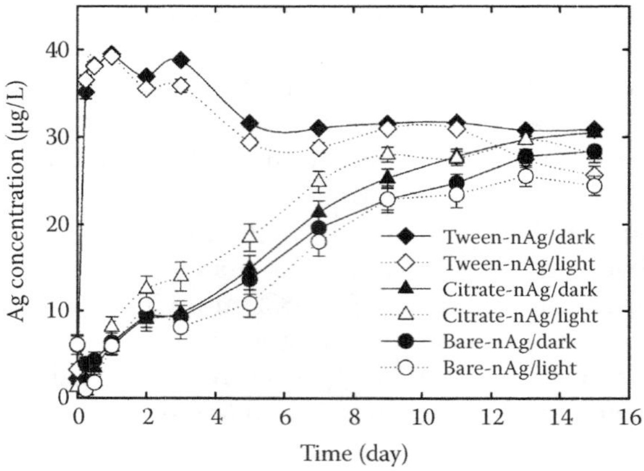

FIGURE 6.14
Concentration of dissolved Ag^+ measured as a function of time during silver nanoparticles dissolution in river water. (From Li, X. and J. J. Lenhart, *Environmental Science & Technology* 46(10) (2012): 5378–5386.)

with times as a result of dissolution (Figure 6.13b). The observed aggregation affected kinetics of Ag^+ release into solution (Figure 6.14; Li and Lenhart 2012). The authors found that Ag^+ concentration rapidly increased within the first few hours of reaction in the suspension of Tween-coated Ag nanoparticles while dissolved Ag^+ remained low in the suspensions of noncoated and citrate-coated Ag nanoparticles (Figure 6.14). However, dissolution of the aggregated nanoparticle was not suppressed. The dissolved Ag^+ concentrations in the suspensions of noncoated and citrate-coated aggregated silver nanoparticles increased at a gradual rate and reached the comparable level of the Tween–silver nanoparticle systems at the end of the experiment (Li and Lenhart 2012).

6.5 Impact of Silver Nanoparticle Dissolution on Their Antibacterial Activity

Silver nanoparticles may exert antibacterial activity through both the interaction of nanoparticles and bacteria (Asghari et al. 2012; Shen et al. 2015) and release of silver ions (Xiu et al. 2012). Oxidative dissolution of silver nanoparticles, therefore, will influence their antibacterial activity and silver nanoparticles with different shape, size and surface chemistry will exhibit different antibacterial properties. An important question in intensive debate over Ag nanoparticle toxicity, however, is to what extent the dissolution of silver nanoparticles influences their antibacterial activity (Asghari et al. 2012; Yang et al. 2011). In order to answer the question, Xiu et al. (2012) studied the antibacterial activity of a variety of silver nanoparticles with different size and surface chemistry. The authors found that the antibacterial activity of silver nanoparticles varied significantly with the change of nanoparticle size and surface chemistry (Figure 6.15a). However, when expressed in terms of the

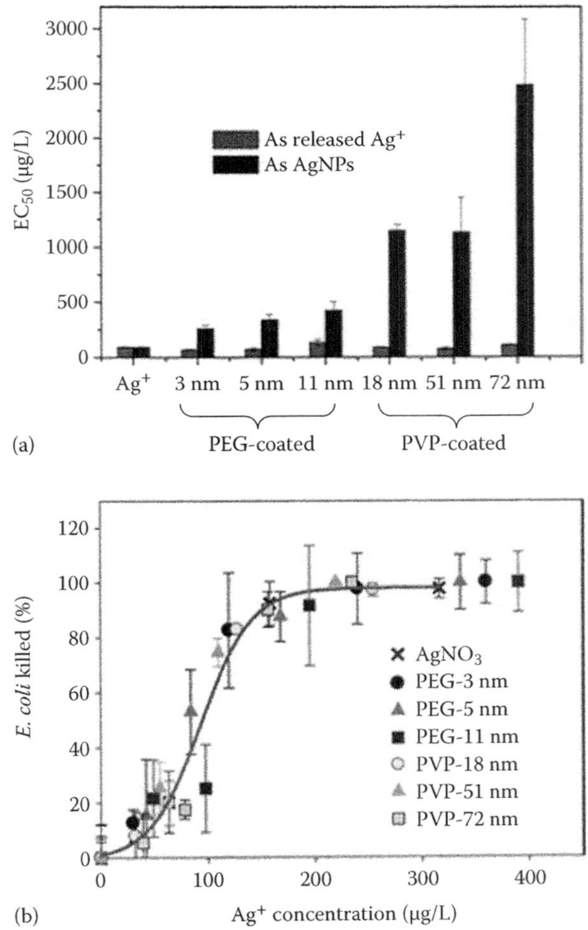

FIGURE 6.15
(a) Dose–response of *E. coli* exposed to various silver nanoparticles under oxic conditions. EC_{50} increases with the increasing particle size (the size was observed by TEM), suggesting size-dependent toxicity. The phenomena are due to indirect effect associated with Ag^+ release (smaller nanoparticles release more Ag^+ and are more toxic). (b) Antibacterial activity expressed as a function of the concentration of the released Ag^+ was statistically indistinguishable from the dose–response patterns of cells exposed to Ag^+ added as Ag NO_3 ($p > 0.05$), illustrating that the released Ag^+ is the critical factor of antibacterial activity. (From Xiu, Z.-M. et al. *Nano Letters* 12(8) (2012): 4271–4275.)

concentration of dissolved Ag^+, the antibacterial activity of silver nanoparticles was statistically indistinguishable from the toxicity of Ag^+ introduced through silver nitrate (Figure 6.15b). The results suggested that the antibacterial activity of silver nanoparticles was dictated by the dissolution of silver nanoparticles (Xiu et al. 2012). The predominant effect of the silver nanoparticle dissolution on their antibacterial activity was also confirmed by the observation that silver nanoparticles without dissolution did not show any measureable effect on bacteria. This conclusion was drawn from the study on PEGSH- and PVP-coated spherical silver nanoparticles over a limited size range using *Escherichia coli* as model bacteria (Figure 6.15b). It is still an open question if this antibacterial mechanism can be extrapolated to other silver nanoparticles or microbes since there is a large library of silver nanoparticles and a great variety of types of microorganisms, which may behave differently.

6.6 Summary and Outlook

This chapter summarises the recent advances in the field of the dissolution of silver nanoparticles in an aqueous system. Silver nanoparticles in water can be oxidised by dissolved oxidant such as oxygen or hydrogen peroxide, leading to the release of silver ions. The dissolution rate of silver nanoparticles usually follows the first order and reaches equilibrium after a few days to a few months. The thermodynamics and kinetics of dissolution are dependent on both the environmental conditions and the characteristics of the nanoparticles. The silver ions generated from the oxidative dissolution of silver nanoparticles plays a predominant role in the antibacterial activity of silver nanoparticles.

While some progress has been made in the understanding of the dissolution of silver nanoparticles, there are still substantial challenges. Current synthesis techniques have led the production of a large library of silver nanoparticles with a different shape, size, aspect ratio, crystallinity and surface chemistry. These nanoparticles may differ substantially in terms of dissolution in complex aquatic systems. Prediction of the dissolution behaviour of various silver nanoparticles under a variety of conditions forms a grand challenge. A detailed fundamental understanding of the dissolution behaviour of silver nanoparticles in solution is essential for the design of silver nanoparticles with a desired performance. Theoretical studies and modelling could be used to supplement the inadequacy of current experimental methods and to reduce the cost of experimentation.

References

Albanese, A., P. S. Tang and W. C. Chan. The effect of nanoparticle size, shape, and surface chemistry on biological systems. *Annual Review of Biomedical Engineering* 14 (2012): 1–16.

Arora, S., J. Jain, J. Rajwade and K. Paknikar. Cellular responses induced by silver nanoparticles: In vitro studies. *Toxicology Letters* 179(2) (2008): 93–100.

Arora, S., J. Jain, J. M. Rajwade and K. M. Paknikar. Interactions of silver nanoparticles with primary mouse fibroblasts and liver cells. *Toxicology and Applied Pharmacology* 236(3) (2009): 310–318.

Asghari, S., S. A. Johari, J. H. Lee et al. Toxicity of various silver nanoparticles compared to silver ions in *Daphnia magna*. *Journal of Nanobiotechnology* 10 (2012): 14.

AshaRani, P., G. Low Kah Mun, M. P. Hande and S. Valiyaveettil. Cytotoxicity and genotoxicity of silver nanoparticles in human cells. *ACS Nano* 3(2) (2008): 279–290.

Badawy, A. M. E., T. P. Luxton, R. G. Silva et al. Impact of environmental conditions (pH, ionic strength, and electrolyte type) on the surface charge and aggregation of silver nanoparticles suspensions. *Environmental Science & Technology* 44(4) (2010): 1260–1266.

Batchelor-McAuley, C., K. Tschulik, C. C. Neumann, E. Laborda and R. G. Compton. Why are silver nanoparticles more toxic than bulk silver? Towards understanding the dissolution and toxicity of silver nanoparticles. *International Journal of Electrochemical Science* 9 (2014): 1132–1138.

Bonet, F., K. Tekaia-Elhsissen and K. V. Sarathy. Study of interaction of ethylene glycol/PVP phase on noble metal powders prepared by polyol process. *Bulletin of Materials Science* 23(3) (2000): 165–168.

Borm, P., F. C. Klaessig, T. D. Landry et al. Research strategies for safety evaluation of nanomaterials, part V: Role of dissolution in biological fate and effects of nanoscale particles. *Toxicological Sciences* 90(1) (2006): 23–32.

Callegari, A., D. Tonti and M. Chergui. Photochemically grown silver nanoparticles with wavelength-controlled size and shape. *Nano Letters* 3(11) (2003): 1565–1568.

Damm, C., H. Münstedt and A. Rösch. The antimicrobial efficacy of polyamide 6/silver-nano-and microcomposites. *Materials Chemistry and Physics* 108(1) (2008): 61–66.

Dastjerdi, R. and M. Montazer. A review on the application of inorganic nanostructured materials in the modification of textiles: Focus on anti-microbial properties. *Colloids Surf B Biointerfaces* 79(1) (2010): 5–18.

Dobias, J. and R. Bernier-Latmani. Silver release from silver nanoparticles in natural waters. *Environmental Science & Technology* 47(9) (2013): 4140–4146.

Elzey, S. and V. H. Grassian. Agglomeration, isolation and dissolution of commercially manufactured silver nanoparticles in aqueous environments. *Journal of Nanoparticle Research* 12(5) (2010): 1945–1958.

Foldbjerg, R., P. Olesen, M. Hougaard et al. PVP-coated silver nanoparticles and silver ions induce reactive oxygen species, apoptosis and necrosis in THP-1 monocytes. *Toxicology Letters* 190(2) (2009): 156–162.

Geranio, L., M. Heuberger and B. Nowack. The behavior of silver nanotextiles during washing. *Environmental Science & Technology* 43(21) (2009): 8113–8118.

Grass, M. E., Y. Yue, S. E. Habas et al. Silver ion mediated shape control of platinum nanoparticles: Removal of silver by selective etching leads to increased catalytic activity. *The Journal of Physical Chemistry C* 112(13) (2008): 4797–4804.

Han, Y., R. Lupitskyy, T.-M. Chou et al. Effect of oxidation on surface-enhanced Raman scattering activity of silver nanoparticles: A quantitative correlation. *Analytical Chemistry* 83(15) (2011): 5873–5880.

He, B. L., J. J. Tan, Y. L. Kong and H. F. Liu. Synthesis of size controlled Ag nanoparticles. *Journal of Molecular Catalysis A – Chemical* 221(1–2) (2004): 121–126.

He, D., S. Garg and T. D. Waite. H_2O_2-mediated oxidation of zero-valent silver and resultant interactions among silver nanoparticles, silver ions, and reactive oxygen species. *Langmuir* 28(27) (2012a): 10266–10275.

He, W., Y.-T. Zhou, W. G. Wamer, M. D. Boudreau and J.-J. Yin. Mechanisms of the pH dependent generation of hydroxyl radicals and oxygen induced by Ag nanoparticles. *Biomaterials* 33(30) (2012b): 7547–7555.

Henglein, A. Colloidal silver nanoparticles: Photochemical preparation and interaction with O_2, CCl_4, and some metal ions. *Chemistry of Materials* 10(1) (1998): 444–450.

Henglein, A., P. Mulvaney and T. Linnert. Chemistry of Agn aggregates in aqueous solution: Non-metallic oligomeric clusters and metallic particles. *Faraday Discuss* 92 (1991): 31–44.

Ho, C.-M., S. K.-W. Yau, C.-N. Lok, M.-H. So and C.-M. Che. Oxidative dissolution of silver nanoparticles by biologically relevant oxidants: A kinetic and mechanistic study. *Chemistry, an Asian Journal* 5(2) (2010): 285.

Hocking, M., K. Bhandari, B. Shell and T. Smyth. Steric and pH effects on the rate of Dakin oxidation of acylphenols. *The Journal of Organic Chemistry* 47(22) (1982): 4208–4215.

Huynh, K. A. and K. L. Chen. Aggregation kinetics of citrate and polyvinylpyrrolidone coated silver nanoparticles in monovalent and divalent electrolyte solutions. *Environmental Science & Technology* 45(13) (2011): 5564–5571.

Iggland, M. and M. Mazzotti. Population balance modeling with size-dependent solubility: Ostwald ripening. *Crystal Growth & Design* 12(3) (2012): 1489–1500.

Iravani, H. K., S. Mirmohammadi and S. B. Zolfaghari. Synthesis of silver nanoparticles: Chemical, physical and biological methods. *Research in Pharmaceutical Sciences* 9(6) (2014): 385–406.

Jang, E., E.-K. Lim, J. Choi et al. Br-assisted Ostwald ripening of Au nanoparticles under H_2O_2 redox. *Crystal Growth & Design* 12(1) (2011): 37–39.

Kent, R. D. and P. J. Vikesland. Controlled evaluation of silver nanoparticle dissolution using atomic force microscopy. *Environmental Science & Technology* 46(13) (2012): 6977–6984.

Kittler, S., C. Greulich, J. Diendorf, M. Koller and M. Epple. Toxicity of silver nanoparticles increases during storage because of slow dissolution under release of silver ions. *Chemistry of Materials* 22(16) (2010): 4548–4554.

Kumar, B., K. Smita, L. Cumbal and A. Debut. Green synthesis of silver nanoparticles using Andean blackberry fruit extract. *Saudi Journal of Biological Sciences* 24(1) (2017): 45–50.

Kuzma, A., M. Weis, S. Flickyngerova et al. Influence of surface oxidation on plasmon resonance in monolayer of gold and silver nanoparticles. *Journal of Applied Physics* 112(10) (2012): 103531.

Laban, G., L. F. Nies, R. F. Turco, J. W. Bickham and M. S. Sepúlveda. The effects of silver nanoparticles on fathead minnow (*Pimephales promelas*) embryos. *Ecotoxicology* 19(1) (2010): 185–195.

Levard, C., E. M. Hotze, G. V. Lowry and G. E. Brown, Jr. Environmental transformations of silver nanoparticles: Impact on stability and toxicity. *Environmental Science & Technology* 46(13) (2012): 6900–6914.

Levard, C., S. Mitra, T. Yang et al. Effect of chloride on the dissolution rate of silver nanoparticles and toxicity to *E. coli*. *Environmental Science & Technology* 47(11) (2013): 5738–5745.

Levard, C., B. C. Reinsch, F. M. Michel et al. Sulfidation processes of PVP-coated silver nanoparticles in aqueous solution: Impact on dissolution rate. *Environmental Science & Technology* 45(12) (2011): 5260–5266.

Li, X. and J. J. Lenhart. Aggregation and dissolution of silver nanoparticles in natural surface water. *Environmental Science & Technology* 46(10) (2012): 5378–5386.

Li, X., J. J. Lenhart and H. W. Walker. Dissolution-accompanied aggregation kinetics of silver nanoparticles. *Langmuir* 26(22) (2010): 16690–16698.

Li, X., J. J. Lenhart and H. W. Walker. Aggregation kinetics and dissolution of coated silver nanoparticles. *Langmuir* 28(2) (2011): 1095–1104.

Liu, J., D. M. Aruguete, M. Murayama and M. F. Hochella, Jr. Influence of size and aggregation on the reactivity of an environmentally and industrially relevant nanomaterial (PbS). *Environmental Science & Technology* 43(21) (2009): 8178–8183.

Liu, J. and R. H. Hurt. Ion release kinetics and particle persistence in aqueous nanosilver colloids. *Environmental Science & Technology* 44(6) (2010): 2169–2175.

Liu, J., D. A. Sonshine, S. Shervani and R. H. Hurt. Controlled release of biologically active silver from nanosilver surfaces. *ACS Nano* 4(11) (2010): 6903–6913.

Lok, C.-N., C.-M. Ho, R. Chen et al. Silver nanoparticles: Partial oxidation and antibacterial activities. *Journal of Biological Inorganic Chemistry* 12(4) (2007): 527–534.

Loza, K., J. Diendorf, C. Sengstock et al. The dissolution and biological effects of silver nanoparticles in biological media. *Journal of Materials Chemistry B* 2(12) (2014): 1634–1643.

Lubick, N. Nanosilver toxicity: Ions, nanoparticles or both? *Environmental Science & Technology* 42(23) (2008): 8617.

Ma, R., C. Levard, S. M. Marinakos et al. Size-controlled dissolution of organic-coated silver nanoparticles. *Environmental Science & Technology* 46(2) (2011): 752–759.

Marambio-Jones, C. and E. M. V. Hoek. A review of the antibacterial effects of silver nanomaterials and potential implications for human health and the environment. *Journal of Nanoparticle Research* 12(5) (2010): 1531–1551.

Maurer-Jones, M. A., M. P. Mousavi, L. D. Chen, P. Bühlmann and C. L. Haynes. Characterization of silver ion dissolution from silver nanoparticles using fluorous-phase ion-selective electrodes and assessment of resultant toxicity to *Shewanella oneidensis*. *Chemical Science* 4(6) (2013): 2564–2572.

Misra, S. K., A. Dybowska, D. Berhanu, S. N. Luoma and E. Valsami-Jones. The complexity of nanoparticle dissolution and its importance in nanotoxicological studies. *Science of the Total Environment* 438 (2012): 225–232.

Molleman, B. and T. Hiemstra. Surface structure of silver nanoparticles as a model for understanding the oxidative dissolution of silver ions. *Langmuir* 31(49) (2015): 13361–13372.

Mueller, N. C. and B. Nowack. Exposure modeling of engineered nanoparticles in the environment. *Environmental Science & Technology* 42(12) (2008): 4447–4453.

Navarro, E., F. Piccapietra, B. Wagner et al. Toxicity of silver nanoparticles to *Chlamydomonas reinhardtii*. *Environmental Science & Technology* 42(23) (2008): 8959–8964.

Özmetin, C., M. Copur, A. Yartasi and M. Kocakerim. Kinetic investigation of reaction between metallic silver and nitric acid solutions. *Chemical Engineering & Technology* 23(8) (2000): 707–711.

Peretyazhko, T. S., Q. Zhang and V. L. Colvin. Size-controlled dissolution of silver nanoparticles at neutral and acidic pH conditions: Kinetics and size changes. *Environmental Science & Technology* 48(20) (2014): 11954–11961.

Pillai, Z. S. and P. V. Kamat. What factors control the size and shape of silver nanoparticles in the citrate ion reduction method? *The Journal of Physical Chemistry B* 108(3) (2004): 945–951.

Ponnaian, P. K., R. Oommen, S. K. C. Kannaiyan et al. Synthesis and characterization of silver nanoparticles for biological applications. *Journal of Environmental Nanotechnology* 4(1) (2015): 23–26.

Qin, X., Z. Miao, Y. Fang et al. Preparation of dendritic nanostructures of silver and their characterization for electroreduction. *Langmuir* 28(11) (2012): 5218–5226.

Rodriguez-Sanchez, L., M. Blanco and M. Lopez-Quintela. Electrochemical synthesis of silver nanoparticles. *The Journal of Physical Chemistry B* 104(41) (2000): 9683–9688.

Shen, M.-H., X.-X. Zhou, X.-Y. Yang et al. Exposure medium: Key in identifying free Ag^+ as the exclusive species of silver nanoparticles with acute toxicity to *Daphnia magna*. *Scientific Reports* 5 (2015): 9674.

Shkilnyy, A., M. Soucé, P. Dubois et al. Poly(ethylene glycol)-stabilized silver nanoparticles for bioanalytical applications of SERS spectroscopy. *Analyst* 134(9) (2009): 1868–1872.

Singh, V., A. Shrivastava and N. Wahi. Biosynthesis of silver nanoparticles by plants crude extracts and their characterization using UV, XRD, TEM and EDX. *African Journal of Biotechnology* 14(33) (2015): 2554–2567.

Sotiriou, G. A., A. Meyer, J. T. Knijnenburg, S. Panke and S. E. Pratsinis. Quantifying the origin of released Ag^+ ions from nanosilver. *Langmuir* 28(45) (2012): 15929–15936.

Sotiriou, G. A. and S. E. Pratsinis. Antibacterial activity of nanosilver ions and particles. *Environmental Science & Technology* 44(14) (2010): 5649–5654.

Stumm, W. and J. J. Morgan. *Aquatic Chemistry: Chemical Equilibria and Rates in Natural Waters*. New York: John Wiley & Sons, 2012.

Tolaymat, T. M., A. M. El Badawy, A. Genaidy et al. An evidence-based environmental perspective of manufactured silver nanoparticle in syntheses and applications: A systematic review and critical appraisal of peer-reviewed scientific papers. *Science of the Total Environment* 408(5) (2010): 999–1006.

Vikesland, P. J., A. M. Heathcock, R. L. Rebodos and K. E. Makus. Particle size and aggregation effects on magnetite reactivity toward carbon tetrachloride. *Environmental Science & Technology* 41(15) (2007): 5277–5283.

Wiesinger, R., I. Martina, C. Kleber and M. Schreiner. Influence of relative humidity and ozone on atmospheric silver corrosion. *Corrosion Science* 77 (2013): 69–76.

Wiley, B., T. Herricks, Y. Sun and Y. Xia. Polyol synthesis of silver nanoparticles: Use of chloride and oxygen to promote the formation of single-crystal, truncated cubes and tetrahedrons. *Nano Letters* 4(9) (2004): 1733–1739.

Wiley, B., Y. Sun and Y. Xia. Synthesis of silver nanostructures with controlled shapes and properties. *Accounts of Chemical Research* 40(10) (2007): 1067–1076.

Xiu, Z.-M., J. Ma and P. J. Alvarez. Differential effect of common ligands and molecular oxygen on antimicrobial activity of silver nanoparticles versus silver ions. *Environmental Science & Technology* 45(20) (2011): 9003–9008.

Xiu, Z.-m., Q.-b. Zhang, H. L. Puppala, V. L. Colvin and P. J. Alvarez. Negligible particle-specific antibacterial activity of silver nanoparticles. *Nano Letters* 12(8) (2012): 4271–4275.

Yang, J., Q. Zhang, J. Y. Lee and H.-P. Too. Dissolution–recrystallization mechanism for the conversion of silver nanospheres to triangular nanoplates. *Journal of Colloid and Interface Science* 308(1) (2007): 157–161.

Yang, X., A. P. Gondikas, S. M. Marinakos et al. Mechanism of silver nanoparticle toxicity is dependent on dissolved silver and surface coating in *Caenorhabditis elegans*. *Environmental Science & Technology* 46(2) (2011): 1119–1127.

Zeng, J., Y. Zheng, M. Rycenga et al. Controlling the shapes of silver nanocrystals with different capping agents. *Journal of the American Chemical Society* 132(25) (2010): 8552–8553.

Zhang, Q., Y. N. Tan, J. Xie and J. Y. Lee. Colloidal synthesis of plasmonic metallic nanoparticles. *Plasmonics* 4(1) (2009): 9–22.

Zhang, Q., J. Xie, Y. Yu and J. Y. Lee. Monodispersity control in the synthesis of monometallic and bimetallic quasi-spherical gold and silver nanoparticles. *Nanoscale* 2(10) (2010): 1962–1975.

Zhang, W., Y. Yao, N. Sullivan and Y. Chen. Modeling the primary size effects of citrate-coated silver nanoparticles on their ion release kinetics. *Environmental Science & Technology* 45(10) (2011): 4422–4428.

Zhang, X., E. M. Hicks, J. Zhao, G. C. Schatz and R. P. Van Duyne. Electrochemical tuning of silver nanoparticles fabricated by nanosphere lithography. *Nano Letters* 5(7) (2005): 1503–1507.

Zhu, J., S. Liu, O. Palchik, Y. Koltypin and A. Gedanken. Shape-controlled synthesis of silver nanoparticles by pulse sonoelectrochemical methods. *Langmuir* 16(16) (2000): 6396–6399.

7

Silver as an Antimicrobial Agent: The Resistance Issue

Kristel Mijnendonckx and Rob Van Houdt

CONTENTS

7.1 Introduction

The history of silver mining goes back 5000 years ago to Anatolia (modern Turkey). Gradually, silver production spread to Central Europe and later on to Eastern Europe. In 1492, the discovery of America boosted silver mining and finally resulted in the worldwide production of silver. In 2014, silver was mined with an estimated production of 27,000 tonnes, with Mexico being the world's leading producer, responsible for 22% of the total amount of silver produced (www.silverinstitute.org).

The unique physical properties of silver including its conductivity, ductility and sensitivity to light facilitated its use in a wide range of technological and industrial applications. It is used for coin and metal fabrication, in electrical and electronic compounds and for jewelry. In addition, its broad-spectrum antimicrobial effects have been well documented. Silver preparations were already used to treat ulcers, to stimulate wound healing and as preservative for food and water by the ancient Greeks, Romans, Egyptians and others (Alexander 2009). In fact, silver was the most important antimicrobial compound before the introduction of antibiotics in the 1940s and is still used in a wide range of medical applications such as in topical creams for the treatment of burn wounds (Klasen 2000), in dental amalgams, in preventative eye care and in silver-impregnated polymers to prevent bacterial (biofilm) growth on medical devices such as catheters and heart valves. In addition, since silver does not affect the colour, taste and odour of water, it is also widely used as a (co-)disinfectant of water systems such as swimming pool water, hospital hot water systems and potable water systems (Yahya et al. 1990). Silver is even used as an alternative to detergents for laundry (Jung et al. 2007). The use and applications of silver are further expanded with the rapid and continuous development of nanotechnology and, today, silver nanoparticles (Ag NPs) are by far the most commonly engineered nanomaterial. Ag NPs are routinely incorporated in a wide range of domestic and personal care products such as laptops, keyboards, refrigerators, dietary supplements, clothing, children's toys and many more (Nanotechnologies). However, the excessive use of silver compounds in clinical and nonclinical applications has raised concerns about the possible development and spread of silver-resistant bacteria (Chopra 2007), which have been reported several times (Choudhury and Kumar 1998; Finley et al. 2015; Haefeli et al. 1984; McHugh et al. 1975). So far, the mechanisms of silver resistance have not been fully elucidated and different preventive strategies have been suggested. In this chapter, an overview of the antimicrobial activity of silver ions and Ag NPs and silver toxicity to human cells will be presented. In addition, resistance mechanisms against silver in bacteria are discussed.

7.2 Human Toxicity of Silver and Ag NPs

The boosted use of silver in antibacterial and antifungal agents in wound care products, medical devices, textiles, cosmetics and domestic appliances raised issues about the safety aspects and potential risks associated with the absorption of Ag^+ into the human body (Drake and Hazelwood 2005; Lansdown 2010). Several recommended exposure limits and guidelines exist, but values vary according to the reference agency that promulgates the recommendations. The World Health Organization decided that a lifetime oral intake of approximately 10 g of silver can be considered as the human no observable adverse effect level. Silver levels up to 0.1 mg/L are tolerated in drinking water (World Health Organization 1996). The American Conference on Governmental Industrial Hygienists established a threshold limit value for metallic silver and silver compounds in air at 0.1 and 0.01 mg/m^3, respectively. The National Institute for Occupational Safety and Health (USA) established a recommended exposure limit at 0.01 mg/m^3 for both soluble silver compounds and silver metal dust. The European Commission recommended an 8-h time-weighted average of 0.1 mg/m^3 total silver dust as occupational exposure limit (Drake and Hazelwood 2005; World Health Organization 1996).

Toxicological studies performed on animals and humans are rather limited, and most toxicity studies are performed *in vitro* (Korani et al. 2015; Lansdown 2010). The main exposure routes of silver compounds are through dermal contact, oral administration and inhalation. Health risks associated with systemic absorption of silver ions seem to be rather low (Drake and Hazelwood 2005; Lansdown 2010). The most common observable changes associated with prolonged exposure to silver compounds are argyria and argyrosis, characterised by an irreversible deposition of silver selenide and silver sulfide precipitates in the skin and the eyes, respectively. The affected area becomes bluish-grey and it becomes worse in the presence of sunlight. However, argyria and argyriosis are not life-threatening and are not associated with irreversible tissue damage (Drake and Hazelwood 2005; Lansdown 2010; Thompson et al. 2009). Like most other xenobiotic metals, silver can elicit delayed contact hypersensitivity reactions and allergy in rare predisposed persons. However, the extent of this risk is not known to date (Lansdown 2010). For Ag NPs, until now, no unambiguous view on the toxic effects has been defined. It has been shown that toxicity depends on numerous factors, including different synthesis methods, capping agents, their various sizes and shapes and the diverse kind of toxicity evaluation tests. Moreover, results vary according to the cell lines or organisms used (reviewed in Gaillet and Rouanet 2015; Korani et al. 2015; Wei et al. 2015). Therefore, risk assessments should be carried out on a case-by-case basis. In their lifetime, humans are unlikely to be exposed to sufficient amounts of silver to provoke symptoms of argyria (World Health Organization 1996). However, care should be taken when using commercially available silver products containing unspecified levels of ionisable silver, for example, 'Jintan Silver Pills', a breath freshener that can be used as remedy for heartburn, nausea, vomiting, motion sickness, hangover, dizziness, bad breath, choking, indisposition and sunstroke (according to the label) (Lansdown 2010; Silver 2003). In addition, people living in highly polluted areas with silver residues from factory wastes (e.g. the San Francisco Bay) also have an increased risk to develop argyria as silver enters the food chain (Flegal et al. 2007).

7.3 Silver Ions

7.3.1 Antimicrobial Activity

For a number of decades, the antimicrobial activity of silver compounds has been studied (Chambers et al. 1962; Gordon et al. 2010; Matsumura et al. 2003;

Russell and Hugo 1994; Yudkins 1937). However, no conclusive mechanism of action was ever observed. Figure 7.1 represents an overview of the antibacterial effects of silver. In first instance, silver replaces the hydrogen atoms of sulfhydryl groups on the surface of microorganisms, resulting in the formation of an S–Ag bond. Consequently, respiration and electron transfer are

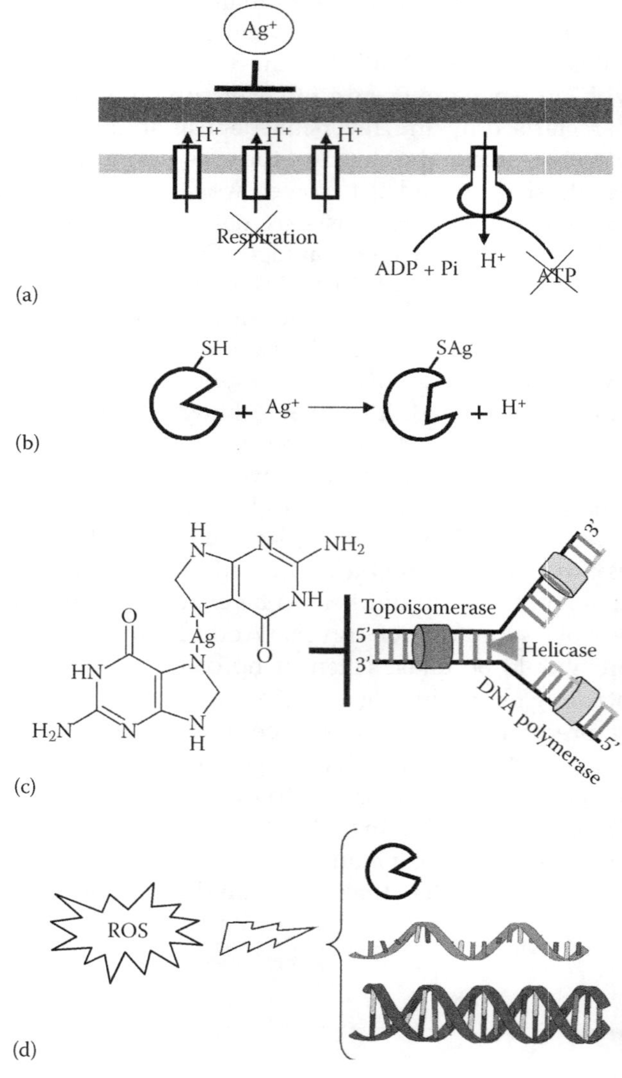

FIGURE 7.1
Antimicrobial effects of Ag^+. (a) Interaction with membrane proteins and blocking respiration and electron transfer, (b) Ag^+ ions interact with proteins, (c) Ag^+ ions interact with DNA, thereby interfering replication, and (d) Ag^+ ions induce ROS production, damaging proteins, RNA and DNA.

completely blocked, hampering the induction of successful rescue mechanisms (Gordon et al. 2010; Russell and Hugo 1994). Furthermore, the collapse of the proton motive force caused by blocking respiration and electron transfer will lead to de-energisation of the membrane and ultimately cell death (Dibrov et al. 2002). For instance, in *Escherichia coli*, a collapse of the proton motive force and subsequent cell death were observed after the addition of $AgNO_3$ (Schreurs and Rosenberg 1982). Similarly, in *Vibrio cholerae*, low concentrations of Ag^+ led to massive proton leakage through the membrane (Dibrov et al. 2002). In *V. cholerae*, this effect was independent of the presence of the Na^+-translocating NADH-ubiquinone oxidoreductase (Dibrov et al. 2002), previously identified as one of the primary targets of Ag^+ ions (Bragg and Rainnie 1974; Hayashi et al. 1992; Semeykina and Skulachev 1990), suggesting that other membrane proteins modified by Ag^+ can cause proton leakage. Once the cell membrane is disrupted, Ag^+ ions can enter the cytoplasm where they can exert additional damage. The most profound effect seem to be the interaction of silver ions with thiol groups (Gordon et al. 2010; Russell and Hugo 1994; Schreurs and Rosenberg 1982). Interaction with the thiol group of cysteine residues, necessary for the activity of many enzymes, leads to conformational changes and to inactivation of enzymatic functions. The activity of $AgNO_3$ against *Pseudomonas aeruginosa* PAO1 was neutralised by cysteine and other thiol compounds (e.g. sodium thioglycolate), in contrast with amino acids containing disulfide bonds, non-sulfur-containing amino acids and other sulfur-containing compounds such as cystathionine, cysteic acid, methyl cysteine, methionine, taurine, sodium bisulfite and sodium thiosulfate (Liau et al. 1997). Furthermore, Ag^+ ions are able to form complexes with nucleic acids and preferentially interact with the nucleosides rather than the phosphate groups of nucleic acids. For instance, binding of Ag^+ to guanine affects the N7-methylation of guanine and enhances pyrimidine dimerisation, thereby, interfering with DNA replication (Russell and Hugo 1994).

It was also demonstrated that Ag^+ treatment promotes the production of reactive oxygen species (ROS) (Gordon et al. 2010; Park et al. 2009). ROS, such as O_2^-, OH^- and H_2O_2, are short-lived, reactive oxidants produced by all aerobic organisms as a by-product of aerobic respiration. They are highly toxic as they cause damage to proteins, DNA, RNA and lipids (Cabiscol et al. 2000). For instance, superoxide anions can cause liberation of iron from iron–sulfur clusters of the respiratory chain enzymes, which, in turn, can induce the production of hydroxyl radicals through the Fenton reaction (Gordon et al. 2010). Consequently, by promoting ROS production, the antibacterial effect of Ag^+ can be enhanced and anti-oxidative enzymes can probably not detoxify the generated ROS as their activity depends on thiol groups, which are blocked by Ag^+. ROS production by silver was evidenced by a similar SoxR-mediated induction of *soxS* transcription after treatment with silver and paraquat, a known superoxide-radical generator (Park et al. 2009). In addition, anaerobically grown bacteria are often less susceptible to Ag^+ ions, putatively reflecting the influence of ROS production on the antibacterial activity of Ag^+ (Matsumura et al. 2003; Park et al. 2009). However, significant differences in silver toxicity under aerobic and anaerobic conditions are not always observed, indicating that other factors are at play. For instance, in *E. coli*, treatment with silver nitrate resulted in a rapid decrease of viability in aerobic and anaerobic conditions, while treatment with silver zeolite only affected viability in aerobic conditions (Matsumura et al. 2003). Similarly, Xiu et al. (2011) did not observe significant differences in the toxicity of $AgNO_3$ to *E. coli* K-12 in the presence or absence of oxygen.

The toxicity of silver ions can be significantly increased in the presence of UV-A and visible light irradiation as shown for *E. coli* and MS2 phages by Kim et al. (2008). Photochemical destruction of silver–cysteine complexes and subsequent formation of monosulfide radicals are probably at the basis of this observation (Kim et al. 2008). Similar to ROS, these radicals may directly interact with polyunsaturated fatty acids in membranes and initiate lipid peroxidation. The latter changes membrane fluidity, which, in turn, leads to altered membrane properties and even disruption of membrane-bound proteins (Cabiscol et al. 2000).

Finally, the toxicity of silver compounds depends on the bioavailability of Ag^+ ions and (among other) on the amount of halides (Gupta et al. 1998). A large fraction of Ag^+ forms complexes with free chloride, phosphate and sulfate ions, and rapidly binds to proteins, hence its use as a general protein stain. Therefore, to sustain antimicrobial activity, Ag^+ should be released slowly and continuously (Edwards-Jones 2009). Several studies showed that the difference between silver resistance and sensitivity was more explicit in the presence of chloride ions (Gupta et al. 1998; Li et al. 1997). Moderate levels of Cl^- interact with Ag^+ and precipitate as AgCl, thereby decreasing available Ag^+. However, higher levels of Cl^- bring the Ag^+ back in solution as $AgCl_2^-$, making it available again. Bromide ions have a similar effect, but because AgBr is less soluble than AgCl, it functions at lower concentrations. Iodide ions remove Ag^+ into a non-bioavailable 1:1 AgI precipitate (Gupta et al. 1998; Silver 2003). These effects have implications for laboratory studies as well as environmental studies since soil and aqueous environments contain several ligands that are able to complex silver ions.

7.3.2 Resistance Mechanisms

In the 1960s, the first recorded silver-resistant bacteria were isolated from silver nitrate-treated burn wounds (Jelenko 1969). Afterwards, silver-resistant bacteria have been recurrently isolated from different clinical environments, burn wounds and even teeth (Davis et al. 2005; Kremer and Hoffmann 2012; McHugh et al. 1975). Silver-resistant microorganisms have also been isolated from nonclinical environments. Examples are a *Pseudomonas stutzeri* strain isolated from the soil of a silver mine in Utah (Haefeli et al. 1984), a *Klebsiella pneumoniae* isolate found in marine shrimps in the coastal waters of India

(Choudhury and Kumar 1998) and the yeast *Candida argentea* obtained from the sediments of an abandoned metal mine in the United Kingdom (Holland et al. 2011).

The molecular basis and mechanism of silver resistance were first described for a *Salmonella enterica* serovar Typhimurium strain that caused the closure of the Massachusetts General Hospital burn ward after septicaemia and death in three patients and is still today the best-characterised (McHugh et al. 1975). This strain harbours pMG101, a 183-kb plasmid assigned to the incHI incompatibility group, which confers resistance to silver, mercury, tellurite as well as to several antibiotics (Gupta et al. 1999). The plasmidic region responsible for silver resistance comprises the *silCFBA(ORF105aa)PRSE* gene cluster, and eight out of the nine gene products were primarily characterised based on homology to the *E. coli cop* and *cus* copper resistance determinants (Silver 2003; Silver et al. 2006). The *sil* gene cluster is highly conserved in several other plasmids from the incHI incompatibility group such as MIP233, MIP235 and WR23 from various *Salmonella* serovars, plasmids pR47b and pR478 from *Serratia marcescens* (Gupta et al. 2001) and plasmid pAPEC-O1-R from avian pathogenic *E. coli* (Johnson et al. 2006). In *Enterobacter cloacae*, the major difference between virulent and avirulent genotypes appears to be the presence of a large IncHI-2 plasmid carrying a functional *sil* gene cluster next to several antibiotic resistant determinants (Kremer and Hoffmann 2012). The environmental isolate *Acinetobacter baumannii* BL88 harbours plasmid pUPI199 that can tolerate up to 0.75 mM $AgNO_3$ and additionally contains resistance determinants for 13 different metals and 10 antibiotics (Deshpande and Chopade 1994). Although studies exploring silver resistance in clinical bacteria showed a rather low prevalence of *sil* genes and limited clinically significant phenotypic expression, recently, two strains resistant to clinically relevant Ag^+ concentrations were isolated from patients in a tertiary care facility (Finley et al. 2015). Both isolates (one *K. pneumoniae* and one *E. cloacae* strain) harbour plasmid-borne *silCBA* and *silP* genes and were able to grow at Ag^+ concentrations up to 5.5 mM. Additionally, both were able to form extracellular Ag NPs. Although the precise mechanism is not yet fully elucidated (Finley et al. 2015), this stresses the importance of continued screening of isolates for silver resistance.

The *silCFBA(orf105)PRSE* gene products mediate silver resistance via active efflux and silver sequestration in the periplasm. SilF, a periplasmic chaperone protein, probably transports Ag^+ to the SilCBA complex (Figure 7.2). This complex forms a three-polypeptide membrane potential-dependent cation/proton antiporter system that spans the entire cell membrane and belongs to the Heavy Metal Efflux-Resistance Nodulation cell Division (HME-RND) family of efflux. The complex consists of an efflux pump (SilA), an outer membrane factor (SilC) and a membrane fusion protein (SilB) and pumps Ag^+ from the periplasm to the exterior of the cell (Franke 2007; Silver 2003). The *orf*105 gene, coding for a hypothetical protein of 105 aa, was recently reanalysed and was predicted to code for a periplasmic metal chaperone of

146 aa that contains the conserved metal-binding site CxxC and shares 45% protein identity with CopG from *Cupriavidus metallidurans* CH34 (Randall et al. 2015). SilP is a putative P-type ATPase efflux pump that transports silver ions from the cell cytoplasm to the periplasm (Franke 2007; Silver 2003). However, neither *silP* nor *orf105* is essential for silver resistance as deletion mutants of *silP* or *orf105* or both did not show an increased silver sensitivity (Randall et al. 2015). The transcription of the *silCFBA(ORF105aa)P* genes is controlled by the two-component regulatory system SilRS, consisting of a transmembrane histidine kinase SilS and a response regulator SilR. This regulatory system is homologous to other two-component regulatory systems involved in the regulation of metal resistance (Franke 2007; Silver 2003). Finally, the *silE* gene located downstream of *silRS,* is not controlled by SilRS; nevertheless, transcription is strongly induced in the presence of Ag^+ (Silver et al. 1999). *SilE* codes for a periplasmic protein that shares 48% identity with PcoE, which acts as a 'metal sponge' because of its ability to bind multiple Cu^+ and Ag^+ ions and is encoded by the *pcoABCDRSE* copper resistance from *E. coli* plasmid pRJ1004 (Zimmermann et al. 2012). SilE could provide a first line of defense by binding Ag^+ before it enters the cytoplasm, as one SilE molecule can bind up to 38 Ag^+ ions depending on the experimental conditions (Silver et al. 1999). Additionally, it could act as a chaperone, transporting Ag^+ ions to the SilCBA complex either directly or via SilF (Franke 2007; Randall et al. 2015; Silver 2003).

Chromosomally located gene clusters that are homologous to the *sil* cluster have been ubiquitously found (Franke et al. 2003). Next to copper resistance, the *cusCFBARS* gene cluster also confers a certain degree of silver resistance, since deletion of *cusA* resulted in silver sensitivity (Franke et al. 2001). Similar to the *sil* system, the *cus* system comprises an RND-driven efflux system (CusCBA), a small periplasmic Cu^+ and Ag^+ binding protein (CusF), which chaperones Cu^+ and Ag^+ ions from the periplasm to CusCBA, and a two-component regulatory system CusRS (Franke et al. 2003; Munson et al. 2000) (Figure 7.2). The cusF gene is able to complement the function of *silF* as deletion of the latter only completely abolishes silver resistance in a *cus*-negative background (Randall et al. 2015). CusA can efflux Ag^+ ions from both the periplasm and the cytoplasm and uses methionine amino acid pairs or clusters to export Cu^+ and Ag^+ (Long et al. 2010). The transcriptional regulatory network of the *cus* system is activated by Ag^+ via binding to the periplasmic domain of CusS. The latter senses the presence of elevated Ag^+ concentrations and is able to bind four Ag^+ ions, which leads to local conformational changes that enhances dimer formations between the sensing domains (Gudipaty and McEvoy 2014). This will activate the response regulator CusR, which, in turn, leads to the induction of the *cusCFBA* genes. The promoter region of *cusCFBA* contains the copper box, a highly conserved palindrome sequence that is present upstream of several copper- and silver-responsive promoters (Munson et al. 2000). This copper box probably constitutes the binding site of the CusR regulator and is also found in the promoter

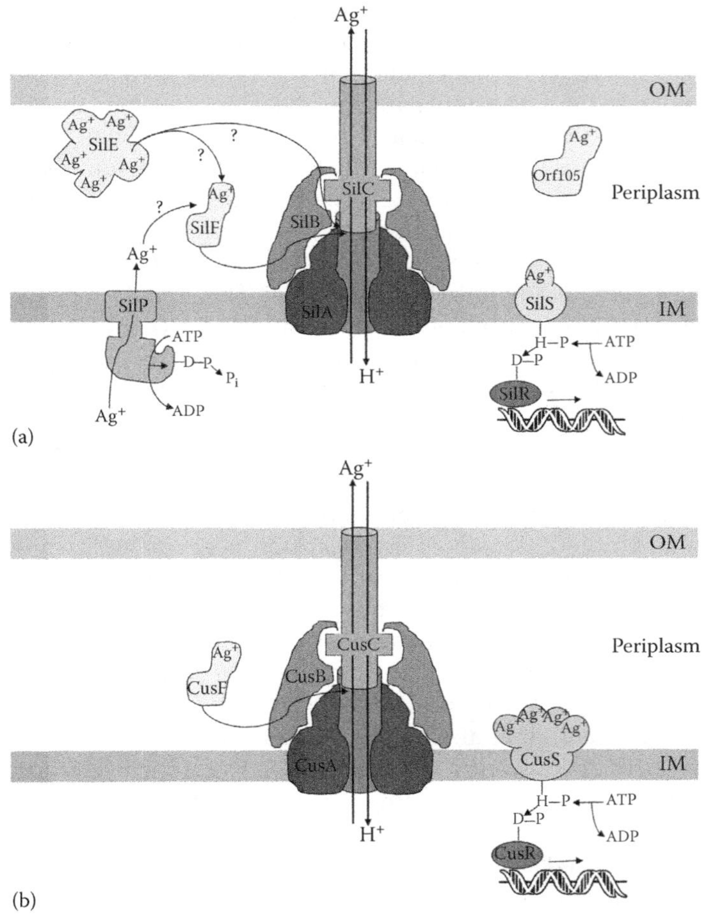

FIGURE 7.2
Overview of the (a) Sil and (b) Cus silver resistance systems.

region of *pcoE* (Munson et al. 2000). Although overexpression of PcoE alone has little effect on overall copper resistance, it is expressed rapidly via the CusRS regulatory cascade and therefore can act as a first line of defense while expression of the other resistance proteins proceeds (Zimmermann et al. 2012).

An alternative silver resistance mechanism was observed in *P. aeruginosa*. Besides its ability to thrive in many diverse terrestrial, marine and freshwater habitats, this bacterium is an important opportunistic pathogen causing severe problems in immune-compromised hosts and cystic fibrosis patients (Rosenfeld et al. 2003). Some strains have the ability to produce pyocyanin, a redox toxin and a reductant for molecular oxygen and ferric (Fe^{3+}) ions (Muller and Merrett 2014). Apparently, pyocyanins can also reduce Ag^+, resulting in the formation of Ag NPs, thereby making Ag^+ less bioavailable and increasing silver resistance fourfold (Muller and Merrett 2014).

Not all species have the same potential to decrease their silver susceptibility after extended exposure. For instance, decreased silver sensitivity was quickly acquired by *E. coli, K. pneumoniae* and *E. cloacae,* in contrast with *Staphylococcus aureus, P. aeruginosa, Shigella sonnei* and *Citrobacter freundii* (Randall et al. 2013, 2015). A silver-resistant *E. coli* mutant, isolated by stepwise selection on increasing concentrations of $AgNO_3$, harboured a single point mutation in *cusS* that resulted in a change of threonine-17 to proline in the N-terminal protein region (Lok et al. 2008). This mutation probably locks CusS in an autophosphorylation state, resulting in constitutive and Ag^+-independent transcriptional activation of the RND-driven CusCFBA system (Gudipaty et al. 2012). The latter was also confirmed at the protein level as CusB and CusF were constitutively expressed in the mutant while both were undetectable in the silver-sensitive parental strain. Differential expression of CusC and CusA was not detected, presumably because these hydrophobic membrane-associated components may not be readily resolved by the used standard two-dimensional gel electrophoresis procedures (Lok et al. 2008). In addition, deletion of *cusF* in the silver-resistant mutant decreased the minimal inhibitory concentration of $AgNO_3$ from 1000 to 12 μM (compared with 3 μM for the parental strain) (Lok et al. 2008). Furthermore, this mutant was deficient in its major outer membrane porins and, consequently, showed decreased outer membrane permeability (Li et al. 1997; Lok et al. 2008). Recently, Randall et al. (2015) observed the same adaptation in three independent silver-resistant *E. coli* mutants, all of which harboured mutations in both *cusS* and *ompR* (coding for the regulator of porin expression) (Figure 7.3).

Similarly, decreased silver susceptibility resulting from a point mutation in *silS* and subsequent increased transcriptional expression of the RND-driven SilCFBA efflux system has been observed for *K. pneumoniae* and *E. cloacae* strains. However, no additional mutation was needed to obtain the silver-resistant phenotype. It seems that the presence of SilE renders porin loss redundant, as addition of *silE* in an *E. coli* strain with a point mutation in *cusS* (but not in *ompR*) results in a silver resistance phenotype (Randall et al. 2015).

Mutations in the sensor kinase of two-component regulatory systems revealing a metal-resistant phenotype is not solely demonstrated for silver. Zinc resistance in *P. aeruginosa* PAO1 was governed by a missense mutation in *czcS*, causing constitutive activation of the czcCBA efflux pump via czcR (Perron et al. 2004). Remarkably, czcR also negatively regulates the expression of *oprD*, coding for a porin through which carbapenems (a class of β-lactam antibiotics) enter the cells, rendering the cells more resistant to these antibiotics (Dieppois et al. 2012; Perron et al. 2004). In addition, CzcR is involved in the regulation of genes involved in virulence processes and biofilm formation (Dieppois et al. 2012). Resistance to the carbepenem antibiotic imipenem, mediated by reduced *oprD* expression, could also be induced by Cu^{2+}. In this case, another

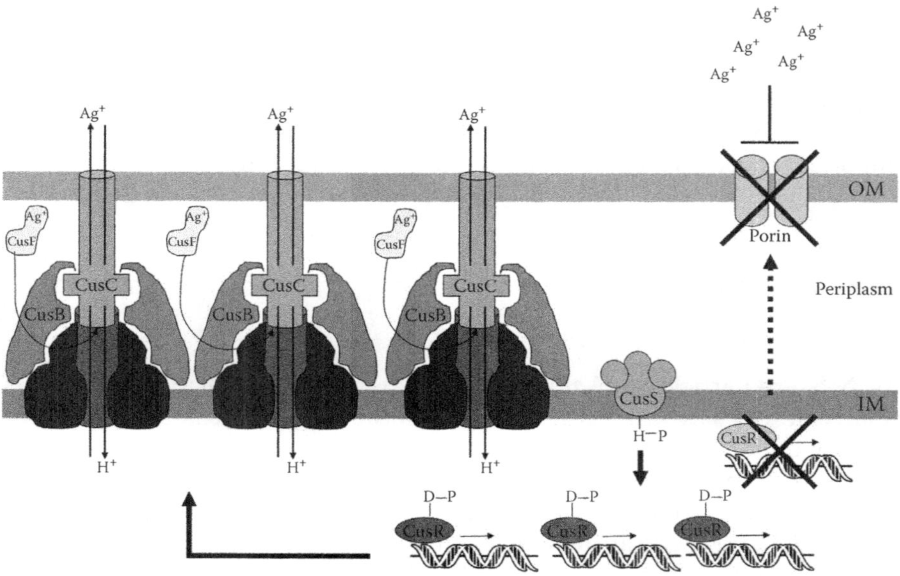

FIGURE 7.3
Overview of how silver resistance is mediated. Mutations in the *ompR* and *cusS* genes decrease influx and increase efflux of Ag^+, resulting in a silver-resistant phenotype.

two-component system, CopRS, was involved and, as for CzcR, increased expression of CopR resulted in downregulation of *oprD*. Interestingly, Cu^{2+}-induced CopR is also able to bind the promoter region of *czcRS*, thereby promoting *czcRS* expression, which, in turn, leads to an increased expression of the RND-driven CzcCBA efflux system and increased Zn^{2+} resistance (Caille et al. 2007). This shows that a complex interplay between two-component systems facilitates the adaptation of microorganisms to different stimuli and stressful conditions. Remarkably, the genomes from clinical and environmental *P. aeruginosa* strains are highly conserved and functionally equivalent with respect to several clinically relevant properties (Alonso et al. 1999; Wolfgang et al. 2003). Thus, the study of cross-regulation is of paramount importance as Cu^{2+} and Zn^{2+} are ubiquitously present not only in the environment as a consequence of agricultural practices but also within the human body and in several medical treatments (Caille et al. 2007; Dieppois et al. 2012). Similarly, a low-level cross-resistance between Ag^+ and cephalosporins (β-lactam antibiotics), probably caused by decreased membrane permeability, was observed in silver-resistant *E. coli* mutants (Li et al. 1997). Cross-resistance caused by alteration of the membrane permeability was also observed in mixed-culture bioreactors, designed for seeding activated sludge systems, dosed with low levels of the β-lactam amoxicillin (Cunningham and Lin 2010). The increased use of silver and Ag NPs in numerous applications lead to elevated Ag^+ concentrations in clinical and nonclinical environments. Moreover, the structural and functional characteristics of metal resistance share common themes with those conferring antibiotic resistance (reviewed in Baker-Austin et al. 2006). Therefore, metal-contaminated soils can be a putative reservoir of harmful, antibiotic resistant strains. The possible long-term effects elicited by this cross-resistance on the environment and human health are not yet known but are an important aspect to take into consideration in future studies.

7.4 Silver Nanoparticles

Ag NPs are particles of Ag(0) with a size ranging from 1 to 100 nm. This small size gives them specific physiochemical characteristics different from those of bulk materials of the same composition, mainly because of the high surface area-to-volume ratio (Rai et al. 2012). The specific characteristics of Ag NPs make them useful in inks (Perelaer et al. 2009), microelectronics (Wu et al. 2006) and medical imaging (Jain et al. 2008). In addition, the broad-spectrum antibacterial activities of Ag NPs made them extremely popular in several medical and nonmedical applications. In medical applications, Ag NPs have been widely used for diagnosis, wound dressings, treatment, medical device coating, medical textiles, drug delivery and contraceptive devices (Ge et al. 2014). Examples of nonmedical applications are the use of Ag NPs in milk bottles and toys for children, clothing, sheets and pillows, cosmetics, refrigerators, vacuum cleaners, washing machines, plenty of personal care applications and many others. The project on emerging nanotechnologies compiles an inventory of nanotechnology-based consumer products. Currently, this database lists 1826 consumer products, of which 925 (±50%) have a defined nanomaterial composition (Nanotechnologies). For the past few years, Ag NP-containing products constitute the largest group of all the commercially available nano-based products and Ag NPs are used in 441 (±47%) of the 925 defined products, while the second most abundant products, titanium dioxide-based nanoparticles, are used in only 92 products (±10%) (Nanotechnologies). This extensive use of Ag NPs leads to an increased release of Ag NPs (and Ag^+ ions) in the environment, which consequently might have harmful ecological effects (Fabrega et al. 2011; Pokhrel and Dubey 2012). Therefore, detailed knowledge about the toxicity mechanism and behaviour of Ag NPs is necessary. Moreover, this will help improve the antimicrobial properties and direct their applications.

7.4.1 Synthesis

Many chemical and physical methods exist to produce Ag NPs including laser ablation, gamma irradiation, electron irradiation, chemical reduction, photochemical methods, microwave processing and others (Iravani et al.

2014). The most common method is chemical reduction from Ag^+ to Ag^0 with an organic or inorganic reducing agent (e.g. $NaBH_4$, ascorbate) together with a stabiliser (e.g. PVP, PEG) to prevent aggregation. The main advantages of physical synthesis methods compared to chemical methods is that there is no need for toxic chemicals, and the resulting Ag NPs have a narrow size distribution. However, the main disadvantage of the physical processes is that they require a high energy consumption (Iravani et al. 2014). To overcome these disadvantages, 'green' synthesis of Ag NPs, in which nontoxic reducing and stabilising agents are used, is of increasing interest. Moreover, it has been shown that biological systems such as yeast (Mourato et al. 2011), algae (Aziz et al. 2015), fungi (Li et al. 2012), plants (Begum et al. 2009) and bacteria have potential in the eco-friendly and economically friendly production of Ag NPs. Extracellular Ag NPs have been produced using *S. aureus* (Nanda and Saravanan 2009), *Bacillus megaterium* (Saravanan et al. 2011), *P. aeruginosa* (Kumar and Mamidyala 2011), *K. pneumoniae* (Shahverdi et al. 2007) and many other bacteria. The formation of intracellular Ag-based crystals was observed in *P. stutzeri* AG259 (Klaus et al. 1999). In addition, periplasmic Ag NPs have been formed by *E. coli*, periplasmically expressing a silver-binding peptide, previously selected from a combinatorial phage display peptide library (Sedlak et al. 2012). These observations indicate that bacteria can be of interest for the biological synthesis of silver nanomaterials and, in addition, for bioremediation of toxic silver waste.

7.4.2 Toxicity

Numerous reports have demonstrated the toxicity of Ag NPs to a wide range of Gram-negative and Gram-positive bacteria (reviewed in Rai et al. 2012), fungi (Hwang et al. 2012) and viruses (De Gusseme et al. 2011; Elechiguerra et al. 2005; Rogers et al. 2008). However, the precise mechanism how Ag NPs exert their toxicity is not yet fully understood. Different toxicity mechanisms have been proposed such as cell membrane damage, thereby increasing the membrane permeability and disrupting respiration, inhibition of DNA replication and modification of intracellular ATP levels (Franci et al. 2015; Morones et al. 2005; Sondi and Salopek-Sondi 2004). Furthermore, toxicity largely depends on several aspects related to the synthesis of the Ag NPs, as size, morphology, surface charge and type of capping agent used all influence the toxicity of Ag NPs. Particle size is inversely proportional to surface area, resulting in a higher specific activity (Morones et al. 2005; Panacek et al. 2006; Sotiriou and Pratsinis 2010). In addition, compared to larger Ag NPs, small Ag NPs release more Ag^+ ions (Sotiriou and Pratsinis 2010; Xiu et al. 2012) and consequently exhibit stronger antimicrobial activities. When larger Ag NPs are used, microbial growth is inhibited as a result of the particle itself rather than through the release of Ag^+ ions (Sotiriou and Pratsinis 2010). The morphology of Ag NPs and more specific their effective surface area in terms of active facets is apparently also important for their toxicity as triangular particles seem to be more effective than spherical particles, which are again more effective than rod-shaped particles (Pal et al. 2007). Also, the surface charge has been shown to be important as *Bacillus* spp. were less susceptible to more negatively charged than to more positively charged Ag NPs. The latter are attracted by the negatively charged cell membrane allowing a higher degree of interaction, while negatively charged Ag NPs are repulsed (El Badawy et al. 2011). Finally, it has been shown that the type of capping agent used to prevent nanoparticle aggregation as well as environmental conditions such as pH, ionic strength and electrolyte type influence the aggregation potential and toxicity of Ag NPs (El Badawy et al. 2010; Xiu et al. 2011).

Furthermore, it is not yet fully elucidated to which degree Ag NP toxicity results from released Ag^+ ions and how much is related to the Ag NPs themselves. Xiu et al. (2012) showed that particle properties only affect Ag NP toxicity in an indirect manner through mechanisms that influence the rate, extent, location or timing of Ag^+ release, the latter being the only factor responsible for the antimicrobial activity of Ag NPs. Their hypothesis was confirmed by testing the antimicrobial activity of self-made glycol-thiol-coated Ag NPs (PEG-Ag NPs) and commercially available polyvinylpyrrolidone-coated Ag NPs (PVP-Ag NPs) of different sizes and with different surface charges. No significant difference between the dose-response patterns of the tested Ag NPs expressed as a function of the released Ag^+ concentration and the dose-response pattern of cells exposed to ionic Ag^+ was observed. In addition, when PEG-Ag NPs of 5 or 11 nm were prepared anaerobically, preventing the release of Ag^+ ions, no measurable toxic effect on *E. coli* K-12 was observed (Xiu et al. 2012). This hypothesis is confirmed by others (Ivask et al. 2014; Loza et al. 2014; Yang et al. 2012) and for different organisms such as *Caenorhabditis elegans* (Yang, Gondikas et al. 2012), *Daphnia magna* (Li et al. 2015) and human cell lines (Beer et al. 2012; De Matteis et al. 2015; Kittler et al. 2010; Park et al. 2010). However, in contrast to PEG-Ag NPs (Xiu et al. 2012), anaerobically prepared, commercially available Ag NPs coated with amorphous carbon (AC-Ag NPs) decreased viability of *E. coli* by 98% (Xiu et al. 2011). Therefore, next to the release of Ag^+ from Ag NPs, the influence of the capping agent cannot be ignored (Figure 7.4).

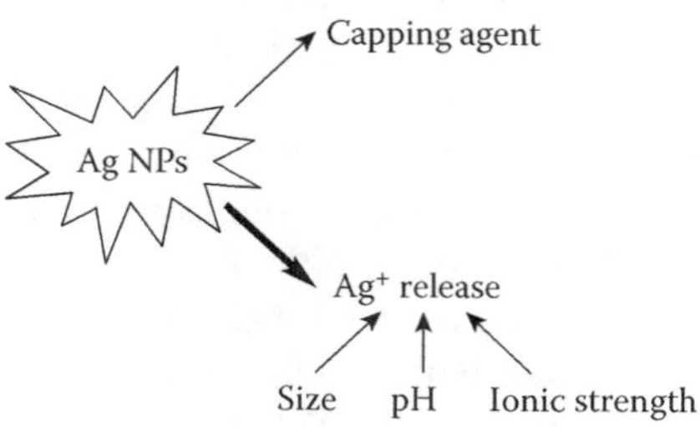

FIGURE 7.4
The antimicrobial effects of Ag NPs depend on (1) the release of Ag^+, which is influenced by their size and environmental conditions, and (2) the capping agent.

Although there is a large amount of data available about the applicability and toxicity of Ag NPs, there are no clear standards for preparing Ag NPs or for assessing their toxicity (Fabrega et al. 2011). Moreover, the mechanism by which they exert their toxic effect can differ depending on the studied organism. In multicellular organisms, there can be an organism-specific immune response to different nanoparticle morphologies leading to different observations, making it difficult to extrapolate results to different biological systems (Xiu et al. 2012).

7.4.3 Resistance Mechanisms

As Ag NPs affect many aspects of bacterial physiology, it is assumed that bacteria are less capable of developing resistance to them (Rai et al. 2012). However, a laboratory evolution experiment showed that *E. coli* MG1655 was able to rapidly adapt to 10-nm-sized citrate-coated Ag NPs. In addition, the mutant showed an increased resistance to 10-nm-sized PVP-coated and 40-nm-sized citrate-coated Ag NPs as well as to $AgNO_3$. The adapted population harboured a single point mutation in the active site of *cusS* and mutations in *ompR* (Graves et al. 2015), which is, as described above, similar to the adaptation to silver ions. The same trend was observed in *Mycobacterium smegmatis* strain mc^2155, which showed increased resistance to Ag NPs and Ag^+ after a single exposure to a toxic concentration of Ag NPs. Furthermore, the adapted strain could tolerate four times more isoniazid, a common mycobacterial antibiotic. However, in this study, the mutation leading to the resistant phenotype was not yet elucidated (Larimer et al. 2014). In addition, exposure of *E. coli* K-12 to Ag NPs resulted in the induction of the *cusCFBA* genes (Du et al. 2012), also shown to be involved in silver ion resistance (Franke et al. 2001). Altogether, this suggests that the resistance mechanisms to Ag NPs and Ag^+ are the same and supports the hypothesis that Ag^+ ions are the main contributors to Ag NPs toxicity.

The antimicrobial activity of Ag NPs is mostly assessed via culture-dependent methods. However, it has been observed that Ag NPs (and Ag^+ as well) can induce a viable but nonculturable state in *P. aeruginosa* AdS. More specifically, exposure to Ag NPs and $AgNO_3$ drastically decreased colony-forming units of planktonic cells and decreased the cellular ATP concentration, whereas the total cell count, membrane integrity and rRNA content were unaffected (Koenigs et al. 2015). This observation should be taken into account by other antimicrobial assessments of Ag NPs.

Notably, hormesis has been observed when *E. coli* K-12 and *Cupriavidus necator* H16 were exposed to sublethal concentrations of Ag NPs (Schacht et al. 2013; Xiu et al. 2012). This stimulatory effect could be elicited by the residual Ag^+ in the Ag NPs stock suspension (Xiu et al. 2012) and is of significant importance to consider in antimicrobial applications of Ag NPs.

7.5 Mobile Genetic Elements and Horizontal Transfer of Silver Resistance

Plasmids from the incHI incompatibility group – in which the *sil* gene cluster is highly conserved – are optimally transferred at temperatures below 25°C, reflecting environmental conditions such as soils and water (Maher and Taylor 1993). Consequently, they are not considered to contribute to the widespread transfer of silver resistance genes in clinical environments (Finley et al. 2015). However, they can be widespread in environmental strains, which consequently can serve as a reservoir for pathogens. Horizontal gene transfer between soil-dwelling organisms and diverse human pathogens has been demonstrated (Forsberg et al. 2012), for instance, the class A extended-spectrum β-lactamase CTX-M, found on plasmids carried by major global pathogens that were traced to environmental *Kluyvera* spp. (Humeniuk et al. 2002). Similarly, the quinolone resistance gene *qnr*, found on a broad-host range conjugative plasmid from a ciprofloxacin-resistant *K. pneumoniae* strain, is traced to several environmental waterborne species (Poirel et al. 2005).

Moreover, *sil* determinants are not only found on plasmids from the incHI incompatibility group and other examples of plasmid-borne *sil* genes are provided below. A *K. pneumoniae* strain and an *E. cloacae* strain, isolated from a tertiary care facility, harbour *sil* genes on a plasmid putatively belonging to the highly persistent and mobile incFII incompatibility group (Finley et al. 2015). The 83-kb plasmid pJT1 of *E. coli* R1, isolated from patients with burn wounds, conferred resistance up to 1 mM $AgNO_3$ (Starodub and Trevors 1989). In *P. stutzeri* AG259, isolated from the soil of a silver mine, silver resistance was also mediated by one of its plasmids (Haefeli et al. 1984). This strain was able to grow on rich medium with 50 mM $AgNO_3$ by accumulation of Ag and Ag_2S crystals in its periplasm (Klaus et al. 1999). Also, *C. metallidurans* CH34, which harbours resistance determinants for at least 20 different metal ions, carries a number of systems putatively involved in silver detoxification, that is, the *silDCBA*, *cusDCBAF* and *cupRAC* clusters. The *C. metallidurans* species is specialised in metal resistance and is often associated with industrial sites linked to mining, metallurgical and chemical industries (Goris et al. 2001) but is also isolated from environments not typified by metal contamination such as different spacecraft-related environments (La Duc et al. 2003; Ott et al. 2004), from patients with cystic fibrosis (Coenye et al. 2005) or as the causative agent of an invasive human infection (Langevin et al. 2011). The *silDCBA* and *cusDCBAF* operons are located on the megaplasmid pMOL30 and the chromid (Janssen et al. 2010; Van Houdt and Mergeay 2012; Van Houdt et al. 2012a), respectively. In fact, the *silDCBA* cluster is located on a genomic island on pMOL30. In contrast, the *cupRAC*, encoding for a P-type ATPase, is located on the chromosome (Janssen et al. 2010). Moreover, comparative whole-genome hybridisation between 17 different *C. metallidurans* strains isolated from diverse biotopes showed that the metal resistance determinants, including the silver-resistant gene clusters, are highly conserved (Van Houdt et al. 2012b). Furthermore, PCR analysis of plasmid extracts from *C. metallidurans* isolates from different potable water management systems of the International Space Station (ISS) and from the air of the Kennedy Space Center Payload Hazardous Servicing Facility indicated that the *silCBA* operon is always located on one of the megaplasmids (Mijnendonckx et al. 2013). Among others, the presence of the *sil* gene cluster in the potable water isolates gives them the ability to withstand the sanitation procedure onboard ISS in which silver is used (Mijnendonckx et al. 2013). In *Delftia acidovorans* and *Bordetella petrii*, the *silCBA* cluster is located on an Integrative Conjugative Element belonging to the Tn*4371* family. The latter family refers to a group of mobile genetic elements that carry functional modules involved in conjugative transfer, integration, maintenance/stability and accessory genes conferring a special phenotype to the host bacteria (Van Houdt et al. 2012c). Often, the *sil* gene cluster is located adjacent to the *pco* gene cluster, a gene cluster originating from an independently isolated plasmid, and this genetic rearrangement is found on the chromosomes and plasmids of a wide variety of species (Hobman and Crossman 2015). Recent resequencing of *E. coli* J53 harbouring the pMG101 plasmid (the original source of the *sil* gene cluster) showed that this rearrangement was mediated by Tn*7*-based transposition (Randall et al. 2015). Altogether, in many strains, the determinants mediating silver resistance are located on mobile genetic elements, facilitating the spread of these traits to other members of the population. Furthermore, mobile genetic elements carrying silver resistance determinants often also harbour genes conferring resistance to other metals or antimicrobials. This stresses the necessity to critically evaluate the current and delineate the future nonmedical use of metals and antimicrobials.

In natural environments, microorganisms are frequently exposed to elevated concentrations of silver. Estuarine and coastal waters exposed to anthropogenic inputs, including those from wastewater effluents (e.g. industry, hospitals, dental offices, etc.) and water flow from metal mines, are an important source of silver, while in pristine freshwaters, the concentration of dissolved silver is generally low (Tappin et al. 2010). Wastewater discharges from hospitals, photographic and electronic industries are shown to be the basis for the enhanced silver concentrations found in the San Francisco Bay (Flegal et al. 2007). Active efforts to reduce discharges and more stringent discharge regulations decreased silver concentrations over the last two to three decades. However, silver contamination is still a matter of concern (Flegal et al. 2007). In estuarine waters contaminated with metal-mine wastes in southwest England, 400 times more silver than background levels were reported in sediments and in residing organisms (Bryan and Langston 1992). Elevated silver concentrations were also observed in Atlantic coastal waters receiving untreated municipal wastewater, whereas the lowest concentrations where found in the Gullmar Fjord, without major sources of water pollution (Tappin et al. 2010). Although the emergence of digital photography and improvements to wastewater treatments reduced silver inputs over the last decades, the extended use of silver and Ag NPs in commercial products will again lead to an increase of silver in the environment. Moreover, sediments will likely remain as a secondary source of silver to marine waters for some time (Tappin et al. 2010). The use of sewage sludge as fertiliser or as organic soil improver can also lead to the spread of silver in the environment (Kaegi et al. 2013). Because silver resistance determinants are frequently located on mobile genetic elements and present in many environmental bacteria, they can be horizontally transferred at high frequencies in particular conditions within natural ecosystems (e.g. in nutritional hot spots such as manure-applied soils) (reviewed in Aminov 2011). Furthermore, this could diversify mobile genetic elements and disseminate novel phenotypes among bacterial populations (Heuer et al. 2009). These observations highlight the necessity to control the release of silver in the environment as this can putatively facilitate the dissemination of silver resistance determinants among environmental microorganisms and to clinically important organisms.

7.6 Conclusions

We reviewed the current insights into silver toxicity of and bacterial resistance to silver ions and nanoparticles, which are widely used in many applications. Although the antimicrobial activity of silver ions and Ag NPs has not yet been fully elucidated, there is a growing consensus about the contributing mechanisms. Silver ions probably interact with the cytoplasmic membrane where they compromise electron transfer and the proton motive force, ultimately resulting in cell death. In addition, ionic silver interacts with enzymes and is able to promote the production of ROS. Ag NPs basically ferry silver ions to bacteria, which are released and exert their action, although additional factors cannot be excluded at this point.

Silver resistance determinants are widely found among environmental and clinically relevant bacteria. Next to chemical detoxification, for instance, by precipitation in the periplasm via reduction to elemental silver or the formation of Ag_2S crystals, bacterial silver resistance mechanisms result from active efflux systems. Efflux pumps are either P-type ATPases, which pump Ag^+ from the cell cytoplasm to the periplasm, or three-polypeptide membrane potential-dependent cation/proton antiporters (HME-RND family), which pump Ag^+ from the periplasm to the exterior of the cell. These resistance mechanisms are often harboured by mobile genetic elements, facilitating their spread. This is of concern because the extensive use of silver-based products will increase the release of silver in the environment, putatively inducing the dissemination of silver resistance (and thereby cross-resistance to antibiotics). Future studies need to pinpoint the precise mechanisms of

Ag^+ and Ag NPs toxicity and resistance. Detailed, comprehensive knowledge can improve and direct the many applications of silver (e.g. antimicrobial, bioremediation, nanomaterials) and will allow assessing the risks associated with human health and ecosystems more accurately.

References

Alexander, J. W. 2009. History of the medical use of silver. *Surg Infect (Larchmt)* 10 (3):289–92.

Alonso, A., F. Rojo, and J. L. Martinez. 1999. Environmental and clinical isolates of *Pseudomonas aeruginosa* show pathogenic and biodegradative properties irrespective of their origin. *Environ Microbiol* 1 (5):421–30.

Aminov, R. I. 2011. Horizontal gene exchange in environmental microbiota. *Front Microbiol* 2:158.

Aziz, N., M. Faraz, R. Pandey, M. Shakir, T. Fatma, A. Varma, I. Barman, and R. Prasad. 2015. Facile algae-derived route to biogenic silver nanoparticles: Synthesis, antibacterial, and photocatalytic properties. *Langmuir* 31 (42):11605–12.

Baker-Austin, C., M. S. Wright, R. Stepanauskas, and J. V. McArthur. 2006. Co-selection of antibiotic and metal resistance. *Trends Microbiol* 14 (4):176–82.

Beer, C., R. Foldbjerg, Y. Hayashi, D. S. Sutherland, and H. Autrup. 2012. Toxicity of silver nanoparticles – Nanoparticle or silver ion? *Toxicol Lett* 208 (3):286–92.

Begum, N. A., S. Mondal, S. Basu, R. A. Laskar, and D. Mandal. 2009. Biogenic synthesis of Au and Ag nanoparticles using aqueous solutions of Black Tea leaf extracts. *Colloids Surf B Biointerfaces* 71 (1):113–8.

Bragg, P. D., and D. J. Rainnie. 1974. Effect of silver ions on the respiratory chain of *Escherichia coli*. *Can J Microbiol* 20 (6):883–9.

Bryan, G. W., and W. J. Langston. 1992. Bioavailability, accumulation and effects of heavy metals in sediments with special reference to United Kingdom estuaries: A review. *Environ Pollut* 76 (2):89–131.

Cabiscol, E., J. Tamarit, and J. Ros. 2000. Oxidative stress in bacteria and protein damage by reactive oxygen species. *Int Microbiol* 3 (1):3–8.

Caille, O., C. Rossier, and K. Perron. 2007. A copper-activated two-component system interacts with zinc and imipenem resistance in *Pseudomonas aeruginosa*. *J Bacteriol* 189 (13):4561–8.

Chambers, C. W., C. M. Proctor, and P. W. Kabler. 1962. Bactericidal effect of low concentrations of silver. *J Am Water Works Assoc* 54:208–16.

Chopra, I. 2007. The increasing use of silver-based products as antimicrobial agents: A useful development or a cause for concern? *J Antimicrob Chemother* 59 (4):587–90.

Choudhury, P., and R. Kumar. 1998. Multidrug- and metal-resistant strains of *Klebsiella pneumoniae* isolated from *Penaeus monodon* of the coastal waters of deltaic Sundarban. *Can J Microbiol* 44 (2):186–9.

Coenye, T., T. Spilker, R. Reik, P. Vandamme, and J. J. Lipuma. 2005. Use of PCR analyses to define the distribution of *Ralstonia* species recovered from patients with cystic fibrosis. *J Clin Microbiol* 43 (7):3463–6.

Cunningham, J. H., and L. S. Lin. 2010. Fate of amoxicillin in mixed-culture bioreactors and its effects on microbial growth and resistance to silver ions. *Environ Sci Technol* 44 (5):1827–32.

Davis, I. J., H. Richards, and P. Mullany. 2005. Isolation of silver- and antibiotic-resistant *Enterobacter cloacae* from teeth. *Oral Microbiol Immunol* 20 (3):191–4.

De Gusseme, B., T. Hennebel, E. Christiaens, H. Saveyn, K. Verbeken, J. P. Fitts, N. Boon, and W. Verstraete. 2011. Virus disinfection in water by biogenic silver immobilized in polyvinylidene fluoride membranes. *Water Res* 45 (4): 1856–64.

De Matteis, V., M. A. Malvindi, A. Galeone, V. Brunetti, E. De Luca, S. Kote, P. Kshirsagar, S. Sabella, G. Bardi, and P. P. Pompa. 2015. Negligible particle-specific toxicity mechanism of silver nanoparticles: The role of Ag^+ ion release in the cytosol. *Nanomed Nanotech Biol Med* 11 (3):731–9.

Deshpande, L. M., and B. A. Chopade. 1994. Plasmid mediated silver resistance in *Acinetobacter baumannii*. *Biometals* 7 (1):49–56.

Dibrov, P., J. Dzioba, K. K. Gosink, and C. C. Hase. 2002. Chemiosmotic mechanism of antimicrobial activity of Ag^+ in *Vibrio cholerae*. *Antimicrob Agents Chemother* 46 (8):2668–70.

Dieppois, G., V. Ducret, O. Caille, and K. Perron. 2012. The transcriptional regulator CzcR modulates antibiotic resistance and quorum sensing in *Pseudomonas aeruginosa*. *PLoS One* 7 (5):e38148.

Drake, P. L., and K. J. Hazelwood. 2005. Exposure-related health effects of silver and silver compounds: A review. *Ann Occup Hyg* 49 (7):575–85.

Du, H., T.-M. Lo, J. Sitompul, and M. Wook Chang. 2012. Systems-level analysis of *Escherichia coli* response to silver nanoparticles: The roles of anaerobic respiration in microbial resistance. *Biochem Biophys Res Commun* 424 (4):657–62.

Edwards-Jones, V. 2009. The benefits of silver in hygiene, personal care and healthcare. *Lett Appl Microbiol* 49 (2):147–52.

El Badawy, A. M., T. P. Luxton, R. G. Silva, K. G. Scheckel, M. T. Suidan, and T. M. Tolaymat. 2010. Impact of environmental conditions (pH, ionic strength, and electrolyte type) on the surface charge and aggregation of silver nanoparticles suspensions. *Environ Sci Technol* 44 (4):1260–6.

El Badawy, A. M., R. G. Silva, B. Morris, K. G. Scheckel, M. T. Suidan, and T. M. Tolaymat. 2011. Surface charge-dependent toxicity of silver nanoparticles. *Environ Sci Technol* 45 (1):283–7.

Elechiguerra, J. L., J. L. Burt, J. R. Morones, A. Camacho-Bragado, X. Gao, H. H. Lara, and M. J. Yacaman. 2005. Interaction of silver nanoparticles with HIV-1. *J Nanobiotechnol* 3:6.

Fabrega, J., S. N. Luoma, C. R. Tyler, T. S. Galloway, and J. R. Lead. 2011. Silver nanoparticles: Behaviour and effects in the aquatic environment. *Environ Int* 37 (2):517–31.

Finley, P. J., R. Norton, C. Austin, A. Mitchell, S. Zank, and P. Durham. 2015. Unprecedented silver resistance in clinically isolated Enterobacteriaceae: Major implications for burn and wound management. *Antimicrob Agents Chemother* 59 (8):4734–41.

Flegal, A. R., C. L. Brown, S. Squire, J. R. Ross, G. M. Scelfo, and S. Hibdon. 2007. Spatial and temporal variations in silver contamination and toxicity in San Francisco Bay. *Environ Res* 105 (1):34–52.

Forsberg, K. J., A. Reyes, B. Wang, E. M. Selleck, M. O. A. Sommer, and G. Dantas. 2012. The shared antibiotic resistome of soil bacteria and human pathogens. *Science* 337 (6098):1107–11.

Franci, G., A. Falanga, S. Galdiero, L. Palomba, M. Rai, G. Morelli, and M. Galdiero. 2015. Silver nanoparticles as potential antibacterial agents. *Molecules* 20 (5):8856–74.

Franke, S. 2007. Microbiology of the Toxic Noble Metal Silver. In Molecular *Microbiology of Heavy Metals*, edited by D.H. Nies and S. Silver, 343–55. Berlin, Heidelberg: Springer Berlin Heidelberg.

Franke, S., G. Grass, and D. H. Nies. 2001. The product of the ybdE gene of the *Escherichia coli* chromosome is involved in detoxification of silver ions. *Microbiology-UK* 147 (Pt 4):965–72.

Franke, S., G. Grass, C. Rensing, and D. H. Nies. 2003. Molecular analysis of the copper-transporting efflux system CusCFBA of *Escherichia coli*. *J Bacteriol* 185 (13):3804–12.

Gaillet, S., and J. M. Rouanet. 2015. Silver nanoparticles: Their potential toxic effects after oral exposure and underlying mechanisms – A review. *Food Chem Toxicol* 77:58–63.

Ge, L., Q. Li, M. Wang, J. Ouyang, X. Li, and M. M. Xing. 2014. Nanosilver particles in medical applications: Synthesis, performance, and toxicity. *Int J Nanomedicine* 9:2399–407.

Gordon, O., T. Vig Slenters, P. S. Brunetto, A. E. Villaruz, D. E. Sturdevant, M. Otto, R. Landmann, and K. M. Fromm. 2010. Silver coordination polymers for prevention of implant infection: Thiol interaction, impact on respiratory chain enzymes, and hydroxyl radical induction. *Antimicrob Agents Chemother* 54 (10):4208–18.

Goris, J., P. De Vos, T. Coenye, B. Hoste, D. Janssens, H. Brim, L. Diels, M. Mergeay, K. Kersters, and P. Vandamme. 2001. Classification of metal-resistant bacteria from industrial biotopes as *Ralstonia campinensis* sp. nov., *Ralstonia metallidurans* sp. nov. and *Ralstonia basilensis* Steinle et al. 1998 emend. *Int J Syst Evol Microbiol* 51 (Pt 5):1773–82.

Graves, J. L. Jr., M. Tajkarimi, Q. Cunningham, A. Campbell, H. Nonga, S. H. Harrison, and J. E. Barrick. 2015. Rapid evolution of silver nanoparticle resistance in *Escherichia coli*. *Front Genet* 6:42.

Gudipaty, S. A., A. S. Larsen, C. Rensing, and M. M. McEvoy. 2012. Regulation of Cu(I)/Ag(I) efflux genes in *Escherichia coli* by the sensor kinase CusS. *FEMS Microbiol Lett* 330 (1):30–7.

Gudipaty, S. A., and M. M. McEvoy. 2014. The histidine kinase CusS senses silver ions through direct binding by its sensor domain. *Biochimica Et Biophysica Acta – Proteins and Proteomics* 1844 (9):1656–61.

Gupta, A., K. Matsui, J. F. Lo, and S. Silver. 1999. Molecular basis for resistance to silver cations in *Salmonella*. *Nat Med* 5 (2):183–8.

Gupta, A., M. Maynes, and S. Silver. 1998. Effects of halides on plasmid-mediated silver resistance in *Escherichia coli*. *Appl Environ Microbiol* 64 (12):5042–5.

Gupta, A., L. T. Phung, D. E. Taylor, and S. Silver. 2001. Diversity of silver resistance genes in IncH incompatibility group plasmids. *Microbiology* 147 (Pt 12):3393–402.

Haefeli, C., C. Franklin, and K. Hardy. 1984. Plasmid-determined silver resistance in *Pseudomonas stutzeri* isolated from a silver mine. *J Bacteriol* 158 (1):389–92.

Hayashi, M., T. Miyoshi, M. Sato, and T. Unemoto. 1992. Properties of respiratory chain-linked Na^+-independent NADH-Quinone reductase in a marine *Vibrio alginolyticus*. *Biochim Biophys Acta* 1099 (2):145–51.

Heuer, H., C. Kopmann, C. T. Binh, E. M. Top, and K. Smalla. 2009. Spreading antibiotic resistance through spread manure: Characteristics of a novel plasmid type with low% G+C content. *Environ Microbiol* 11 (4):937–49.

Hobman, J. L., and L. C. Crossman. 2015. Bacterial antimicrobial metal ion resistance. *J Med Microbiol* 64 (Pt 5):471–97.

Holland, S. L., P. S. Dyer, C. J. Bond, S. A. James, I. N. Roberts, and S. V. Avery. 2011. *Candida argentea* sp. nov., a copper and silver resistant yeast species. *Fungal Biol* 115 (9):909–18.

Humeniuk, C., G. Arlet, V. Gautier, P. Grimont, R. Labia, and A. Philippon. 2002. β-Lactamases of *Kluyvera ascorbata*, probable progenitors of some plasmid-encoded CTX-M types. *Antimicrob Agents Chemother* 46 (9):3045–9.

Hwang, I. S., J. Lee, J. H. Hwang, K. J. Kim, and D. G. Lee. 2012. Silver nanoparticles induce apoptotic cell death in *Candida albicans* through the increase of hydroxyl radicals. *Febs Journal* 279 (7):1327–38.

Iravani, S., H. Korbekandi, S. V. Mirmohammadi, and B. Zolfaghari. 2014. Synthesis of silver nanoparticles: Chemical, physical and biological methods. *Res Pharm Sci* 9 (6):385–406.

Ivask, A., I. Kurvet, K. Kasemets, I. Blinova, V. Aruoja, S. Suppi, H. Vija, A. Kaekinen, T. Titma, M. Heinlaan, M. Visnapuu, D. Koller, V. Kisand, and A. Kahru. 2014. Size-dependent toxicity of silver nanoparticles to bacteria, yeast, algae, crustaceans and mammalian cells in vitro. *Plos One* 9 (7):e102108.

Jain, P. K., X. H. Huang, I. H. El-Sayed, and M. A. El-Sayed. 2008. Noble metals on the nanoscale: Optical and photothermal properties and some applications in imaging, sensing, biology, and medicine. *Acc Chem Res* 41 (12):1578–86.

Janssen, P. J., R. Van Houdt, H. Moors, P. Monsieurs, N. Morin, A. Michaux, M. A. Benotmane, N. Leys, T. Vallaeys, A. Lapidus, S. Monchy, C. Medigue, S. Taghavi, S. McCorkle, J. Dunn, D. van der Lelie, and M. Mergeay. 2010. The complete genome sequence of *Cupriavidus metallidurans* strain CH34, a master survivalist in harsh and anthropogenic environments. *PLoS One* 5 (5):e10433.

Jelenko, C., 3rd. 1969. Silver nitrate resistant *E. coli*: Report of case. *Ann Surg* 170 (2):296–9.

Johnson, T. J., Y. M. Wannemeuhler, J. A. Scaccianoce, S. J. Johnson, and L. K. Nolan. 2006. Complete DNA sequence comparative genomics, and prevalence of an IncHI2 plasmid occurring among extraintestinal pathogenic *Escherichia coli* isolates. *Antimicrob Agents Chemother* 50 (11):3929–33.

Jung, W. K., S. H. Kim, H. C. Koo, S. Shin, J. M. Kim, Y. K. Park, S. Y. Hwang, H. Yang, and Y. H. Park. 2007. Antifungal activity of the silver ion against contaminated fabric. *Mycoses* 50 (4):265–69.

Kaegi, R., A. Voegelin, C. Ort, B. Sinnet, B. Thalmann, J. Krismer, H. Hagendorfer, M. Elumelu, and E. Mueller. 2013. Fate and transformation of silver nanoparticles in urban wastewater systems. *Water Res* 47 (12):3866–77.

Kim, J. Y., C. Lee, M. Cho, and J. Yoon. 2008. Enhanced inactivation of *E. coli* and MS-2 phage by silver ions combined with UV-A and visible light irradiation. *Water Res* 42 (1–2):356–62.

Kittler, S., C. Greulich, J. Diendorf, M. Koeller, and M. Epple. 2010. Toxicity of silver nanoparticles increases during storage because of slow dissolution under release of silver ions. *Chem Mater* 22 (16):4548–54.

Klasen, H. J. 2000. Historical review of the use of silver in the treatment of burns. I. Early uses. *Burns* 26 (2):117–30.

Klaus, T., R. Joerger, E. Olsson, and C. G. Granqvist. 1999. Silver-based crystalline nanoparticles, microbially fabricated. *Proc Natl Acad Sci U S A* 96 (24):13611–4.

Koenigs, Alexa M., Hans-Curt Flemming, and Jost Wingender. 2015. Nanosilver induces a non-culturable but metabolically active state in *Pseudomonas aeruginosa*. *Front Microbiol* 6:395.

Korani, M., E. Ghazizadeh, S. Korani, Z. Hami, and A. Mohammadi-Bardbori. 2015. Effects of silver nanoparticles on human health. *Eur J Nanomed* 7 (1):51–62.

Kremer, A. N., and H. Hoffmann. 2012. Subtractive hybridization yields a silver resistance determinant unique to nosocomial pathogens in the *Enterobacter cloacae* complex. *J Clin Microbiol* 50 (10):3249–57.

Kumar, C. G., and S. K. Mamidyala. 2011. Extracellular synthesis of silver nanoparticles using culture supernatant of *Pseudomonas aeruginosa*. *Colloids Surf, B* 84 (2):462–6.

La Duc, M. T., W. Nicholson, R. Kern, and K. Venkateswaran. 2003. Microbial characterization of the Mars Odyssey spacecraft and its encapsulation facility. *Environ Microbiol* 5 (10):977–85.

Langevin, S., J. Vincelette, S. Bekal, and C. Gaudreau. 2011. First case of invasive human infection caused by *Cupriavidus metallidurans*. *J Clin Microbiol* 49 (2):744–5.

Lansdown, A. B. 2010. A pharmacological and toxicological profile of silver as an antimicrobial agent in medical devices. *Adv Pharmacol Sci* 2010:910686.

Larimer, Curtis, Mohammad Shyful Islam, Anil Ojha, and Ian Nettleship. 2014. Mutation of environmental mycobacteria to resist silver nanoparticles also confers resistance to a common antibiotic. *Biometals* 27 (4):695–702.

Li, G., D. He, Y. Qian, B. Guan, S. Gao, Y. Cui, K. Yokoyama, and L. Wang. 2012. Fungus-mediated green synthesis of silver nanoparticles using *Aspergillus terreus*. *Int J Mol Sci* 13 (1):466–76.

Li, L., H. Wu, C. Ji, C. A. van Gestel, H. E. Allen, and W. J. Peijnenburg. 2015. A metabolomic study on the responses of *Daphnia magna* exposed to silver nitrate and coated silver nanoparticles. *Ecotoxicol Environ Saf* 119:66–73.

Li, X. Z., H. Nikaido, and K. E. Williams. 1997. Silver-resistant mutants of *Escherichia coli* display active efflux of Ag^+ and are deficient in porins. *J Bacteriol* 179 (19):6127–32.

Liau, S. Y., D. C. Read, W. J. Pugh, J. R. Furr, and A. D. Russell. 1997. Interaction of silver nitrate with readily identifiable groups: Relationship to the antibacterial action of silver ions. *Lett Appl Microbiol* 25 (4):279–83.

Lok, C. N., C. M. Ho, R. Chen, P. K. Tam, J. F. Chiu, and C. M. Che. 2008. Proteomic identification of the Cus system as a major determinant of constitutive *Escherichia coli* silver resistance of chromosomal origin. *J Proteome Res* 7 (6):2351–6.

Long, F., C. C. Su, M. T. Zimmermann, S. E. Boyken, K. R. Rajashankar, R. L. Jernigan, and E. W. Yu. 2010. Crystal structures of the CusA efflux pump suggest methionine-mediated metal transport. *Nature* 467 (7314):484–8.

Loza, K., J. Diendorf, C. Sengstock, L. Ruiz-Gonzalez, J. M. Gonzalez-Calbet, M. Vallet-Regi, M. Koller, and M. Epple. 2014. The dissolution and biological effects of silver nanoparticles in biological media. *J Mater Chem B* 2 (12):1634–43.

Maher, D., and D. E. Taylor. 1993. Host-range and transfer efficiency of incompatibility group-HI plasmids. *Can J Microbiol* 39 (6):581–7.

Matsumura, Y., K. Yoshikata, S. Kunisaki, and T. Tsuchido. 2003. Mode of bactericidal action of silver zeolite and its comparison with that of silver nitrate. *Appl Environ Microbiol* 69 (7):4278–81.

McHugh, G. L., R. C. Moellering, C. C. Hopkins, and M. N. Swartz. 1975. *Salmonella typhimurium* resistant to silver nitrate, chloramphenicol, and ampicillin. *Lancet* 1 (7901):235–40.

Mijnendonckx, K., A. Provoost, C. M. Ott, K. Venkateswaran, J. Mahillon, N. Leys, and R. Van Houdt. 2013. Characterization of the survival ability of *Cupriavidus metallidurans* and *Ralstonia pickettii* from space-related environments. *Microb Ecol* 56 (2):347–60.

Morones, J. R., J. L. Elechiguerra, A. Camacho, K. Holt, J. B. Kouri, J. T. Ramirez, and M. J. Yacaman. 2005. The bactericidal effect of silver nanoparticles. *Nanotechnology* 16 (10):2346–53.

Mourato, A., M. Gadanho, A. R. Lino, and R. Tenreiro. 2011. Biosynthesis of crystalline silver and gold nanoparticles by extremophilic yeasts. *Bioinorg Chem Appl* 2011:546074.

Muller, M., and N. D. Merrett. 2014. Pyocyanin production by *Pseudomonas aeruginosa* confers resistance to ionic silver. *Antimicrob Agents Chemother* 58 (9):5492–9.

Munson, G. P., D. L. Lam, F. W. Outten, and T. V. O'Halloran. 2000. Identification of a copper-responsive two-component system on the chromosome of *Escherichia coli* K-12. *J Bacteriol* 182 (20):5864–71.

Nanda, A., and M. Saravanan. 2009. Biosynthesis of silver nanoparticles from *Staphylococcus aureus* and its antimicrobial activity against MRSA and MRSE. *Nanomed Nanotech Biol Med* 5 (4):452–6.

Nanotechnologies, Project on Emerging. http://www.nanotechproject.org/cpi/.

Ott, C. M., R. J. Bruce, and D. L. Pierson. 2004. Microbial characterization of free floating condensate aboard the Mir space station. *Microb Ecol* 47 (2):133–6.

Pal, S., Y. K. Tak, and J. M. Song. 2007. Does the antibacterial activity of silver nanoparticles depend on the shape of the nanoparticle? A study of the Gram-negative bacterium *Escherichia coli*. *Appl Environ Microbiol* 73 (6):1712–20.

Panacek, A., L. Kvitek, R. Prucek, M. Kolar, R. Vecerova, N. Pizurova, V. K. Sharma, T. Nevecna, and R. Zboril. 2006. Silver colloid nanoparticles: Synthesis, characterization, and their antibacterial activity. *J Phys Chem B* 110 (33):16248–53.

Park, E.-J., J. Yi, Y. Kim, K. Choi, and K. Park. 2010. Silver nanoparticles induce cytotoxicity by a Trojan-horse type mechanism. *Toxicol In Vitro* 24 (3):872–8.

Park, H. J., J. Y. Kim, J. Kim, J. H. Lee, J. S. Hahn, M. B. Gu, and J. Yoon. 2009. Silver-ion-mediated reactive oxygen species generation affecting bactericidal activity. *Water Res* 43 (4):1027–32.

Perelaer, J., C. E. Hendriks, A. W. de Laat, and U. S. Schubert. 2009. One-step inkjet printing of conductive silver tracks on polymer substrates. *Nanotechnology* 20 (16):165303.

Perron, K., O. Caille, C. Rossier, C. Van Delden, J. L. Dumas, and T. Kohler. 2004. CzcR–CzcS, a two-component system involved in heavy metal and carbapenem resistance in *Pseudomonas aeruginosa*. *J Biol Chem* 279 (10):8761–8.

Poirel, L., J. M. Rodriguez-Martinez, H. Mammeri, A. Liard, and P. Nordmann. 2005. Origin of plasmid-mediated quinolone resistance determinant QnrA. *Antimicrob Agents Chemother* 49 (8):3523–5.

Pokhrel, L. R., and B. Dubey. 2012. Potential impact of low-concentration silver nanoparticles on predator–prey interactions between predatory dragonfly nymphs and *Daphnia magna* as a prey. *Environ Sci Technol* 46 (14):7755–62.

Rai, M. K., S. D. Deshmukh, A. P. Ingle, and A. K. Gade. 2012. Silver nanoparticles: The powerful nanoweapon against multidrug-resistant bacteria. *J Appl Microbiol* 112 (5):841–52.

Randall, C. P., A. Gupta, N. Jackson, D. Busse, and A. J. O'Neill. 2015. Silver resistance in Gram-negative bacteria: A dissection of endogenous and exogenous mechanisms. *J Antimicrob Chemother* 70 (4):1037–46.

Randall, C. P., L. B. Oyama, J. M. Bostock, I. Chopra, and A. J. Oneill. 2013. The silver cation (Ag): Antistaphylococcal activity, mode of action and resistance studies. *J Antimicrob Chemother* 68 (1):131–8.

Rogers, J. V., C. V. Parkinson, Y. W. Choi, J. L. Speshock, and S. M. Hussain. 2008. A preliminary assessment of silver nanoparticle inhibition of monkeypox virus plaque formation. *Nanoscale Res Lett* 3 (4):129–33.

Rosenfeld, M., B. W. Ramsey, and R. L. Gibson. 2003. *Pseudomonas* acquisition in young patients with cystic fibrosis: Pathophysiology, diagnosis, and management. *Curr Opin Pulm Med* 9 (6):492–7.

Russell, A. D., and W. B. Hugo. 1994. Antimicrobial activity and action of silver. *Prog Med Chem* 31:351–70.

Saravanan, M., A. K. Vemu, and S. K. Bank. 2011. Rapid biosynthesis of silver nanoparticles from *Bacillus megaterium* (NCIM 2326) and their antibacterial activity on multi drug resistant clinical pathogens. *Colloids and Surfaces B – Biointerfaces* 88 (1):325–31.

Schacht, V. J., L. V. Neumann, S. K. Sandhi, L. Chen, T. Henning, P. J. Klar, K. Theophel, S. Schnell, and M. Bunge. 2013. Effects of silver nanoparticles on microbial growth dynamics. *J Appl Microbiol* 114 (1):25–35.

Schreurs, W. J., and H. Rosenberg. 1982. Effect of silver ions on transport and retention of phosphate by *Escherichia coli*. *J Bacteriol* 152 (1):7–13.

Sedlak, R. H., M. Hnilova, C. Grosh, H. Fong, F. Baneyx, D. Schwartz, M. Sarikaya, C. Tamerler, and B. Traxler. 2012. Engineered *Escherichia coli* silver-binding periplasmic protein that promotes silver tolerance. *Appl Environ Microbiol* 78 (7):2289–96.

Semeykina, A. L., and V. P. Skulachev. 1990. Submicromolar Ag^+ increases passive Na^+ permeability and inhibits the respiration-supported formation of Na^+ gradient in *Bacillus* FTU vesicles. *FEBS Letters* 269 (1):69–72.

Shahverdi, A. R., A. Fakhimi, H. R. Shahverdi, and S. Minaian. 2007. Synthesis and effect of silver nanoparticles on the antibacterial activity of different antibiotics against *Staphylococcus aureus* and *Escherichia coli*. *Nanomedicine – Nanotechnology Biology and Medicine* 3 (2):168–71.

Silver, S. 2003. Bacterial silver resistance: Molecular biology and uses and misuses of silver compounds. *FEMS Microbiol Rev* 27 (2–3):341–53.

Silver, S., A. Gupta, K. Matsui, and J. F. Lo. 1999. Resistance to Ag^+ cations in bacteria: Environments, genes and proteins. *Metal Based Drugs* 6 (4–5):315–20.

Silver, S., T. Phung le, and G. Silver. 2006. Silver as biocides in burn and wound dressings and bacterial resistance to silver compounds. *J Ind Microbiol Biotechnol* 33 (7):627–34.

Sondi, I., and B. Salopek-Sondi. 2004. Silver nanoparticles as antimicrobial agent: A case study on *E. coli* as a model for Gram-negative bacteria. *Journal of Colloid and Interface Science* 275 (1):177–82.

Sotiriou, G. A., and S. E. Pratsinis. 2010. Antibacterial activity of nanosilver ions and particles. *Environmental Science & Technology* 44 (14):5649–54.

Starodub, M. E., and J. T. Trevors. 1989. Silver resistance in *Escherichia coli* R1. *J Med Microbiol* 29 (2):101–10.

Tappin, A. D., J. L. Barriada, C. B. Braungardt, E. H. Evans, M. D. Patey, and E. P. Achterberg. 2010. Dissolved silver in European estuarine and coastal waters. *Water Res* 44 (14):4204–16.

Thompson, R., V. Elliott, and A. Mondry. 2009. Argyria: Permanent skin discoloration following protracted colloid silver ingestion. *BMJ Case Rep* 2009:1.

Van Houdt, R., and M. Mergeay. 2012. Plasmids as secondary chromosomes. In *Molecular Life Sciences: An Encyclopedic Reference*, edited by Ellis Bell, Prof. Judith S Bond, Prof. Judith P Klinman, Dr. Bettie Sue Siler Masters and Prof. Robert D Wells: Springer-Verlag Berlin Heidelberg, Germany.

Van Houdt, R., R. Leplae, G. Lima-Mendez, M. Mergeay, and A. Toussaint. 2012a. Towards a more accurate annotation of tyrosine-based site-specific recombinases in bacterial genomes. *Mob DNA* 3 (1):6.

Van Houdt, R., P. Monsieurs, K. Mijnendonckx, A. Provoost, A. Janssen, M. Mergeay, and N. Leys. 2012b. Variation in genomic islands contribute to genome plasticity in *Cupriavidus metallidurans*. *BMC Genomics* 13:111.

Van Houdt, R., A. Toussaint, M. P. Ryan, J. T. Pembroke, M. Mergeay, and C. C. Adley. 2012c. The Tn4371 ICE family of bacterial mobile genetic elements. In *Bacterial Integrative Mobile Genetic Elements*, edited by A. P. Roberts and P. Mullany, 1–22. Austin, TX: Landes Bioscience.

Wei, L., J. Lu, H. Xu, A. Patel, Z. S. Chen, and G. Chen. 2015. Silver nanoparticles: Synthesis, properties, and therapeutic applications. *Drug Discov Today* 20 (5): 595–601.

Wolfgang, M. C., B. R. Kulasekara, X. Liang, D. Boyd, K. Wu, Q. Yang, C. G. Miyada, and S. Lory. 2003. Conservation of genome content and virulence determinants among clinical and environmental isolates of *Pseudomonas aeruginosa*. *Proc Natl Acad Sci U S A* 100 (14):8484–9.

World Health Organization. 1996. Silver in drinking water: Background document for the development of WHO Guidelines for drinking water quality. WHO, Geneva, Switzerland, WHO/SDE/WSH/03.04/14.

Wu, H. P., J. F. Liu, X. J. Wu, M. Y. Ge, Y. W. Wang, G. Q. Zhang, and J. Z. Jiang. 2006. High conductivity of isotropic conductive adhesives filled with silver nanowires. *International Journal of Adhesion and Adhesives* 26 (8):617–21.

Xiu, Z. M., J. Ma, and P. J. Alvarez. 2011. Differential effect of common ligands and molecular oxygen on antimicrobial activity of silver nanoparticles versus silver ions. *Environ Sci Technol* 45 (20):9003–8.

Xiu, Z. M., Q. B. Zhang, H. L. Puppala, V. L. Colvin, and P. J. Alvarez. 2012. Negligible particle-specific antibacterial activity of silver nanoparticles. *Nano Lett* 12 (8):4271–5.

Yahya, M. T., L. K. Landeen, M. C. Messina, S. M. Kutz, R. Schulze, and C. P. Gerba. 1990. Disinfection of bacteria in water systems by using electrolytically generated copper:silver and reduced levels of free chlorine. *Can J Microbiol* 36 (2):109–16.

Yang, X., A. P. Gondikas, S. M. Marinakos, M. Auffan, J. Liu, H. Hsu-Kim, and J. N. Meyer. 2012. Mechanism of silver nanoparticle toxicity is dependent on dissolved silver and surface coating in *Caenorhabditis elegans*. *Environ Sci Technol* 46 (2):1119–27.

Yang, Y., Q. Chen, J. D. Wall, and Z. Hu. 2012. Potential nanosilver impact on anaerobic digestion at moderate silver concentrations. *Water Research* 46 (4):1176–84.

Yudkins, J. 1937. The effect of silver ions on some enzymes of *Bacterium coli*. *Enzymologia* 2:161–70.

Zimmermann, M., S. R. Udagedara, C. M. Sze, T. M. Ryan, G. J. Howlett, Z. Xiao, and A. G. Wedd. 2012. PcoE – A metal sponge expressed to the periplasm of copper resistance *Escherichia coli*. Implication of its function role in copper resistance. *J Inorg Biochem* 115:186–97.

8

The Risks of Silver Nanoparticles to the Human Body

Krzysztof Siemianowicz and Wirginia Likus

CONTENTS

8.1 The Use of Nanosilver in Medicine

Antimicrobial properties of silver have been known for many centuries. In ancient Egypt, silver bars were kept in water in order to make medicine for the treatment of ulcers. In ancient Rome, soldiers put silver coins on their wounds to accelerate healing. Probably the first scientifically documented medical usage of silver took place in 1884 when German obstetrician C.S.F. Crede administered a 1% silver nitrate solution to prevent gonococcal conjunctivitis in neonates (Russell and Hugo 1994). Chemical compounds containing silver were used during World War II to treat infections.

Although silver has been known in medicine for a very long time, the history of nanosilver began in the second half of the 20th century. Nobel prize winner Richard A. Frey gave a lecture in 1959 at the meeting of the American Physical Society entitled 'There is a plenty room at the bottom'. He is considered the father of nanotechnology. Nanotechnology is aimed at research that notices, comprehends, measures and manipulates matter at the level of atoms and molecules (Scott 2005). While reducing the overall dimensions of a single particle to the nanoscale, a change of its properties is being noticed and unique physical, optical, chemical and biological properties appear.

Silver nanoparticles often termed nanosilver are clusters of silver atoms ranging in diameter from 1 to 100 nm. In nanoparticles, the relation of their surface to mass is big enough to change the properties of such particles. Nanoparticles have ultra large surface per mass allowing a larger number of atoms to be in immediate contact with ambience. It allows them a quicker and easier reaction with other atoms or particles. At the nanoscale, quantum mechanics plays a big enough role to alter the physical, optical and chemical properties of the particle. Although the term 'nanosilver' is relatively young, this form of silver has been known for a long time as colloidal silver. It took centuries to understand its nature (Świdwińska-Gajewska and Czerczak 2014).

In medicine, silver can be used in various forms: bulk silver, silver ions and nanosilver. The strong antibacterial properties of nanosilver open a wide spectrum of its medical and paramedical applications (Figure 8.1). It is added to numerous products that should present antibacterial properties. Such products include cosmetics that are applied for everyday hygiene such as soaps, deodorants, gels, shampoos and creams. Nanosilver may also be used to impregnate cloth, in the production of socks to reduce odour. Sometimes, it is also used in the production of refrigerators and washing machines. Because of its antimicrobial properties, nanosilver is also used in water-purifying systems. It may be also used to impregnate food packaging. Nanosilver may be a component of paints used to cover walls of hospital wards and operating rooms. It is also used in the production of protective medical cloth, mattresses, bed sheets, gloves and masks. Nanosilver may also be applied in medical equipment, namely, syringes, respirator tubes and surgical tools. A very important medical application of nanosilver is its use

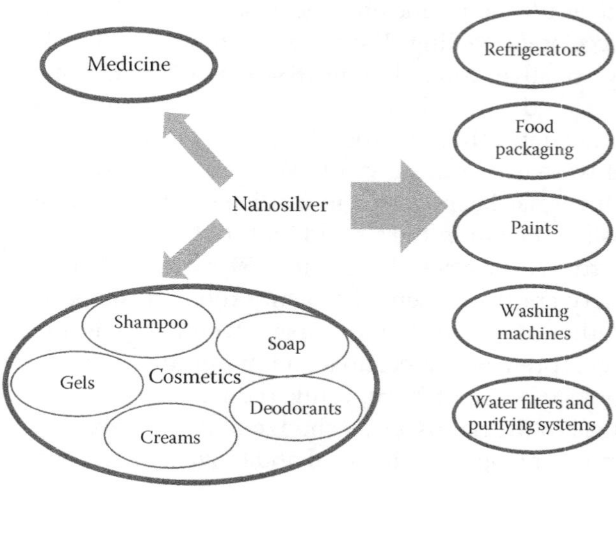

FIGURE 8.1
Nanosilver applications in everyday life.

in fighting infections and treating wounds, burns, ulcers and pemphigus (Figures 8.2 and 8.3) (Benn et al. 2010; Drake and Hazelwood 2005; Lee et al. 2002; Likus et al. 2013; Vigneshwaran et al. 2007).

Silver nitrate as a component of ointments, creams and solutions has been used for a long time to accelerate healing of burns. Nanosilver has also been introduced into this field of medicine. Dressings and bandages containing polyethylene nets with small nanosilver particles ranging from 10 to 15 nm can accelerate healing of burns. Some researchers have proven that this application of nanosilver can accelerate this process by 3 days (Huang et al. 2007). Some experimental studies have revealed that nanosilver treatment can be useful in the treatment of dermatitis and ulcers.

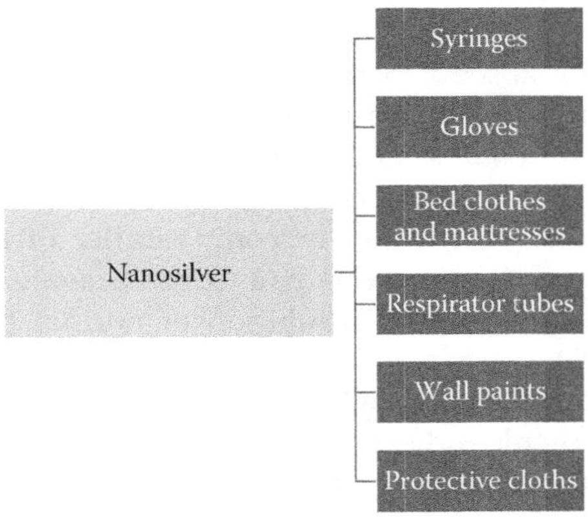

FIGURE 8.2
Medical and paramedical applications of nanosilver (part 1).

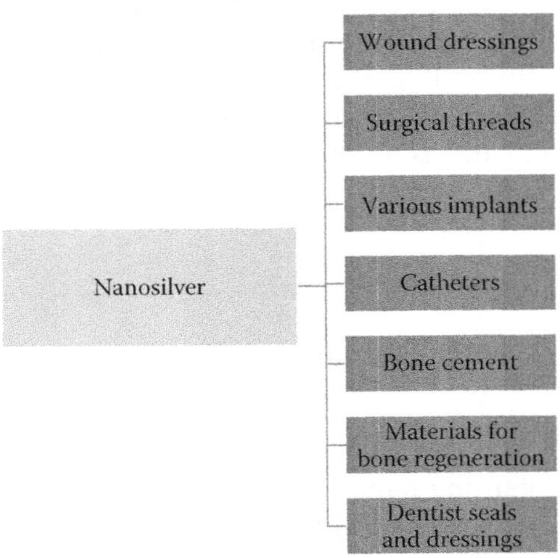

FIGURE 8.3
Medical and paramedical applications of nanosilver (part 2).

Catheters introduced into a patient's body provide an easy access to administer drugs intravenously, collect blood samples or evacuate fluids from various parts in the body (e.g. after surgical procedures). They, however, are a potential gateway for infections. Bacteria can infect catheters, leading to the growth of bacterial biofilms, and in such cases, catheter removal is necessary. *In vitro* testing has proven that plastic catheter tubes coated with a nanosilver layer could be an effective antibacterial tool (Chaloupka et al. 2010; Roe et al. 2008).

Neurosurgical catheters used for draining an excess of cerebrospinal fluid (CSF) can be used as a fully implanted device to drain CSF into the peritoneal cavity or as a temporary external drainage. In both cases, catheters are prone to bacterial infections, which can lead to very serious consequences such as meningitis, inflammation of the ventricles of brain (catheter-associated ventriculitis) or brain abscess. Nanosilver has been introduced into everyday neurosurgical usage because of its antibacterial properties (Bayston et al. 2007; Galiano et al. 2008; Lackner et al. 2008).

Nanosilver was also tested as a coating for prosthetic silicon heart valves. Although toxicity testing showed biocompatibility of these valves, they were withdrawn because of elevated rates of paravalvular leakage. This complication was caused by an inhibition of normal fibroblast function (Jamieson et al. 2009).

Orthopaedics is another field where infections are dangerous and their treatment is very difficult and expensive. Nanosilver has been used to cover both orthopaedic implants and materials used for bone regeneration. An interesting example of the latter approach is the use of complexes of bone morphogenic protein-2 (BMP-2) and nanosilver sized 20–40 nm placed in poly(lactic-co-glycolic) acid. They showed strong antibacterial properties and did not present cytotoxic properties that could inhibit an osteoinductive action of BMP-2. The use of bone cement in orthopaedic procedures presents another risk of infections. Experimental studies with bone cement enriched in nanosilver have provided promising results (Alt et al. 2004). Dental seals and dental dressings can also be enriched with nanosilver.

8.2 Entry Portal of Nanosilver into the Human Body

The wide use of nanosilver in both everyday life and medicine provides an avenue for nanosilver to enter the human body in various ways (Figure 8.4). Many cosmetics containing nanosilver make contact with skin. Absorption through the skin is one way nanosilver can enter the body. The human skin is the largest organ of the body. It reaches more than 10% of body mass and provides a large area of contact with the external environment, approximately 1.73 m^2 in adult individuals. Some materials containing nanosilver,

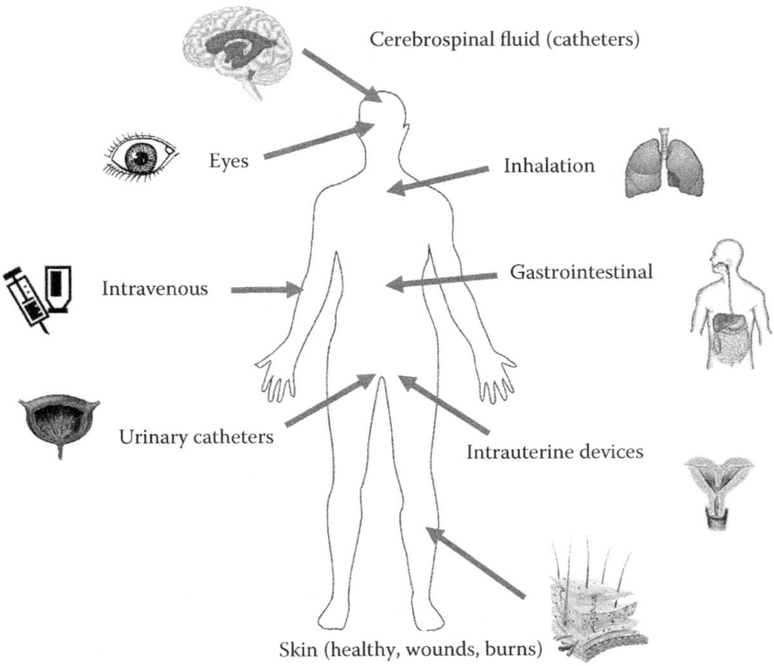

FIGURE 8.4
Entry portal of nanosilver into the human body.

such as clothes, mattresses, bed sheets, socks and masks, may also come in contact with skin. Researchers have evaluated the effects of dermal exposure to nanosilver. In experimental studies, nanosilver was applied to the skin of various animals. The results are not consistent. Kim et al. (2013) observed that rats and rabbits that underwent an acute dermal toxicity test did not present any signs of toxicity. A skin sensation test in guinea pigs showed a discrete or patchy erythema in 5% of the animals. These results classify nanosilver as a weak skin sensitiser. Korani et al. (2011) reported that dose-dependent abnormalities in skin, liver and spleen were detected in an acute dermal toxicity test. A subchronic dermal toxicity test revealed greater tissue abnormalities than an acute test. These results indicate that nanosilver can penetrate the skin and provide organ toxicities in a dose- and time-dependent manner. Similar results were obtained in a subsequent study of this research team, allowing them to make the following ranking of nanosilver organ toxicities: kidney, muscle, bone, skin, liver, heart and spleen (Korani et al. 2013).

Because of obvious ethical issues, an evaluation of the impact of nanosilver on human skin by means of experimental studies could not be carried out. However, researchers can evaluate its influence on cultured human epidermal keratinocytes (HEKs). Samberg et al. compared the influence of various types of nanosilver particles on HEKs. Both washed nanosilver particles and carbon-coated nanosilver showed no significant decrease of cell viability (Samberg et al. 2010). Unwashed nanosilver particles caused a significant dose-dependent decrease of this parameter. All kinds of tested nanosilver particles could be found in cytoplasmic vacuoles of HEKs. Their study indicates that the dermal toxicity of nanosilver depends on the type of nanosilver particle. In the same study, nanosilver particles were applied to porcine skin. Only focal inflammation and deposition of nanosilver on the surface and in the upper stratum corneum layers of the skin could be detected.

Nanosilver is often used for treatment of burns, wounds and ulcers. It may be a component of ointments, creams, solutions or an impregnate of a medical dressing. Although these medicines and materials are intended to be used topically to prevent infections, damaged skin makes the penetration of nanosilver into the body easier. The chemical compounds can penetrate the skin in four ways: intracellular, transcellular and two transappendageal – through sweat glands and through hair follicles. It depends on the physicochemical properties of nanoparticles. Skin absorption depends on many factors, which can be roughly classified into two major groups – based on the condition of the skin and based on external factors. Anatomical localisation results in healthy skin to have various epidermis thicknesses and different skin barrier integrity. The presence of wounds, scratches, burns and skin diseases, such as allergic or irritant contact dermatitis, atopic eczema and psoriasis, affects the skin condition and function. External factors include a contaminated skin surface, irritant detergent and chemicals, mechanical flexion and exposure to physical stimuli such as heat, infrared or ultraviolet radiation. All these factors can increase the dermal uptake of nanosilver (Siemianowicz et al. 2015).

Intravenous entry into the body is usually well controlled when nanoparticles are administered as drugs or imaging agents. However, nanosilver is usually not used in these applications. Nanosilver enters the body when catheters containing nanosilver are introduced into blood vessels, and nanosilver may be slowly released from the catheters to the blood. This route seems to play a marginal role. Nanosilver can also be released to the blood and tissues from various implants covered with it.

Inhalation is also a means by which nanosilver enters the body. It is not a way of medical application of NS, but it may be important in a case of occupational hazard. Workers employed in the production of nanosilver or products containing nanosilver may be exposed to inhalation of nanosilver. People who are also at risk of nanosilver inhalation are those who use sprays containing nanosilver in their work or everyday life. Workers cleaning and maintaining air-condition systems may use cleaning sprays containing nanosilver. Careless use of sprays may increase the amount of inhaled nanosilver (Świdwińska-Gajewska and Czerczak 2015). Quadros and Marr evaluated the risk of nanosilver inhalation in everyday use of sprays containing the material. The results of their study indicate that such a risk does exist and exposure models estimate that even 70 ng of silver may deposit in the respiratory tract during product use (Quadros and Marr 2011). Experimental studies performed on mice showed that subacute exposure to inhalation of small nanosilver particles (sized 3–7 nm) resulted in minimal inflammatory response or toxicity (Stebounova et al. 2011). While discussing the occupational hazards of nanosilver, one should remember that a new form of nanosilver – silver nanowires (AgNWs) – has been recently introduced. In their case, the diameter and the shape of the nanoparticle are important (Theodorou et al. 2015).

Nanosilver can also enter the human body by gastrointestinal absorption. Nanoparticles are used as 'food contact substances' and thus may come in contact with drinking water (e.g. nanosilver being present in various water filters and purifiers). NS present in inhaled air may be dammed by ciliated epithelium in airways and absorbed in the mucosa of airways. During the process of cleansing of the ciliated epithelium the mucus containing absorbed NS can be swallowed. Nanosilver is unstable to oxidation and can release ions through gradual reaction with dioxygen and protons. Gastric juice contains hydrochloric acid that is responsible for its acidic pH and accelerates this process. Silver ions generated in the digestive tract can enter the bloodstream through ion or nutrient uptake channels. Both microparticles and nanoparticles can be taken up in the gut via endocytosis by M-cells in Peyer's patches. Once nanosilver enters the bloodstream, it is distributed throughout the body (Liu et al. 2012).

Nanosilver may come in contact with eyes, mainly as a result of the careless use of sprays or because of occupational hazards. Nanosilver can also be used in some intrauterine devices, creating another gateway. Urinary catheters are another means by which nanosilver can enter the human body. These plausible gateways of nanosilver have not been widely studied.

8.3 Toxicity of Silver and Nanosilver

For a long time, both silver and nanosilver have been thought to be safe antibacterial agents. The only reported side effect of overdose was irreversible pigmentation of skin or eyes termed argyria or argyrosis. Silver deposits in these patients are often localised in skin regions exposed to light. This phenomenon has not been explained until recently. Engineered silver nanoparticles can undergo a profound transformation between the time of their synthesis and the time they reach various tissues and intracellular spaces. These changes may involve adsorption, chemical reaction, dissolution and aggregation. Biological fluids have a wide range of pH. Slight local acidification of biological fluids may take place in some pathological conditions, for example, in infected tissues, and accelerate the release of silver ions from nanosilver. When Ag^+ enters the bloodstream from the gut or diseased skin, it is transported into the blood bound to albumin. Cysteine, methionine and disulfide bridges are the major functional groups involved in the binding of Ag^+ (Liu et al. 2012). Silver ions have a high affinity for protein thiol groups; however, they are easily exchangeable, giving silver significant biomolecular mobility. Sulfides and selenides have a higher binding affinity for silver. Their concentration in biological fluids is lower than that in tissues. When silver complexed with thiol groups reaches the near-skin region, it becomes exposed to sunlight and can be easily reduced by ultraviolet and visible light to metallic nanosilver particles, leading to their immobilisation. These silver deposits can be detected in histiocytes, fibroblasts and multinucleated giant cells of the skin. Transmission electron microscopy showed that these deposits are located inside lysosomes and residual bodies of phagocytes as well in the extracellular connective tissue matrix (Jonas et al. 2007). Unlike ions, metallic nanosilver cannot undergo chemical thiol exchange reactions. These findings put new light on the pathogenesis of an old complication of a therapy with silver compounds and explain why only uncovered skin regions are the favourite sites of discolouration termed argyria (Figure 8.5).

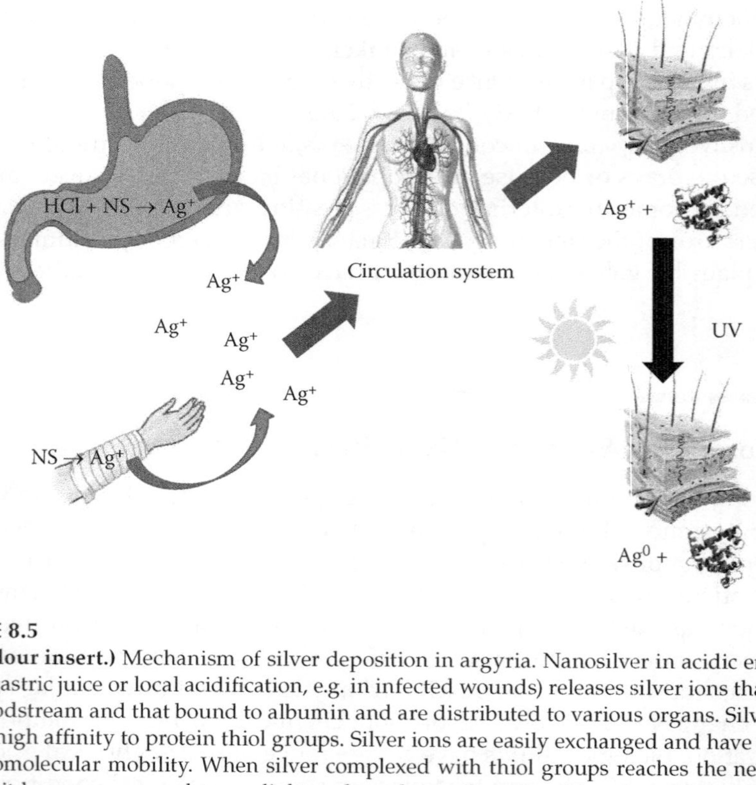

FIGURE 8.5
(See colour insert.) Mechanism of silver deposition in argyria. Nanosilver in acidic environment (gastric juice or local acidification, e.g. in infected wounds) releases silver ions that enter the bloodstream and that bound to albumin and are distributed to various organs. Silver ions have a high affinity to protein thiol groups. Silver ions are easily exchanged and have significant biomolecular mobility. When silver complexed with thiol groups reaches the near-skin region, it becomes exposed to sunlight and can be easily reduced by ultraviolet and visible light to metallic nanosilver particles, leading to their immobilisation.

Deposition of silver in skin is not the only dermatological symptom of silver toxicity. Crosera et al. (2009) analysed studies on the toxicity of nanosilver released from several types of nanosilver containing dressings for cultured human dermal fibroblasts, keratinocytes and other skin-derived cells. Nanosilver crystallines were toxic to both keratinocytes and fibroblasts. Cell proliferation was inhibited, cell morphology was affected and cell viability was decreased. Fibroblasts appeared to be more sensitive to nanosilver than keratinocytes. Ma et al. investigated molecular mechanisms of influence of nanosilver on cultured human dermal fibroblasts-fetal (DHF-f). Their results suggest that nanosilver might cause several cellular damages such as disruption of cytoskeleton and cellular membrane, disturbance of energy metabolism and gene expression–associated pathways (Ma and Huang 2011). Exposition to nanosilver resulted also in DNA damage accompanied by cell cycle arrest. Dermal exposure to nanosilver may also lead to skin inflammatory response (Crosera et al. 2009; Korani et al. 2013). The plausible proinflammatory properties of nanosilver were also evaluated by Martinez-Gutrierrez et al. on cultured human monocytes. An induction of secretion of proinflammatory cytokines and interleukin-6 and -10 (IL-6 and IL-10) was detected. In this study, a relatively low concentration of nanosilver (10 μg/ml) was used, but the nanosilver particles were small, which were known to be more toxic (Martinez-Gutierrez et al. 2011).The chosen size of nanosilver particles could have an important influence on observed results. As monocytes and macrophages constitute an important part of our immune response system, these observations should be taken into consideration while estimating safety issues of prolonged human exposure to nanosilver, in both medical and occupational settings.

Nanosilver can also interact with a coagulation system. The same team of researchers tested 24-nm silver particles. This size was chosen because the range of 20–25 nm had the strongest antibacterial activity among 15 tested nanosilver particles. No influence on the extrinsic coagulation pathway measured by prothrombin time was observed, whereas measurement of activated partial thromboplastin time (APTT) showed an inhibition of the intrinsic pathway of coagulation (Martinez-Gutierrez et al. 2010, 2011). An animal study performed by Shrivastava et al. (2009) showed that mice injected with nanosilver presented a decrease in platelet aggregation. These findings should be remembered while considering an application of nanosilver in patients with coagulation disorders or receiving anticoagulant therapy.

Haase et al. (2011) observed that nanosilver could affect the lipid composition of cellular membrane and its fluidity. In human macrophages, nanosilver also affected their phagocytic ability. Experimental studies have shown that nanosilver can cross the blood–brain barrier and accumulate in rat brains, causing necrosis and neuronal degeneration (Tang et al. 2008). Nanosilver can also accumulate in rodent olfactory bulb and brain after inhalation (Sung et al. 2009). A study performed on cultured rat cerebellum granule cells showed that nanosilver caused an increase of calcium ion uptake into neurons and an increase in their intracellular level. The calcium imbalance was accompanied by destabilisation of mitochondrial function and reactive oxygen species production. This study also showed that activation of glutamatergic NMDA receptor played an important role in neurotoxicity evoked by nanosilver as the addition of a noncompetitive inhibitor of NMDA receptor, MK-801, abolished the increase in the intracellular level of Ca^{2+} and its consequences (Ziemińska et al. 2014).

In cell cultures, nanosilver was documented to be cytotoxic to several types of cells including human alveolar epithelial cell line (A549) and human alveolar macrophage cell line (Ge et al. 2014). However, an experimental study showed that mice undergoing subacute inhalation exposure to nanosilver had minimal pulmonary inflammation and cytotoxicity (Stebounova et al. 2011).

Theodorou et al. (2015) observed that, when inhaled, AgNWs could interact with components of lung lining fluid (LLF) containing phospholipids and surfactants. Some of the components of LLF can modify the dissolution kinetics of AgNWs and induce their agglomeration and finally a generation of a secondary population of nanosilver particles with altered properties. The ability of nanosilver to interact with proteins present in biological fluids seems to be underappreciated. When nanoparticles enter a biological fluid, they become coated with proteins, which may transmit biological effects owing to an altered protein conformation, exposure of novel epitopes or perturbated function (Cedervall et al. 2007). This protein coating is termed 'corona'. Monteiro-Riviere et al. (2013) observed that nanosilver association with various serum proteins purportedly forming different coronas significantly modulated nanosilver uptake into HEK compared to native nanosilver particle uptake. Albumins and fibrinogen as well as lipoproteins can compete to create corona. The nature of protein corona may give nanosilver new important biological properties. It may alter biodistribution, pattern of cellular uptake, biological activity and toxicity (El-Ansary and Al-Daihan 2009; Monteiro-Riviere et al. 2013). The chemical properties of biological fluids can also lead to an agglomeration of nanosilver particles without forming a corona. The agglomeration alters the particle size, with agglomerated nanosilver changing from being a nanoparticle to becoming bulk material (De Stefano et al. 2012). The biological and antibacterial properties and the toxicity of nanosilver are dependent on nanoparticle size. Thus, while extrapolating the results of various experimental studies, especially those performed on various cultured cell lines, one should be careful because the aforementioned procedures for the formation of a corona or for the agglomeration of nanoparticles can take place in a living organism and change the properties of applied nanosilver particles.

Some authors observed that, in experimental animals, exposure to nanosilver resulted in various degrees of liver function impairment. Bigdoli et al. observed that although nanosilver-containing wound dressing accelerated the healing of burns, a significant increase of plasma alanine transaminase was detected. However, liver histopathological examination did not show any abnormalities (Bigdoli et al. 2013). A 28-day oral toxicity test showed that, in rats, nanosilver caused slight liver damage (Kim et al. 2008). Lamb et al. (2010) observed that in the human hepatoma cell line, nanosilver could inhibit an activity of cytochrome P-450 and microsomal NADPH cytochrome c reductase. Hepatic cytochrome P-450 takes part in the metabolism of many xenobiotics, including a variety of drugs. The inhibition of cytochrome P-450 by nanosilver can influence drug metabolism and may be a potential source of drug–drug interactions. Despite the fact that nanosilver is not a drug itself, it may happen if the organism is exposed daily to nanosilver-containing items such as cosmetics and various health care products (Lamb et al. 2010). Albers et al. investigated the effect of nanosilver on osteoblasts and osteoclasts. Silver particles sized 50 nm had a strong cytotoxic effect on both tested cell types, whereas the cytotoxic effect of silver microparticles (3 μm) was weak (Albers et al. 2013). The cytotoxicity was mediated by the release of silver ions. This study also gave an interesting comparison of the concentrations of silver ions necessary to elicit antibacterial and cytotoxic effects. The antimicrobial effect occurred at Ag^+ concentrations that are two to four times higher than those inducing a cytotoxic effect. The results of this study indicate the need for a more detailed research on the safety of nanosilver-covered orthopedic implants and the impact of nanosilver on the biocompatibility of these implants. The plausible toxic effects of nanosilver are shown in Figure 8.6.

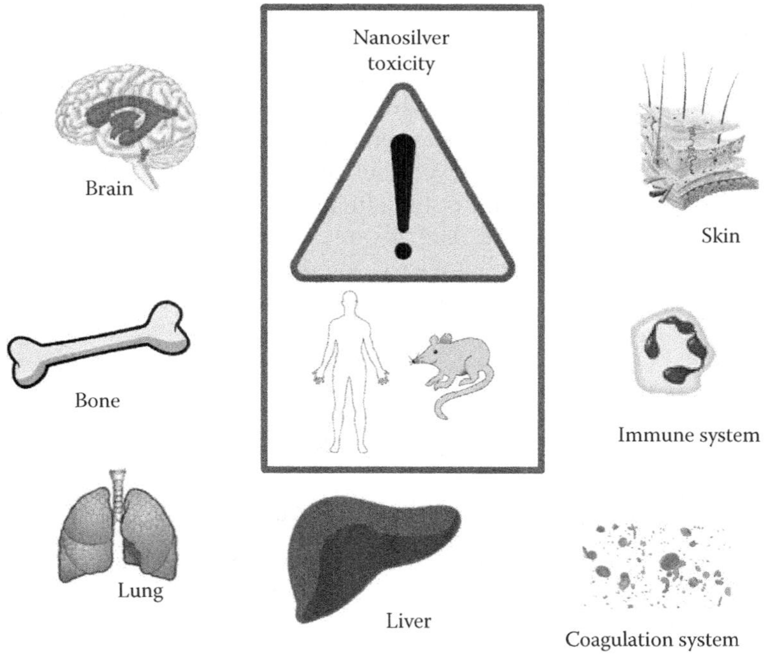

FIGURE 8.6
Plausible goals of nanosilver toxicity.

8.4 Cytotoxic Effects of Nanosilver on Neoplasmatic Cells

Researchers have been interested in evaluating the effect of nanosilver on neoplasmatic cells. Very small silver particles (4.5 nm) presented a dose-dependent toxicity for cultured human osteoblast cancer cells. An IC_{50} of as low as 3.42 μg/ml suggests these nanosilver particles to be more toxic for the studied neoplasmatic cell line than other heavy metal ions (Moaddab et al. 2011). Nanosilver was also shown to be toxic and to elicit a genotoxic effect on human glioblastoma cells (AshaRani et al. 2009). Nanosilver of different sizes was tested in various human neoplasmatic cell lines and was proven to be toxic to human: skin carcinoma, fibrosarcoma, glioblastoma, lung adenocarcinoma, colon carcinoma and hepatoma (Kim and Ryu 2013). Sahu et al. compared the impact of 20 nm of nanosilver on two human cancer cell lines, liver cancer HepG2 and colon cancer Caco2. In both cell lines, nanosilver elicited a dose- and time-dependent cytotoxicity and genotoxicity. Each used an indicator of cytotoxicity and genotoxicity – micronucleus formation, a frequency of binucleated cells with micronuclei or a decrease of ds-DNA content; Alamar Blue reduction assay showed that Hep2G cells were more sensitive to nanosilver exposure than Caco2 cells. The concentration of nanosilver sufficient enough to elicit a cytotoxic effect for Hep2G was 1 μg/ml, whereas for Caco2, it was 10 μg/ml (Sahu et al. 2014a,b,c). These authors observed that in tested neoplasmatic cell lines, nanosilver elicited its cytotoxic and genotoxic effects in a mechanism different from the mechanism that cause an increase in cellular oxidative stress. This observation indicates that the differences in the mechanism of toxicity induced by nanosilver may be largely attributed to differences in types of cell lines used in a study.

Although nanosilver is toxic to various neoplasmatic cells, it is not considered an anticancer drug. Sahu et al. (2014b) indicate that the use of human neoplasmatic cell line cultures Hep2G and Caco2 may be a good model for the rapid screening of the genotoxicity potential of nanosilver. Their results, although indirect, indicate that human liver is more sensitive than colon to the toxicity of nanosilver.

8.5 Exposure Limits of Silver and Nanosilver

The rapid development of nanotechnology creates new fields where nanosilver is used. An increasing number of products containing nanosilver increase the risk of its toxic influence on humans. It requires an introduction of safety exposure limits.

The first attempt to evaluate the exposure limit of silver was made in 1939 when Hill and Pillsbury established a threshold value of 0.9 g silver for a whole life intake. Above this value, argyria could develop (Nowack et al. 2011). Although this value was established 78 years ago, the standard silver level (<100 μg/L) in drinking water in America is based on this calculation. Discussing the toxicology and safety limits of silver, a distinction between three forms of silver – bulk metallic silver, silver ions and nanosilver – should be considered. The American Conference of Governmental Industrial Hygienists established a threshold value of 0.1 mg/m^3 for metallic silver in inhaled air. Many countries have established the same value. This value is the exposure limit in most European Union countries. However, three of them have more severe values: Poland, 0.05 mg/m^3, and Austria and Denmark, 0.01 mg/m^3. In the United States, this value is also the threshold limit established by two other agencies – the Occupational Safety and Health Administration and the National Institute for Occupational Safety and Health. Apart from the abovementioned values concerning 8 h working time, in some countries, there are also limits concerning short-term exposure (15 min). They are higher in Germany and Switzerland (0.8 mg/m^3), in Hungary (0.4 mg/m^3) and in Denmark (0.02 mg/m^3). The next safety threshold limits concerning silver-soluble compounds and silver compounds (both calculated as Ag) in most countries are 0.01 mg/m^3 for 8 h occupational exposure. In some countries, there are also short-term exposure limits for silver compounds, usually 0.02 mg/m^3, but in Austria, the limit is 0.1 mg/m^3 (GESTIS-database on hazardous substances 2015).

Some researchers use other normative values for nanosilver. The authors of ENRHES (Engineered Nanoparticles: Review Health and Environmental Safety) introduced a novel limit value – DNEL (derived no-effect level). It is based on a 90-day exposure study in which rats are exposed to inhalation of nanosilver particles sized 18–19 nm, 6 hours a day, 5 days a week. The nanosilver concentration of 49 $\mu g/m^3$ was the lowest concentration that causes an inflammatory response in lungs. This concentration was set as LOAEL (lowest observed adverse effect level). For lung effects of nanosilver, it was set at 49 $\mu g/m^3$. For 8 h working time, LOAEL is set at another level –25 $\mu g/m^3$ (equal to 300,000 particles/cm^3). Another introduced parameter is NOAL (no observed adverse effect level). As there are two ways of extrapolating LOAEL into NOAEL, the values of NOAEL may differ. This value may be calculated for organs (e.g. lung or liver) or for a whole organism. Another coefficient, OAF (overall assessment factor), is calculated with a consideration of inter- and intraspecies variability and extrapolation of subchronic into chronic exposure. Experts from The Netherlands National Institute for Public Health and the Environment (Rijksinstituut voor Volksgezondheid en Milieu [RIVM]) introduced nano reference values (NRVs) for nanomaterials calculated for both 8 h working time and short-term exposure. NRV is expressed as the number of particles per cubic centimetre. For nanosilver, it is set at 20,000 particles/cm^3. This parameter may be difficult to evaluate as it requires a measurement of a number of particles. With the same amount of nanosilver in 1 cm^3 expressed as mass, the number of particles may be different depending on their size. Some scientists point out that defining exposure limits for nanosilver should be made with special care and that it is difficult as ion release plays an important role in the mechanisms of nanosilver toxicity. Thus, the control of exposure risk factors should be the same as in the case of soluble silver compounds (Sung et al. 2009; Świdwińska-Gajewska and Czerczak 2015).

Various normative parameters have been proposed for estimating safety limits of exposure to nanosilver, and none of them is ideal. The exposure limits mentioned in the beginning of this chapter should be treated as MAC-TWA (maximum admissible concentration–time-weighted average). This value is different in various countries, but in some of them, it is the same as that for soluble silver compounds (which release silver ions). New European Union Regulation no. 528/2012, which replaced the older Biocidal Product Directive (BPD), clarifies that active substances undergo a rigorous hazard characterisation and that any approval for a biocidal active substance will not include its nanoform unless specified (Schäfer et al. 2013).

8.6 Conclusion

Nanosilver represents a prominent nanoparticle and has already been used in many medical applications and has been added in products for every-day use. Since the size and shape of nanosilver and the composition of nanoparticles containing silver (i.e. nanosilver with biomolecule corona) have a significant impact on the biological properties of nanosilver and its toxicity, more attention should be paid to the diversity of nanosilver particles. Nanosilver can induce toxic effects on cells and tissue that are mediated by various mechanisms including oxidative stress and genotoxicity. The specific mechanisms accounting for these cytotoxic effects and their dependence on silver particle size and shape still require further elucidation.

Studies that evaluated risk assessment of nanosilver exposure have shown different approaches. It can also be seen in various settings of exposure limits. This makes it difficult to compare the results of various studies or the exposure limits of different countries. The wide range of parameters used results in differing numerical values; comparing them would thus require much attention and could not be directly made. The rapid commercialisation of nanosilver necessitates meaningful discussion and overseeing the safety of nanosilver use.

References

Albers, C.E., Hofstetter, W., Siebenrock, K.A., Landmann, R., Klenke, F.M. In vitro cytotoxicity of silver nanoparticles on osteoblasts and osteoclasts at antibacterial concentrations. *Nanotoxicology* 7(2013): 30–6.

Alt, V., Bechert, T., Steinrücke, P., Wagener, M., Seidel, P., Dingeldein, E., Domann, E., Schnettler, R. An in vitro assessment of the antibacterial properties and cytotoxicity of nanoparticulate silver bone cement. *Biomaterials* 25(2004): 4383–91.

AshaRani, P.V., Mun, G., Low, K., Hande, M.P., Valiyaveettil. Cytotoxicity and genotoxicity of silver nanoparticles in human cells. *ACS Nano* 3(2009): 279–90.

Bayston, R., Ashraf, W., Fisher, L. Prevention of infection in neurosurgery: A role of 'antimicrobial' catheters. *J Hosp Infect* 65(2007): 39–42.

Benn, T., Cavanagh, B., Hristovski, K., Posner, J.D., Westerhoff, P. The release of nanosilver from consumer products used in the home. *J Envir Qual* 39(2010): 1875–82.

Bigdoli, S.A., Mahdavi, M., Rezayat, S.M., Korani, M., Amani, A., Ziarai, P. Toxicity assessment of nanosilver wound dressing in Wistar rat. *Acta Med Iran* 51(2013): 203–8.

Cedervall, T., Lynch, I., Lindman, S., Berggård, T., Thulin, E., Nilsson, H., Dawson, K.A., Linse, S. Understanding the nanoparticle-protein corona using methods to quantify exchange rates and affinities of proteins for nanoparticles. *Proc Natl Acad Sci U S A* 104(2007): 2050–5.

Chaloupka, K., Malam, Y., Seifalian, A.M. Nanosilver as a new generation of nanoproduct in biomedical applications. *Trends Biotechnol* 28(2010): 580–8.

Crosera, M., Bovenzi, M., Maina, G., Adami, G., Zanette, C., Florio, C., Larese, F.F. Nanoparticle dermal absorption and toxicity: A review of the literature. *Int Arch Occup Environ Health* 82(2009): 1043–55.

De Stefano, D., Carnuccio, R., Maiuri, M.C. Nanomaterials toxicity and cell death modalities. *J Drug Deliv* 2012(2012): 167896.

Drake, P.L., Hazelwood, K.J. Exposure-related health effects of silver and silver compounds: A review. *Ann Occup Hyg* 49(2005): 575–85.

El-Ansary, A., Al-Daihan, S. On the toxicity of therapeutically used nanoparticles: An overview. *J Toxicol* 2009(2009): 754810.

Galiano, K., Pleifer, C., Engelhardt, K., Brössner, G., Lackner, P., Huck, C., Lass-Flörl, C., Obwegeser, A. Silver segregation and bacterial growth of intraventricular catheters impregnated with silver nanoparticles in cerebrospinal fluid drainages. *Neurol Res* 30(2008): 285–7.

Ge, L., Li, Q., Wang, M., Ouyang, J., Li, X., Xing, M.M. Nanosilver particles in medical applications: Synthesis, performance, and toxicity. *Int J Nanomedicine* 9(2014): 2399–407.

GESTIS-database on hazardous substances-DGUV – International limit values for chemical agents. http://limitvalue.ifa.dguv.de/WebForm_ueliste2.aspx (accessed 21 Oct. 2015)

Haase, A., Arlinghaus, H.F., Tentschert, J., Jungnickel, H., Graf, P., Mantion, A., Draude, F., Galla, S., Plendl, J., Goetz, M.E., Masic, A., Meier, W., Thünemann, A.F., Taubert, A., Luch, A. Application of laser postionization secondary neutral mass spectrometry/time-of-flight secondary ion mass spectrometry in nanotoxicology: Visualization of nanosilver in human macrophages and cellular responses. *ACS Nano* 5(2011): 3059–68.

Huang, Y., Li, X., Liao, Z., Zhang, G., Liu, Q., Tang, J., Peng, Y., Liu, X., Luo, Q. A randomized comparative trial between Acticoat and SD-Ag in the treatment of residual burn wounds, including safety analysis. *Burns* 33(2007): 161–6.

Jamieson, W.R., Fradet, G.J., Abel, J.G., Janusz, M.T., Lichtenstein, S.V., MacNab, J.S., Stanford, E.A., Chan, F. Seven-year results with the St Jude Medical Silzone mechanical prosthesis. *J Thorac Cardiovasc Surg* 137(2009): 1109–15.

Jonas, L., Bloch, C., Zimmermann, R., Stadie, V., Gross, G.E., Schäd, S.G. Detection of silver sulfide deposits in the skin of patients with argyria after long-term use of silver-containing drugs. *Ultrastruct Pathol* 31(2007): 379–84.

Kim, S., Ryu, D.Y. Silver nanoparticle-induced oxidative stress, genotoxicity and apoptosis in cultured cells and animal tissues. *J Appl Toxicol* 33(2013): 78–89.

Kim, J.S., Song, K.S., Sung, J.H., Ryu, H.R., Choi, B.G., Cho, H.S., Lee, J.K., Yu, I.J. Genotoxicity, acute oral and dermal toxicity, eye and dermal irritation and corrosion and skin sensitization evaluation of silver nanoparticles. *Nanotoxicology* 7(2013): 953–60.

Kim, Y.S., Kim, J.S., Cho, H.S., Rha, D.S., Kim, J.M., Park, J.D., Choi, B.S., Lim, R., Chang, H.K., Chung, Y.H., Kwon, I.H., Jeong, J., Han, B.S., Yu, I.J. Twenty-eight-day oral toxicity, genotoxicity, and gender-related tissue distribution of silver nanoparticles in Sprague-Dawley rats. *Inhal Toxicol* 20(2008): 575–83.

Korani, M., Rezayat, S.M., Gilani, K., Arbabi Bidgoli, S., Adeli, S. 2011. Acute and subchronic dermal toxicity of nanosilver in guinea pig. *Int J Nanomedicine* 6: 855–62.

Korani, M., Rezayet, S.M., Nigdoli, S.A. Sub-chronic dermal toxicity of silver nanoparticles in guinea pig: Special emphasis to heart, bone and kidney toxicities. *Iran J Pharm Res* 12(2013): 511–9.

Lackner, P., Beer, R., Broessner, G., Helbok, R., Galiano, K., Pleifer, C., Pfausler, B., Brenneis, C., Huck, C., Engelhardt, K., Obwegeser, A.A., Schmutzhard, E. Efficacy of silver nanoparticles-impregnated external ventricular drain catheters in patients with acute occlusive hydrocephalus. *Neurocrit Care* 8(2008): 360–5.

Lamb, J.G., Hathaway, L.B., Munger, M.A., Raucy, J.L., Franklin, M.R. Nanosilver particle effects on drug metabolism in vitro. *Drug Metab Dispos* 38(2010): 2246–51.

Lee, J.E., Park, J.C., Lee, K.H., Oh, S.H., Suh, H. Laminin modified infection-preventing collagen membrane containing silver sulfadiazine hyaluronan microparticles. *Artif Organs* 26(2002): 521–8.

Likus, W., Bajor, G., Siemianowicz, K. Nanosilver – Does it have only one face? *Acta Bioch Pol* 60(2013): 495–501.

Liu, J., Wang, Z., Liu, F.D., Kane, A.B., Hurt, R.H. Chemical transformations of nanosilver in biological environments. *ACS Nano* 6(2012): 9887–99.

Ma, J., Lü, X., Huang, Y. Genomic analysis of cytotoxicity response to nanosilver in human dermal fibroblast. *Biomed Nanotechnol* 7(2011): 263–75.

Martinez-Gutierrez, F., Olive, P.L., Banuelos, A., Orrantia, E., Nino, N., Sanchez, E.M., Ruiz, F., Bach, H., Av-Gay, Y. Synthesis, characterization, and evaluation of antimicrobial and cytotoxic effect of silver and titanium nanoparticles. *Nanomedicine NBM* 6(2010): 681–8.

Martinez-Gutierrez, F., Thi, E.P., Silverman, J.M., de Oliveira, C.C., Svensson, S.L., Vanden Hoek, A., Sánchez, E.M., Reiner, N.E., Gaynor, E.C., Pryzdial, E.L., Conway, E.M., Orrantia, E., Ruiz, F., Av-Gay, Y., Bach, H. Antibacterial activity, inflammatory response, coagulation and cytotoxicity effects of silver nanoparticles. *Nanomedicine* 8(2011): 328–36.

Moaddab, S., Ahari H., Shahbazzadeh, D., Motallebi, A.A., Anva, A.A., Rahman-Ny, J., Shokrgozar, M.R. Toxicity study of nanosilver (Nanocid®) on osteoblast cancer cell line. *Int Nano Lett* 1(2011): 11–6.

Monteiro-Riviere, N.A., Samberg, M.E., Oldenburg, S.J., Riviere, J.E. Protein binding modulates the cellular uptake of silver nanoparticles into human cells: Implications for in vitro to in vivo extrapolations? *Toxicol Lett* 220(2013): 286–93.

Nowack, B., Harald, F.K., Height, M. 120 years of nanosilver history: Implications for policy makers. *Environ Sci Technol* 45(2011): 1177–83.

Quadros, M.E., Marr, L.C. Silver nanoparticles and total aerosols emitted by nanotechnology-related consumer spray products. *Environ Sci Technol* 45(2011): 10713–9.

Roe, D., Karandikar, B., Bonn-Savage, N., Gibbins, B., Roullet, J.B. Antimicrobial surface functionalization of plastic catheters by silver nanoparticles. *J Antimicrob Chemother* 61(2008): 869–76.

Russell, A.D., Hugo, W.B. Antimicrobial activity and action of silver. *Prog Med Chem* 31(1994): 351–70.

Sahu, S.C., Roy, S., Zheng, J., Yourick, J.J., Sprando, R.L. Comparative genotoxicity of nanosilver in human liver Hep2G and colon Caco2 cells evaluated by fluorescent microscopy of cytochalasin B-blocked micronucleus formation. *J Appl Toxicol* 34(2014a): 1200–8.

Sahu, S.C., Njoroge, J., Bryce, S.M., Yourick, J.J., Sprando, R.L. Comparative genotoxicity of nanosilver in human liver HepG2 and colon Caco2 cells evaluated by a flow cytometric in vitro micronucleus assay. *J Appl Toxicol* 34(2014b): 1226–34.

Sahu, S.C., Zheng, J., Graham, L., Chen, L., Ihrie, J., Yourick, J.J., Sprando, R.L. Comparative cytotoxicity of nanosilver in human liver HepG2 and colon Caco2 cells in culture. *J Appl Toxicol* 34(2014c): 1155–66.

Samberg, M.E., Oldenburg, S.J., Monteiro-Riviere, A. Evaluation of silver nanoparticle toxicity in skin in vivo and keratinocytes in vitro. *Environ Health Perspect* 118(2010): 407–13.

Schäfer, B., Brocke, J.V., Epp, A., Götz, M., Herzberg, F., Kneuer, C., Sommer, Y., Tentschert, J., Noll, M., Günther, I., Banasiak, U., Böl, G.F., Lampen, A., Luch, A., Hensel, A. State of the art in human risk assessment of silver compounds in consumer products: A conference report on silver and nanosilver held at the BfR in 2012. *Arch Toxicol* 87(2013): 2249–62.

Scott, N.R. Nanotechnology and animal health. *Rev Sci Tech* 24(2005): 425–32.

Shrivastava, S., Bera, T., Singh, S.K., Singh, G., Ramachandrarao, P., Dash, D. Characterization of antiplatelet properties of silver nanoparticles. *ACS Nano* 3(2009): 1357–64.

Siemianowicz, K., Likus, W., Markowski, J. Medical aspects of nanomaterial toxicity. In *Nanomaterials Toxicity and Risk Assessment*. ed. S.Solenski, M.L. Larramendy, 161–175. Rijeka: InTech (2015).

Stebounova, L.V., Adamcakova-Dodd, A., Kim, J.S., Park, H., O'Shaughnessy, P.T., Grassian, V.H., Thorne, P.S. Nanosilver induces minimal lung toxicity or inflammation in a subacute murine inhalation model. *Part Fibre Toxicol* 8(2011): 5.

Sung, J.H., Ji, J.H., Park, J.D., Yoon, J.U., Kim, D.S., Jeon, K.S., Song, M.Y., Jeong, J., Han, B.S., Han, J.H., Chung, Y.H., Chang, H.K., Lee, J.H., Cho, M.H., Kelman, B.J., Yu, I.J. Subchronic inhalation toxicity of silver nanoparticles. *Toxicol Sci* 108(2009): 452–61.

Świdwińska-Gajewska, A.M., Czerczak, S. Nanosilver – Harmful effects of biological activity. *Med Pr* 65(2014): 831–45 (article in Polish).

Świdwińska-Gajewska, A.M., Czerczak, S. Nanosilver – Occupational exposure limits. *Med Pr* 66(2015): 429–42 (article in Polish).

Tang, J., Xiong, L., Wang, S., Xiong, L., Wang, S., Wang, J., Liu, L., Li, J., Wan, Z., Xi, T. Influence of silver nanoparticles on neurons and blood–brain barrier via subcutaneous injection in rats. *Appl Surf Sci* 255(2008): 502–4.

Theodorou, I.G., Botelho, D., Schwander, S., Zhang, J., Chung, K.F., Tetley, T.D., Shaffer, M.S., Gow, A., Ryan, M.P., Porter, A.E. Static and dynamic microscopy of the chemical stability and aggregation state of silver nanowires in components of murine pulmonary surfactant. *Environ Sci Technol* 49(2015): 8048–56.

Vigneshwaran, N., Kathe, A.A., Varadarajan, P.V., Nachane, R.P., Balasubramanya, R.H. Functional finishing of cotton fabrics using silver nanoparticles. *J Nanosci Nanotechnol* 7(2007): 1893–7.

Ziemińska, E., Stafiej, A., Strużyńska, L. The role of the glutamatergic NMDA receptor in nanosilver-evoked neurotoxicity in primary cultures of cerebellar granule cells. *Toxicology* 315(2014): 38–48.

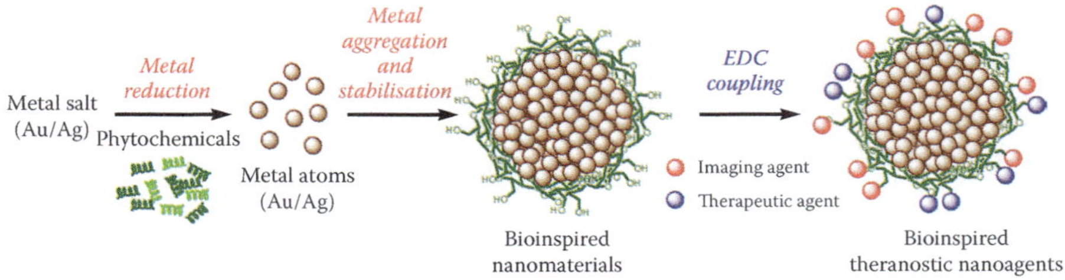

SCHEME 1.1
Diagrammatic representation of bioinspired synthesis and surface functionalisation of the theranostic nanoagents. (Reproduced with permission from Bhaumik, Thakur et al. *ACS Biomat Sci Eng*, 1:382–392. Copyright 2015 American Chemical Society.)

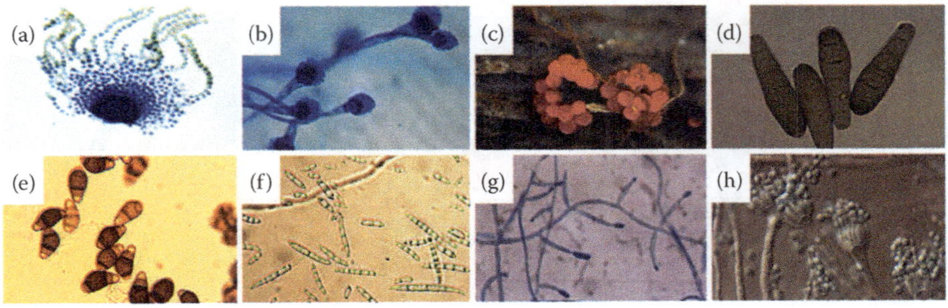

FIGURE 1.1
Image of fungi used in the biosynthesis of AgNPs: (a) *Aspergillus flavus*, (b) *Aspergillus fumigatus*, (c) *Bionectria ochroleuca*, (d) *Bipolaris nodulosa*, (e) *Cochliobolus lunatus*, (f) *Fusarium oxysporum*, (g) *Fusarium semitectum*, (h) *Penicillium fellutanum*. (Picture courtesy of Google images.)

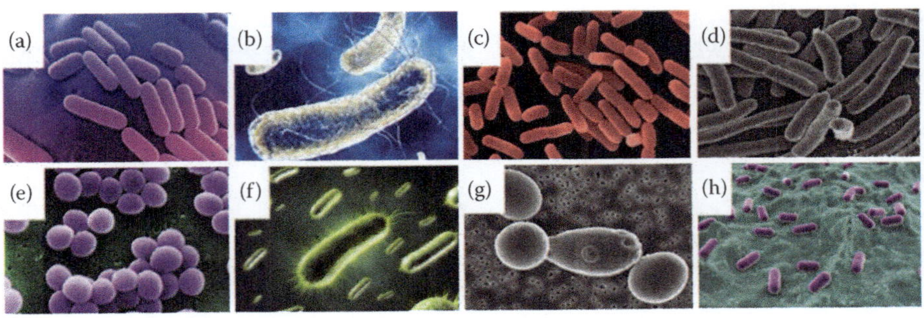

FIGURE 1.2
Image of bacteria used in the biosynthesis of AgNPs: (a) *Klebsiella pneumonia*, (b) *Bacillus licheniformis*, (c) *Bacillus subtilis*, (d) *Escherichia coli*, (e) *Staphylococcus aureus*, (f) *Bacillus cereus*, (g) *Saccharomyces boulardii*, (h) *Lactobacillus* strains. (Picture courtesy of Google images.)

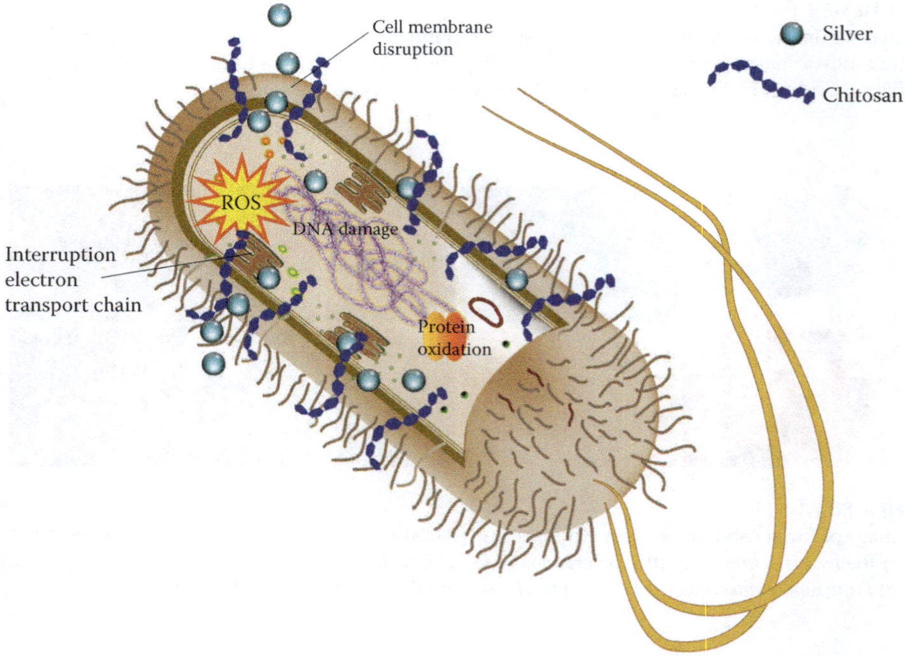

FIGURE 3.6
The synergistic antimicrobial effect of chitosan and nanoparticle silver. Chitosan increases the permeability of the bacterial outer membrane, which would allow the silver nanoparticles to penetrate into the bacterial cells. Silver ions bind the bacterial DNA with subsequent DNA damage, protein oxidation and interruption of the electron transport chain.

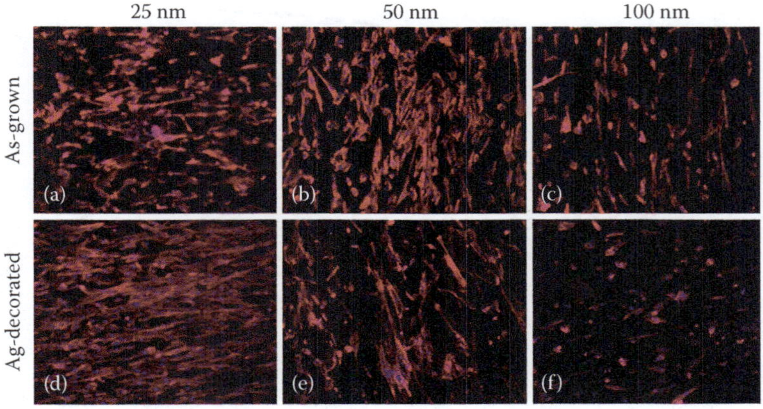

FIGURE 4.8
Fluorescence microscopy images of human fibroblasts attached to the as-grown (a through c) and Ag-decorated (d through f) TiO_2 NTs with different diameters. The red fluorescence indicates cytoskeletal actin and the blue fluorescence indicates cell nuclei. For both as-grown and Ag-decorated TiO_2 NTs, longer and better-defined actin cytoskeleton and a higher density of fibroblasts are observed from NTs with a smaller diameter.

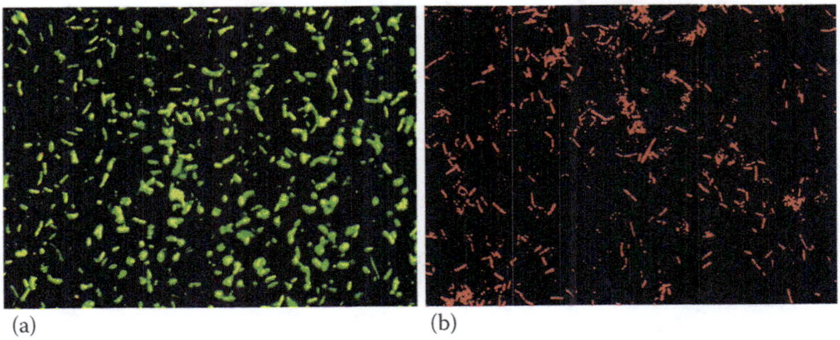

FIGURE 5.6
Fluorescence micrograph of *P. aeruginosa* after being treated with the nanocomposites for 0 (a) and 20 min (b), respectively. (Reprinted with permission from Mei, L., Lu, Z. T., Zhang, X. G., Li, C. X., Jia, Y. X. Polymer–Ag nanocomposites with enhanced antimicrobial activity against bacterial infection. *ACS Appl Mater Inter* 6(2014): 15813–15821. Copyright 2014 American Chemical Society.)

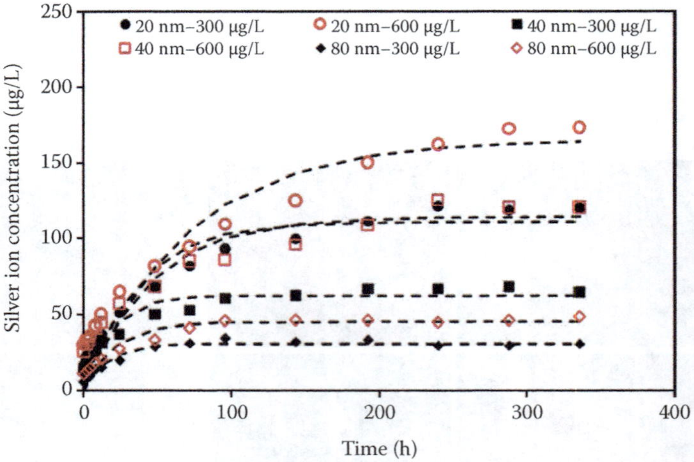

FIGURE 6.2
Kinetics of Ag^+ release from Ag nanoparticles in Hoagland medium; the model fits by Equation 6.4 are shown by the dashed lines. (From Zhang, W. et al., *Environmental Science & Technology* 45(10) (2011): 4422–4428.)

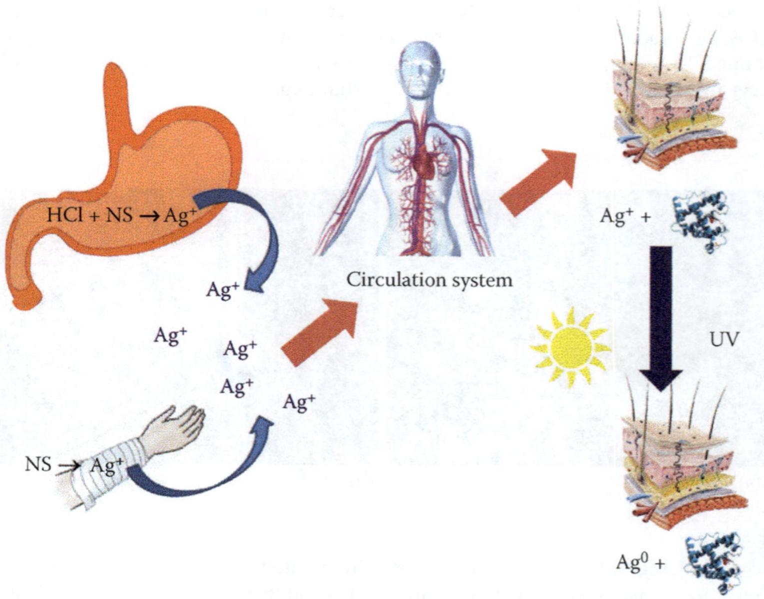

FIGURE 8.5
Mechanism of silver deposition in argyria. Nanosilver in acidic environment (gastric juice or local acidification, e.g. in infected wounds) releases silver ions that enter the bloodstream and that bound to albumin and are distributed to various organs. Silver ions have a high affinity to protein thiol groups. Silver ions are easily exchanged and have significant biomolecular mobility. When silver complexed with thiol groups reaches the near-skin region, it becomes exposed to sunlight and can be easily reduced by ultraviolet and visible light to metallic nanosilver particles, leading to their immobilisation.

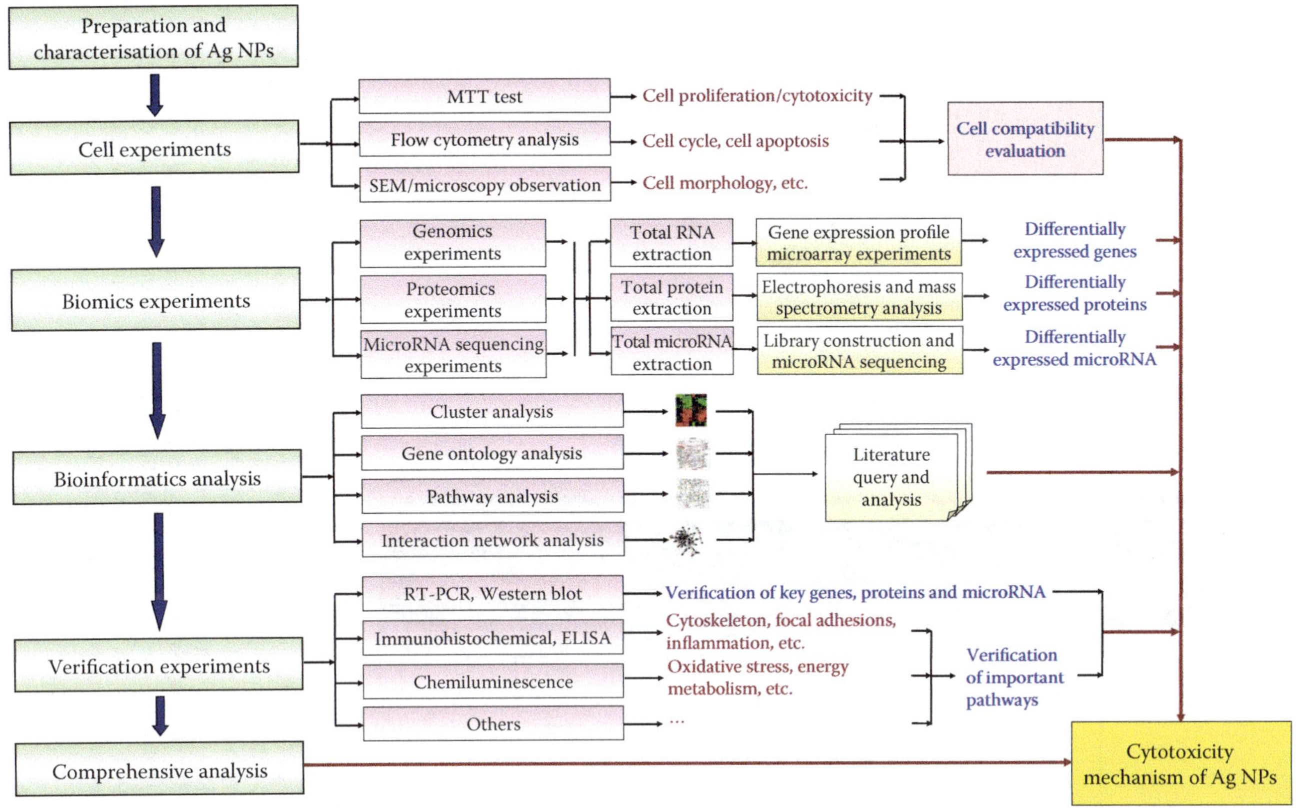

FIGURE 10.1
The research route for investigating the cytotoxicity mechanism of Ag NPs based on biomics and bioinformatics technologies. (From Lü, X.Y. et al., *Journal of Inorganic Materials* 28(2013):21–8.)

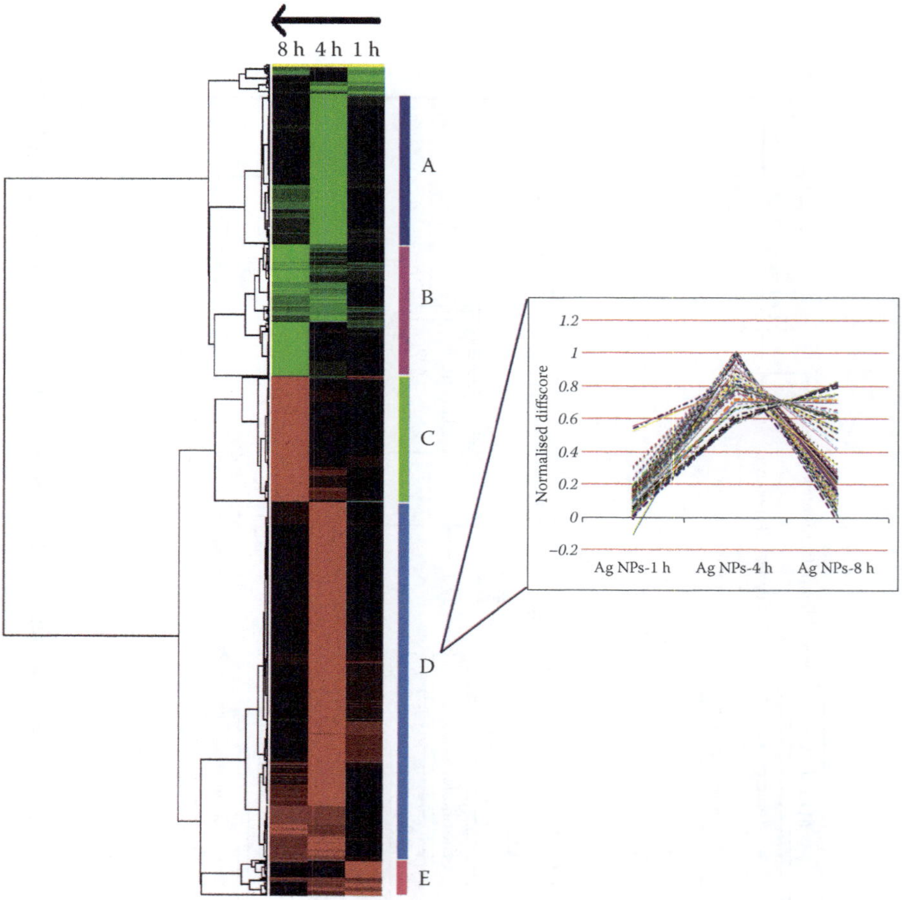

FIGURE 10.2
Global view of expression patterns of 1593 differentially expressed genes by hierarchical clustering analysis. The left heat map is the hierarchical clustering diagram, each row represents the expression level for one gene during the treatment and each column represents a time point. The intensity of red/green represents the magnitude of change in expression for each gene. Red means that the gene was up-regulated, while green means that the gene was down-regulated. Five clusters that demonstrate specific expression patterns during the entire treatment were regarded as clusters A, B, C, D and E; the zoomed-in view was a sketch diagram of expression pattern for cluster D, representing the expression trend over time. (From Ma, J.W. et al., *Journal of Biomedical Nanotechnology* 7(2011):263–75.)

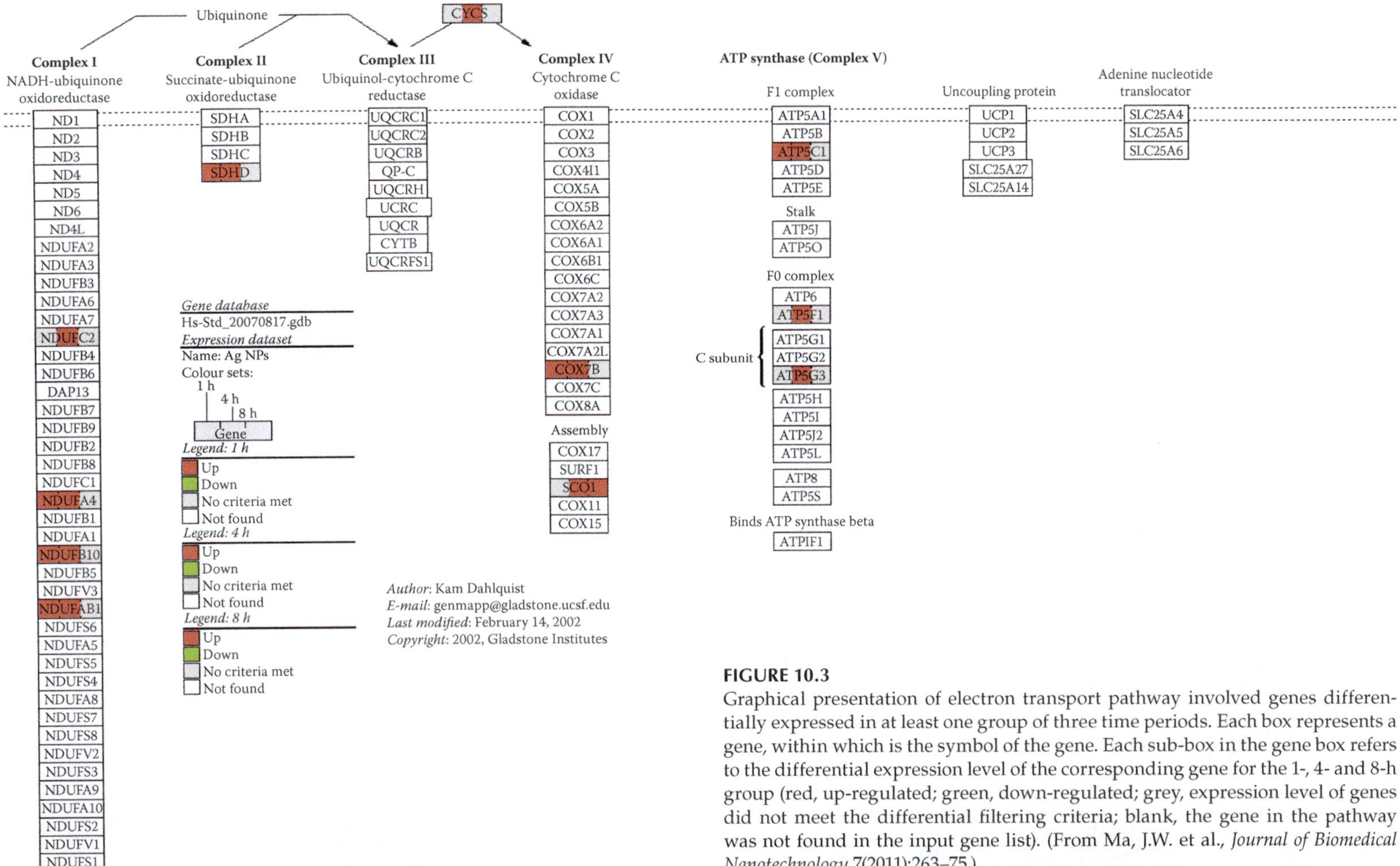

FIGURE 10.3

Graphical presentation of electron transport pathway involved genes differentially expressed in at least one group of three time periods. Each box represents a gene, within which is the symbol of the gene. Each sub-box in the gene box refers to the differential expression level of the corresponding gene for the 1-, 4- and 8-h group (red, up-regulated; green, down-regulated; grey, expression level of genes did not meet the differential filtering criteria; blank, the gene in the pathway was not found in the input gene list). (From Ma, J.W. et al., *Journal of Biomedical Nanotechnology* 7(2011):263–75.)

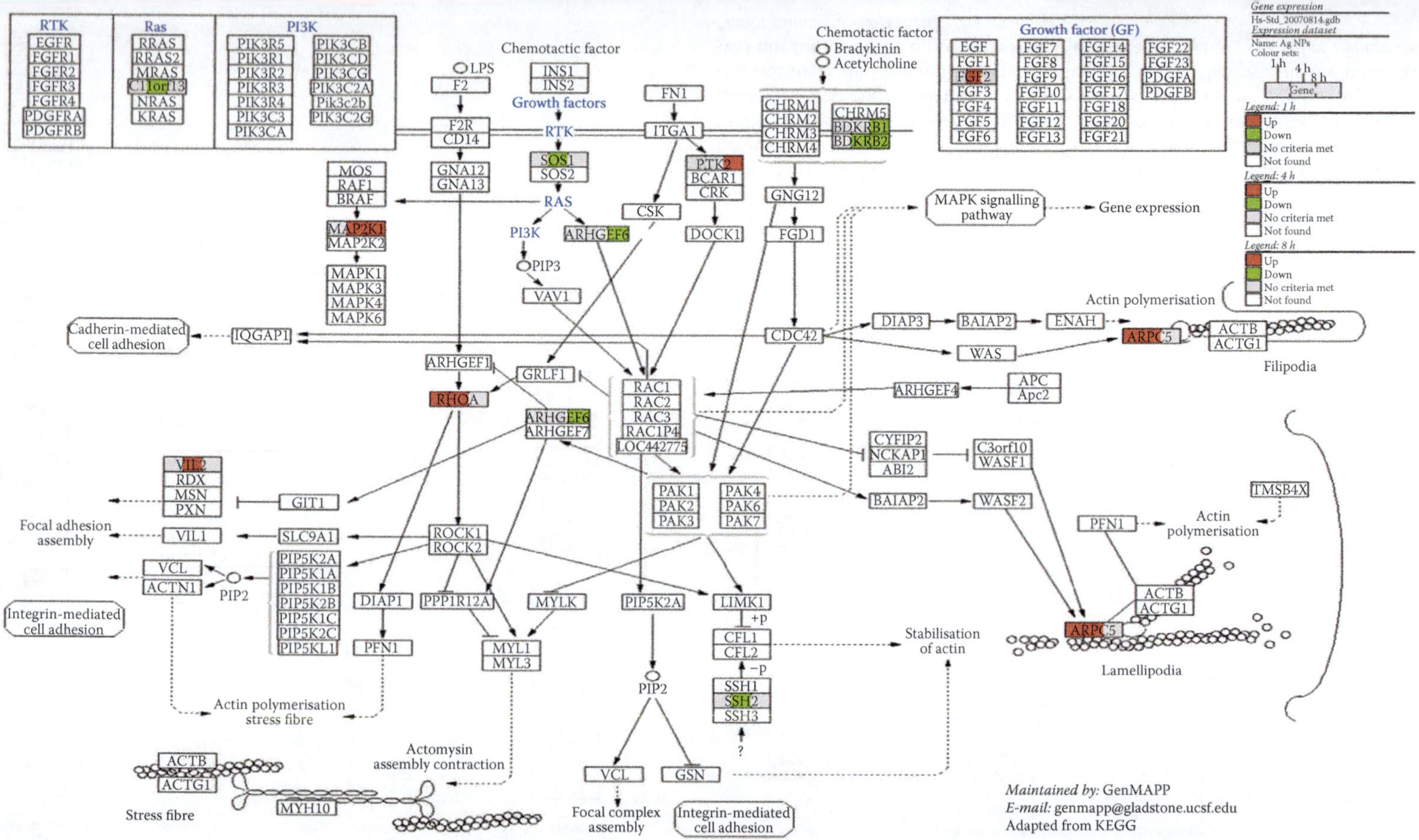

FIGURE 10.4

Graphical presentation of regulation of the actin cytoskeleton pathway involved genes differentially expressed in at least one group of three time periods. Each box represents a gene, within which is the symbol of the gene. Each sub-box in the gene box refers to the differential expression level of the corresponding gene for the 1-, 4- and 8-h group. (From Ma, J.W. et al., *Journal of Biomedical Nanotechnology* 7(2011):263–75.)

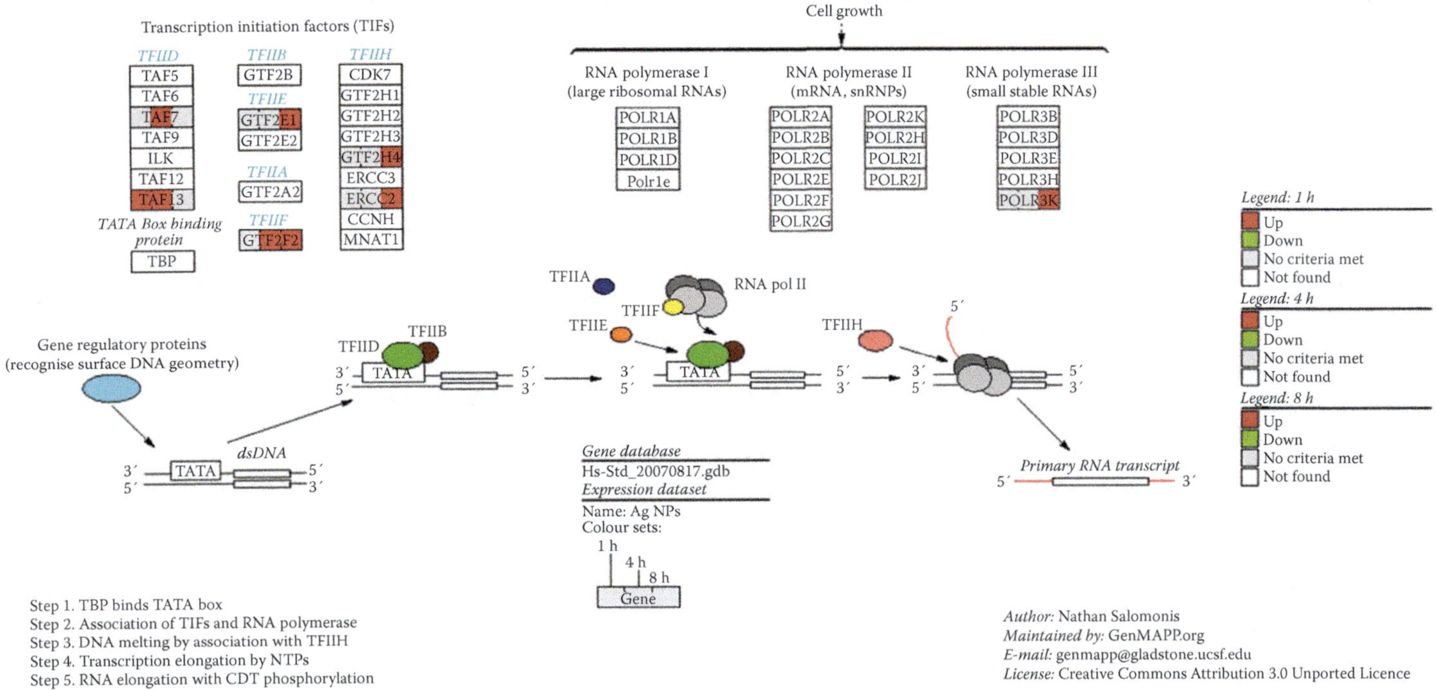

(a)

FIGURE 10.5
Graphical presentation of regulation of four pathways associated with gene expression processes. (a) Eukaryotic transcription initiation pathway. Each box represents a gene, within which is the symbol of the gene. Each sub-box in the gene box refers to the differential expression level of the corresponding gene for the 1-, 4- and 8-h group. *(Continued)*

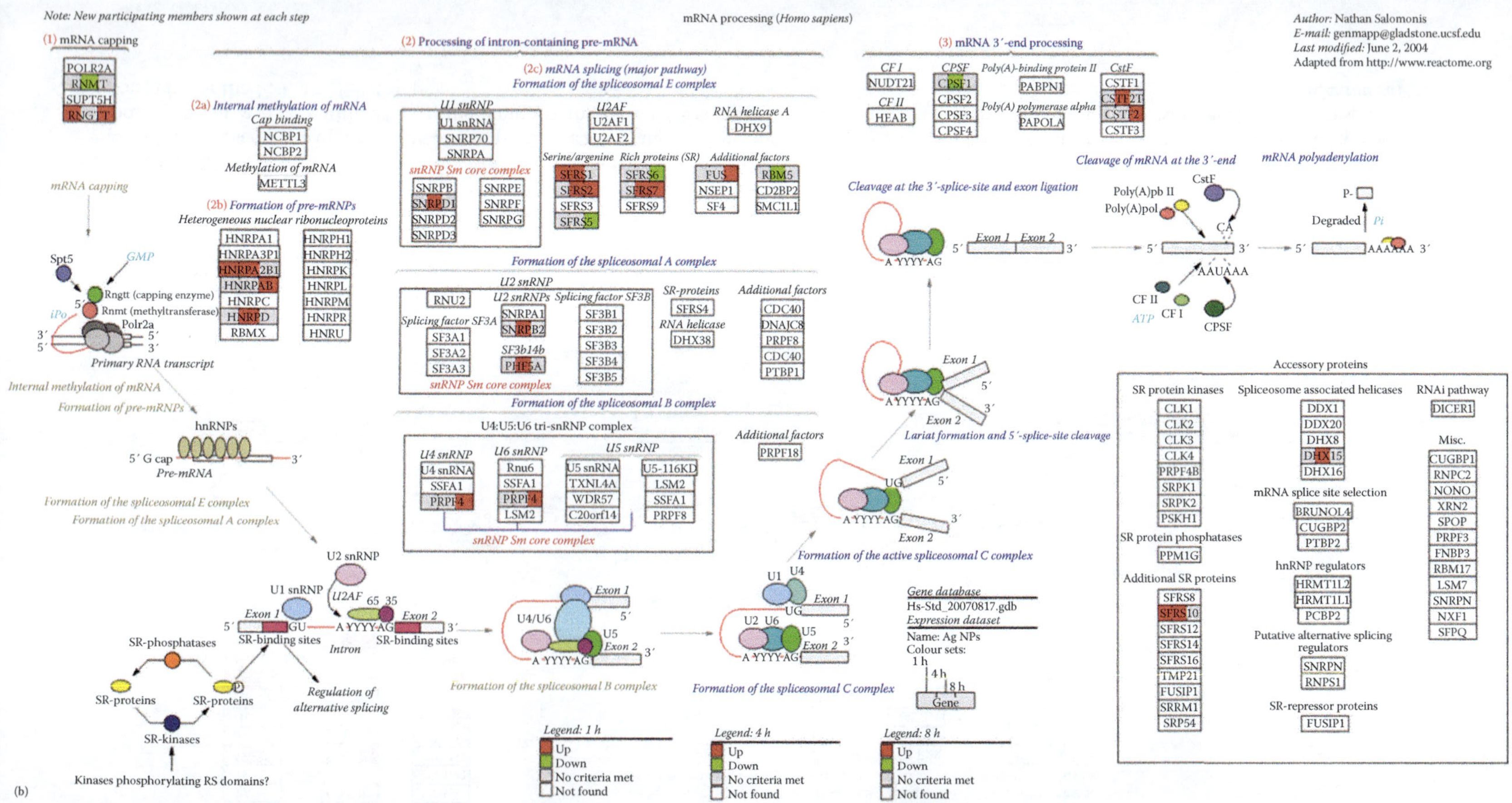

FIGURE 10.5 (CONTINUED)

Graphical presentation of regulation of four pathways associated with gene expression processes. (b) mRNA processing pathway. Each box represents a gene, within which is the symbol of the gene. Each sub-box in the gene box refers to the differential expression level of the corresponding gene for the 1-, 4- and 8-h group. *(Continued)*

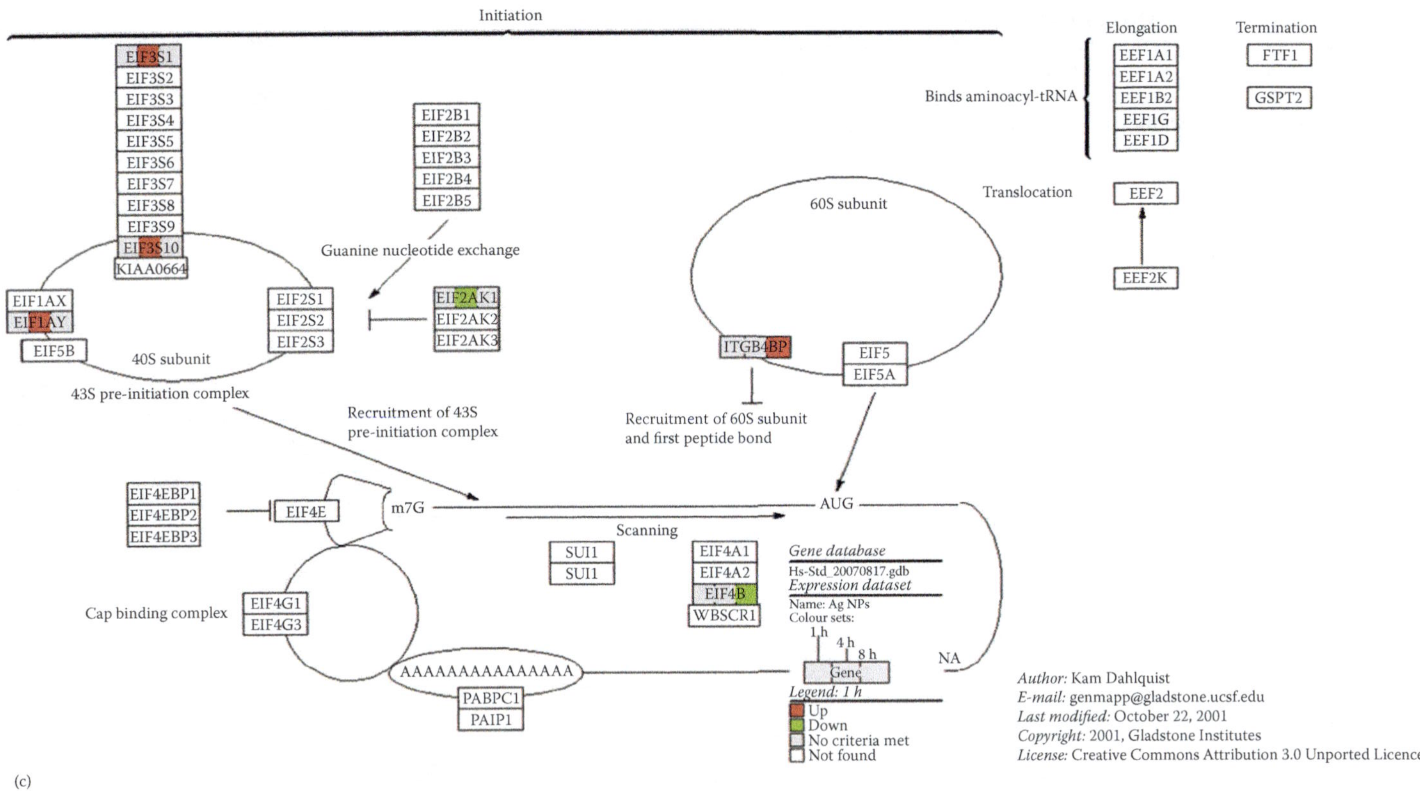

FIGURE 10.5 (CONTINUED)
Graphical presentation of regulation of four pathways associated with gene expression processes. (c) Translation factors pathway. Each box represents a gene, within which is the symbol of the gene. Each sub-box in the gene box refers to the differential expression level of the corresponding gene for the 1-, 4- and 8-h group.

(Continued)

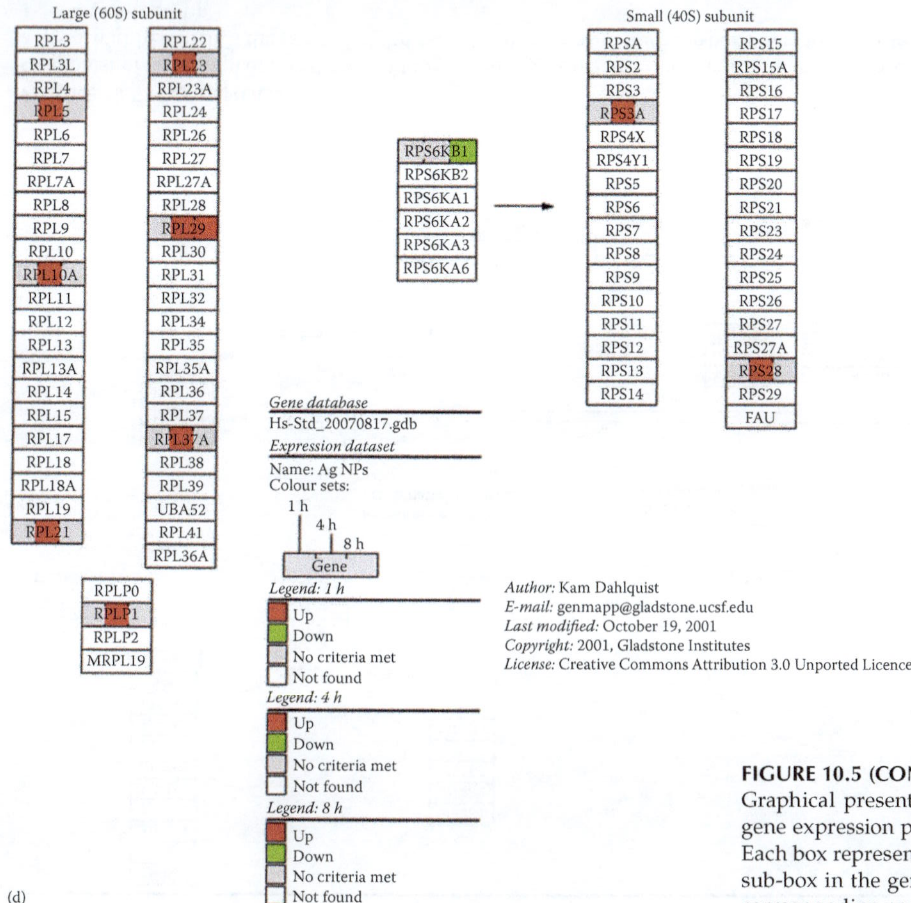

(d)

FIGURE 10.5 (CONTINUED)
Graphical presentation of regulation of four pathways associated with gene expression processes. (d) Cytoplasmic ribosomal proteins pathway. Each box represents a gene, within which is the symbol of the gene. Each sub-box in the gene box refers to the differential expression level of the corresponding gene for the 1-, 4- and 8-h group.

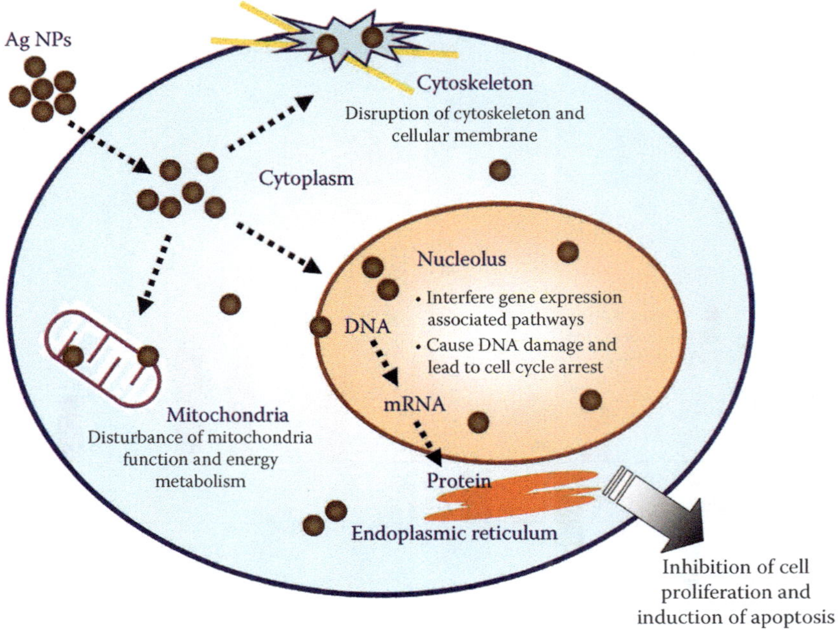

FIGURE 10.6
The proposed molecular mechanism of the Ag NP–cell interaction. (From Ma, J.W. et al., *Journal of Biomedical Nanotechnology* 7(2011):263–75.)

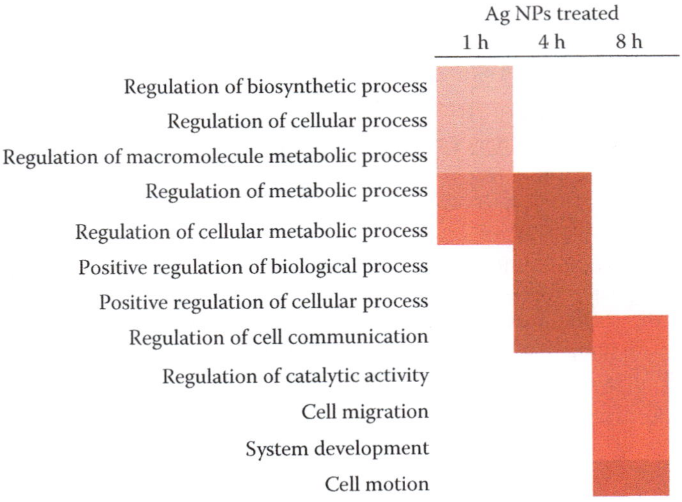

FIGURE 10.8
The enriched biological process GO categories of the miRNA target mRNAs and target proteins that matched HDFs treated with 200 μM Ag NPs for 1, 4 and 8 h. Each GO category was represented by a single row of red boxes, and each time point was represented by a single column. The depth of red represents the p value of the categories; a deeper colour indicates a smaller p value. A smaller p value indicates a higher correlation between the specific GO category and the target mRNAs and target proteins. (From Huang, Y. et al., *Journal of Biomedical Nanotechnology* 10(2014):3304–17.)

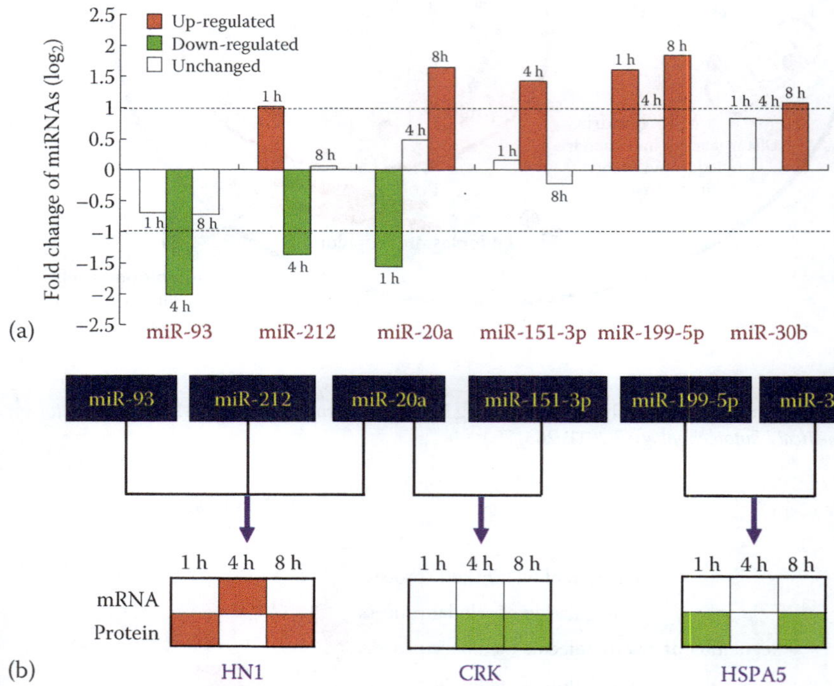

FIGURE 10.9
(a) The expression of six miRNAs identified by SOLiD sequencing. The two dotted lines mark the up-regulated (upper line, fold change = 2) and down-regulated (lower line, fold change = 0.5) threshold limits. The *y* axis refers to the relative expression levels in 200 μM Ag NP–treated HDFs compared to the control. (b) The regulatory relationships of six miRNAs to three target mRNA–protein pairs. (From Huang, Y. et al., *Journal of Biomedical Nanotechnology* 10(2014):3304–17.)

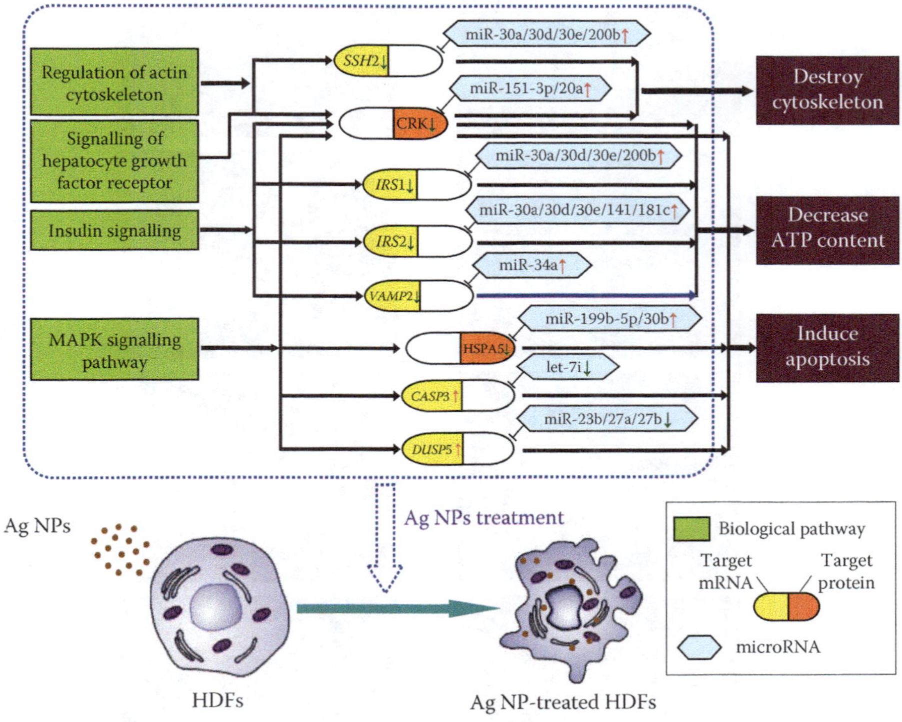

FIGURE 10.10
The four key pathways identified by differentially expressed miRNAs and regulated target mRNAs and target proteins that participated in the toxicity of 200 μM Ag NPs in HDFs. (From Huang, Y. et al., *Journal of Biomedical Nanotechnology* 10(2014):3304–17.)

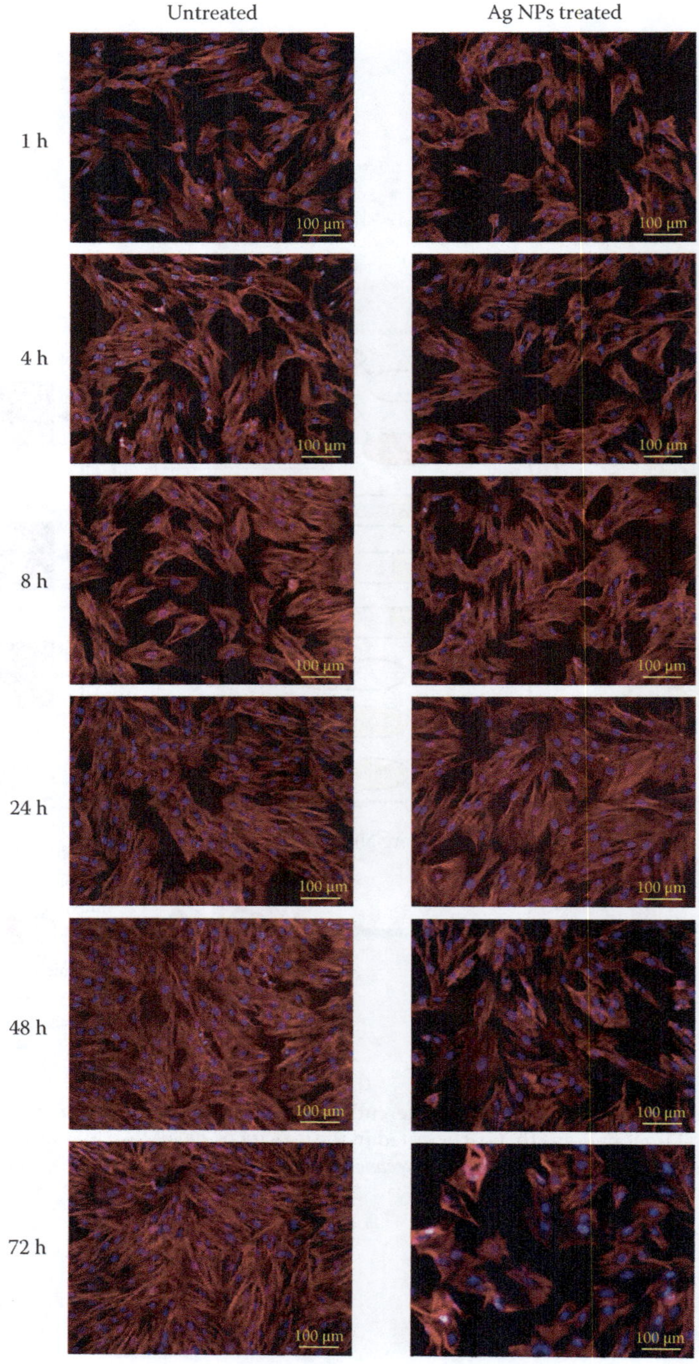

FIGURE 10.11
Fluorescence microscopy images of HDFs showing F-actin (red) and cell nuclei (blue). The left-hand column contains the images of untreated cells, while the right-hand column contains the images of cells treated with 200 μM Ag NPs. The scale bars correspond to 100 μm. (From Huang, Y. et al., *Journal of Biomedical Nanotechnology* 10(2014):3304–17.)

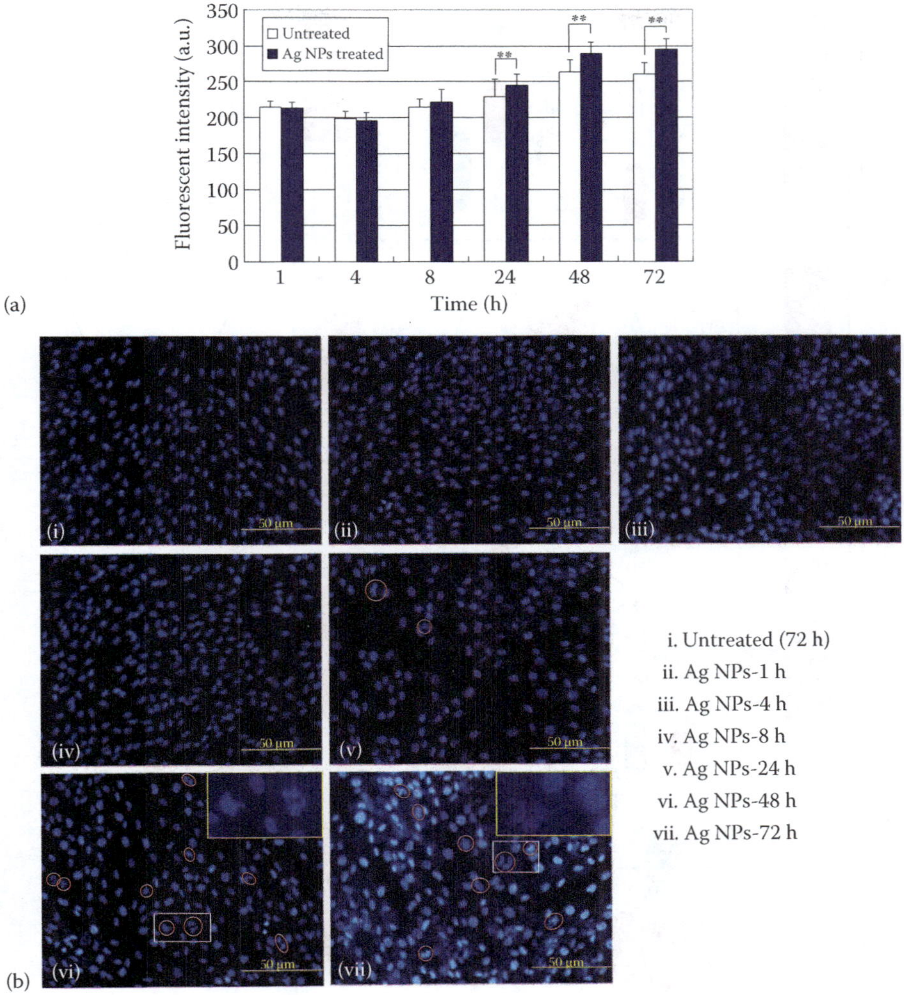

FIGURE 10.13
HDF apoptosis induced by 200 μM Ag NPs. (a) Fluorescence intensity of Hoechst 33342 in HDFs. $^{**}p < 0.01$. (b) Fluorescence microscopy images of HDFs stained with Hoechst 33342 for nuclei (blue colour) (original magnification ×200, inset ×400). The red circle indicates the apoptotic cell nuclei. The scale bars correspond to 50 μm. (From Huang, Y. et al., *Journal of Biomedical Nanotechnology* 10(2014):3304–17.)

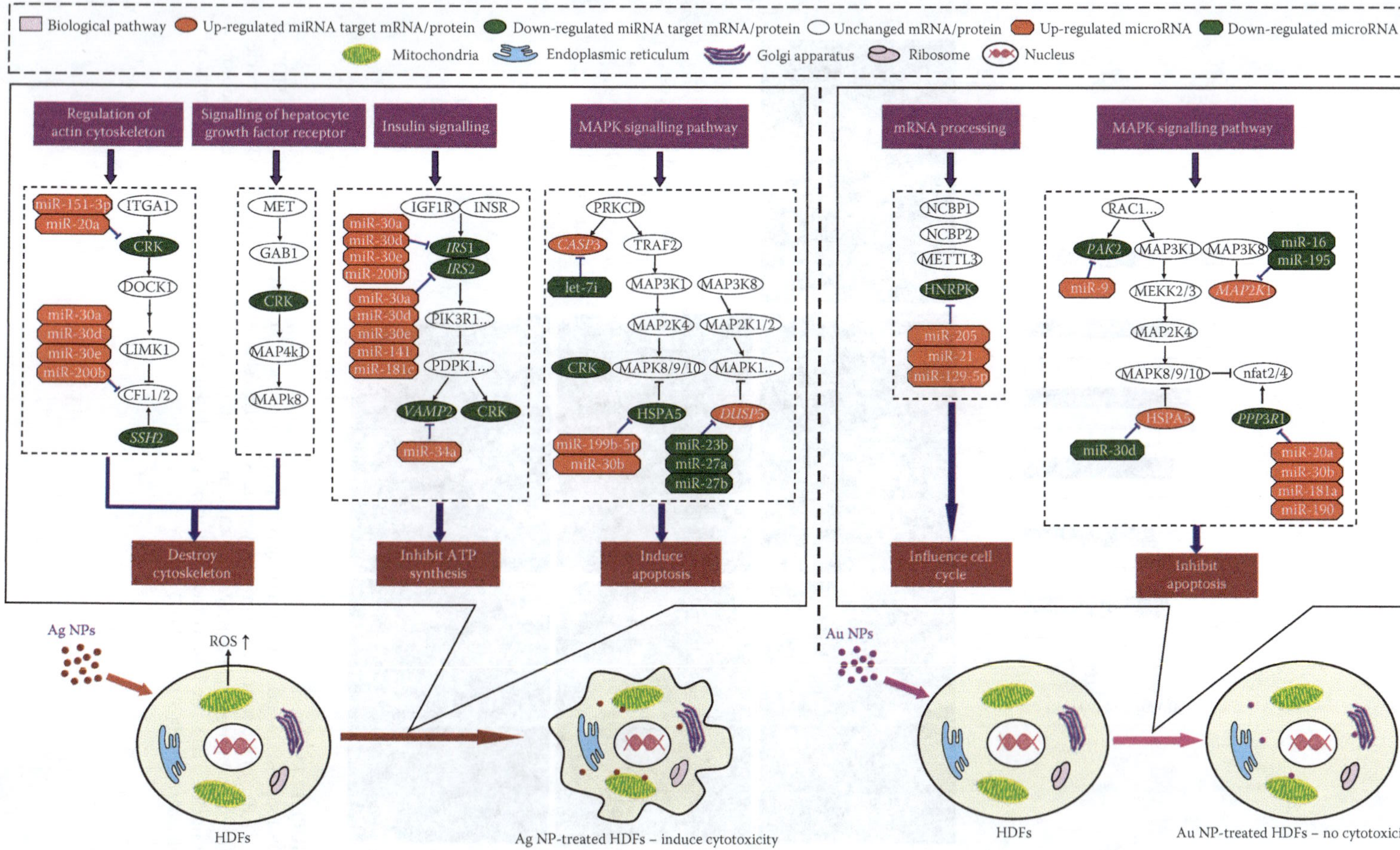

FIGURE 10.15
Comparison of the interaction mechanisms of Ag NPs and Au NPs on HDFs. (From Huang, Y. et al., *Biomaterials* 37(2015):13–24.)

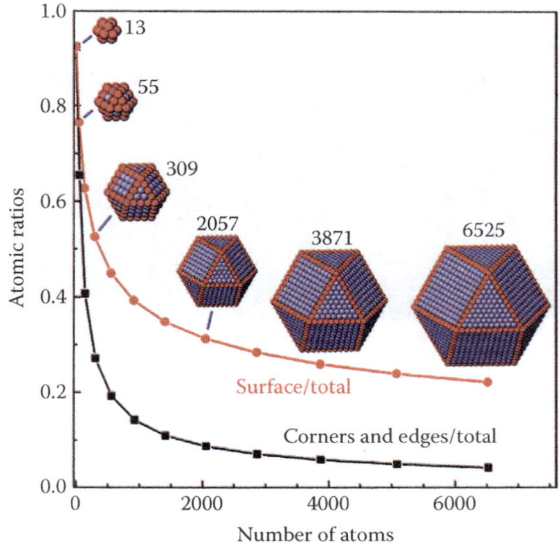

FIGURE 12.3
Reducing particle size results in an increased ratio of the surface atoms to the total number of atoms (red circles) and the atoms at corner and edge sites to the total number of atoms (black squares), calculated by using the cuboctahedron-shaped FCC model. (Adapted from *Surf Sci Rep*, 70, Cuenya, B. and Behafarid, F., Nanocatalysis: Size- and shape-dependent chemisorption and catalytic reactivity, 135–87, Copyright 2015, with permission from Elsevier.)

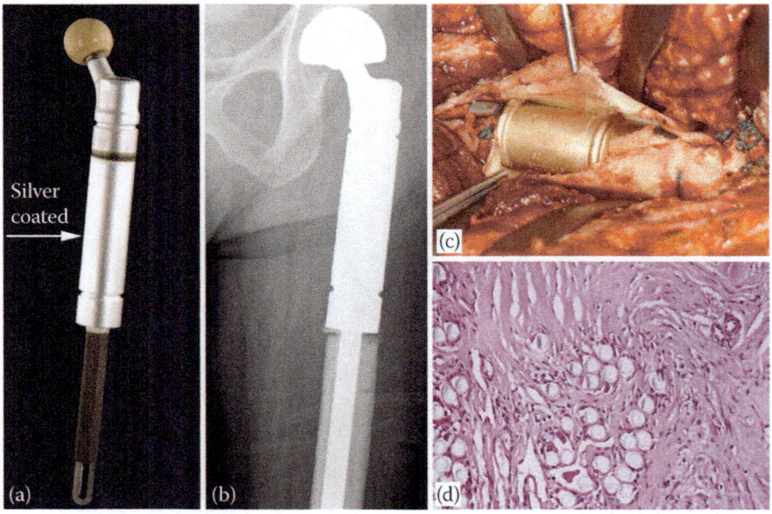

FIGURE 12.5
(a) The corpus of the megaprosthesis was elementary-silver coated (the arrow) and the stem was not treated; (b) x-ray of the silver-coated implant placed in bone; (c) a picture of a silver-coated proximal femur replacement showing no signs of corrosion, local inflammation and argyria at 7 months postoperation; (d) histopathological view of the periprosthetic environment (stained by the hematoxylin and eosin assay) showing ingrowth of the polyethylenterepthalate tube in the surrounding tissue without any foreign body granulomas or silver particle depositions. (Adapted from *Biomaterials*, 28, Hardes, J. et al., Lack of toxicological side-effects in silver-coated megaprostheses in humans, 2869–75, Copyright 2007, with permission from Elsevier.)

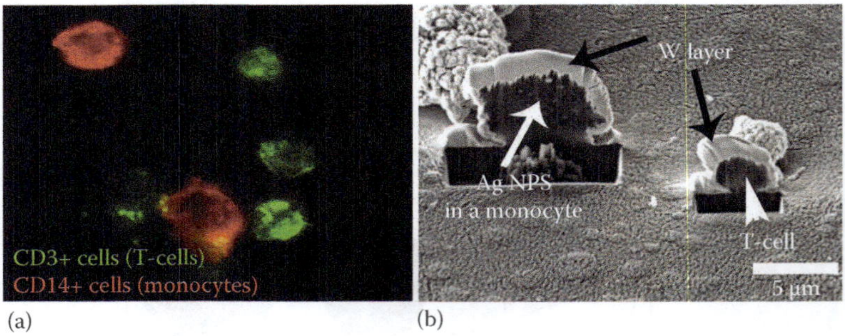

FIGURE 12.8
(a) Fluorescence micrograph of the peripheral monocytes (CD14+) and lymphocytes (T-cells, CD3+); (b) detection of the intracellular Ag NPs in monocytes (cultured with 20 μg/mL Ag NPs for 24 h) by focused ion beam, scanning electron microscopy (FIB/SEM) technique; before carrying out the FIB process, the specimens were protected by coating a thin tungsten (W) layer. (Adapted from *Acta Biomater*, 7, Greulich, C. et al., Cell type-specific responses of peripheral blood mononuclear cells to silver nanoparticles, 3505–14, Copyright 2011, with permission from Elsevier.)

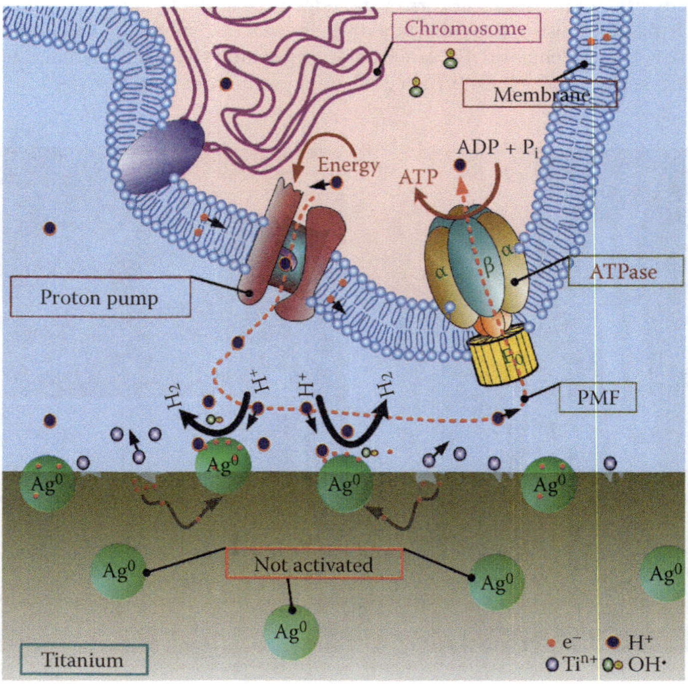

FIGURE 12.11
The microgalvanic effects controlled bactericidal actions of titanium surface immobilised of Ag NPs (Ag^o) by silver plasma immersion ion implantation (Ag PIII). PMF denotes the electrochemical gradient of proton-motive force. (Modified according to *Biomaterials*, 32, Cao, H. et al., Biological actions of silver nanoparticles embedded in titanium controlled by micro-galvanic effects, 693–705, Copyright 2011, with permission from Elsevier.)

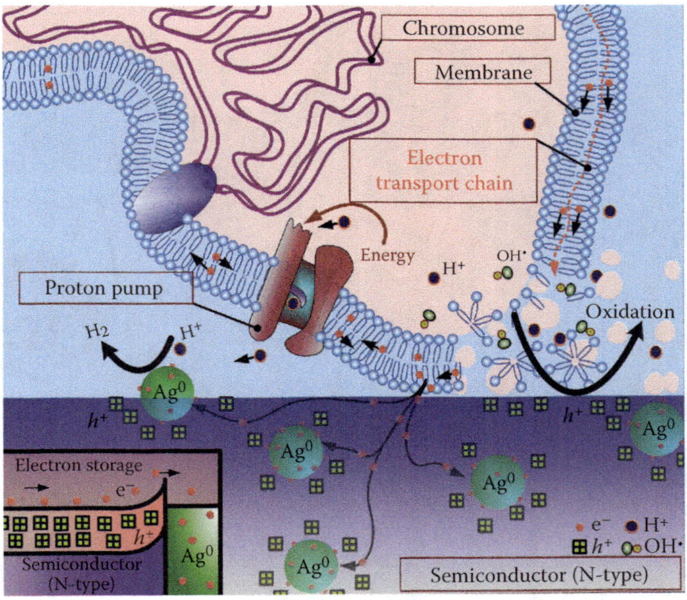

FIGURE 12.12

The Schottky–Mott barrier controlled bactericidal actions of a semiconductor (N-type) immobilised of Ag NPs (Ag^o) by silver plasma immersion ion implantation (Ag PIII). That is, the electrons are transferred from the bacterial membranes to the semiconductor surface, stored on the Ag NPs (electron storage) and induce valence-band hole (h^+) accumulation at the semiconductor side answer for the cytosolic content leakage (oxidation) of the adherent bacteria in the dark. (Modified according to *Acta Biomater*, 9, Cao, H. et al., Electron storage mediated dark antibacterial action of bound silver nanoparticles: Smaller is not always better, 5100–10, Copyright 2013, with permission from Elsevier.)

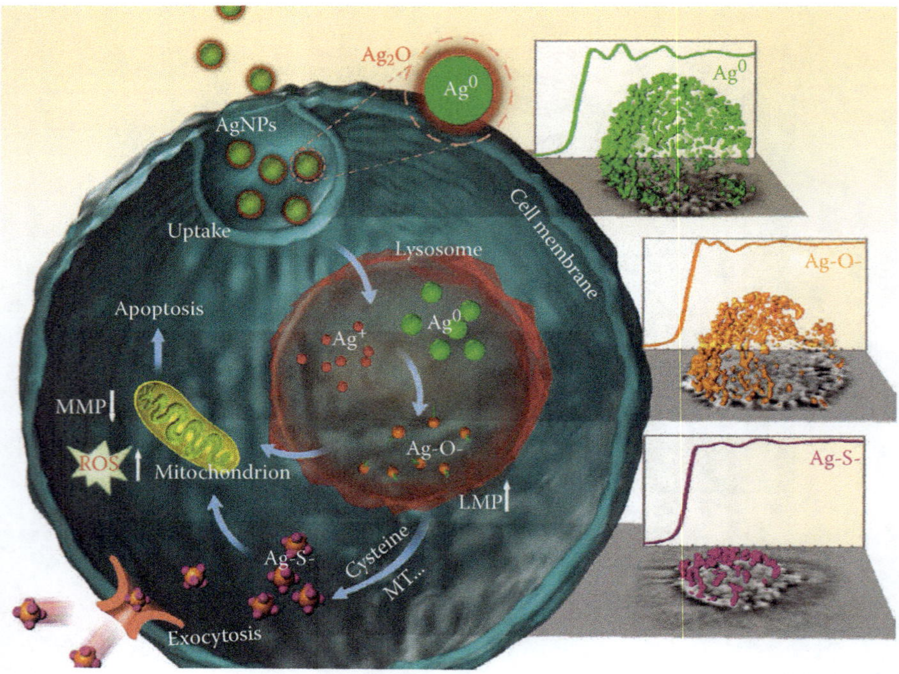

FIGURE 12.17
A schematic diagram illustrating the chemical transformation of Ag NPs in human monocytes (THP-1): Ag NPs were uptaken by the cells and trafficked from engulfed vesicles to the lysosomes. Because of the acidic environment in the lysosome, silver transferred from elemental silver (Ag^0) to silver ions and Ag-O-, and then to Ag-S- species. (Adapted with permission from Wang, L. et al., *ACS Nano* 9: 6532–47. Copyright 2015 American Chemical Society.)

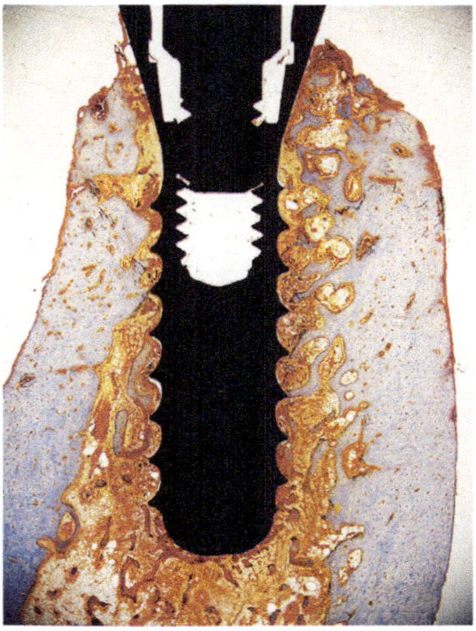

FIGURE 14.1
Titanium dental implants with ideal osseointegration.

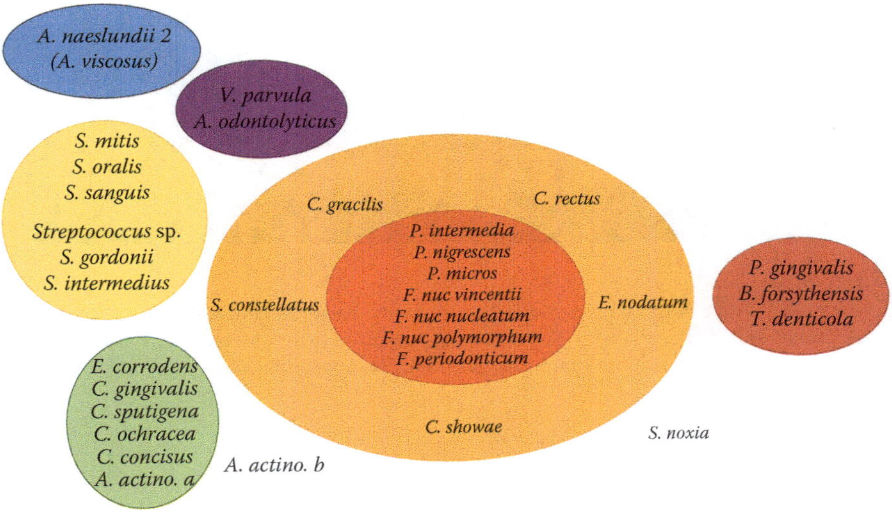

FIGURE 14.3
The microbial complexes identified in subgingival plaque surround natural teeth. (Adapted from Socransky et al.: Microbial complexes in subgingival plaque. *J Clin Periodontol.* 1998. 25. 134–44. Copyright Wiley-VCH Verlag GmbH & Co. KGaA. Reproduced with permission.)

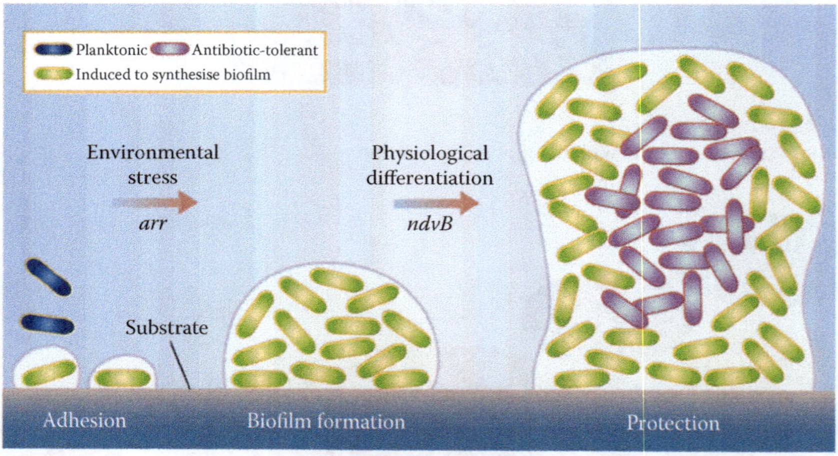

FIGURE 15.4
General scheme (for both Gram-positive and -negative bacteria) conceptualising the biofilm development and its behaviours. (Reprinted by permission from Macmillan Publishers Ltd. *Nat Biotech* O'Toole, G.A. and Stewart, P.S. 23:1378–1379, copyright 2005.)

9

Immunomodulatory Activities of Silver Nanoparticles (AgNPs) in Human Neutrophils

Denis Girard

CONTENTS

9.1 Introduction

9.1.1 Nanoparticles at a Glance

Nanoparticles (NPs) certainly have a great potential for human needs. However, there are increasing concerns that the same features that make NPs so attractive also represent potential risks to human health (Maynard 2007). In the past few years, interest in the use of nanomaterials and NPs in medicine has increased tremendously, especially for drug delivery in cancer therapies. However, there are several studies investigating the potential use of NPs as carriers to detect allergies or to alleviate inflammatory symptoms. Although the use of NPs for diagnostic and therapeutic purposes in medicine represents a potentially interesting avenue to develop nanodrug systems, there are some potential toxic risks. Indeed, cytotoxicity, oxidative stress, genotoxicity and inflammation have been reported in both *in vitro* and *in vivo* models as major adverse effects of NPs.

A variety of sectors other than medicine use NPs. These include, but are not limited to, sports, aerospace, electronics, cosmetics, textile industries and food. Therefore, human exposure to NPs is unavoidable and this leads to the possibility that NPs may reach the blood circulation and interact with immune blood cells. Thus, it becomes crucial to evaluate the potential risk that NPs represent to human health. In this respect, different studies using *in vivo* models of inflammation, especially those investigating airway NP exposure, have been performed and several reported an increased number of leukocytes, mainly polymorphonuclear neutrophils (PMNs), in lungs and bronchoalveolar lavages (BALs). In fact, neutrophil counts are frequently used as biomarkers of inflammation in several studies. However, despite this, and knowing that PMNs are key player cells in inflammation, it is only recently that some studies, including our own, have focused on the direct interaction between NPs and human PMNs (Abrikossova et al. 2012; Babin et al. 2013; Couto et al. 2014; Goncalves et al. 2011).

As previously mentioned, one of the most adverse effects of NPs reported in the literature is inflammation. Indeed, a variety of NPs were found to possess pro-inflammatory activities, principally based on their ability to increase the production of different pro-inflammatory cytokines (Elsabahy and Wooley 2013; Nagakura et al. 2014; Skuland et al. 2014; Wu et al. 2010) and on the observations that NPs can exacerbate airway inflammation *in vivo* (Brandenberger et al. 2013; Chen et al. 2006; Hussain et al. 2011; Srinivas et al. 2011). However, inflammation is a normal biological response of the body to various assaults, including microorganisms, injuries, dusts, drugs and other chemicals. Under normal circumstances, inflammation will subside and resolve itself in a healthy individual through a series of tightly regulated responses. However, when deregulation occurs, inflammation can lead to inflammatory disorders and diseases including asthma and several pulmonary lung diseases, dermatitis, arthritis, inflammatory bowel diseases and so on (Edwards and Hallett 1997; Watt et al. 2005).

9.1.2 Silver Nanoparticles

AgNPs are increasingly used in electronics, food adjuvants, paints, sunscreens, cosmetics and in a wide range of medical applications, including wound treatment with different silver-containing bandages (Bartlomiejczyk et al. 2013; Rai et al. 2009). Also, a variety of silver compounds are used for topical applications such as treatment of burn injuries (Franci et al. 2015; Klasen 2000). Therefore, exposure of humans to AgNPs is unavoidable and it is highly plausible that AgNPs will reach the bloodstream and interact with cells of the innate immunity, including neutrophils. Further, AgNPs are very attractive for developing new therapeutic strategies, including drug delivery. However, substantial toxic properties have been associated with the use of AgNPs, even at noncytotoxic concentrations, and have been attributed to either nanosized particles of Ag or silver ions (Ag^+) themselves (Asharani et al. 2012; AshaRani et al. 2009; de Lima et al. 2012). In addition, a large number of *in vitro* and *in vivo* studies show that AgNPs have the potential to induce toxic effects in different mammalian cells, including inflammation, and to cause a deposition in several organs (Anderson et al. 2015; AshaRani et al. 2009; Chen et al. 2007; de Lima et al. 2012; Foldbjerg et al. 2011; Lee et al. 2014). Nevertheless, the safety of these NPs, as well as their effects in the host defense system, remain unestablished. Particularly, direct activation of PMNs by different AgNPs is poorly documented, despite the fact that accumulating data indicate that PMN biology could be altered by different kinds of NPs, including titanium dioxide, cerium dioxide, zinc oxide, gadolinium oxide, iron oxide, cholesteryl butyrate solid lipid, sirolimus-loaded NP and polymethylmethacrylate NP (Abrikossova et al. 2012; Babin et al. 2013; Couto et al. 2014; Dianzani et al. 2006; Goncalves et al. 2010; Goncalves and Girard 2014; Moeller et al. 2012; Papatheofanis and Barmada 1991).

9.2 Introducing Neutrophils

PMNs are the most abundant type of leukocytes in human blood, representing more than 65% of total leukocytes. These cells are primordial players of innate immunity and provide a very effective defense against pathogens, especially bacteria and fungus. They are terminally mature nondividing cells that, as other immune cells, develop in the bone marrow from $CD34^+$ stem cells. Importantly, more than 50% of the bone marrow is dedicated to the generation of PMNs. It takes approximately 14 days to obtain fully mature PMNs from precursor cells resulting from a series of cell divisions and stages: myeloblasts, promyelocytes, myelocytes, metamyelocytes, band neutrophils and mature neutrophils. Although the mechanism is still not well understood, it occurs under the influence of regulatory cytokines (Edwards and Hallett 1997; Edwards and Watson 1995; Ward et al. 1999). In a normal adult, it has been estimated that approximately 5×10^{10} neutrophils are released from the bone marrow per day, representing one of the fastest cell turnovers in the human body (Edwards and Watson 1995; Ward et al. 1999). Therefore, it is easy to imagine that PMN cell turnover must be under strict control in order to prevent cell overproduction leading to diseases, including cancer. Indeed, one type of cancer, acute promyelocytic leukemia, is a cancer of the white blood cells characterised by an abnormal accumulation of immature neutrophils, the promyelocytes. In healthy individuals, the number of PMNs remains relatively constant, and this could be explained by the fact that these cells possess a short lifespan with a half-life of ~12 h in circulation. Further, PMNs are well known to undergo constitutive or spontaneous apoptosis, certainly largely responsible for maintaining adequate cell number under normal circumstances. Apoptotic PMNs become unresponsive to extracellular stimuli and will lose and express different kinds of molecules on their surfaces (Akgul et al. 2001; Duffin et al. 2010; Ren and Savill 1998), including some named as 'eat-me' signals involved in the elimination of apoptotic PMNs by professional phagocytes (a process called efferocytosis), largely responsible for the resolution of inflammation (Akgul et al. 2001; Duffin et al. 2010; Savill 1997; Silva 2010). Therefore, identification of any agents that could induce or delay PMN apoptosis is of major importance to help control the number of PMNs. In this respect, when the rate of PMN apoptosis is accelerated, this could increase bacterial susceptibility, and inversely, when apoptosis is delayed or suppressed, this could aggravate inflammation and lead to autoimmune diseases (Duffin et al. 2010; Savill 1997).

Although different biochemical hallmarks of apoptosis are observable in neutrophils (Akgul et al. 2001; Duffin et al. 2010; Fox et al. 2010), including cell shrinkage, chromatin condensation and internucleosomal DNA degradation, appearance of pyknotic nuclei, caspase activation, flip-flop of phosphatidylserines (from the inner to the outer surface of the cell) and so on, it is important to specify that PMNs are also different from several other cell types. In this respect, the common caspase substrates such as poly(ADP-ribose) polymerase, the catalytic subunit of DNA-dependent protein kinase, the small ribonucleoprotein U1-70 kDa and the nuclear/mitotic apparatus proteins are not detected in PMNs (Bhatia et al. 1995; Sanghavi et al. 1998). Also, human PMNs do not express caspase-2 and the antiapoptotic Bcl-2 (B-cell lymphoma 2) proteins (Santos-Beneit and Mollinedo 2000). Inversely, PMNs highly express the antiapoptotic protein myeloid cell leukemia-1 (Mcl-1). In addition, PMNs are known to possess a very low number of mitochondria that may have a role restricted to apoptosis rather than for energy generation (Maianski et al. 2004). During apoptosis, mature PMNs can release different proteases from azurophilic granules, including cathepsin D, contributing to caspase-3 activation through processing of caspase-8 (Conus et al. 2008). Also, unusual roles for nuclear proteins have been reported in PMNs (Witko-Sarsat et al. 2010). One good example is that, unlike other cells, the proliferating cell nuclear antigen protein is rather expressed in the cytoplasm of mature PMNs where it could bind to pro-caspases, affecting their apoptotic rates.

Apoptosis is a highly regulated process that could be triggered through either the extrinsic pathway, the intrinsic pathway or the endoplasmic reticulum (ER) stress-induced pathway (Bettigole and Glimcher 2015; Boyce and Yuan 2006; Roy et al. 2014). The intrinsic pathway is initiated through the intracellular release of different mitochondrial signal factors. In brief, after its release, cytochrome c will form a complex with adenosine triphosphate (ATP) and the enzymatic protein Apaf-1. This complex will in turn activate the initiator caspase-9 that will interact with the complex cytochrome c–ATP–Apaf-1, forming an apoptosome, leading to activation of the effector caspase-3 and degradation of cellular structures, including the cytoskeleton (Robertson et al. 2002; Roy et al. 2014). The extrinsic pathway is rather initiated via the stimulation of the transmembrane death receptors, including Fas receptors (CD95), one of the best characterised ones (Lavrik 2014). During activation of this pathway, some ligand molecules will be released by other cells and will bind to transmembrane death receptors on the target cell, inducing apoptosis. For example, the binding of the Fas ligands (CD95L) to their receptors (CD95) will trigger cell surface receptor aggregation, leading to the recruitment of an intracellular adaptor protein, Fas-associated death domain protein or FADD, which, in turn, will interact with the initiator caspase-8 protein, forming a complex, the death-inducing signal complex or DISC (Ashkenazi and Dixit 1998; Lavrik 2014; Li et al. 1998). Then, activated caspase-8 could activate caspase-3, indicating that both intrinsic and intrinsic pathway can overlap. In this respect, activated caspase-8 can also activate a protein, BID, known to act as a signal on the membrane of mitochondria facilitating cytochrome c release.

Both intrinsic and extrinsic pathways of cell apoptosis are known to be activated during spontaneous human neutrophil apoptosis as evidenced by several parameters, including caspase-9 (intrinsic) and caspase-8 (extrinsic) activation (Bruno et al. 2005; Cross et al. 2008; Ge and Rikihisa 2006). More recently, we were the first to determine that the ER stress-induced cell apoptotic pathway is also operational in human PMNs (Binet et al. 2010). Indeed, PMNs were found to express inositol-requiring protein-1 (IRE1), activating transcription factor-6 (ATF6) and protein kinase RNA (PKR)–like ER kinase (PERK), the three major sensors of protein folding status in the ER (Ron and Walter 2007; Todd et al. 2008).

During acute inflammation, PMNs are among the first cells to migrate to an inflammatory site, where they will produce several pro-inflammatory mediators (especially chemokines), attracting other PMNs first and then other cell types, including monocytes, macrophages and lymphocytes; this corresponds to chronic inflammation. The ability of PMNs to eliminate invading pathogens occurs via two important mechanisms. First, the respiratory burst, an oxygen-dependent process, leads to the generation of reactive oxygen species (ROS) known as important messengers and to regulate several functions. Second, degranulation is rather an oxygen-independent mechanism by which PMNs release potent toxic degradative products stored in granules. PMNs are also known as a cellular source of a variety of compounds involved in inflammation, including leukotriene B_4, platelet-activating factor and various cytokines such as IL-1α, IL-8, IL-12, TNF-α, TGF-β and GRO-α, to name a few (Edwards and Hallett 1997). Of note, several PMN priming and activating agents such as IL-1β, IL-8, IL-15, GM-CSF, TGF-β, C5a, C9 and so on are found in human fluids in diverse diseases as, for example, in the synovial fluids of rheumatic patients (Cordero et al. 2001; Ottonello et al. 2002; Steiner et al. 1999). These cells are also known to adhere onto cell substratum (e.g. endothelial cells) (Kasper et al. 2006) or onto extracellular matrix proteins, including fibronectin (Anceriz et al. 2007). They can also move toward a chemotactic gradient (chemotaxis) and exert phagocytosis, two important functions also involved in killing and elimination of pathogens. An important new discovery was made concerning the biology of

PMNs, one decade ago. Upon activation, PMNs release neutrophil extracellular traps (NETs) composed of decondensed chromatin DNA in association with histones, granular proteins and a few cytoplasmic proteins, which are able to trap and kill extracellular bacteria, fungi and parasites (Brinkmann et al. 2004).

9.3 Indirect Interaction between AgNPs and Neutrophils *In Vivo*

Some reports indicate that AgNPs can induce inflammation and attract specifically neutrophils in a variety of *in vivo* models. For example, 50 or 250 μg of 70-nm PVP-coated AgNP ($AgNP_{70}$) was instilled intratracheally in rats, and after 24 h, several parameters were analysed from the bronchoalveolar lavage fluids (BALF), including lactate dehydrogenase (LDH), total protein, cytokine levels and differential cell counts. No parameters were significantly altered when using the lowest concentration of the NP, whereas treatment with the concentration of 250 μg significantly increased LDH, total protein and some cytokines. In addition, the number of neutrophils was increased by a factor of 60, when compared with controls (Haberl et al. 2013). In another study, the effects of a 28-day oral administration of different concentrations of silver nanocolloid (0.25, 2.5 and 25 parts per million [ppm]) on hematological parameters were determined in mice (Malaczewska 2014). In brief, a decreased count of monocytes in the blood was observed at all tested concentrations as well as the counts of NK and NKT cells (at 0.25 and 2.5 ppm) and an increase in the $CD4^+/CD8^+$ T cell distribution. Interestingly, at all concentrations, NPs also stimulated phagocytosis and ROS production of PMNs. By exposing rats, nose-only, to clean air, $AgNP_{15}$ (179 μg/m^3) or $AgNP_{410}$ (167 μg/m^3) 6 h/day for 4 consecutive days, Braakhuis et al. (2014) reported a 175-fold increase of PMN influx in the lungs in response to $AgNP_{15}$ only. In another study, four types of AgNPs were tested in rats after intratracheal instillation: citrate-stabilised $AgNP_{20}$ and $AgNP_{110}$ and PVP-stabilised $AgNP_{20}$ and $AgNP_{110}$ at a concentration of 0, 0.1, 0.5 or 1.0 mg/kg body weight. BALs and lung tissues were obtained after 1, 7 and 21 days after exposure. They reported that all types of AgNP increased the number of PMNs at all tested periods and at a concentration of 0.5 or 1.0 mg/kg body weight (Silva et al. 2015).

These examples ably illustrate the fact that several *in vivo* studies that aim at evaluating the potential adverse effects of AgNPs in humans use the PMN count as an important biomarker of inflammation in a variety of *in vivo* rodent models. In addition, these studies (and others) indirectly promote the necessity and importance of investigating how AgNPs could directly alter the biology of PMNs. We and others have performed some studies in order to determine how AgNPs can alter the biology of human neutrophils. This will be discussed in Section 9.4.

9.4 Direct Interaction between AgNPs and Neutrophils *In Vitro*

Although we (Babin et al. 2013; Goncalves and Girard 2014; Goncalves et al. 2010) and others (Abrikossova et al. 2012; Bartneck et al. 2010; Couto et al. 2014; Dianzani et al. 2006; Hwang et al. 2015) have reported that some NPs can alter the biology of neutrophils, the direct interaction between AgNPs and human neutrophils is not well documented. In 2014, we reported that AgNPs with an initial size of 20 nm ($AgNP_{20}$) increased the cell size of human neutrophils as evidenced by optical microscopy and by flow cytometry based on the cell size forward scattered light (FSC) and the inner complexity or granularity based on the FSC (Poirier et al. 2014). Because of these results, and since some rodent phagocytes (the murine macrophage RAW 264.7 and J774.1 cell lines) were found to internalise AgNP (Singh and Ramarao 2012), we then hypothesised that $AgNP_{20}$ could penetrate neutrophils. Indeed, using transmission electronic microscopy, we found that $AgNP_{20}$ can rapidly interact with the cell membrane, penetrate PMNs and localise in vacuole-like structures even within 1 min in some cases. Interestingly, AgNPs appeared to be then randomly distributed in the cytosol after 24 h (Poirier et al. 2014). Also, we demonstrated that treatment of freshly isolated human PMNs with 100 µg/ml $AgNP_{20}$ for 24h (but not at 10 µg/ml) increased the apoptotic rate, identifying for the first time that AgNPs are proapoptotic in these cells. Because we are interested on the mode of action of AgNP and since we previously documented that some different modulators of PMN apoptosis can alter the biosynthesis of new polypeptides (*de novo* protein synthesis) (Binet et al. 2006; Savoie et al. 2000; Girard et al. 1997), now including some NPs such as zinc oxide (Goncalves and Girard 2014), we next determine how AgNPs will alter such an important biological process. After metabolic cell labelling, we found that AgNP-induced human PMNs induce a marked suppression of *de novo* protein synthesis and therefore act as potent protein synthesis inhibitors at a proapoptotic concentration of 100 µg/ml, but not at 10 µg/ml, a concentration that did not affect the basal level of PMN spontaneous apoptosis (Poirier et al. 2014).

In about the same time, one study investigated the impact of AgNPs and silver ions on innate immune cells, including PMNs (Haase et al. 2014). However, unlike our study, they used AgNPs synthesised within hydroxylated polyester dendrimers generating AgNPs with mean particle sizes of 2.0, 3.4, 5.7, 15.4 and 34.7 nm. They reported that AgNPs did not affect the capacity of PMNs to exert phagocytosis of bacteria as well as oxidative burst. However, they found that AgNPs, as well as Ag^+, could induce NET formation.

Because different biological activities and toxicities of NPs could be related to their initial size (Kim et al. 2015; Mendes et al. 2014; Yin et al. 2015), we performed another study aiming at comparing the effects of $AgNP_{20}$ to an AgNP with a larger diameter of 70 nm, $AgNP_{70}$, on the biology of PMNs (Poirier et al. 2015). We demonstrated that unlike $AgNP_{20}$, $AgNP_{70}$ did not alter the cell size of PMNs. Also, in contrast to the proapoptotic effect of $AgNP_{20}$, we found that $AgNP_{70}$ delay spontaneous neutrophil apoptosis. Interestingly, but intriguingly, $AgNP_{70}$ were also found to inhibit de novo protein synthesis similarly to $AgNP_{20}$. Of note, throughout this study, all experiments with $AgNP_{70}$ and $AgNP_{20}$ were performed in parallel in the same experimental conditions with PMNs isolated from the same blood donors. In this study, using the general oxidative stress indicator, CM-H_2DCFDA, in flow cytometry experiments, we showed that both $AgNP_{20}$ and $AgNP_{70}$ did not induce intracellular ROS production. In contrast to $AgNP_{70}$, $AgNP_{20}$ were found to increase the production of the potent chemoattractant CXCL8 (IL-8) by PMNs, indicating a different mechanism of action between both AgNPs. Further, in the same order of ideas, we demonstrated that $AgNP_{20}$, but not $AgNP_{70}$, induce PMN degranulation, as evidenced by the release of albumin and metalloproteinase-9 (MMP-9/Gelatinase B) in the supernatants (Poirier et al. 2015). This was also confirmed by the detection of gelatinase activity induced by $AgNP_{20}$ as assessed by zymography experiments. Therefore, collectively, the results of these two studies demonstrate that two AgNPs with different initial diameters, namely, 20 nm or 70 nm, can possess similar as well as different immunomodulatory activities on PMN functions, indicating different modes of action.

We then performed another study using smaller AgNPs with a diameter of 15 nm, $AgNP_{15}$. Similarly to $AgNP_{20}$, $AgNP_{15}$ were found to rapidly penetrate human PMNs (Liz et al. 2015). However, $AgNP_{15}$ appears to induce unconventional apoptosis. Indeed, in contrast to the cell shrinkage and CD16 cell surface shedding (Dransfield et al. 1994) normally observed in human apoptotic PMNs that we routinely used in our laboratory as markers of apoptotic cells, we rather observed that $AgNP_{15}$ increase the cell volume and do not induce CD16 shedding. This unconventional cell death was clearly distinct from cell necrosis and was reversed by the addition of a pan-caspase inhibitor known to mostly inhibit caspase-1, caspase-3, caspase-4 and caspase-7. Because of this, and since we previously published that the ER stress-induced cell apoptotic pathway was operational in human PMNs, including the fact that these cells were also found to express caspase-4 and that it could be activated (Binet et al. 2010), we then tried to inhibit $AgNP_{15}$-induced atypical cell death by adding specific inhibitors to caspase-1 and to caspase-4. Interestingly, both of these inhibitors were found to prevent the effect of $AgNP_{15}$. Knowing that these two inflammatory caspases are known to be involved in inflammasome activation and IL-1β production (Fernandes-Alnemri et al. 2007; Man and Kanneganti 2015), it was logical to verify if $AgNP_{15}$ increase the IL-1β production and, if so, to determine if caspase-1 or caspase-4 is involved.

We found that, indeed, $AgNP_{15}$ increased the neutrophil IL-1β production and that both caspases are involved, although caspase-4 is more importantly implicated (Liz et al. 2015). In this study, we also demonstrated that $AgNP_{15}$ increased ROS production and that ROS participate in $AgNP_{15}$-induced cell death. Finally, we reported in this study that when PMNs were forced to adhere, $AgNP_{15}$ induced the NET formation.

Recently, the interaction between AgNP–polyvinyl alcohol (AgNP–PVA) and human PMNs was reported. In this study, ROS production was increased in PMNs incubated with 10 µM AgNP–PVA, as assessed by flow cytometry using the DCFH-DA probe (Paino and Zucolotto 2014). Curiously, although the authors demonstrated that cell necrosis and apoptosis were significantly increased after treatment with the NPs, as assessed by flow cytometry after staining with PI and Annexin V in human hepatocellular carcinoma (HepG2) and in peripheral blood mononuclear cells (PBMCs), this was not performed in PMNs. Moreover, they investigated the cellular uptake of AgNP–PVA in HepG2 and PBMCs based on increased SSC fluorescence intensity recorded by flow cytometry, but, again, not in human PMNs.

During the writing of this review, one study reported the cytotoxic effect of AgNPs on human neutrophils, according to the size of the NPs (Soares et al. 2016). Even if they used a similar approach to us, they however used polyvinyl pyrrolidone-coated AgNPs (10 and 50 nm) and neutrophils were plated at a cell density of 2×10^6 cells/ml. They found that the smaller $AgNP_{10}$ were more toxic for neutrophils than $AgNP_{50}$; they lead to membrane damage and altered lysosomal activity and induce oxidative burst. The authors mentioned that $AgNP_{10}$ induced cell necrosis after 16 h of incubation based on morphological examination. Interestingly, using TEM, they confirmed our observations that AgNPs ($AgNP_{20}$ in our case) can penetrate neutrophils.

9.5 Conclusions

AgNPs are already used in medicine, and it is highly probable that, in the forthcoming years, they will probably be used increasingly in a variety of other sectors. It is therefore crucial not only to determine their potential effect on inflammation but also to understand their modes of action. Several of the *in vitro* studies discussed above evaluated the cytotoxicity and only one or few PMN response(s) of different kinds of NPs, including AgNP. Yet, few studies other than our own have determined the effects of AgNPs on PMN apoptosis and the mechanism involved in cell death, a very important issue involved in the regulation of PMN numbers. However, more recent reports have investigated the interaction between NPs and PMNs by studying different functions/responses, an approach that we encourage. Although there is a growing interest in developing *in vitro* assays in nanotoxicology

(Arora et al. 2012) to evaluate the potential risk of using NPs, including AgNPs, it is also strongly encouraged to use primary human cells as a source of *in vitro* cells for testing them, especially PMNs, knowing their importance in inflammation.

Acknowledgement

This study was supported by the Institut de recherche Robert-Sauvé en santé et en sécurité du travail (IRSST).

References

Abrikossova, N., C. Skoglund, M. Ahren, T. Bengtsson, and K. Uvdal. 2012. Effects of gadolinium oxide nanoparticles on the oxidative burst from human neutrophil granulocytes. *Nanotechnology* 23 (27):275101.

Akgul, C., D. A. Moulding, and S. W. Edwards. 2001. Molecular control of neutrophil apoptosis. *FEBS Lett* 487 (3):318–22.

Anceriz, N., K. Vandal, and P. A. Tessier. 2007. S100A9 mediates neutrophil adhesion to fibronectin through activation of beta2 integrins. *Biochem Biophys Res Commun* 354 (1):84–9.

Anderson, D. S., R. M. Silva, D. Lee, P. C. Edwards, A. Sharmah, T. Guo, K. E. Pinkerton, and L. S. Van Winkle. 2015. Persistence of silver nanoparticles in the rat lung: Influence of dose, size, and chemical composition. *Nanotoxicology* 9 (5):591–602.

Arora, S., J. M. Rajwade, and K. M. Paknikar. 2012. Nanotoxicology and in vitro studies: The need of the hour. *Toxicol Appl Pharmacol* 258 (2):151–65.

Asharani, P., S. Sethu, H. K. Lim, G. Balaji, S. Valiyaveettil, and M. P. Hande. 2012. Differential regulation of intracellular factors mediating cell cycle, DNA repair and inflammation following exposure to silver nanoparticles in human cells. *Genome Integr* 3 (1):1–14.

AshaRani, P. V., G. Low Kah Mun, M. P. Hande, and S. Valiyaveettil. 2009. Cytotoxicity and genotoxicity of silver nanoparticles in human cells. *ACS Nano* 3 (2):279–90.

Ashkenazi, A., and V. M. Dixit. 1998. Death receptors: Signaling and modulation. *Science* 281 (5381):1305–8.

Babin, K., F. Antoine, D. M. Goncalves, and D. Girard. 2013. TiO_2, CeO_2 and ZnO nanoparticles and modulation of the degranulation process in human neutrophils. *Toxicol Lett* 221 (1):57–63.

Bartlomiejczyk, T., A. Lankoff, M. Kruszewski, and I. Szumiel. 2013. Silver nanoparticles – Allies or adversaries? *Ann Agric Environ Med* 20 (1):48–54.

Bartneck, M., H. A. Keul, G. Zwadlo-Klarwasser, and J. Groll. 2010. Phagocytosis independent extracellular nanoparticle clearance by human immune cells. *Nano Lett* 10 (1):59–63.

Bettigole, S. E., and L. H. Glimcher. 2015. Endoplasmic reticulum stress in immunity. *Annu Rev Immunol* 33:107–38.

Bhatia, M., J. B. Kirkland, and K. A. Meckling-Gill. 1995. Modulation of poly(ADP-ribose) polymerase during neutrophilic and monocytic differentiation of promyelocytic (NB4) and myelocytic (HL-60) leukaemia cells. *Biochem J* 308 (Pt 1):131–7.

Binet, F., H. Cavalli, E. Moisan, and D. Girard. 2006. Arsenic trioxide (AT) is a novel human neutrophil pro-apoptotic agent: Effects of catalase on AT-induced apoptosis, degradation of cytoskeletal proteins and de novo protein synthesis. *Br J Haematol* 132 (3):349–58.

Binet, F., S. Chiasson, and D. Girard. 2010. Evidence that endoplasmic reticulum (ER) stress and caspase-4 activation occur in human neutrophils. *Biochem Biophys Res Commun* 391 (1):18–23.

Boyce, M., and J. Yuan. 2006. Cellular response to endoplasmic reticulum stress: A matter of life or death. *Cell Death Differ* 13 (3):363–73.

Braakhuis, H. M., I. Gosens, P. Krystek, J. A. Boere, F. R. Cassee, P. H. Fokkens, J. A. Post, H. van Loveren, and M. V. Park. 2014. Particle size dependent deposition and pulmonary inflammation after short-term inhalation of silver nanoparticles. *Part Fibre Toxicol* 11:49.

Brandenberger, C., N. L. Rowley, D. N. Jackson-Humbles, Q. Zhang, L. A. Bramble, R. P. Lewandowski, J. G. Wagner, W. Chen, B. L. Kaplan, N. E. Kaminski, G. L. Baker, R. M. Worden, and J. R. Harkema. 2013. Engineered silica nanoparticles act as adjuvants to enhance allergic airway disease in mice. *Part Fibre Toxicol* 10 (1):26.

Brinkmann, V., U. Reichard, C. Goosmann, B. Fauler, Y. Uhlemann, D. S. Weiss, Y. Weinrauch, and A. Zychlinsky. 2004. Neutrophil extracellular traps kill bacteria. *Science* 303 (5663):1532–5.

Bruno, A., S. Conus, I. Schmid, and H. U. Simon. 2005. Apoptotic pathways are inhibited by leptin receptor activation in neutrophils. *J Immunol* 174 (12):8090–6.

Chen, D., T. Xi, and J. Bai. 2007. Biological effects induced by nanosilver particles: In vivo study. *Biomed Mater* 2 (3):S126–8.

Chen, H. W., S. F. Su, C. T. Chien, W. H. Lin, S. L. Yu, C. C. Chou, J. J. Chen, and P. C. Yang. 2006. Titanium dioxide nanoparticles induce emphysema-like lung injury in mice. *Faseb J* 20 (13):2393–5.

Conus, S., R. Perozzo, T. Reinheckel, C. Peters, L. Scapozza, S. Yousefi, and H. U. Simon. 2008. Caspase-8 is activated by cathepsin D initiating neutrophil apoptosis during the resolution of inflammation. *J Exp Med* 205 (3):685–98.

Cordero, O. J., F. J. Salgado, A. Mera-Varela, and M. Nogueira. 2001. Serum interleukin-12, interleukin-15, soluble CD26, and adenosine deaminase in patients with rheumatoid arthritis. *Rheumatol Int* 21 (2):69–74.

Couto, D., M. Freitas, V. Vilas-Boas, I. Dias, G. Porto, M. A. Lopez-Quintela, J. Rivas, P. Freitas, F. Carvalho, and E. Fernandes. 2014. Interaction of polyacrylic acid coated and non-coated iron oxide nanoparticles with human neutrophils. *Toxicol Lett* 225 (1):57–65.

Cross, A., R. J. Moots, and S. W. Edwards. 2008. The dual effects of TNFalpha on neutrophil apoptosis are mediated via differential effects on expression of Mcl-1 and Bfl-1. *Blood* 111 (2):878–84.

de Lima, R., A. B. Seabra, and N. Duran. 2012. Silver nanoparticles: A brief review of cytotoxicity and genotoxicity of chemically and biogenically synthesized nanoparticles. *J Appl Toxicol* 32 (11):867–79.

Dianzani, C., R. Cavalli, G. P. Zara, M. Gallicchio, G. Lombardi, M. R. Gasco, P. Panzanelli, and R. Fantozzi. 2006. Cholesteryl butyrate solid lipid nanoparticles inhibit adhesion of human neutrophils to endothelial cells. *Br J Pharmacol* 148 (5):648–56.

Dransfield, I., A. M. Buckle, J. S. Savill, A. McDowall, C. Haslett, and N. Hogg. 1994. Neutrophil apoptosis is associated with a reduction in CD16 (Fc gamma RIII) expression. *J Immunol* 153 (3):1254–63.

Duffin, R., A. E. Leitch, S. Fox, C. Haslett, and A. G. Rossi. 2010. Targeting granulocyte apoptosis: Mechanisms, models, and therapies. *Immunol Rev* 236: 28–40.

Edwards, S. W., and M. B. Hallett. 1997. Seeing the wood for the trees: The forgotten role of neutrophils in rheumatoid arthritis. *Immunol Today* 18 (7):320–4.

Edwards, S. W., and F. Watson. 1995. The cell biology of phagocytes. *Immunol Today* 16 (11):508–10.

Elsabahy, M., and K. L. Wooley. 2013. Cytokines as biomarkers of nanoparticle immunotoxicity. *Chem Soc Rev* 42 (12):5552–76.

Fernandes-Alnemri, T., J. Wu, J. W. Yu, P. Datta, B. Miller, W. Jankowski, S. Rosenberg, J. Zhang, and E. S. Alnemri. 2007. The pyroptosome: A supramolecular assembly of ASC dimers mediating inflammatory cell death via caspase-1 activation. *Cell Death Differ* 14 (9):1590–604.

Foldbjerg, R., D. A. Dang, and H. Autrup. 2011. Cytotoxicity and genotoxicity of silver nanoparticles in the human lung cancer cell line, A549. *Arch Toxicol* 85 (7):743–50.

Fox, S., A. E. Leitch, R. Duffin, C. Haslett, and A. G. Rossi. 2010. Neutrophil apoptosis: Relevance to the innate immune response and inflammatory disease. *J Innate Immun* 2 (3):216–27.

Franci, G., A. Falanga, S. Galdiero, L. Palomba, M. Rai, G. Morelli, and M. Galdiero. 2015. Silver nanoparticles as potential antibacterial agents. *Molecules* 20 (5):8856–74.

Ge, Y., and Y. Rikihisa. 2006. *Anaplasma phagocytophilum* delays spontaneous human neutrophil apoptosis by modulation of multiple apoptotic pathways. *Cell Microbiol* 8 (9):1406–16.

Girard, D., R. Paquin, and A. D. Beaulieu. 1997. Responsiveness of human neutrophils to interleukin-4: Induction of cytoskeletal rearrangements, de novo protein synthesis and delay of apoptosis. *Biochem J* 325 (Pt 1):147–53.

Goncalves, D. M., S. Chiasson, and D. Girard. 2010. Activation of human neutrophils by titanium dioxide (TiO_2) nanoparticles. *Toxicol In Vitro* 24 (3):1002–8.

Goncalves, D. M., R. de Liz, and D. Girard. 2011. Activation of neutrophils by nanoparticles. *Scientific World J* 11:1877–85.

Goncalves, D. M., and D. Girard. 2014. Zinc oxide nanoparticles delay human neutrophil apoptosis by a de novo protein synthesis-dependent and reactive oxygen species-independent mechanism. *Toxicol In Vitro* 28 (5):926–31.

Haase, H., A. Fahmi, and B. Mahltig. 2014. Impact of silver nanoparticles and silver ions on innate immune cells. *J Biomed Nanotechnol* 10 (6):1146–56.

Haberl, N., S. Hirn, A. Wenk, J. Diendorf, M. Epple, B. D. Johnston, F. Krombach, W. G. Kreyling, and C. Schleh. 2013. Cytotoxic and proinflammatory effects of PVP-coated silver nanoparticles after intratracheal instillation in rats. *Beilstein J Nanotechnol* 4:933–40.

Hussain, S., J. A. Vanoirbeek, K. Luyts, V. De Vooght, E. Verbeken, L. C. Thomassen, J. A. Martens, D. Dinsdale, S. Boland, F. Marano, B. Nemery, and P. H. Hoet. 2011. Lung exposure to nanoparticles modulates an asthmatic response in a mouse model. *Eur Respir J* 37 (2):299–309.

Hwang, T. L., I. A. Aljuffali, C. F. Hung, C. H. Chen, and J. Y. Fang. 2015. The impact of cationic solid lipid nanoparticles on human neutrophil activation and formation of neutrophil extracellular traps (NETs). *Chem Biol Interact* 235:106–14.

Kasper, B., E. Brandt, M. Ernst, and F. Petersen. 2006. Neutrophil adhesion to endothelial cells induced by platelet factor 4 requires sequential activation of Ras, Syk, and JNK MAP kinases. *Blood* 107 (5):1768–75.

Kim, I. Y., E. Joachim, H. Choi, and K. Kim. 2015. Toxicity of silica nanoparticles depends on size, dose, and cell type. *Nanomedicine* 11 (6):1407–16.

Klasen, H. J. 2000. A historical review of the use of silver in the treatment of burns. II. Renewed interest for silver. *Burns* 26 (2):131–8.

Lavrik, I. N. 2014. Systems biology of death receptor networks: Live and let die. *Cell Death Dis* 5:e1259.

Lee, Y. H., F. Y. Cheng, H. W. Chiu, J. C. Tsai, C. Y. Fang, C. W. Chen, and Y. J. Wang. 2014. Cytotoxicity, oxidative stress, apoptosis and the autophagic effects of silver nanoparticles in mouse embryonic fibroblasts. *Biomaterials* 35 (16):4706–15.

Li, H., H. Zhu, C. J. Xu, and J. Yuan. 1998. Cleavage of BID by caspase 8 mediates the mitochondrial damage in the Fas pathway of apoptosis. *Cell* 94 (4):491–501.

Liz, R., J. C. Simard, L. B. Leonardi, and D. Girard. 2015. Silver nanoparticles rapidly induce atypical human neutrophil cell death by a process involving inflammatory caspases and reactive oxygen species and induce neutrophil extracellular traps release upon cell adhesion. *Int Immunopharmacol* 28 (1):616–25.

Maianski, N. A., J. Geissler, S. M. Srinivasula, E. S. Alnemri, D. Roos, and T. W. Kuijpers. 2004. Functional characterization of mitochondria in neutrophils: A role restricted to apoptosis. *Cell Death Differ* 11 (2):143–53.

Malaczewska, J. 2014. Effect of 28-day oral administration of silver nanocolloid on the peripheral blood leukocytes in mice. *Pol J Vet Sci* 17 (2):263–73.

Man, S. M., and T. D. Kanneganti. 2015. Regulation of inflammasome activation. *Immunol Rev* 265 (1):6–21.

Maynard, A. D. 2007. Nanotechnology: The next big thing, or much ado about nothing? *Ann Occup Hyg* 51 (1):1–12.

Mendes, R. G., B. Koch, A. Bachmatiuk, A. A. El-Gendy, Y. Krupskaya, A. Springer, R. Klingeler, O. Schmidt, B. Buchner, S. Sanchez, and M. H. Rummeli. 2014. Synthesis and toxicity characterization of carbon coated iron oxide nanoparticles with highly defined size distributions. *Biochim Biophys Acta* 1840 (1):160–9.

Moeller, S., R. Kegler, K. Sternberg, and R. G. Mundkowski. 2012. Influence of sirolimus-loaded nanoparticles on physiological functions of native human polymorphonuclear neutrophils. *Nanomedicine* 8 (8):1293–300.

Nagakura, C., Y. Negishi, M. Tsukimoto, S. Itou, T. Kondo, K. Takeda, and S. Kojima. 2014. Involvement of P2Y11 receptor in silica nanoparticles 30-induced IL-6 production by human keratinocytes. *Toxicology* 322:61–8.

Ottonello, L., G. Frumento, N. Arduino, M. Bertolotto, M. Mancini, E. Sottofattori, F. Dallegri, and M. Cutolo. 2002. Delayed neutrophil apoptosis induced by synovial fluid in rheumatoid arthritis: Role of cytokines, estrogens, and adenosine. *Ann N Y Acad Sci* 966:226–31.

Paino, I. M., and V. Zucolotto. 2014. Poly(vinyl alcohol)-coated silver nanoparticles: Activation of neutrophils and nanotoxicology effects in human hepatocarcinoma and mononuclear cells. *Environ Toxicol Pharmacol* 39 (2):614–21.

Papatheofanis, F. J., and R. Barmada. 1991. Polymorphonuclear leukocyte degranulation with exposure to polymethylmethacrylate nanoparticles. *J Biomed Mater Res* 25 (6):761–71.

Poirier, M., J. C. Simard, F. Antoine, and D. Girard. 2014. Interaction between silver nanoparticles of 20 nm (AgNP20) and human neutrophils: Induction of apoptosis and inhibition of de novo protein synthesis by AgNP20 aggregates. *J Appl Toxicol* 34 (4):404–12.

Poirier, M., J. C. Simard, and D. Girard. 2015. Silver nanoparticles of 70 nm and 20 nm affect differently the biology of human neutrophils. *J Immunotoxicol* 13 (3):375–85.

Rai, M., A. Yadav, and A. Gade. 2009. Silver nanoparticles as a new generation of antimicrobials. *Biotechnol Adv* 27 (1):76–83.

Ren, Y., and J. Savill. 1998. Apoptosis: The importance of being eaten. *Cell Death Differ* 5 (7):563–8.

Robertson, J. D., M. Enoksson, M. Suomela, B. Zhivotovsky, and S. Orrenius. 2002. Caspase-2 acts upstream of mitochondria to promote cytochrome c release during etoposide-induced apoptosis. *J Biol Chem* 277 (33):29803–9.

Ron, D., and P. Walter. 2007. Signal integration in the endoplasmic reticulum unfolded protein response. *Nat Rev Mol Cell Biol* 8 (7):519–29.

Roy, M. J., A. Vom, P. E. Czabotar, and G. Lessene. 2014. Cell death and the mitochondria: Therapeutic targeting of the BCL-2 family-driven pathway. *Br J Pharmacol* 171 (8):1973–87.

Sanghavi, D. M., M. Thelen, N. A. Thornberry, L. Casciola-Rosen, and A. Rosen. 1998. Caspase-mediated proteolysis during apoptosis: Insights from apoptotic neutrophils. *FEBS Lett* 422 (2):179–84.

Santos-Beneit, A. M., and F. Mollinedo. 2000. Expression of genes involved in initiation, regulation, and execution of apoptosis in human neutrophils and during neutrophil differentiation of HL-60 cells. *J Leukoc Biol* 67 (5):712–24.

Savill, J. 1997. Apoptosis in resolution of inflammation. *J Leukoc Biol* 61 (4):375–80.

Savoie, A., V. Lavastre, M. Pelletier, T. Hajto, K. Hostanska, and D. Girard. 2000. Activation of human neutrophils by the plant lectin *Viscum album* agglutinin-I: Modulation of de novo protein synthesis and evidence that caspases are involved in induction of apoptosis. *J Leukoc Biol* 68 (6):845–53.

Silva, M. T. 2010. Secondary necrosis: The natural outcome of the complete apoptotic program. *FEBS Lett* 584 (22):4491–9.

Silva, R. M., D. S. Anderson, L. M. Franzi, J. L. Peake, P. C. Edwards, L. S. Van Winkle, and K. E. Pinkerton. 2015. Pulmonary effects of silver nanoparticle size, coating, and dose over time upon intratracheal instillation. *Toxicol Sci* 144 (1):151–62.

Singh, R. P., and P. Ramarao. 2012. Cellular uptake, intracellular trafficking and cytotoxicity of silver nanoparticles. *Toxicol Lett* 213 (2):249–59.

Skuland, T., J. Ovrevik, M. Lag, P. Schwarze, and M. Refsnes. 2014. Silica nanoparticles induce cytokine responses in lung epithelial cells through activation of a p38/TACE/TGF-alpha/EGFR-pathway and NF-kappaBeta signalling. *Toxicol Appl Pharmacol* 279 (1):76–86.

Soares, T., D. Ribeiro, C. Proenca, R. C. Chiste, E. Fernandes, and M. Freitas. 2016. Size-dependent cytotoxicity of silver nanoparticles in human neutrophils assessed by multiple analytical approaches. *Life Sci* 145: 247–54.

Srinivas, A., P. J. Rao, G. Selvam, P. B. Murthy, and P. N. Reddy. 2011. Acute inhalation toxicity of cerium oxide nanoparticles in rats. *Toxicol Lett* 23:23.

Steiner, G., M. Tohidast-Akrad, G. Witzmann, M. Vesely, A. Studnicka-Benke, A. Gal, M. Kunaver, P. Zenz, and J. S. Smolen. 1999. Cytokine production by synovial T cells in rheumatoid arthritis. *Rheumatology (Oxford)* 38 (3):202–13.

Todd, D. J., A. H. Lee, and L. H. Glimcher. 2008. The endoplasmic reticulum stress response in immunity and autoimmunity. *Nat Rev Immunol* 8 (9):663–674.

Ward, C., I. Dransfield, E. R. Chilvers, C. Haslett, and A. G. Rossi. 1999. Pharmacological manipulation of granulocyte apoptosis: Potential therapeutic targets. *Trends Pharmacol Sci* 20 (12):503–9.

Watt, A. P., B. C. Schock, and M. Ennis. 2005. Neutrophils and eosinophils: Clinical implications of their appearance, presence and disappearance in asthma and COPD. *Curr Drug Targets Inflamm Allergy* 4 (4):415–23.

Witko-Sarsat, V., J. Mocek, D. Bouayad, N. Tamassia, J. A. Ribeil, C. Candalh, N. Davezac, N. Reuter, L. Mouthon, O. Hermine, M. Pederzoli-Ribeil, and M. A. Cassatella. 2010. Proliferating cell nuclear antigen acts as a cytoplasmic platform controlling human neutrophil survival. *J Exp Med* 207 (12):2631–45.

Wu, W., J. M. Samet, D. B. Peden, and P. A. Bromberg. 2010. Phosphorylation of p65 is required for zinc oxide nanoparticle-induced interleukin 8 expression in human bronchial epithelial cells. *Environ Health Perspect* 118 (7):982–7.

Yin, H., P. S. Casey, M. J. McCall, and M. Fenech. 2015. Size-dependent cytotoxicity and genotoxicity of ZnO particles to human lymphoblastoid (WIL2-NS) cells. *Environ Mol Mutagen* 56 (9):767–76.

Section III

Techniques and Concepts for Risk Control

10

Evaluating the Interactions of Silver Nanoparticles and Mammalian Cells Based on Biomics Technologies

Xiaoying Lü and Yan Huang

CONTENTS

10.1 Introduction of Silver Nanoparticles

On 18 October 2011, the European Union redefined nanomaterial as a natural, incidental or manufactured material containing particles, with one or more external dimensions in the size range 1–100 nm (Kang et al. 2015). Among nanoparticles, silver nanoparticles (Ag NPs) are the most commercialised nano-compound at present (Ip et al. 2006). In fact, silver had been believed to have beneficial healing and antidisease properties before the emergence of antibiotics (Kulthong et al. 2012) and had been used for decades because of its health benefits as an antimicrobial and antifungal substance (Ahamed et al. 2010). Recently, studies suggest that the antimicrobial activity is retained in Ag NPs (Melaiye et al. 2005). Thus, Ag NPs are frequently used for medical purposes in both surgical and nonsurgical equipment such as wound dressings, bandages, catheters, medical face masks, heart valves, skin, bone grafts and other implants (Awasthi et al. 2015; Funez et al. 2013). Beside their antimicrobial potential, Ag NPs have also been proven to be active against several types of viruses including human immunodeficiency virus, hepatitis B virus, herpes simplex virus and so on (Galdiero et al. 2011).

10.2 Biocompatibility Evaluation of Ag NPs

Biocompatibility evaluation is an important task in the research of biomaterials. Up to now, preclinical evaluation of biocompatibility has been carried out at three different levels: the animal level, the cellular level and the molecular level. As one kind of biomaterial, the biocompatibility evaluation of Ag NPs has also been carried out at these three levels (Lü et al. 2009).

10.2.1 At the Animal Level

Since Ag NPs will eventually be used in the human body, animal experiment is still a common method to study the biological properties of Ag NPs. Takenaka et al. (2001) treated rats with 15-nm Ag NPs and found that the particles entered the lungs, blood, liver, kidney, spleen, brain, heart, nasal cavities and lung-associated lymph nodes. Garcia et al. found that a low dose (1 mg/kg) of Ag NPs resulted in no changes in body and testis weights, sperm concentration and motility, fertility indices or follicle-stimulating hormone and luteinising hormone serum concentrations. While serum and intratesticular testosterone concentrations were increased, epithelium morphology, germ cell apoptosis and Leydig cell size were significantly changed (Garcia et al. 2014). Shahare et al. observed the effect of Ag NPs (3–20 nm) on small intestinal mucosa of Swiss albino male mice. The results revealed that Ag NPs significantly decreased the body weight of mice and damage to the epithelial cell microvilli and intestinal glands. The loss of microvilli might reduce the absorptive capacity of the intestinal epithelium and has led to weight loss (Shahare et al. 2013). Al Gurabi et al. (2015) investigated the intraperitoneal toxicity of Ag NPs in Swiss albino mice. Ag NPs induced a significant increase in serum liver injury markers including alkaline phosphatase, alanine aminotransferase and aspartate aminotransferase; they also caused severe damage to the liver.

10.2.2 At the Cellular Level

The evaluation at the animal level can comprehensively reflect the effect of Ag NPs on the body; however, the experimental cycle is long, it is expensive, the process is complex and it is difficult to control the individual differences and interference factors. Moreover, the results from animal experiments might not be extrapolated to human beings very well. In contrast, the cellular experiment has the following advantages: it is simple, it is rapid, it is sensitive, it is economic, it makes standardisation easy to achieve and it has good repeatability; hence, the *in vitro* cytotoxicity test is often used as a screening test in assessing the biocompatibility of Ag NPs. Hussain et al. evaluated the acute toxic effects of Ag NPs, MoO_3, Al, Fe_3O_4 and TiO_2 on BRL3A cells. Results showed that Ag NPs had the highest toxicity, depleted glutathione, reduced mitochondrial membrane potential and increased reactive oxygen species (ROS) production. The cytotoxicity of Ag NPs might mediate through oxidative stress (Hussain et al. 2005). AshaRani et al. investigated the toxicity of Ag NPs to IMR-90 and U251 cells. Results showed that uptake of Ag NPs occurred mainly through endocytosis and distributed in the cytoplasm and nucleus. The toxicity of Ag NP was mediated through intracellular calcium transients and significant change of cell morphology, spreading and surface ruffling. The signalling cascades played key roles in cytoskeleton deformations and in inhibiting cell proliferation (AshaRani et al. 2009a). AshaRani et al. further studied the cytotoxicity and genotoxicity of starch-coated Ag NPs. Ag NPs were found to be present inside the mitochondria and nucleus, reduced ATP content, caused mitochondria damage and increased production of ROS. Ag NP treatment also caused DNA damage, which led to cell cycle arrest in the G2/M phase. A possible mechanism of toxicity was proposed (AshaRani et al. 2009b). Kang et al. compared the cytotoxicity of ZnO NPs with Ag NPs to human epithelial colorectal adenocarcinoma (Caco-2) cells. The results showed that NPs with a higher concentration and treated for a longer time induced more serious cytotoxicity. Their cytotoxicity in Caco-2 cells might be mediated through oxidative stress (Kang et al. 2015). Awasthi et al. studied the toxicity of Ag NPs with different dose concentrations (25, 50 and 100 μg/mL) to Chinese hamster ovary cells. Ag NPs decreased mitochondrial membrane potential, comparable catalase, SOD, glutathione peroxidase, glutathione-*S*-transferase, glutathione reductase activities and glutathione level. DNA damage was also increased in a dose-dependent manner (Awasthi et al. 2015).

10.2.3 At the Molecular Level

With the cell-level evaluations, we can only know whether the cell died or not and how many cells died, but what happened before the cells died and how cells responded to Ag NPs at the molecular level are unknown (Lü et al. 2013).

10.2.3.1 Traditional Molecular Biology Methods

In 1995, Dr. Chou Laisheng first put forward the concept of molecular biocompatibility, and the regulation of surface topography on fibronectin mRNA expression was investigated with Northern hybridisation analysis (Chou et al. 1995). Subsequently, some molecular biological methods, such as Reverse Transcription–Polymerase Chain Reaction (RT-PCR), *in situ* hybridisation, Northern blotting, Western blotting and ELISA, were gradually applied in evaluating the molecular biocompatibility of biomaterials. Jeyaraj et al. studied the cytotoxicity of Ag NPs on human cervical carcinoma cells. RT-PCR and Western blot results indicated that Ag NPs could selectively inhibit the cellular mechanism of HeLa by DNA damage and caspase-mediated cell death (Jeyaraj et al. 2013). Qin et al. analysed the cytotoxicity of Ag NPs and their effects on osteogenic differentiation of stem cells with RT-PCR. The results stated that Ag NPs could promote osteogenic differentiation at a suitable concentration without inducing cytotoxicity (Qin et al. 2014). Rahman et al. evaluated the effects of 25-nm Ag NPs on gene expression in different regions of the mouse brain with mouse oxidative stress and antioxidant defence arrays. The expression of genes found varied in the caudate nucleus, frontal cortex and hippocampus after treatment with Ag NPs. Ag NPs might produce apoptosis and neurotoxicity by generating free radical–induced oxidative stress and by altering gene expression (Rahman et al. 2009). However, these technologies could only analyse the expression of one or a few genes at one time after Ag NP treatment; they could not explain the interaction mechanism of Ag NPs with cells.

10.2.3.2 High-Throughput Biomics Technologies

The rapid developments in high-throughput biomics technologies enable researchers to comprehensively and systematically analyse the molecular mechanisms of toxicity of Ag NPs. Microarray is an effective means for detecting and characterising DNA. It is a collection of microscopic DNA spots attached to a solid surface. One spot contains picomole amounts of one DNA probe. Probe-target hybridisation is usually detected and quantified by detection of fluorophore-, silver- or chemiluminescence-labelled targets to determine relative abundance of nucleic acid sequences in the sample (Krizkova et al. 2016). Microarray-based toxicogenomics studies serve as a suitable technique to explore the genome-wide effects of Ag NPs on any organism through a single experiment (Das et al. 2012). Kawata et al. applied DNA microarray to study the *in vitro* toxicity of Ag NPs at non-cytotoxic doses to human hepatoma cells (Kawata et al. 2009). Most of the differentially expressed genes were involved in chromosome segregation, cell division, proliferation, DNA biosynthesis and restoration of DNA after DNA damage. Bouwmeester et al. (2011) used human intestinal epithelium consisting of Caco-2 and M-cells to study the effects of Ag NPs with different sizes (20, 34, 61 and 113 nm) on whole-genome mRNA expression. The results showed that Ag NPs induced the change of expression of a series of stress response–related genes. Lim et al. (2012) studied the effects of 5- and 100-nm Ag NPs on inflammatory and stress genes in human macrophages using cDNA microarray analysis. The results showed that low-level and early-stage exposure to 5-nm Ag NPs induced expression of IL-8 as well as stress genes against ROS.

After genomics and transcriptomics, proteomics is the next step in the study of biological systems. Proteomics is the large-scale study of proteins within a cell, tissue or organism, which was first defined in 1995. It is a rapidly evolving field focussed on identification and characterisation of these proteins and their proteoforms. Quantitative methods in proteomics have enabled comparative analysis of protein expression profiles, providing information of cells and proteins in different stages of bio-production (Landels et al. 2015). Verano-Braga et al. used mass spectrometry–based proteomic technologies to investigate the Ag NP–protein interaction in human LoVo cells. The data indicated that 100-nm nanoparticles played indirect effects via three pathways. Twenty-nanometre nanoparticles induced direct effects on cellular stress and up-regulated the expression of proteins involved in SUMOylation. Protein ubiquitination and degradation were triggered by both 20- and 100-nm nanoparticles (Verano-Braga et al. 2014). Miethling-Graff et al. (2014) evaluated the cellular proteomic response of the human LoVo cell line to 10 μg/mL Ag NPs (size, 20 and 100 nm) for 24 h using iTRAQ-based proteomics technology. It was found that Ag NPs down-regulated the expression of mitochondrial proteins. The influence of 20-nm Ag NPs on cell death and mitochondrial activity–related proteins and ATP synthesis was stronger than that of 100-nm Ag NPs.

10.2.4 Bioinformatics Analysis

With biomics experiments, a large amount of complex biological data will be produced. How to make an accurate and reasonable analysis of the data and how to find out the biological significance is an important topic in biomics research. Bioinformatics tools can be applied to achieve the above objectives. Among them, clustering, gene ontology (GO) functional annotation and biological pathway analysis are three important methods.

Cluster analysis is a common technique for statistical data analysis. It is the task of grouping a set of objects in such a way that objects in the same group are more similar to each other than to those in other groups. GO is a controlled vocabulary used to describe the molecular function, biological process and cellular component of genes and gene products in a cell (Lü et al. 2009; Yang et al. 2010). Pathway analysis can identify subtle changes in related genes or proteins by representing interacting networks (Lü et al. 2010). By examining the changes in gene or protein expression in a pathway, the biological causes of Ag NPs can be explored. Clustering, GO and biological pathway analysis reflect three different aspects of the same set of biological data. Combining these three methods together could incorporate expression pattern, functional annotations and biological pathways, so as to describe biological processes comprehensively and to illustrate the molecular mechanism of cytotoxicity of Ag NPs effectively (Lü et al. 2010; Yang et al. 2010).

10.3 Studying the Cytotoxicity Mechanism of Ag NPs via Multilevel Biomics

10.3.1 Our Research Route

In the past 10 years of studying the cytotoxicity mechanism of Ag NPs using multilevel biomics methods, a complete research route has been formed (Figure 10.1) by our group: (1) Ag NPs were prepared and characterised; (2) the effects of Ag NPs on the morphology, proliferation, cell cycle and apoptosis of human dermal fibroblasts (HDFs) were evaluated at the cellular level; (3) biomics experiments were carried out to obtain the mRNA, microRNA (miRNA) and protein expression in Ag NP–treated HDFs; (4) bioinformatics analyses were performed to filter important mRNA/miRNA/protein and key biological pathways;

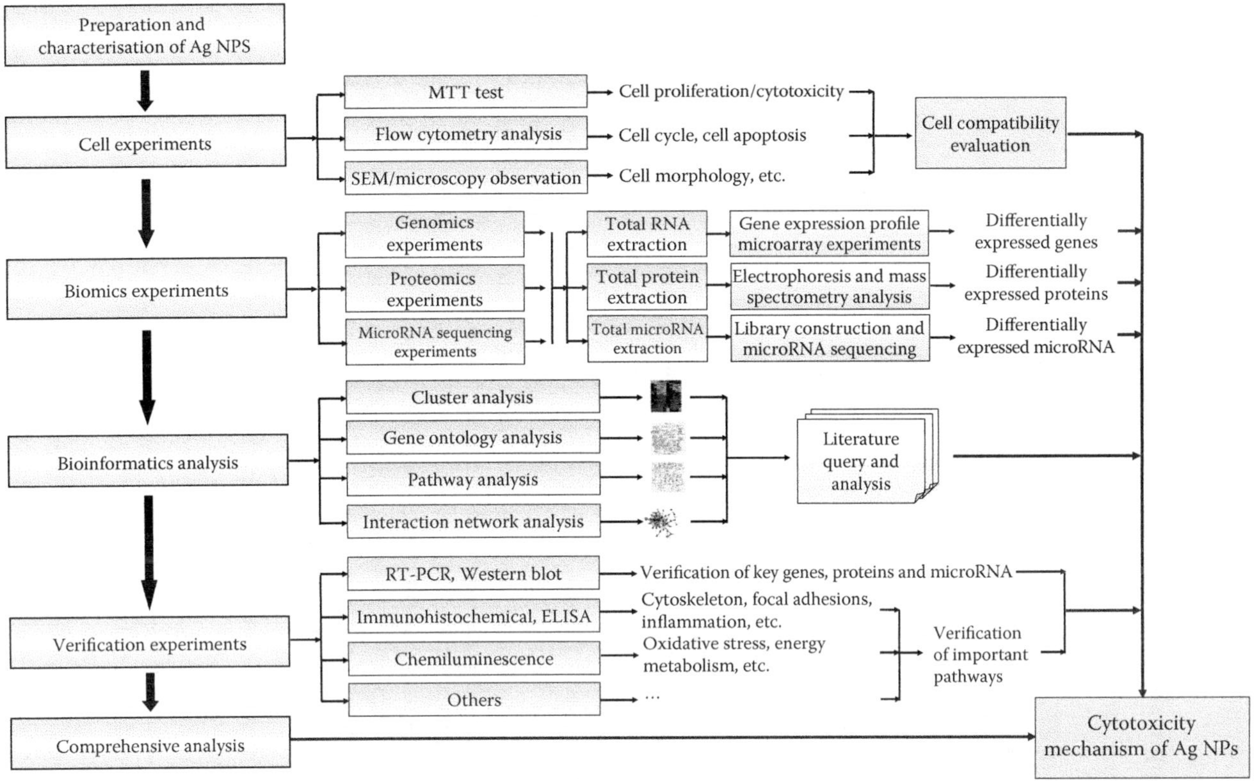

FIGURE 10.1
(See colour insert.) The research route for investigating the cytotoxicity mechanism of Ag NPs based on biomics and bioinformatics technologies. (From Lü, X.Y. et al., *Journal of Inorganic Materials* 28(2013):21–8.)

(5) a variety of traditional cellular/molecular biology methods were used to verify the bioinformatics analysis results; (6) the above results from cellular and biomics experiments, bioinformatics analysis and validation experiments were combined to explore the cytotoxicity mechanism of Ag NPs.

10.3.2 Application of Gene Expression Profile Microarray

Our research group (Ma et al. 2011) investigated the interaction mechanism between Ag NPs and HDFs at the gene level. After the treatment of Ag NPs for 1, 4 and 8 h, 237, 1149 and 684 genes were found differentially expressed, with 1593 different genes in total. Among them, more genes were up-regulated in all three groups. Here, hierarchical clustering and GO analysis were combined for investigating the trend of GO function with time passed after Ag NPs treatment. Figure 10.2 showed the diagram of agglomerative hierarchical clustering of 1593 differentially expressed genes. All genes were divided into five clusters, and Database for Annotation, Visualization and Integrated Discovery (DAVID, http://david.abcc.ncifcrf.gov/) was used for GO functional annotation analysis. Table 10.1 lists the involved gene number and related five significant GO terms with smallest p values in each of the five clusters. Genes in cluster A were down-regulated, and the expression pattern was increased first and then decreased (Figure 10.2). It could be seen from Table 10.1 that these genes were associated with 'regulation of cell process', 'biopolymer metabolic process', 'nucleobase nucleoside nucleotide and nucleic acid metabolic process' and so on. Genes in cluster B were also down-regulated, while the expression level of most genes showed a downward trend as time passed, with the lowest expression value appearing at 8 h. The GO categories including 'cellular lipid metabolic process', 'signal transduction' and 'response to wounding' were affected. An increasing trend was found in up-regulated genes in cluster C, which suggested that Ag NPs might enhance their influence on those genes whose functions related to 'organelle organisation and biogenesis', 'cell cycle process' and so on. Our previous flow cytometry results had shown that Ag NPs mainly affected the S and G2/M phases, resulting in cell cycle arrest (Ma et al. 2011). Thus, the GO analysis results coincided with the flow cytometry results. Up-regulated genes in cluster D, which also first increased and then decreased, were enriched in 'Ribonucleoprotein complex biogenesis and assembly', 'rRNA processing', 'Nucleobase nucleoside nucleotide and nucleic acid metabolic process' and so on. Genes in Cluster E were up-regulated extremely at 1 h and back to normal state at 8 h, implying that changes in 'negative regulation of cellular process' and 'negative regulation of biological process' might appear at the early stage of Ag NP treatment.

The biological responses of cells to nanoparticles, such as mRNA expression, protein expression and toxicity, had been suggested to be time-dependent. Here, at 1 h, Ag NPs mainly affected the regulation of cellular processes (cluster E), and at 4 h, the influence changed to the metabolism of various biomolecules (clusters A and D). Table 10.1 also shows that the largest numbers of

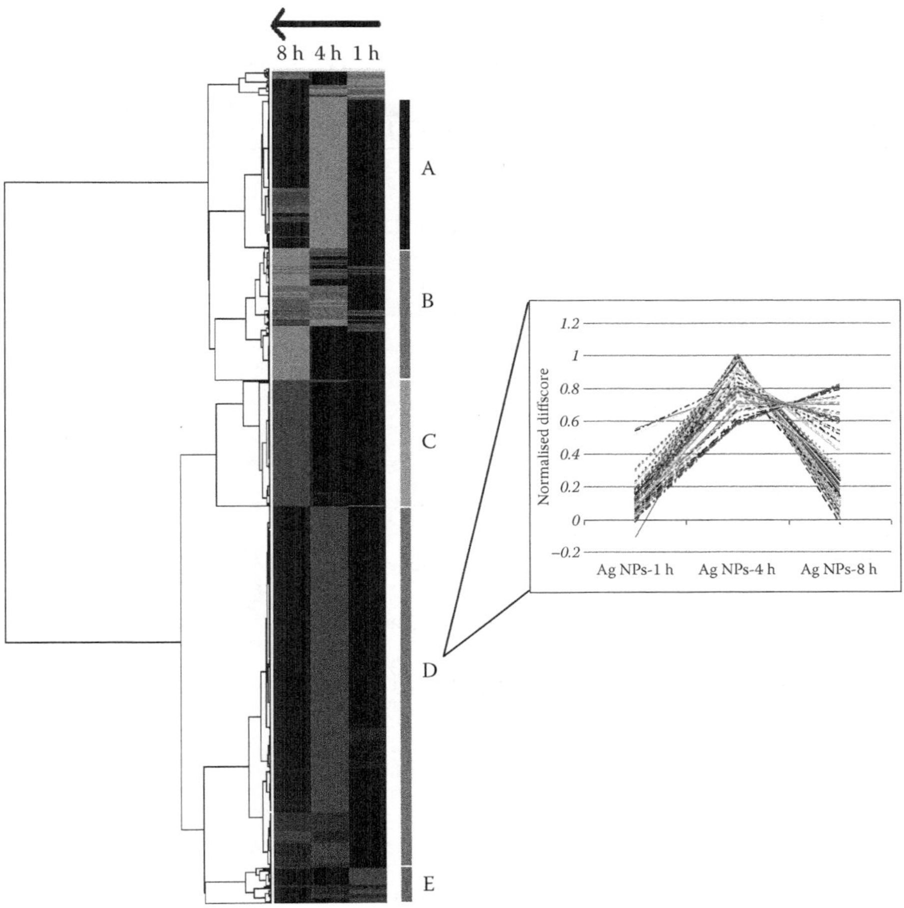

FIGURE 10.2
(See colour insert.) Global view of expression patterns of 1593 differentially expressed genes by hierarchical clustering analysis. The left heat map is the hierarchical clustering diagram, each row represents the expression level for one gene during the treatment and each column represents a time point. The intensity of red/green represents the magnitude of change in expression for each gene. Red means that the gene was up-regulated, while green means that the gene was down-regulated. Five clusters that demonstrate specific expression patterns during the entire treatment were regarded as clusters A, B, C, D and E; the zoomed-in view was a sketch diagram of expression pattern for cluster D, representing the expression trend over time. (From Ma, J.W. et al., *Journal of Biomedical Nanotechnology* 7(2011):263–75.)

genes were classified in clusters A and D and were most significantly regulated at 4 h. Thus, 4 h might be a key time point at which nucleic acid metabolic processes and gene expression regulation might be obviously affected. Finally, at 8 h, the impact on cellular organelles and the entire cell appeared (clusters B and C). Hence, at the mRNA level, Ag NPs also showed a time-dependent influence on HDFs. With the integration of clustering and GO analyses for Ag

TABLE 10.1

Enriched Biological Process GO Term in Each of the Five Clusters

Cluster	No. of Genes	Biological Process GO Term	Counts per Cluster	*p* Value[a]
A	290	Regulation of cell process	93	1.7E–8
		Biopolymer metabolic process	99	3.6E–6
		Nucleobase nucleoside nucleotide and nucleic acid metabolic process	73	5.5E–4
		Regulation of gene expression	54	7.3E–4
		Regulation of metabolic process	57	8.0E–4
B	252	Cellular lipid metabolic process	16	2.4E–3
		Lipid metabolic process	18	2.8E–3
		Signal transduction	55	5.8E–3
		Response to wounding	12	5.9E–3
		Lymphocyte activation	7	1.4E–2
C	240	Organelle organisation and biogenesis	33	3.1E–7
		Cell cycle process	17	4.0E–3
		Ribonucleoprotein complex biogenesis and assembly	8	4.7E–3
		Anatomical structure morphogenesis	21	1.1E–2
		Mitotic cell cycle	9	1.6E–2
D	686	Ribonucleoprotein complex biogenesis and assembly	29	1.0E–11
		rRNA processing	11	1.7E–5
		Nucleobase nucleoside nucleotide and nucleic acid metabolic process	159	3.0E–5
		Cellular biosynthetic process	56	2.9E–4
		tRNA processing	9	5.1E–4
E	66	Negative regulation of cellular process	10	7.8E–3
		Negative regulation of biological process	10	1.0E–2
		Biopolymer metabolic process	25	2.2E–2
		Anatomical structure morphogenesis	9	2.3E–2
		Regulation of metabolic process	16	3.4E–2

Source: Ma, J.W., Lü, X.Y., Huang, Y. Genomic analysis of cytotoxicity response to nanosilver in human dermal fibroblasts. *Journal of Biomedical Nanotechnology* 7(2011):263–75.

[a] *p* values were calculated to determine the significance of enriched terms in each cluster. The lower the *p* value, the more significant correlation was between the specific GO term and the cluster of genes.

NP–induced gene expression data, a more comprehensive understanding of the impact of Ag NPs on HDFs was obtained. Ag NPs might have considerable effects on HDFs by affecting gene expression regulation, biomolecule metabolism, cell cycle process and some other aspects.

GenMAPP analysis showed that 90 local MAPP biological pathways belonging to cellular processes, metabolic processes, molecular functions and physiological processes in HDFs were influenced by Ag NPs. According to the proportions of the involved genes in each pathway and the number, six biological pathways listed in Table 10.2 were discussed, with 67 differentially expressed genes in total.

1. *Electron Transport Chain Pathway*

   ATP is mostly generated by electron transport chains in mitochondria. In the 'electron transport chain pathway' (Figure 10.3), 11 genes were found involved, with all up-regulated and vital for mitochondrial complexes. Among them, 10 genes belonged to cluster D (Figure 10.1), which suggested that HDFs had the greatest impact on ATP synthesis at 4 h.

TABLE 10.2

Six Concerned Biological Pathways and the Number of Differentially Expressed Genes Respectively Generated by GenMAPP Software

No.	Pathways	Description of Function	Total Number	Up-Regulated Gene Number	Down-Regulated Gene Number
1	Electron transport chain	ATP synthesis and provides energy for cells	11	11	0
2	Regulation of actin cytoskeleton	Functions in the maintenance of cell morphology and intracellular trafficking	12	6	6
3	Eukaryotic transcription initiation	The initiation process where genetic information stored in DNA is copied into mRNA	7	7	0
4	mRNA processing	Conversion of precursor messenger RNA into mature messenger RNA, which occurs in the cell nucleus before the RNA is translated	21	16	5
5	Translation factors	The phosphorylation of translation factors can activate (or inhibit) protein synthesis, which is the ultimate step of gene expression	6	4	2
6	Cytoplasmic ribosomal proteins	In conjunction with rRNA, they make up the ribosomal subunits involved in translation	10	9	1

Source: Ma, J.W., Lü, X.Y., Huang, Y. Genomic analysis of cytotoxicity response to nanosilver in human dermal fibroblasts. *Journal of Biomedical Nanotechnology* 7(2011):263–75.

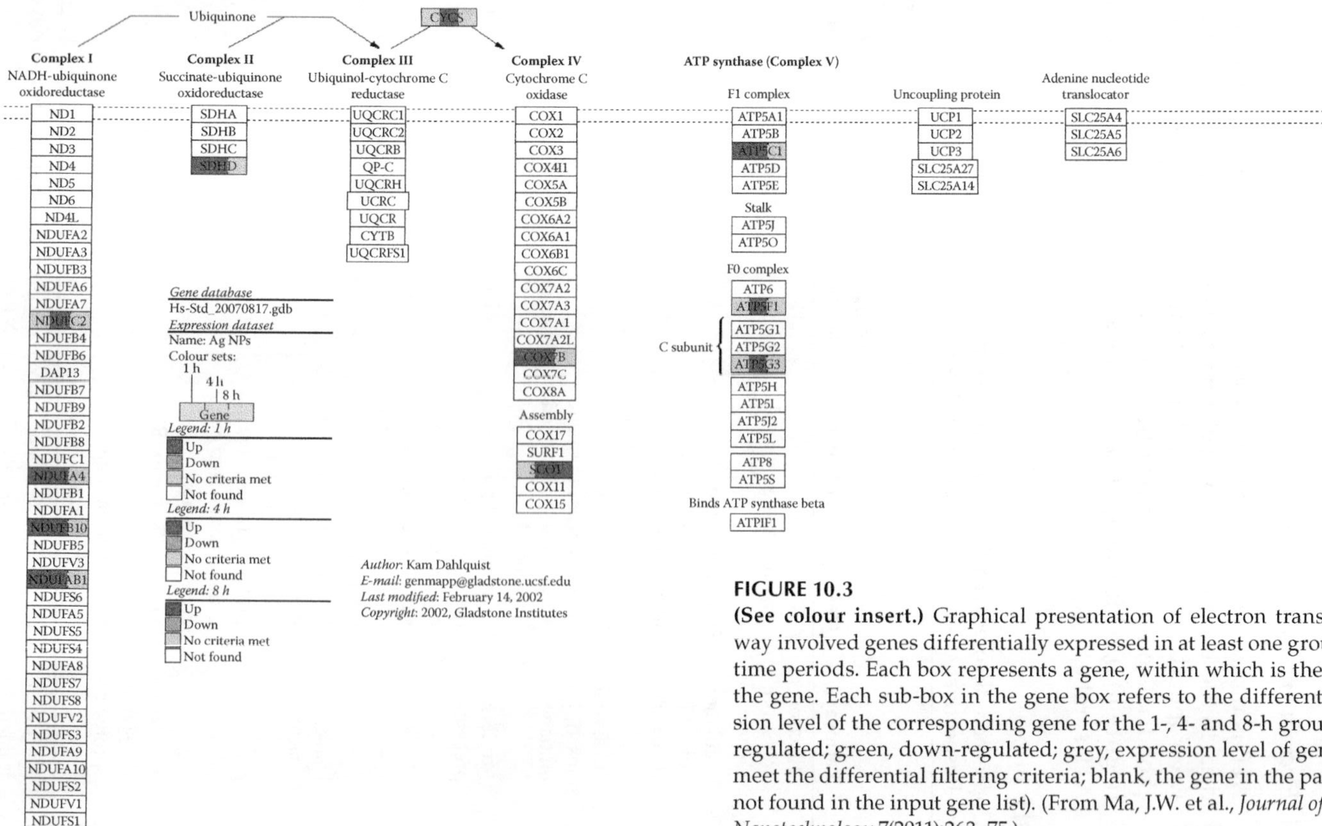

FIGURE 10.3
(See colour insert.) Graphical presentation of electron transport pathway involved genes differentially expressed in at least one group of three time periods. Each box represents a gene, within which is the symbol of the gene. Each sub-box in the gene box refers to the differential expression level of the corresponding gene for the 1-, 4- and 8-h group (red, up-regulated; green, down-regulated; grey, expression level of genes did not meet the differential filtering criteria; blank, the gene in the pathway was not found in the input gene list). (From Ma, J.W. et al., *Journal of Biomedical Nanotechnology* 7(2011):263–75.)

ATP5C1 encodes one ATP synthase, which benefits for catalysing ATP synthesis. The up-regulation of *ATP5C1* might imply the enhancement of ATP synthesis. This might be assumed that after cells were treated with Ag NPs, a self-defence mechanism in cells was activated in a short time, and ATP synthesis was enhanced to meet the increased demands of energy, but ATP synthesis was interrupted as time passed.

CYCS encodes cytochrome c, a strategic intermediate in cell apoptosis, and was up-regulated. Cytochrome c is usually considered as a marker of cell apoptosis, and its release is mastered by voltage-dependent anion channel on mitochondrial outer membrane. The up-regulation of *CYCS* might indicate the damage of mitochondrial membrane in HDFs (Qiu et al. 2000).

The inhibition of the electron transport chain is known to evoke cell death by generating ROS. Some reports indicated that the cytotoxicity of Ag NPs is attributed to the accumulation of ROS (Hsin et al. 2008; Rahman et al. 2009), whereas several reports showed that Ag NPs led to minimal oxidative stress (Cha et al. 2008; Farkas et al. 2010). Here, four genes (*NDUFC2, NDUFA4, NDUFB10* and *NDUFAB1*), which encode NADH-ubiquinone oxidoreductase of mitochondrial complex I (the major ROS generation site), were up-regulated after Ag NP treatment. This might be because the treatment time of Ag NPs was too short to generate discernible ROS and affect gene expression.

2. *Regulation of Actin Cytoskeleton Pathway*

Actin cytoskeleton plays its role in the conservation of cell morphology and polarity, endocytosis, intracellular trafficking, contractility, motility and cell division (Gourlay and Ayscough 2005). In Figure 10.4, 12 differentially expressed genes were found included in the 'regulation of actin cytoskeleton pathway', with 6 genes up-regulated and 6 genes down-regulated. Up-regulated *ARPC5* is very important for the organisation of the Arp2/3 protein complex, which is related to the control of actin polymerisation. Actin polymerisation can be regulated by external stimuli and plays the main role in many physiological functions, particularly in cell motility (Mitchison and Cramer 1996). Thus, the up-regulation of *ARPC5* might imply the abnormality of actin polymerisation. Gourlay et al. reported that actin cytoskeleton could regulate ROS release from mitochondria and played a key role in activating cell death pathways. The supposed mechanism is that actin can master the opening and closing of the voltage-dependent anion channel on the mitochondria outer membrane and then control the release of apoptogenic proteins, including cytochrome c (Gourlay and Ayscough 2005).

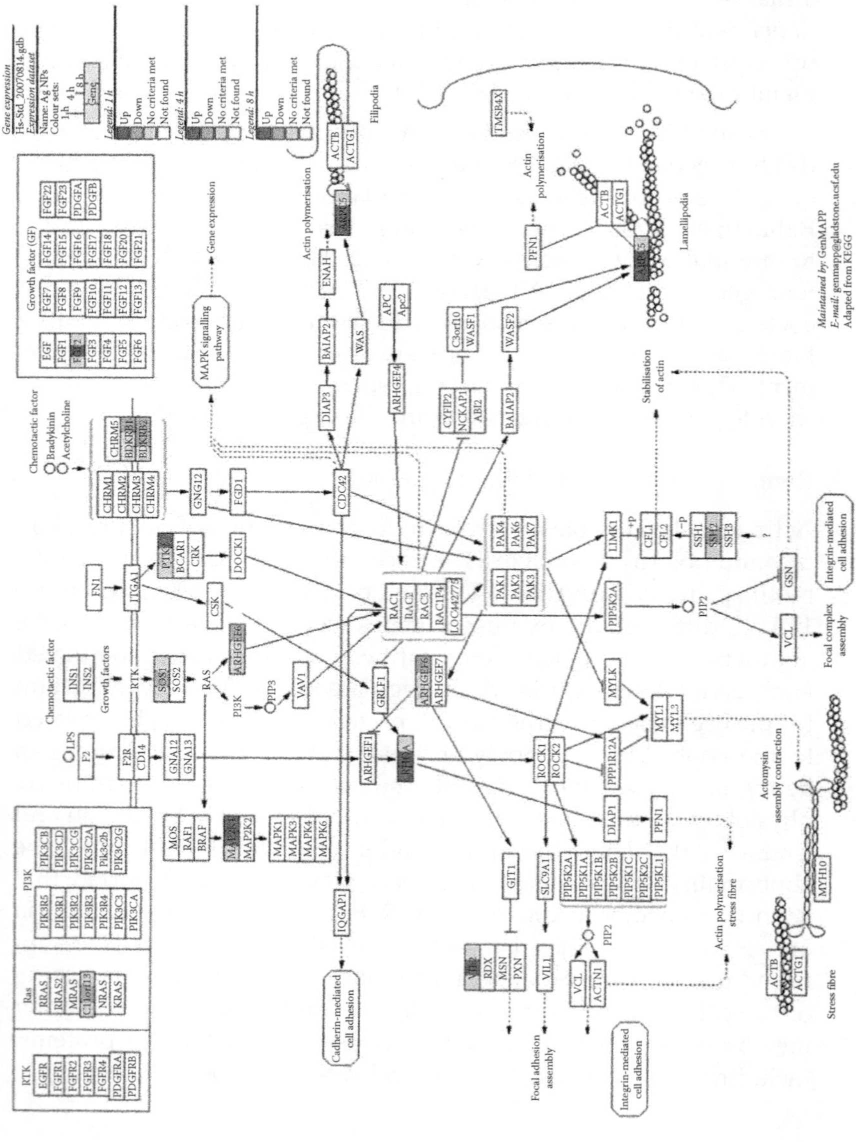

FIGURE 10.4
(See colour insert.) Graphical presentation of regulation of the actin cytoskeleton pathway involved genes differentially expressed in at least one group of three time periods. Each box represents a gene, within which is the symbol of the gene. Each sub-box in the gene box refers to the differential expression level of the corresponding gene for the 1-, 4- and 8-h group. (From Ma, J.W. et al., *Journal of Biomedical Nanotechnology* 7 (2011):263–75.)

3. *Four Pathways Associated with Gene Expression Processes*

Gene expression is the process by which the genetic information stored in the DNA sequence is synthesised through transcription and translation. In gene expression, several steps, including transcription, RNA splicing, translation and posttranslational modification of protein, can be modulated. Because they are closely related to the gene expression process, four pathways including 'eukaryotic transcription initiation', 'mRNA processing', 'translation factors' and 'cytoplasmic ribosomal proteins' (nos. 3–6 in Table 10.2) were discussed as a group. Forty-four differentially expressed genes participated in these four pathways, and most of them were up-regulated (Figure 10.5).

In the 'eukaryotic transcription initiation pathway' (Figure 10.5a), most involved genes code transcription initiation factors, which have functions in the downstream of signalling cascades and are relevant to biological and extracellular stimuli. 'mRNA processing pathway' contains three main steps, including mRNA capping, processing of intron-containing and mRNA 3′-end processing (Figure 10.5b). It could be seen that most differentially expressed genes were relevant to the mRNA splicing process. Among them, up-regulated *SFRS*1, *SFRS*2 and *SFRS7* belong to the SR family of splicing factor and act as key regulators of mRNA metabolism (Long and Caceres 2009). 'Translation factors pathway' (Figure 10.5c) and 'cytoplasmic ribosomal proteins pathway' (Figure 10.5d) are related to the translational regulation of gene expression. The results implied that Ag NPs regulated gene expression processes in HDFs.

DNA damage was regarded as a key aspect in the cytotoxicity mechanism of Ag NPs. Some studies reported that Ag NPs could induce DNA damage, collapse chromosome strands, evoke DNA repair progress and arrest the cell cycle (AshaRani et al. 2009a; Kim et al. 2009; Kumari et al. 2009). Here, *GADD45B* was the significantly up-regulated gene, which belongs to the gene group whose transcript levels would increase under stress conditions or DNA-damaging agents' exposure. Expression of the *GADD*45-like genes can lead to the activation of p38/JNK via MTK1/MEKK4 and affect cell cycle and apoptosis (Takekawa and Saito 1998). JNK activation had been found in Ag NP–induced cell apoptosis (Hsin et al. 2008). Hence, the up-regulation of *GADD45B* might suggest that Ag NPs can induce DNA damage and then cause cell cycle arrest.

Beside the abovementioned pathways, some other pathways were also found to be affected by Ag NP–induced differentially expressed genes, such as focal adhesion, insulin signalling, TCA cycle and so on. Genes participating in focal adhesion might imply that the

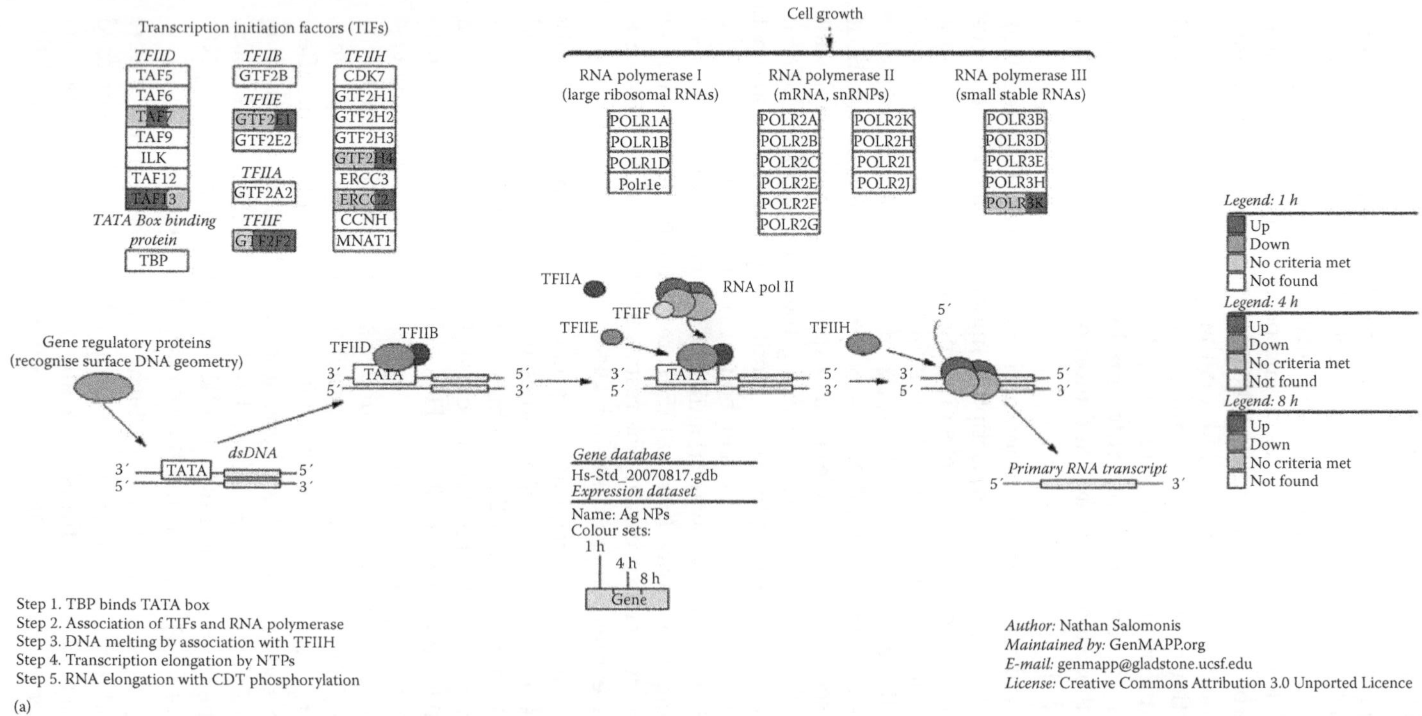

FIGURE 10.5
(See colour insert.) Graphical presentation of regulation of four pathways associated with gene expression processes. (a) Eukaryotic transcription initiation pathway. Each box represents a gene, within which is the symbol of the gene. Each sub-box in the gene box refers to the differential expression level of the corresponding gene for the 1-, 4- and 8-h group. *(Continued)*

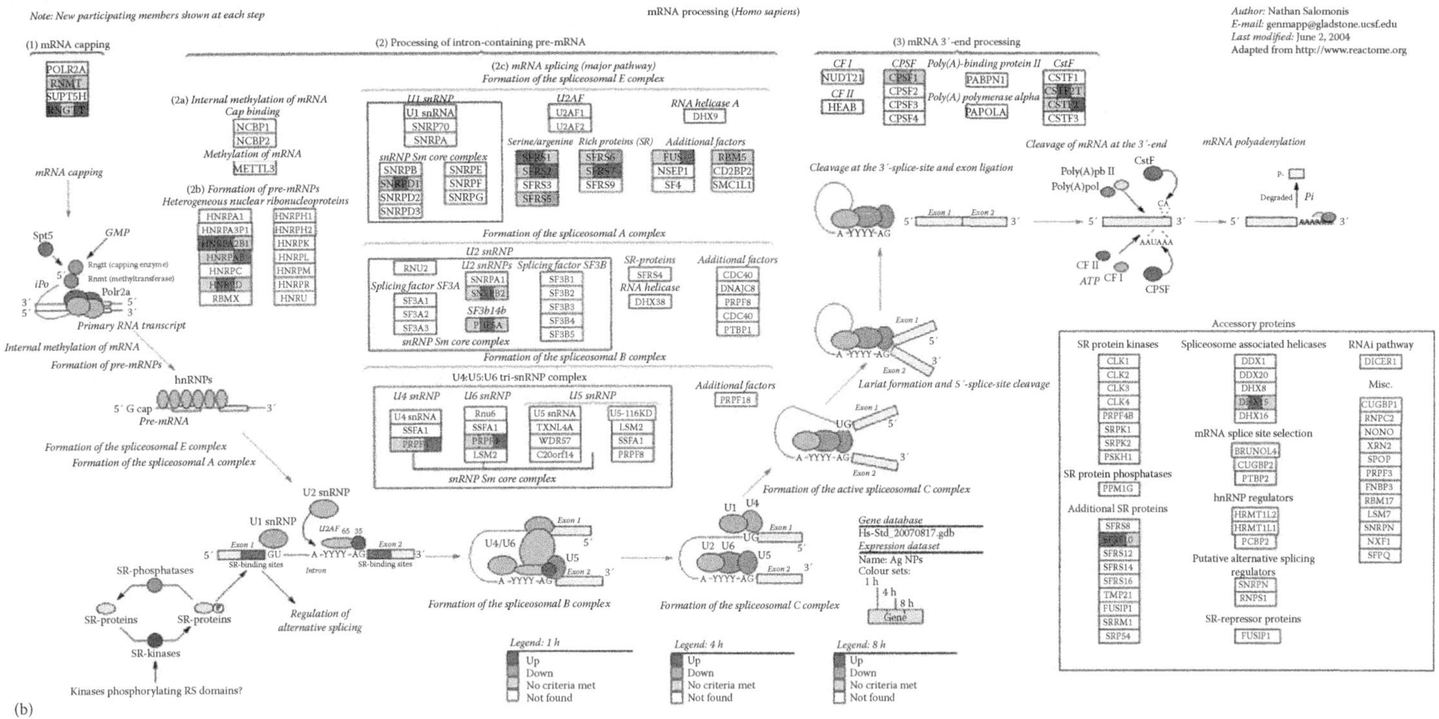

FIGURE 10.5 (CONTINUED)
(See colour insert.) Graphical presentation of regulation of four pathways associated with gene expression processes. (b) mRNA processing pathway. Each box represents a gene, within which is the symbol of the gene. Each sub-box in the gene box refers to the differential expression level of the corresponding gene for the 1-, 4- and 8-h group. *(Continued)*

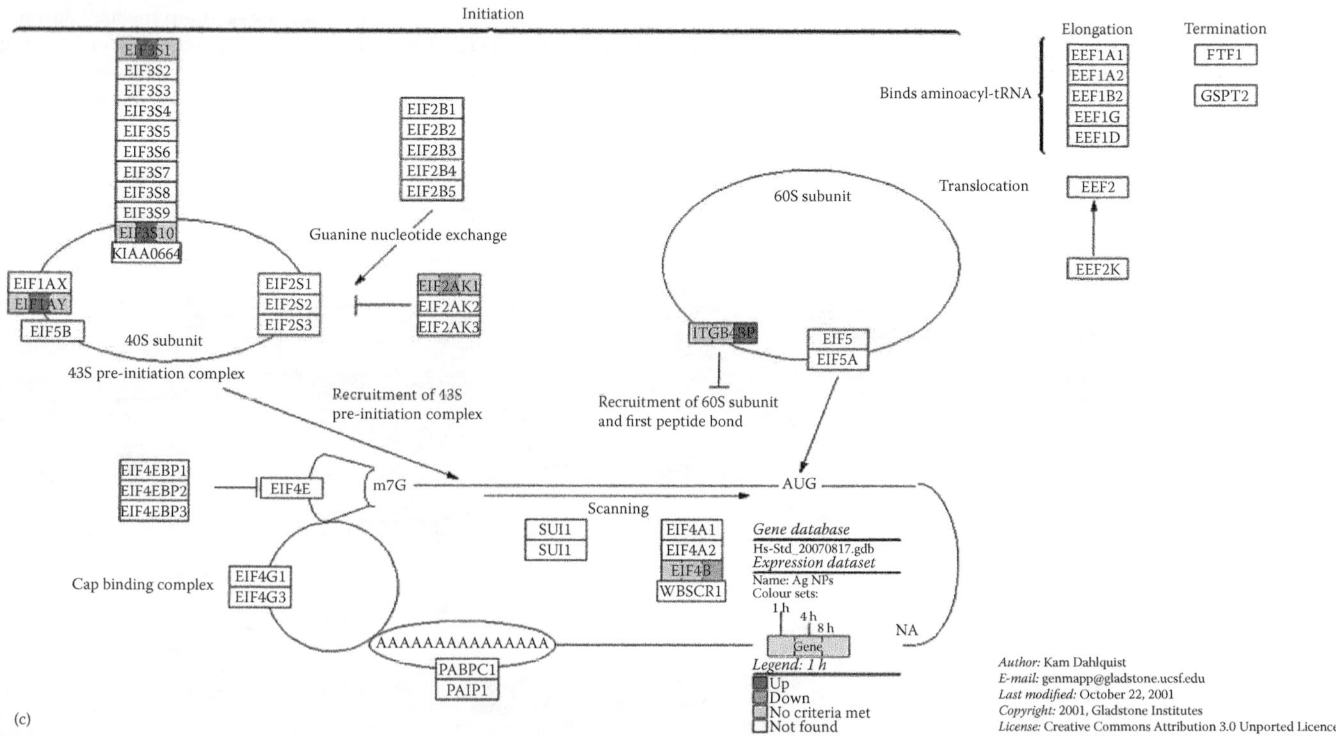

FIGURE 10.5 (CONTINUED)
(See colour insert.) Graphical presentation of regulation of four pathways associated with gene expression processes. (c) Translation factors pathway. Each box represents a gene, within which is the symbol of the gene. Each sub-box in the gene box refers to the differential expression level of the corresponding gene for the 1-, 4- and 8-h group. *(Continued)*

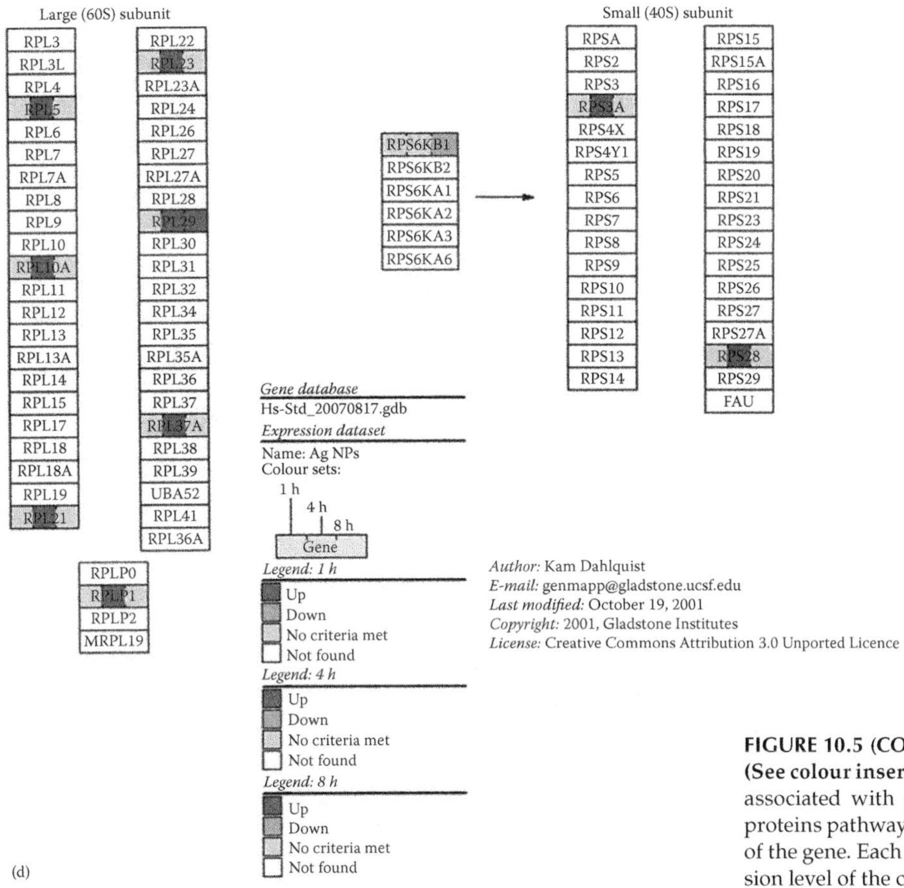

FIGURE 10.5 (CONTINUED)
(See colour insert.) Graphical presentation of regulation of four pathways associated with gene expression processes. (d) Cytoplasmic ribosomal proteins pathway. Each box represents a gene, within which is the symbol of the gene. Each sub-box in the gene box refers to the differential expression level of the corresponding gene for the 1-, 4- and 8-h group.

apoptosis of HDFs could be prevented. The influence on insulin signalling and TCA cycle pathways suggested that energy metabolism might increase soon after Ag NP treatment.

On the whole, the interaction molecular mechanism between Ag NPs and HDFs is illustrated in Figure 10.6 by combining clustering, GO and pathway analysis results.

1. After Ag NPs were not taken, 'regulation of actin cytoskeleton' and 'focal adhesion' were regulated, which suggested that Ag NPs might affect cell shape, mobility and adhesion. Intracellular transportation disturbance might be induced by Ag NPs through regulating transportation-related genes.
2. Glucose transportation was promoted, and genes encoding enzymes in the electron transportation chain and TCA cycle were up-regulated, implying that Ag NPs might disturb mitochondria function and energy metabolism.
3. Ag NPs might affect the entire gene expression process inside the cell nucleus, that is, from transcription to translation. Ag NPs might also cause DNA damage, leading to cell cycle arrest.
4. Finally, apoptosis-related genes like *CYCS* and *CASP3* were stimulated, which suggested that the programmed cell death might be triggered.

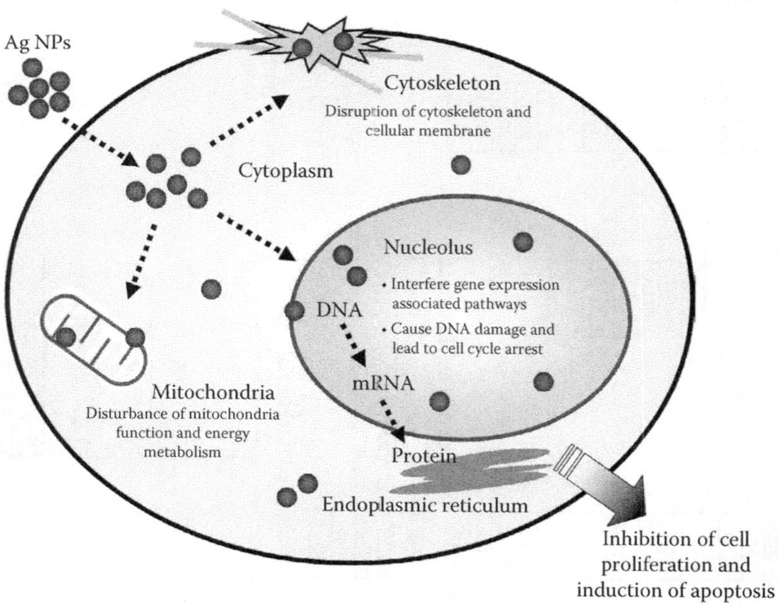

FIGURE 10.6
(See colour insert.) The proposed molecular mechanism of the Ag NP–cell interaction. (From Ma, J.W. et al., *Journal of Biomedical Nanotechnology* 7(2011):263–75.)

10.3.3 Application of Proteomics

Our research group further carried out proteomics analysis of Ag NPs on HDFs based on 2D-DIGE and mass identification. Twenty-five functional proteins were finally obtained after 200 μM Ag NP treatment for 1, 4 and 8 h (Table 10.3) (Huang et al. 2014). Comparing the protein and gene expression data, it was found that the number of differentially expressed proteins (25) was far less than that of differentially expressed genes (1593). Table 10.4 lists

TABLE 10.3

Twenty-Five Differentially Expressed Proteins Identified by MS Analysis in HDF after the Treatment of 200 μM Ag NPs for 1, 4 and 8 h Compared to Untreated HDF

No.	Accession ID	Protein Name	Symbol
19 Up-Regulated Proteins			
1	gi|62896815	Heat shock 70 kDa protein 8 isoform 2 variant	HSPA8
2	gi|5031875	Lamin A/C isoform 2	LMNA
3	gi|62414289	Vimentin	VIM
4	gi|19743875	Fumarate hydratase precursor	FH
5	gi|28626510	Reticulocalbin 3, EF-hand calcium binding domain	RCN3
6	gi|56417849	ER membrane protein complex subunit 1	EMC1
7	gi|6093248	FARP2 FERM, RhoGEF and pleckstrin domain protein 2	FARP2
8	gi|108935845	Heterogeneous nuclear ribonucleoproteins C1/C2	HNRNPC
9	gi|83304912	Myosin-7	MYH7
10	gi|4502101	Annexin I	ANXA1
11	gi|119597993	Annexin A2, isoform CRA_c	ANXA2
12	gi|854189	Tropomyosin isoform	TPM1
13	gi|30581141	Proteasome activator subunit 1 isoform 2	PSME1
14	gi|4505753	Phosphoglycerate mutase 1 (brain)	PGAM1
15	gi|662841	Heat shock protein 27	HSPB1
16	gi|5453549	Thioredoxin peroxidase	PRDX4
17	gi|31543380	Parkinson disease protein 7	PARK7
18	gi|50345294	Hematological and neurological expressed 1 isoform 2	HN1
19	gi|46255705	BTF3L4 protein	BTF3L4
4 Down-Regulated Proteins			
20	gi|16507237	Heat shock 70 kDa protein 5	HSPA5
21	gi|15277503	ACTB protein	ACTB
22	gi|119581148	Keratin 9 (epidermolytic palmoplantar keratoderma)	KRT9
23	gi|41327710	V-crk sarcoma virus CT10 oncogene homolog isoform b	CRK
2 Up- and Down-Regulated Proteins			
24	gi|89574029	Mitochondrial ATP synthase, H+ transporting F1 complex beta subunit	ATP5B
25	gi|32492940	Medulloblastoma antigen MU-MB-20.201	FAM184A

Source: Huang, Y., Lü, X.Y., Ma, J.W. Toxicity of silver nanoparticles to human dermal fibroblasts on microRNA level. *Journal of Biomedical Nanotechnology* 10(2014):3304–17.

TABLE 10.4

Expression Level of 25 Differentially Expressed Proteins and Encoding mRNAs in HDFs with the Treatment of 200 μM Ag NPs for 1, 4 and 8 h Compared to Untreated HDF

No.	Official Symbol	Ag NPs, 1 h		Ag NPs, 4 h		Ag NPs, 8 h	
		Protein	mRNA	Protein	mRNA	Protein	mRNA
1	FH	↑	↑	↑	↑	↑	ND
2	HSPA8	↑	ND	↑	↑	↑	↑
3	EMC1	↑	ND	↑	↑	↑	ND
4	HN1	↑	ND	ND	↑	↑	ND
5	LMNA	↑	ND	↑	ND	↑	ND
6	VIM	↑	ND	↑	ND	↑	ND
7	RCN3	↑	ND	↑	ND	↑	ND
8	FARP2	↑	ND	↑	ND	↑	ND
9	HNRNPC	↑	ND	↑	ND	↑	ND
10	MYH7	↑	ND	↑	ND	↑	ND
11	ANXA1	↑	ND	↑	ND	ND	ND
12	ANXA2	↑	ND	ND	ND	↑	ND
13	TPM1	↑	ND	↑	ND	↑	ND
14	PSME1	↑	ND	↑	ND	↑	ND
15	PGAM1	↑	ND	↑	ND	↑	ND
16	HSPB1	↑	ND	ND	ND	ND	ND
17	PARK7	↑	ND	↑	ND	↑	ND
18	BTF3L4	↑	ND	↑	ND	↑	ND
19	PRDX4	ND	ND	↑	ND	↑	ND
20	ACTB	↓	ND	↓	ND	↓	ND
21	KRT9	↓	ND	↓	ND	↓	ND
22	CRK	ND	ND	↓	ND	↓	ND
23	HSPA5	↓	ND	ND	ND	↓	ND
24	ATP5B	↓	ND	ND	ND	↑	ND
25	FAM184A	↑	ND	↓	ND	↓	ND

Source: Huang, Y., Lü, X.Y., Ma, J.W. Toxicity of silver nanoparticles to human dermal fibroblasts on microRNA level. *Journal of Biomedical Nanotechnology* 10(2014):3304–17.

Note: ↑, Up-regulated; ↓, down-regulated; ND, not differentially expressed.

the expression pattern of 25 differentially expressed proteins and encoding mRNAs in HDFs treated with Ag NPs. Among them, only four differentially expressed mRNA–protein pairs were obtained (FH, HSPA8, EMC1 and HN1), with not exactly the same expression patterns.

Some studies revealed that the mRNA and protein expression levels did not have a quantitative correlation or had weak or opposite correlation (Qu et al. 2013; Yang et al. 2010). The limited technology, sensitivity, depth and database for protein research compared to mRNA are the reasons for the poor correlation (Griffin et al. 2002). According to the central dogma of molecular biology (Figure 10.7), mRNA expression will affect protein expression

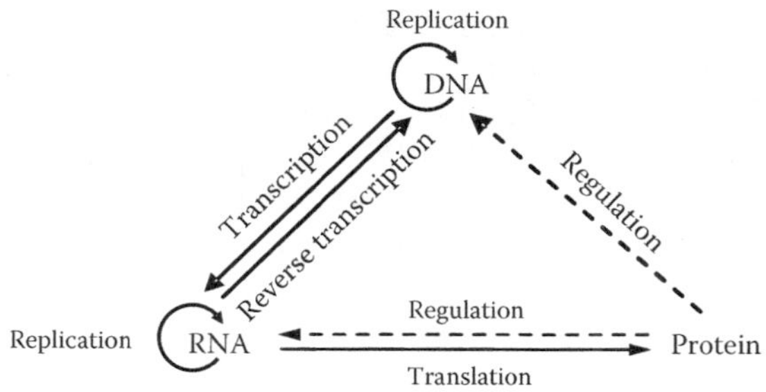

FIGURE 10.7
The central dogma of molecular biology. (Modified according to Crick, F. Central dogma of molecular biology. *Nature* 227(1970):561–3.)

through the translation process, and protein expression shows a certain reverse regulation on mRNA expression (Crick 1970). Hence, the main reason that mRNA and protein have different expression patterns is that there may be regulatory mechanisms in gene expression, posttranslational modifications and protein degradation, as well as other independent mechanisms (Tian et al. 2004).

10.3.4 Application of miRNA Sequencing

For a long time, gene transcription regulation is one research hotspot, as transcription is the first and the most crucial step of gene expression. With the discovery and an in-depth study of a variety of small RNAs, such as miRNA and small interfering RNA, the importance and complexity of post-transcriptional regulation mechanism were gradually recognised.

The first miRNA, *lin-4*, was discovered in 1993, which was found as a short noncoding RNA containing ~22 nucleotide sequences. It was partially complementary to multiple sequences in the 3 UTR of the *lin-14* mRNA and was proposed to inhibit the translation of the *lin-14* mRNA into the LIN-14 protein (Lee et al. 1993). In 2000, the second small RNA, *let-7* RNA, which represses *lin-41* to promote a later developmental transition in *Caenorhabditis elegans*, was found (Reinhart et al. 2000). With more and more miRNAs being discovered, there was a research upsurge on miRNA. The miRNA is a small noncoding RNA molecule (containing approximately 22 nucleotides) found in animals, plants and some viruses. It acts as an endogenous factor that can regulate the expression of mRNA and protein (Takane et al. 2011), plays a pivotal regulatory role in many biological processes (including cell differentiation, cell proliferation/growth, cell mobility and apoptosis) (Farh et al. 2005) and regulates 50% of protein-coding genes and the simultaneous down-modulation of many genes (which can be achieved by a single miRNA or several miRNAs); thus, the global expression profile of a cell is drastically modified (Baek et al. 2008). Because miRNA-mediated gene regulation is situated at the stage immediately before protein synthesis, it plays a critical role in determining the level of protein expression via mRNA degradation or translational repression (Chen et al. 2013). In order to reveal the reason why the differentially expressed mRNA and protein had different expression patterns in Ag NP–treated HDFs and to find out key pathways in Ag NP–induced cytotoxicy, our group investigated miRNA expression profile subsequently.

10.3.4.1 miRNA Sequencing

At present, real-time quantitative PCR and miRNA microarray are mainly used for studying miRNA expression. These methods focus on studying the expression and quantification of known miRNAs, although they cannot be used to find new miRNAs.

The high-throughput miRNA sequencing technology breaks through the limitations of the current research techniques and enables researchers to directly sequence all miRNA molecules as well as to find and identify new miRNAs. SOLiD sequencing is one example of the second generation of sequencing instruments. It was developed by Applied Biosystems and applied for commercial sequencing in 2007, with advantages such as high efficiency, short time and low cost. After treatment with 200 μM Ag NPs for 1, 4 and 8 h in HDFs, 59, 143 and 142 differentially expressed miRNAs were identified using SOLiD sequencing, with 246 miRNAs in total. Far fewer miRNAs were differentially expressed in the Ag NP 1 h group (59) than in the Ag NP 4 h (143) and Ag NP 8 h groups (142), indicating that the influences of Ag NPs on miRNA expression at 4 h and 8 h after treatment were larger than those at 1 h.

10.3.4.2 Prediction of Target Genes of Differentially Expressed miRNAs

The functional research of miRNA is one of the most popular and difficult topics in miRNA research. As an important regulatory factor in gene post-transcription, miRNA plays its role by regulating the corresponding target genes. Therefore, the analysis of miRNA target genes is the first and key step for understanding the function of miRNA. The methods to determine miRNA target genes include bioinformatics prediction and experimental assays (Xia et al. 2009). Compared with the complexity and time-consuming nature of experimental assays, bioinformatics prediction can determine a group of miRNA target genes easily and quickly. Hence, bioinformatics prediction was first carried out with bioinformatical algorithms. In order to improve accuracy, the target genes of the differentially expressed miRNAs were predicted using the three most common algorithms, including miRanda, PicTar and TargetScan with the public database miRecord (http://mirecords.biolead.org/prediction_query.php), and only those predicted by all these three algorithms were filtered. Because most miRNAs do not combine with target genes in a completely complementary pairing manner in animal cells,

TABLE 10.5

The Number of Differentially Expressed miRNAs and Corresponding Predicted miRNA Target Genes in HDFs with the Treatment of 200 μM Ag NPs for 1, 4 and 8 h

Group	Ag NPs, 1 h	Ag NPs, 4 h	Ag NPs, 8 h
miRNA	59	143	142
Predicted miRNA target genes	1747	2928	2667

one miRNA may have multiple target genes (Bartel 2004). Finally, 1747, 2928 and 2667 target genes were predicted in HDFs treated with 200 μM Ag NPs for 1, 4 and 8 h, respectively (Table 10.5).

10.3.4.3 Identifying Matched miRNA, Target mRNA and Target Proteins

After bioinformatics prediction, theoretical target genes of miRNAs were obtained, and then mRNAs and proteins that have same name as the predicted miRNA target genes were chosen from our gene expression profile microarray and proteomics experiments previously (Sections 10.3.2 and 10.3.3), and these mRNAs and proteins that appeared in both prediction and experiment were called matched miRNA target mRNA and miRNA target protein, respectively. Table 10.6 shows the number of matched miRNA target mRNA and target protein.

10.3.4.4 Bioinformatics Analysis of Matched miRNA, Target mRNAs and Target Proteins

By matching mRNA, protein and miRNA expression profiles, the regulatory relationship between miRNA and target mRNA and that between miRNA and target protein were obtained. Because the expressions of three components (mRNA, protein and miRNA) are closely related with each other in cells, for the 255 matched miRNA target mRNA and 3 target proteins (257 matched miRNA target mRNAs and target proteins in

TABLE 10.6

The Number of Matched miRNA Target mRNA and Target Protein in HDFs with the Treatment of 200 μM Ag NPs for 1, 4 and 8 h

Group	Ag NPs, 1 h	Ag NPs, 4 h	Ag NPs, 8 h
Matched miRNA target mRNA	26	185	80
Total matched miRNA target mRNA		255	
Matched miRNA target protein	2	1	2
Total matched miRNA target protein		3	
Total matched miRNA target mRNA and protein		257	

total), GO functional annotation and biological pathway analysis were carried out together.

10.3.4.4.1 GO Functional Annotation Analysis

DAVID was used for the functional annotation analysis of all 257 matched miRNA target mRNAs and target proteins in HDFs, and 80 GO biological process categories were obtained. Among them, 'regulation of cell communication', 'regulation of cellular metabolic process', 'regulation of metabolic process', 'regulation of cellular process' and 'regulation of primary metabolic process' were the top five enriched categories having the smallest *p* value. Thus, the primary functions of these 257 miRNA target mRNAs and target proteins were related to cell communication and metabolism.

Figure 10.8 shows the five enriched biological process GO categories (with the smallest *p* values) of 28, 186 and 82 matched miRNA target mRNAs and target proteins in the Ag NP 1 h, 4 h and 8 h groups by DAVID analysis. It could be observed that the functions of the miRNA target mRNAs and target proteins were different among the three groups. In the Ag NP 1 h group,

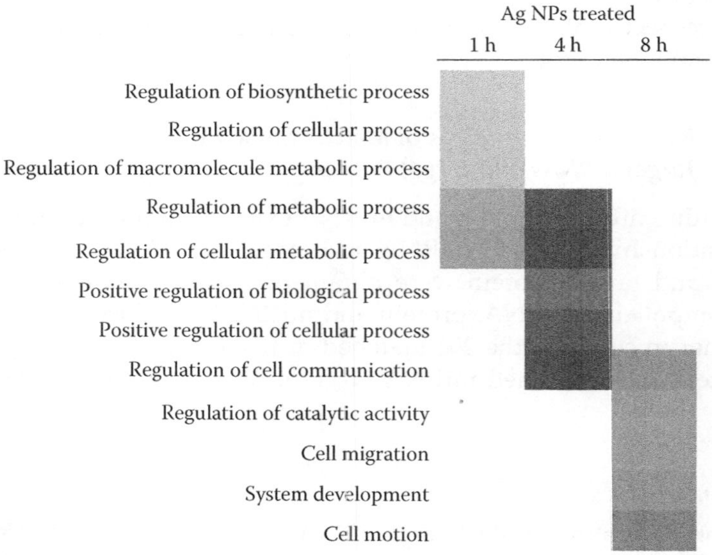

FIGURE 10.8
(See colour insert.) The enriched biological process GO categories of the miRNA target mRNAs and target proteins that matched HDFs treated with 200 μM Ag NPs for 1, 4 and 8 h. Each GO category was represented by a single row of red boxes, and each time point was represented by a single column. The depth of red represents the *p* value of the categories; a deeper colour indicates a smaller *p* value. A smaller *p* value indicates a higher correlation between the specific GO category and the target mRNAs and target proteins. (From Huang, Y. et al., *Journal of Biomedical Nanotechnology* 10(2014):3304–17.)

the functions of miRNA target mRNAs and target proteins were mainly associated with metabolism-related processes. In the Ag NP 4 h group, cell communication began to be affected. In the Ag NP 8 h group, cell migration and cell motion were influenced eventually.

10.3.4.4.2 Biological Pathway Analysis

GenMAPP was utilised for biological pathway analysis for 257 matched miRNA target mRNAs and target proteins, and 57 pathways were found to have participated. The number of involved pathways rose from 18 (Ag NP 1 h) to 45 (Ag NP 4 h and Ag NP 8 h), which suggested that the effect of miRNAs on target mRNAs/proteins increased with the passage of time.

Among the 57 pathways, 5 cell adhesion-related pathways, 3 cytoskeleton-related pathways, 3 energy metabolism–related pathways, 3 transcription and translation–related process pathways, 2 cell cycle–related pathways, 10 apoptosis-related pathways, 8 inflammation-related pathways and 9 signal transduction–related pathways were included. These results suggested that Ag NPs might have effects on cell adhesion, cytoskeleton, energy metabolism, DNA transcription and mRNA translation, cell cycle, apoptosis and inflammatory responses.

10.3.4.5 Analysing the Role of miRNAs on Target mRNA–Protein Pair Expression

To reveal the regulatory role of miRNA on mRNA–protein pairs that had different expression patterns, the relationship among the three components (miRNA, mRNA and encoded protein [mRNA–protein pair]) should be found out. Among the 257 matched miRNA target mRNAs and target proteins, 3 target mRNA–protein pairs (HN1, HSPA5 and CRK) were found regulated by 6 miRNAs, and their regulatory relationships are listed in Table 10.7.

TABLE 10.7

The Regulatory Relationship of Six miRNAs to Three Target mRNA–Protein Pairs in 200 μM SNP-Treated HDFs for 1, 4 and 8 h

Group	miRNAs	Target mRNA	Target Protein
Ag NPs, 1 h	miR-20a		HN1
	miR-199b-5p		HSPA5
Ag NPs, 4 h	miR-93	*HN1*	
	miR-212	*HN1*	
	miR-151-3p		CRK
Ag NPs, 8 h	miR-20a		CRK
	miR-30b		HSPA5
	miR-199b-5p		HSPA5

Source: Huang, Y., Lü, X.Y., Ma, J.W. Toxicity of silver nanoparticles to human dermal fibroblasts on microRNA level. *Journal of Biomedical Nanotechnology* 10(2014):3304–17.

The expression value and expression pattern of these six miRNAs are shown in Figure 10.9a. Figure 10.9b shows the regulatory relationship between six miRNAs and three target mRNA–protein pairs visually. It could be observed that there exist four expression patterns for the three mRNA–protein pairs: (1) the mRNA was unchanged while the protein was up-regulated, (2) the mRNA was up-regulated while the protein was unchanged, (3) both the mRNA and protein were unchanged, and (4) the mRNA was unchanged while the protein was down-regulated. No correlation was found between mRNA and protein expression levels.

In our research, three miRNAs (miR-93, miR-212 and miR-20a) were found to co-regulate the HN1 mRNA–protein pair (Figure 10.9b). In the Ag NP 1 h group, inverse correlation was only presented between the down-regulated miR-20a and the up-regulated HN1 protein, proposing that miR-20a restrained the translation of *HN*1 mRNA. In the Ag NP 4 h group, inverse correlations

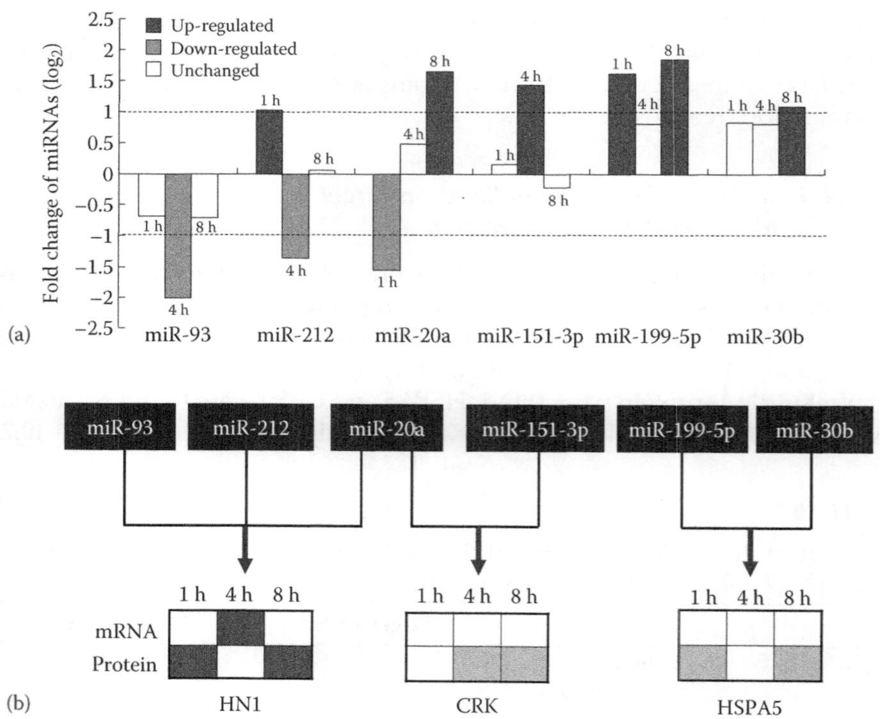

FIGURE 10.9
(See colour insert.) (a) The expression of six miRNAs identified by SOLiD sequencing. The two dotted lines mark the up-regulated (upper line, fold change = 2) and down-regulated (lower line, fold change = 0.5) threshold limits. The *y* axis refers to the relative expression levels in 200 μM Ag NP–treated HDFs compared to the control. (b) The regulatory relationships of six miRNAs to three target mRNA–protein pairs. (From Huang, Y. et al., *Journal of Biomedical Nanotechnology* 10(2014):3304–17.)

existed between miR-93, miR-212 and the *HN*1 mRNA, suggesting that these two miRNAs affected mRNA degradation. In the Ag NP 8 h group, no inverse correlation between any miRNA and HN1 mRNA/protein was found; hence, there might exist other regulatory mechanisms posttranscription (Perco et al. 2010). Our research showed that miRNAs regulated the expression target mRNA/protein pairs via mRNA degradation or translational repression at different time points. The results coincided with those of Gu and Kay (2010) who proposed that mRNA degradation and translational repression might overlap under some conditions.

10.3.4.6 Identification of the Key Pathway in Ag NP–Induced Cytotoxicity

Because mRNA expression can affect protein expression through the translation process and miRNA can regulate mRNA and protein expression via mRNA degradation or translational repression, the pathway that differentially expressed miRNAs, target mRNAs and target proteins that participated simultaneously would be very important for comprehensively revealing the cytotoxicity mechanism of Ag NPs. Thus, we identify such a pathway as a key pathway. Here, the six miRNAs and three corresponding target mRNA–protein pairs (Table 10.6) were found to be involved in four key pathways, including 'Regulation of actin cytoskeleton', 'Signalling of hepatocyte growth factor receptor', 'Insulin signalling' and 'MAPK signalling pathway'. The miR-151-3p/20a-CRK pair participated in all four pathways, the miR-199b-5p/30b-HSPA5 pair was only involved in the 'MAPK signalling pathway' and the miR-93/212/20a-HN1 pair did not join any pathway. Figure 10.10 showed the four abovementioned pathways and included differentially expressed miRNAs, target mRNAs and proteins whose functions were associated with cytoskeleton, ATP production and apoptosis according to the findings in the literature.

The 'Regulation of actin cytoskeleton' and 'Signalling of hepatocyte growth factor receptor' pathways were related to cytoskeletal function. Slingshot protein phosphatase 2 (SSH2) is a member of the SSH family and can activate cofilin, causing abnormal migration behaviours of epidermal cells (Kligys et al. 2007). CRK is an adaptor protein, whose genetic knockdown can result in cytoskeleton disorder and cellular boundary damage (Birge et al. 2009). The down-regulation of *SSH*2 mRNA and CRK protein might suggest that Ag NPs could impair the cytoskeleton of HDFs.

The 'Insulin signalling' pathway can affect the energy balance in cells. Insulin receptor substrates *IRS*1 and *IRS*2 play their roles in regulating the growth of skeletal muscle and metabolism through Akt and AMPK pathways. The absence of insulin signalling (such as *IRS*1, *IRS*2, etc.) may injure mitochondrial oxidative phosphorylation and production of ATP (Long et al. 2011). Vesicle-associated membrane protein 2 (VAMP2) and CRK lie at the downstream of the Akt pathway. The down-regulation of

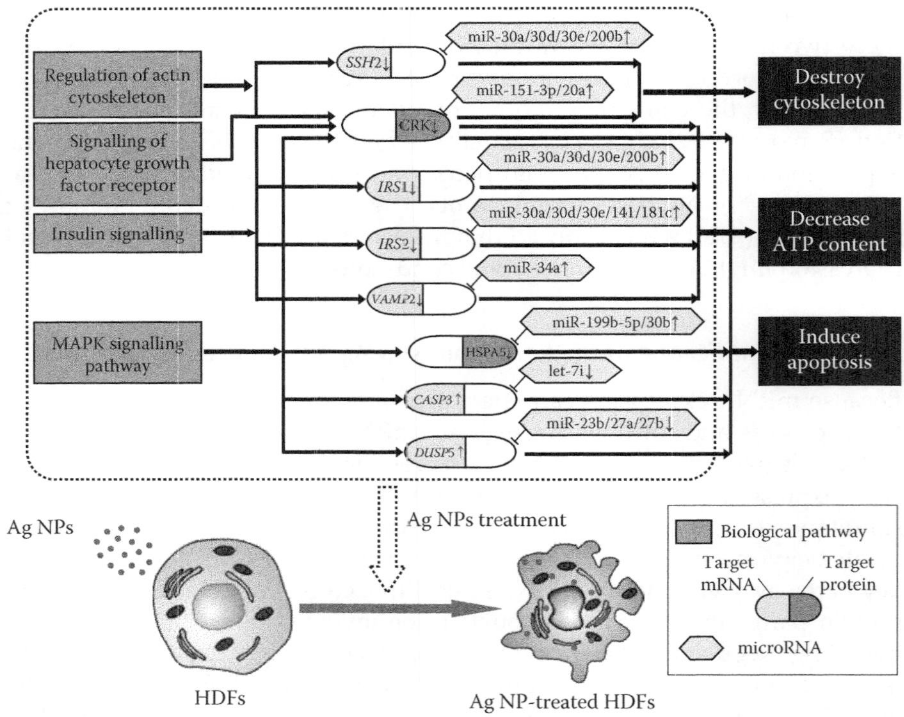

FIGURE 10.10
(See colour insert.) The four key pathways identified by differentially expressed miRNAs and regulated target mRNAs and target proteins that participated in the toxicity of 200 μM Ag NPs in HDFs. (From Huang, Y. et al., *Journal of Biomedical Nanotechnology* 10(2014):3304–17.)

*IRS*1, *IRS*2, *VAMP*2 and CRK implied that Ag NPs might resist ATP production in HDFs.

The 'MAPK signalling pathway' plays vital roles in cell apoptosis regulation. Down-regulated CRK can lead to JNK-mediated apoptotic response (Hrincius et al. 2010). HSPA5 is a member of the heat shock protein 70 (HSP70) family, and its high expression may accelerate Ca^{2+} binding, resist calcium signalling and then prevent the activation of some pro-apoptotic proteins (Zimmermann et al. 2010). On the contrary, down-regulation of HSPA5 will be beneficial for inducing apoptosis. Caspase-3 (*CASP*3) gene-encoded protein plays a primary role in the execution phase of cell apoptosis, is up-regulated in apoptotic cells through extrinsic and intrinsic pathways (Ghavami et al. 2009), and has been considered as a reliable marker of apoptosis (Duan et al. 2003). Dual-specificity phosphatase 5 (*DUSP*5) could be invoked by the p53 protein, which was up-regulated in response to cellular stress and could evoke apoptosis (Ueda et al. 2003). Thus, the down-regulation of CRK and HSPA5 and the up-regulation of *CASP*3 and *DUSP*5 might imply that Ag NPs can cause apoptosis.

According to the above analysis, Ag NPs were considered to be capable of destroying cytoskeleton via *SSH2* and CRK in the 'Regulation of actin cytoskeleton' and 'Signalling of hepatocyte growth factor receptor' pathways, which were regulated by miR-30a, miR-20a and so on. Ag NPs might reduce ATP content in HDFs via CRK, *IRS1*, *IRS2* and *VAMP2* in the 'Insulin signalling' pathway, which were regulatd by miR-20a, miR-30a, miR-30d and so on. Moreover, Ag NPs might cause cell apoptosis via CRK, HSPA5, *CASP3* and *DUSP5* in the 'MAPK signalling pathway' regulated by miR-20a, miR-30b, let-7i, miR-23b and so on (Figure 10.10). Hence, these four pathways might play critical roles in Ag NP-induced toxicity.

10.3.4.7 Validation of Bioinformatics Analysis

Biomics experiments produce huge amounts of data. With bioinformatics analysis, the biological significance under the experimental data can be determined. However, the accuracy of these theoretical analysis results should be verified with cellular experiment. Thus, validation of bioinformatics analysis is an important step in the biomics experiments. To verify the bioinformatics analysis result that Ag NP might induce HDFs toxicity via damaging cytoskeleton, reducing ATP content and inducing cell apoptosis (Figure 10.10), three cellular experiments were performed.

10.3.4.7.1 Cytoskeleton Observation

Figure 10.11 shows the cytoskeleton of untreated and 200 μM Ag NP–treated HDFs. Longer F-actin filaments at a high density were found to be arranged in an orderly manner inside untreated HDFs. After HDFs were treated with Ag NPs for 1, 4, 8 or 24 h, no distinct changes in actin cytoskeleton happened. However, cytoskeletal contraction began at 48 h. After 72 h, actin filaments were shorter and more disordered, with the edges becoming shadowy and the cells becoming triangular in shape. The results showed that Ag NPs could cause cytoskeleton deformation in HDFs.

10.3.4.7.2 ATP Content Analysis

Figure 10.12 shows the measured intracellular ATP content in untreated and 200 μM Ag NP–treated HDFs. The ATP content in all Ag NP–treated cells was decreased significantly compared to the untreated group ($p < 0.01$), which illustrated that Ag NPs could resist ATP production in HDFs.

10.3.4.7.3 Cell Apoptosis Assay

Figure 10.13 shows the cell apoptosis assay results with Hoechst staining. The fluorescence intensity increased significantly ($p < 0.01$), and the nucleus was partly destroyed and apoptotic bodies were formed in the Ag NP 24, 48 and 72 h groups compared to the untreated group, which stated that Ag NPs could gradually induce HDF apoptosis after 24 h. Our study showed that differentially expressed miRNAs in Ag NP–treated

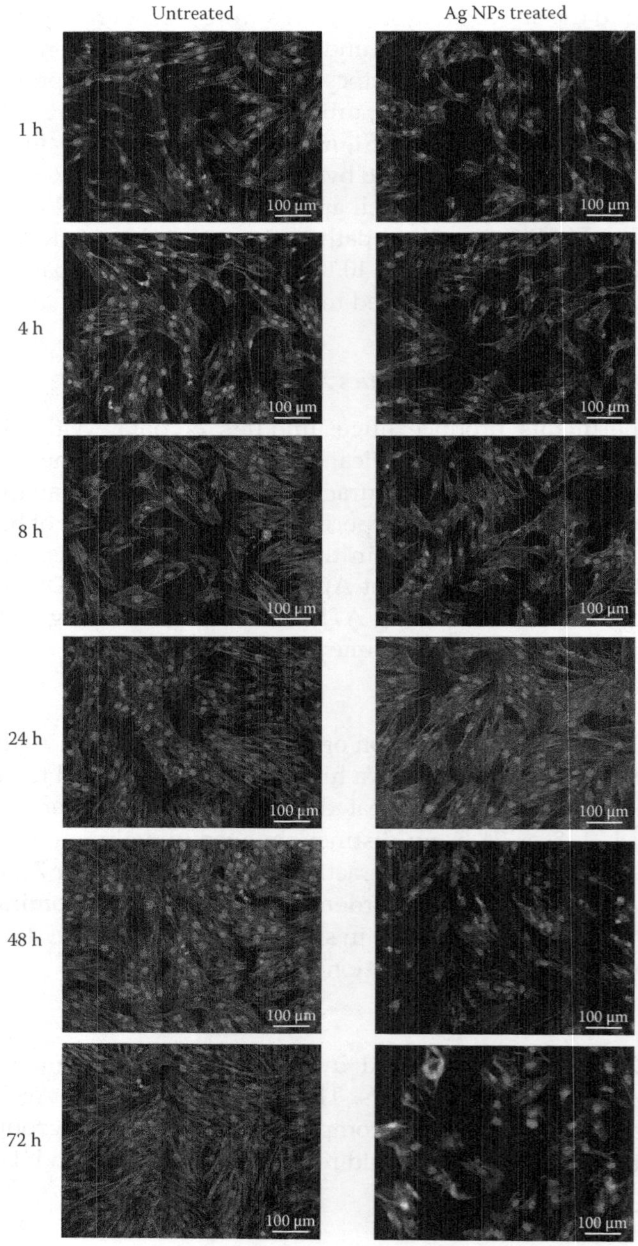

FIGURE 10.11
(See colour insert.) Fluorescence microscopy images of HDFs showing F-actin (red) and cell nuclei (blue). The left-hand column contains the images of untreated cells, while the right-hand column contains the images of cells treated with 200 μM Ag NPs. The scale bars correspond to 100 μm. (From Huang, Y. et al., *Journal of Biomedical Nanotechnology* 10(2014):3304–17.)

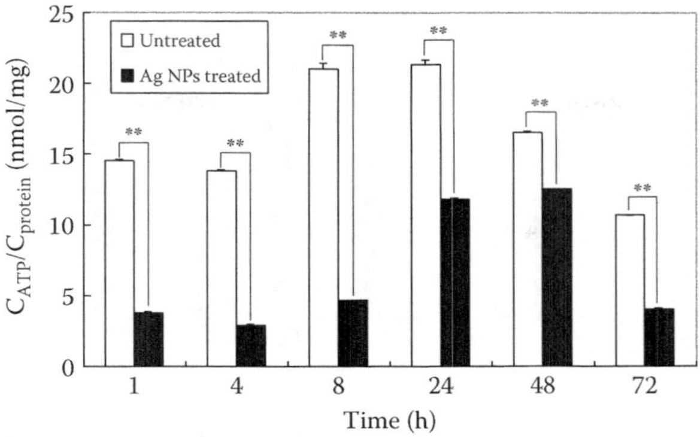

FIGURE 10.12
The ATP content in untreated HDFs and those treated with 200 μM Ag NPs. The ATP content is the ATP concentrations normalised with the cellular proteins, and the results are the mean ± SD of the triplicate experiments. $^{**}p < 0.01$. (From Huang, Y. et al., *Journal of Biomedical Nanotechnology* 10(2014):3304–17.)

HDFs affected the expression of target genes and proteins, resulting in toxicity via destroying the cytoskeleton, reducing ATP production and inducing apoptosis.

10.3.5 Cytotoxicity Mechanism of Ag NPs Obtained by Different Approaches

Previous studies had reported that Ag NPs damaged the cytoskeleton and restricted cell spread (AshaRani et al. 2009a,b), decreased ATP levels and caused functional disorders in mitochondria (AshaRani et al. 2009b), induced oxidative stress (Eom et al. 2010; Hsin et al. 2008; Nishanth et al. 2011; Piao et al. 2011), promoted DNA damage and cell cycle arrest (AshaRani et al. 2009a,b; Kawata et al. 2009), led to differential expression of apoptosis and inflammation-related genes and resisted cell viability (AshaRani et al. 2009b; Hsin et al. 2008; Kalishwaralal et al. 2009).

Table 10.8 shows the comparison of Ag NP–induced cytotoxicity mechanisms from references and our studies. It could be found that our results are in agreement with the previous research in many ways, such as the effect on the cytoskeleton and cellular membrane, the effect on mitochondria function and energy metabolism, DNA damage being induced and cell cycle arrest. Different from some previous reports, transcription and translation process pathways, apoptosis pathways, inflammation pathways and signal transduction pathways that contained a series of differentially expressed mRNA, protein and miRNA were found. Our group not only found differentially expressed genes/miRNAs/proteins in Ag NP–treated HDFs but also filtered

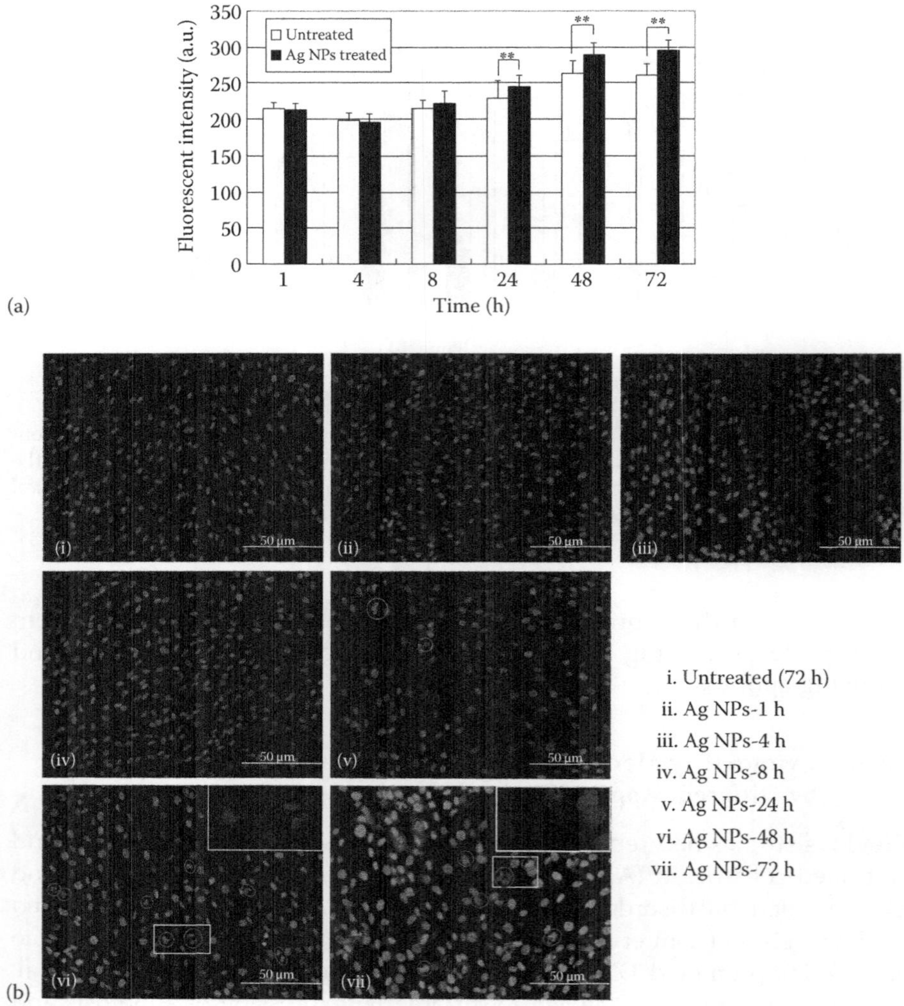

FIGURE 10.13
(See colour insert.) HDF apoptosis induced by 200 μM Ag NPs. (a) Fluorescence intensity of Hoechst 33342 in HDFs. $^{**}p < 0.01$. (b) Fluorescence microscopy images of HDFs stained with Hoechst 33342 for nuclei (blue colour) (original magnification ×200, inset ×400). The red circle indicates the apoptotic cell nuclei. The scale bars correspond to 50 μm. (From Huang, Y. et al., *Journal of Biomedical Nanotechnology* 10(2014):3304–17.)

TABLE 10.8

The Comparison of Ag NP–Induced Cytotoxicity Mechanisms Based on Different Approaches

	Results from References	Results from Our Studies
Impact on cytoskeleton and cell membrane	• Disruption and deformation of cytoskeleton • Degradation of plasma and mitochondrial membrane integrity • Na^+/K^+-ATPase inhibition, Ca^{2+} homeostasis disruption	• 5 cell adhesion pathways, 3 cytoskeleton pathways where the affected mRNA, protein and miRNA were filtered • Regulation of transportation-associated genes indicates that the intracellular transportation was affected • Destroy cytoskeleton via miR-30a, miR-20a, etc. by regulating *SSH2* and CRK in the 'Regulation of actin cytoskeleton' and 'Signalling of hepatocyte growth factor receptor' pathways
Mitochondria function and energy metabolism	• Disruption of the mitochondrial respiratory chain, leading to ROS production and interruption of ATP synthesis	• Multiple genes coding enzymes in tricarboxylic acid cycle and electron transportation chain were up-regulated • 3 energy metabolism pathways where the involved mRNA, protein and miRNA were found • Might decrease intracellular ATP content via miR-20a, miR-30a, miR-30d, etc. by regulating CRK, *IRS1*, *IRS2* and *VAMP2* in the 'Insulin signalling' pathway
DNA damage	• DNA damage and chromosome fragmentation, which led to cell cycle arrest	• 2 cell cycle pathways were affected by mRNA, protein and miRNA • DNA damage was induced and the cell cycle process was influenced
Oxidative stress	• Generation of ROS • Reduction of superoxide dismutase activity and glutathione levels • Lipid peroxidation increased • Expression of oxidative stress–related genes changed	• Expression of metallothionein mRNA increased • 39 oxidative stress–related miRNAs were differentially expressed • miRNA-target gene regulatory network related to oxidative stress was found • ROS production was not repressed

(*Continued*)

TABLE 10.8 (CONTINUED)

The Comparison of Ag NP–Induced Cytotoxicity Mechanisms Based on Different Approaches

	Results from References	Results from Our Studies
Others	• N/A	• 3 transcription and translation process pathways, 10 apoptosis pathways, 8 inflammation pathways and 9 signal transduction pathways that contained a series of differentially expressed mRNA, protein and miRNA were found • Ag NPs might induce cell apoptosis via miR-20a, miR-30b, let-7i, miR-23b, etc. by regulating CRK, HSPA5, *CASP*3 and *DUSP*5 in the 'MAPK signalling pathway'.

Sources: Ma, J.W., Lü, X. Y., Huang, Y. Genomic analysis of cytotoxicity response to nanosilver in human dermal fibroblasts. *Journal of Biomedical Nanotechnology* 7(2011):263–75; Huang, Y., Lü, X.Y., Ma, J.W. Toxicity of silver nanoparticles to human dermal fibroblasts on microRNA level. *Journal of Biomedical Nanotechnology* 10(2014):3304–17; and Huang, Y., Lü, X.Y. The influence of silver nanoparticle-induced oxidative stress on microRNA expression and cytotoxicity. *Science of Advanced Materials* 6(2014):1907–18.

four pathways (namely, 'Regulation of actin cytoskeleton', 'Signalling of hepatocyte growth factor receptor', 'Insulin signalling' and 'MAPK signalling pathway') that played key roles in Ag NP–induced toxicity and revealed the key interaction mechanism of Ag NPs on cells.

10.4 Comparing the Molecular Actions of Ag NPs with Au NPs in HDFs

Ag NPs and gold nanoparticles (Au NPs) are two kinds of metal nanobiomaterials that are commonly used in the field of biomedicine. Au NPs have often been considered as a relatively nontoxic nanomaterial, while Ag NPs exhibit certain toxicity. Some studies had reported the different influences between Au NPs and Ag NPs on cells. Farkas et al. (2010) found that Ag NPs decreased membrane integrity and metabolic levels while Au NPs had no cytotoxicity, which might be attributed to the release of Ag^+ or Au^+. The research of Bachand et al. (2012) showed that both Au NPs and Ag NPs did not induce oxidative stress and cytotoxicity; however, their effects on the release of interleukin (IL)-8 were significantly different. These studies investigated the impact of physicochemical properties of nanoparticles on cells, whereas no studies on molecular mechanism have been performed.

To reveal the mechanism of the different effects of Ag NPs and Au NPs on cells, a comparison at the cellular and molecular levels was conducted by our group (Huang et al. 2015).

10.4.1 At the Cellular Level

Cellular experiments showed that Ag NPs and Au NPs had several different impacts on HDFs (Huang and Lu 2014; Huang et al. 2014, 2015; Qu et al. 2009). First, Ag NPs induced cytotoxicity after 48 h, whereas Au NPs had no cytotoxicity. Second, Ag NPs damaged cytoskeleton after 48 h, whereas Au NPs did not change the cytoskeleton. Third, the decrease of ATP production in Ag NP–treated HDFs was more distinct than that in AU NP–treated cells. Furthermore, Ag NPs caused oxidative stress and apoptosis, whereas Au NPs decreased ROS level and did not cause apparent apoptosis.

10.4.2 At the mRNA and Protein Levels

The comparison results at the mRNA and protein levels revealed that Au NPs and Ag NPs had different effects on the type and expression pattern of differentially expressed mRNAs and proteins, although the involved GO functions and pathways showed many similarities (Huang et al. 2014; Ma et al. 2011; Qu et al. 2013; Yang et al. 2010). The nanoparticle–cell interaction mechanisms induced by Ag NPs and Au NPs at the mRNA level are listed in Table 10.9. In general, although many similarities were found between the interactions of these two kinds of nanoparticles on HDFs, different effects on biological functions and regulations of gene expression still existed. For example, Ag NPs up-regulated the expression of *GADD45B* in HDFs, which might cause DNA damage; however, a similar change had not been observed in the Au NP–treated group. Oxidative stress–related genes such as *SOD3* and *MT1X* were up-regulated after Au NPs exposure, whereas in the Ag NP-treated group, genes encoding metallothioneins were up-regulated. The above differences might be attributed to the distinct physicochemical properties between Ag NPs and Au NPs (Ma et al. 2011).

Table 10.10 lists the biological pathways affected by the differentially expressed proteins in Ag NP– and Au NP–treated HDFs (Huang et al. 2015). A total of 31 and 24 pathways were obtained in the Ag NP and Au NP groups, respectively, and 16 pathways were same. Among these pathways, 4 contained more proteins in Ag NP–treated HDFs than in Au NP–treated cells, and their functions were related to apoptosis and cytoskeleton. More proteins were involved in only one pathway ('glycolysis and gluconeogenesis pathway') in the Au NP–treated group than in the Ag NP–treated group, while the function of the involved proteins in the Au NP–treated group enhanced ATP synthesis. Moreover, Ag NP–induced, differentially

TABLE 10.9

The Comparison of Ag NP– and Au NP–cell Interaction Mechanisms at the mRNA Level

	Ag NPs	Au NPs
Oxidative stress	• Significant increase of metallothionein mRNA expression was found, which could scavenge the excessive intracellular ROS	• Genes related to oxidative stress showed up-regulation, such as *SOD3* and *MT1X*, and indicated that potential oxidative stress could be induced
DNA damage and cell cycle arrest	• DNA damage was induced, as reflected by the up-regulation of *GADD45B* • Cell cycle arrested at the S phase and could provide enough time for the cells to repair the damaged DNA	• The portion of cells in the S phase increased while the portion of G2/M cells decreased
Electron-transport chain	• All differentially expressed genes in the electron-transport chain pathway were down-regulated, such as *ATP5C1*, *NDUFA4* and *COX7B*	• Most genes involved in the electron-transport chain pathway were up-regulated, such as *NDUFA4*, *SDHD* and *COX7B*
Cytoskeleton	• The elevated expression of *ARPC5* reflected the disorder of actin polymerisation	• Actin-based cytoskeleton stability; actin filament polymerisation might be affected

Source: Ma, J.W., Lü, X. Y., Huang, Y. Genomic analysis of cytotoxicity response to nanosilver in human dermal fibroblasts. *Journal of Biomedical Nanotechnology* 7(2011):263–75.

expressed proteins were involved in another 15 pathways, whose functions were associated with cell adhesion, energy metabolism, apoptosis and so on. On the contrary, Au NPs affected an additional eight pathways related to signal transduction, glutathione metabolism, mRNA translation and so on. The above results also indicated that Ag NPs induced greater influences on HDFs than Au NPs at the protein level.

10.4.3 At the miRNA Level

10.4.3.1 The Expressed miRNAs, Matched miRNA and Target mRNAs/Proteins

After treatment with Au NPs for 1, 4 and 8 h, 109, 78 and 124 differentially expressed miRNAs in HDFs were identified using SOLiD sequencing, with 202 miRNAs in total. Table 10.11 lists the distribution of differentially expressed miRNAs in Ag NP– and Au NP–treated HDFs. It could be found that, in all three time points, the number of differentially expressed miRNAs in the Ag NP– or Au NP–treated group was larger than those both regulated in these two groups. The result implied that the miRNA expression profile

TABLE 10.10

Comparison of Pathways That Involved Differentially Expressed Proteins in Ag NP– and Au NP–Treated HDFs

No.	MAPPs	Number of Differentially Expressed Proteins in SNP-Treated HDFs	Number of Differentially Expressed Proteins in GNP-Treated HDFs
1	MAPK signalling pathway	4	1
2	FAS pathway and stress induction of HSP regulation	2	1
3	Regulation of actin cytoskeleton	2	1
4	Striated muscle contraction	2	1
5	Glycolysis and gluconeogenesis	1	2
6	Adipogenesis	1	1
7	α6-β4 Integrin signalling pathway	1	1
8	B cell receptor signalling pathway	1	1
9	EGFR1 signalling pathway	1	1
10	Electron transport chain	1	1
11	mRNA processing	1	1
12	Oxidative phosphorylation	1	1
13	Proteasome degradation	1	1
14	Selenium	1	1
15	T cell receptor signalling pathway	1	1
16	TCA cycle	1	1
17	Focal adhesion	3	
18	IL-3 signalling pathway	2	
19	Prostaglandin synthesis and regulation	2	
20	Diurnally regulated genes with circadian orthologs	1	
21	ErbB signalling pathway	1	
22	IL-2 signalling pathway	1	
23	IL-6 signalling pathway	1	
24	Insulin signalling	1	
25	Integrin-mediated cell adhesion	1	
26	Kit receptor signalling pathway	1	
27	Myometrial relaxation and contraction pathways	1	
28	p38 MAPK signalling pathway	1	
29	Signalling of hepatocyte growth factor receptor	1	
30	TGF-β receptor signalling pathway	1	
31	TNF-α-NF-kB signalling pathway	1	
32	AMPK signalling		1
33	Androgen receptor signalling pathway		1

(Continued)

TABLE 10.10 (CONTINUED)

Comparison of Pathways That Involved Differentially Expressed Proteins in Ag NP– and Au NP–Treated HDFs

No.	MAPPs	Number of Differentially Expressed Proteins in SNP-Treated HDFs	Number of Differentially Expressed Proteins in GNP-Treated HDFs
34	Delta-notch signalling pathway		1
35	G13 signalling pathway		1
36	Glutathione metabolism		1
37	Metapathway biotransformation		1
38	SIDS susceptibility pathways		1
39	Translation factors		1

Source: Huang, Y., Lü, X.Y., Qu, Y.H., Yang, Y.M., Wu, S. MicroRNA sequencing and molecular mechanisms analysis of the effects of gold nanoparticles on human dermal fibroblasts. *Biomaterials* 37(2015):13–24.

TABLE 10.11

Differentially Expressed miRNAs in 200 μM Ag NP– and Au NP–Treated HDFs

Time Point	Differentially Expressed miRNAs in Both SNP- and GNP-Treated Groups	Differentially Expressed miRNAs Only in the SNP-Treated Group	Differentially Expressed miRNAs Only in the GNP-Treated Group
1 h	29	30	80
4 h	32	111	46
8 h	53	89	71

Source: Huang, Y., Lü, X.Y., Qu, Y.H., Yang, Y.M., Wu, S. MicroRNA sequencing and molecular mechanisms analysis of the effects of gold nanoparticles on human dermal fibroblasts. *Biomaterials* 37(2015):13–24.

was closely related to the type of nanoparticle. Furthermore, more miRNAs were only differentially expressed in Au NP–treated cells than in the Ag NP–treated group at 1 h, and less at both 4 and 8 h. These results suggested that Ag NPs induced greater effects on miRNA expression than Au NPs with the passage of time.

With target gene prediction of differentially expressed miRNAs, 2403, 2044 and 3002 target genes were obtained in Au NP–treated HDFs for 1, 4 and 8 h. By matching with 1794 mRNAs (Yang et al. 2010) and 24 proteins (Qu et al. 2013), 102, 29 and 72 matched target mRNAs and target proteins were identified with 187 targets in total. Comparing the number of matched miRNA target mRNAs and target proteins in Ag NP– and Au NP–treated HDFs (Table 10.12), more miRNA target mRNAs and target proteins were obtained in the Ag NP– or Au NP–treated group, although

TABLE 10.12

Comparison of the Number of Matched miRNA Target mRNAs and Target Proteins in Ag NP– and Au NP–Treated HDFs

Time Point	Matched miRNA Target mRNAs and Target Proteins in Both Ag NP– and Au NP–Treated Groups	Matched miRNA Target mRNAs and Target Proteins Only in the Ag NP–Treated Group	Matched miRNA Target mRNAs and Target Proteins Only in the Au NP–Treated Group
1 h	6	22	96
4 h	12	174	17
8 h	27	55	45

some miRNA target mRNAs and target proteins were common in both Au NP– and Ag NP–treated groups.

10.4.3.2 The Affected GO Functions

Table 10.13 lists the significantly down-regulated biological processes ($p < 0.05$) of matched miRNA target mRNAs and target proteins in Ag NP– or Au NP–treated HDFs analysed with DAVID. It could be noticed that 11 and 8 biological processes were obtained in the Ag NP– and Au NP–treated group, respectively, with seven terms in common. Among the seven terms, six were related to metabolism, and more matched miRNA target mRNAs and target proteins

TABLE 10.13

Significantly Down-Regulated Biological Processes ($p < 0.05$) in HDFs Treated with 200 μM Ag NPs or Au NPs for 1, 4 and 8 h

		Ag NPs			Au NPs		
No.	GO Term	1 h	4 h	8 h	1 h	4 h	8 h
1	Cellular macromolecule metabolic process		21		20	6	15
2	Regulation of metabolic process		17				12
3	Regulation of cellular metabolic process		17				12
4	Regulation of cellular process			16			18
5	Regulation of macromolecule metabolic process		16				11
6	Regulation of primary metabolic process		16				11
7	Regulation of biosynthetic process		14				11
8	Regulation of cell communication			7			
9	Regulation of catalytic activity			5			
10	Response to extracellular stimulus			3			
11	Negative regulation of cell communication			3			
12	Nucleobase, nucleoside, nucleotide and nucleic acid metabolic process						11

Source: Huang, Y., Lü, X.Y., Qu, Y.H., Yang, Y.M., Wu, S. MicroRNA sequencing and molecular mechanisms analysis of the effects of gold nanoparticles on human dermal fibroblasts. *Biomaterials* 37(2015):13–24.

were found involved in the Ag NP–treated group than in the Au NP–treated group, which suggested that Ag NPs had stronger effects on energy metabolism than Au NPs. Moreover, Ag NPs also affected other processes such as cell communication, response to extracellular stimuli and so on, which implied that the whole impact of Ag NPs on physiological functions of HDFs was stronger.

10.4.3.3 ***The Affected Biological Pathways***

Figure 10.14 shows the biological pathways that contain more than five matched miRNA target mRNAs and target proteins in Ag NP– or Au NP–treated HDFs. In the Au NP–treated group, eight pathways were found affected, whose function related to cytoskeleton and cell adhesion, energy metabolism, inflammatory response, signal transduction and adipogenesis. In the Ag NP–treated group, 18 pathways were identified, with additional functions such as apoptosis and calcium regulation in cardiac and smooth muscle cell contraction. It could also be found that 14 pathways in the Ag NP–treated group contained more miRNA target mRNAs and target proteins than the Au NP–treated group, including all energy metabolism (one pathway) and apoptosis pathways (three pathways). The result agreed with the phenomenon that Ag NPs had wider effects on ATP production and apoptosis than Au NPs (Huang et al. 2014, 2015). In addition, two pathways ('regulation of actin cytoskeleton' and 'integrin-mediated cell adhesion') were found to contain more miRNA target mRNAs and target proteins in the Au NP–treated group than in the Ag NP–treated group. In Au NP–treated HDFs, six miRNA target mRNAs and target proteins were involved in the 'regulation of actin cytoskeleton' pathway (Table 10.14), with four (*PIK3R2*, *ACTN*1, ACTG1 and PAK2) down-regulated at 1 h, one (*SSH*2) down-regulated at 4 h and one (MAP2K1) up-regulated at 8 h. Therefore, the cytoskeleton in Au NP–treated HDFs might be repaired as time passed (Huang et al. 2015). In Ag NP–treated cells, miRNA target mRNAs and target proteins associated with cytoskeleton arrangement and cell edge stability were down-regulated in both 4 h and 8 h groups (Table 10.14), indicating that Ag NPs could cause increasing cytoskeleton damage as time passes. The results from fluorescent staining of F-actin verified that the effect of Ag NPs on cytoskeleton was stronger than that of Au NPs (Huang et al. 2014, 2015).

Table 10.15 lists five key pathways filtered in Au NP– and Ag NP–treated HDFs. More pathways were found in the Ag NP–treated group (four pathways) than in the Au NP–treated group (two pathways), with only one pathway ('MAPK signalling pathway') in common. According to the above discussion, the interaction mechanisms of Ag NPs and Au NPs on HDFs were summarised in Figure 10.15. It could be observed that Au NPs and Ag NPs played different roles via key biological pathways and related key mRNAs, proteins and miRNAs. For Au NPs, they might affect cell cycle via miR-205, miR-21 and so on, and target HNRPK was involved in the 'mRNA

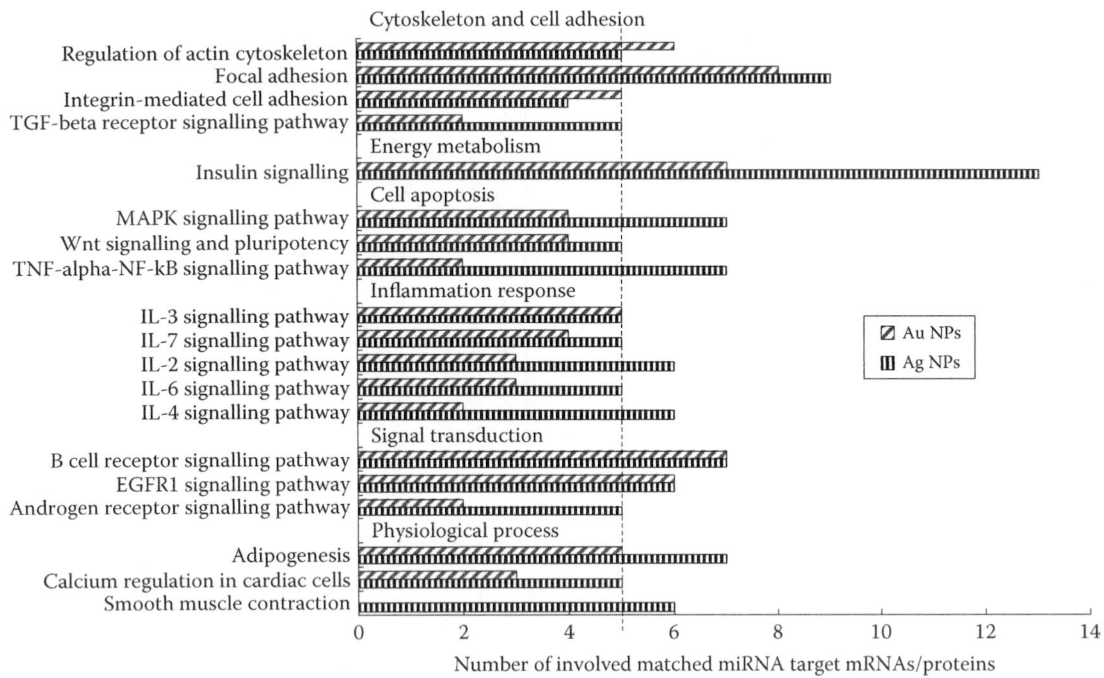

FIGURE 10.14
Biological pathways containing more than five matched miRNA target mRNAs and target proteins in the Au NP– or Ag NP–treated groups. (From Huang, Y. et al., *Biomaterials* 37(2015):13–24.)

TABLE 10.14

miRNA–mRNA and miRNA–Protein Target Pairs Involved in 'Regulation of Actin Cytoskeleton' Pathways in Au NP– and Ag NP–Treated HDFs

Group	1 h	4 h	8 h
Au NPs	miR-30b↑-*PIK3R2*↓ miR-19b↑-*ACTN1*↓ miR-145↑-ACTG1↓ miR-9↑-PAK2↓	miR-20a↑-*SSH2*↓	miR-195↓-MAP2K1↑
Ag NPs		miR-30a↑-*SSH2*↓ miR-30d↑-*SSH2*↓ miR-30e↑-*SSH2*↓ miR-200b↑-*SSH2*↓ miR-151-3p↑-CRK↓	miR-20a↑-CRK↓

TABLE 10.15

Five Key Pathways That Differentially Expressed miRNAs, Target mRNAs and Target Proteins That Participated Simultaneously in Au NP– and Ag NP–Treated HDFs

No.	Pathway	Ag NPs	Au NPs
1	MAPK signalling pathway	√	√
2	mRNA processing		√
3	Regulation of actin cytoskeleton	√	
4	Signalling of hepatocyte growth factor receptor	√	
5	Insulin signalling	√	

Source: Huang, Y., Lü, X.Y., Qu, Y.H., Yang, Y.M., Wu, S. MicroRNA sequencing and molecular mechanisms analysis of the effects of gold nanoparticles on human dermal fibroblasts. *Biomaterials* 37(2015):13–24.

processing pathway'. They resisted apoptosis via miR-9, miR-20a, miR-16, miR-30d and so on, and target *PAK*2, *PPP3R*1, *MAP2K*1 and HSPA5 participated in the 'MAPK signalling pathway'. Finally, Au NPs did not result in cytotoxicity (Huang et al. 2015). On the contrary, Ag NPs induced cytoskeleton damage via miR-30a, miR-20a and so on, and target *SSH*2 and CRK joined in the 'regulation of actin cytoskeleton' and 'signalling of hepatocyte growth factor receptor' pathways. Ag NPs decreased ATP production via miR-20a, miR-30a, miR-30d, miR-34a and so on, and target CRK, *IRS*1, *IRS*2 and *VAMP*2 were involved in the 'insulin signalling pathway'. Ag NPs also promoted apoptosis via miR-20a, miR-30b, let-7i, miR-23b and so on, and target CRK, HSPA5, *CASP*3 and *DUSP*5 were involved in the 'MAPK signalling pathway'. Ag NPs led to cytotoxicity ultimately (Huang et al. 2014). Nel et al. suggested that one of the primary mechanisms of inorganic nanoparticles that caused toxicity was ROS induction. High levels of ROS can cause oxidative stress and other secondary effects including denaturation of protein, regulation of particular signal transduction pathways, damage of mitochondrial membrane and damage of DNA (Nel et al. 2006). Ag NPs promoted ROS accumulation in HDFs (Huang and Lu 2014), whereas Au NPs

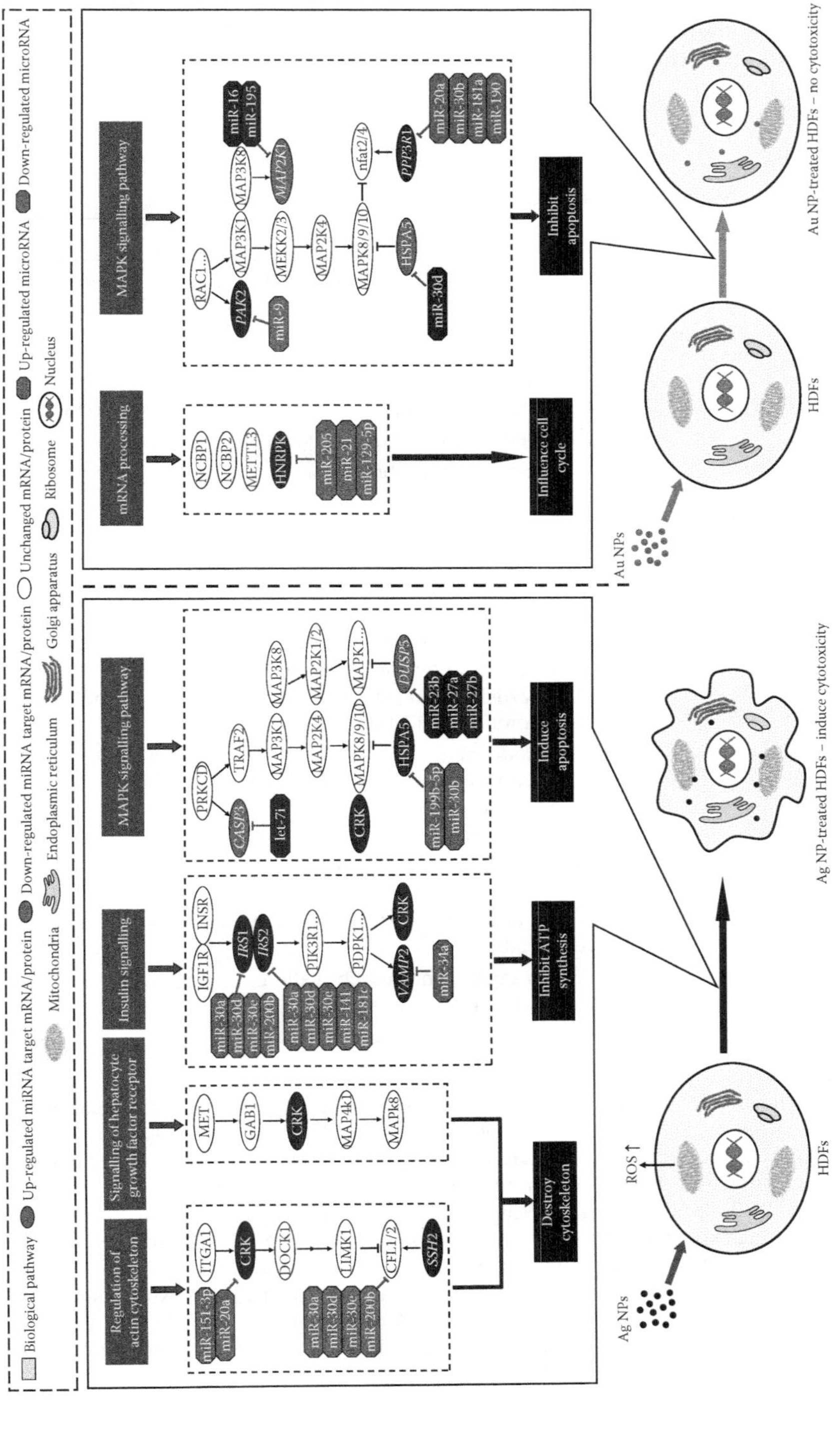

FIGURE 10.15
(See colour insert.) Comparison of the interaction mechanisms of Ag NPs and Au NPs on HDFs. (From Huang, Y. et al., *Biomaterials* 37(2015):13–24.)

decreased ROS level compared to untreated cells (Huang et al. 2015). Thus, the different results on ROS induction between Ag NPs and Au NPs might be the reason that they had adverse effects on HDFs at both the cellular and molecular levels.

TABLE 10.16

Mechanisms of Metal Nanoparticle Cytotoxicity

Nanoparticles	Cytotoxicity Mechanism
Ag	• Dissolution and Ag^+ release inhibits respiratory enzymes and ATP production • Destroy cytoskeleton • Induce apoptosis • ROS production • Disruption of membrane integrity and transport processes
Au	• Disruption of protein conformation
Co/Ni ferrite nanoparticles, magnetic metallic nanoparticles	• Liberation of toxic cations
Cu/CuO	• DNA damage and oxidative stress
CdSe	• Dissolution and release of toxic Cd and Se ions
TiO_2	• ROS production mediated by electron–hole pairs • Glutathione depletion and toxic oxidative stress as a result of photoactivity and redox properties • Nanoparticle-mediated cell membrane disruption lead to cell death; protein fibrillation
ZnO	• ROS production • Dissolution and release of toxic cations • Lysosomal damage • Inflammation
Fe_3O_4	• ROS production and oxidative stress • Liberation of toxic Fe^{2+} • Disturbance of the electronic or ion transport activity in the cell membrane
CeO_2	• Protein aggregation and fibrillation
Al_2O_3	• ROS production • Pro-inflammatory response
MoO_3	• Membrane disruption

Sources: Huang, Y., Lü, X.Y., Ma, J.W. Toxicity of silver nanoparticles to human dermal fibroblasts on microRNA level. *Journal of Biomedical Nanotechnology* 10(2014):3304–17; Qu, Y.H., Huang, Y., Lü, X.Y. Proteomic analysis of molecular biocompatibility of gold nanoparticles to human dermal fibroblasts-fetal. *Journal of Biomedical Nanotechnology* 9(2013):40–52; Li, S., Wang, Y., Wang, H., Bai, Y., Liang, G., Huang, N. et al. MicroRNAs as participants in cytotoxicity of CdTe quantum dots in NIH/3T3 cells. *Biomaterials* 32(2011a):3807–14; Li, S., Wang, H., Qi, Y., Tu, J., Bai, Y., Tian, T. et al. Assessment of nanomaterial cytotoxicity with SOLiD sequencing-based microRNA expression profiling. *Biomaterials* 32(2011b):9021–30; and Nel, A.E., Madler, L., Velegol, D., Xia, T., Hoek, EMV, Somasundaran, P. et al. Understanding biophysicochemical interactions at the nano-bio interface. *Nature Materials* 8(2009):543–57.

10.5 Comparing the Cytotoxicity Mechanism of Ag NPs with Other Nanoparticles

Generally, a single type of nanoparticle may cause toxicity via a combination of different mechanisms such as the induction of ROS, genotoxicity, morphological modifications, nanoparticle degradation and immunological effects (George et al. 2010; Joris et al. 2013; Soenen et al. 2011). Table 10.16 lists the cytotoxicity mechanisms of several metal nanoparticles. It could be seen from Table 10.16 that most metal nanoparticles can induce ROS and oxidative stress, but some will disrupt membrane integrity (such as Ag, TiO_2 and MoO_3), and others will lead to DNA damage (such as Cu/CuO) and inflammatory response. The results implied that the toxic effects of metal nanoparticles are in common but differentiated.

10.6 Summary

Research on the biocompatibility of biomaterials made use of integrative analysis of mRNA, protein and miRNA expression profile data. First, the complex regulatory relationship between miRNA, target mRNA and target protein was discussed. It was found that miRNA itself showed a variety of expression pattern (up-/down-regulated or not differentially expressed). Differentially expressed miRNAs could regulate target mRNA–protein pairs via mRNA degradation and translational repression, leading to different expression patterns of mRNAs and encoded proteins. Then, with bioinformatics analysis, the key pathways in which miRNAs, target mRNAs and target proteins were simultaneously involved were identified. Biological experiments further verified the reliability of bioinformatic analysis results, and the toxic effects of Ag NPs on HDF (including destroying the cytoskeleton, reducing intracellular ATP content and inducing apoptosis) were theoretically and experimentally demonstrated.

By comparing the effect of Ag NPs and Au NPs at the cellular and molecular level, the mechanisms behind the different effects of these two kinds of nanoparticles on HDFs were revealed. In contrast to Ag NPs, Au NPs affected cell cycle, diminished the inhibition of ATP synthesis and damage to the cytoskeleton, suppressed apoptosis and, last, did not lead to cytotoxicity.

Through the above research, a 'bioinformatics mode' based on mechanism and quantitative research was explored to assess the biocompatibility of biomaterials. A new research system (including gene expression profile microarray, proteomics technology, and miRNA sequencing combining bioinformatics analysis and biological experiment verification) for evaluating the molecular compatibility of biomaterials was established.

References

Ahamed, M., Posgai, R., Gorey, T.J., Nielsen, M., Hussain, S.M., Rowe, J.J. Silver nanoparticles induced heat shock protein 70, oxidative stress and apoptosis in *Drosophila melanogaster*. *Toxicology and Applied Pharmacology* 242 (2010):263–9.

Al Gurabi, M.A., Ali, D., Alkahtani, S., Alarifi, S. In vivo DNA damaging and apoptotic potential of silver nanoparticles in Swiss albino mice. *OncoTargets and Therapy* 8(2015):295–302.

AshaRani, P.V., Hande, M.P., Valiyaveettil, S. Anti-proliferative activity of silver nanoparticles. *BMC Cell Biology* 10(2009a):65.

AshaRani, P.V., Mun, G.L.K., Hande, M.P., Valiyaveettil, S. Cytotoxicity and genotoxicity of silver nanoparticles in human cells. *ACS Nano* 3(2009b):279–90.

Awasthi, K.K., Awasthi, A., Verma, R., Kumar, N., Roy, P., Awasthi, K. et al. Cytotoxicity, genotoxicity and alteration of cellular antioxidant enzymes in silver nanoparticles exposed CHO cells. *RSC Advances* 5(2015):34927–35.

Bachand, G.D., Allen, A., Bachand, M., Achyuthan, K.E., Seagrave, J.C., Brozik, S.M. Cytotoxicity and inflammation in human alveolar epithelial cells following exposure to occupational levels of gold and silver nanoparticles. *Journal of Nanoparticle Research* 14(2012):1212.

Baek, D., Villen, J., Shin, C., Camargo, F.D., Gygi, S.P., Bartel, D.P. The impact of microRNAs on protein output. *Nature* 455(2008):64-U38.

Bartel, D.P. MicroRNAs: Genomics, biogenesis, mechanism, and function. *Cell* 116(2004):281–97.

Birge, R.B., Kalodimos, C., Inagaki, F., Tanaka, S. Crk and CrkL adaptor proteins: Networks for physiological and pathological signalling. *Cell Communication and Signalling* 7(2009):13.

Bouwmeester, H., Poortman, J., Peters, R.J., Wijma, E., Kramer, E., Makama, S. et al. Characterization of translocation of silver nanoparticles and effects on whole-genome gene expression using an in vitro intestinal epithelium coculture model. *ACS Nano* 5(2011):4091–103.

Cha, K., Hong, H.W., Choi, Y.G., Lee, M.J., Park, J.H., Chae, H.K. et al. Comparison of acute responses of mice livers to short-term exposure to nano-sized or micro-sized silver particles. *Biotechnology Letters* 30(2008):1893–9.

Chen, C.Z., Schaffert, S., Fragoso, R., Loh, C. Regulation of immune responses and tolerance: The microRNA perspective. *Immunological Reviews* 253(2013):112–28.

Chou, L., Firth, J.D., Uitto, V.J., Brunette, D.M. Substratum surface topography alters cell shape and regulates fibronectin mRNA level, mRNA stability, secretion and assembly in human fibroblasts. *Journal of Cell Science* 108(1995):1563–73.

Crick, F. Central dogma of molecular biology. *Nature* 227(1970):561–3.

Das, S., Debnath, N., Patra, P., Datta, A., Goswami, A. Nanoparticles influence on expression of cell cycle related genes in *Drosophila*: A microarray-based toxicogenomics study. *Toxicological and Environmental Chemistry* 94(2012):952–7.

Duan, W.R., Garner, D.S., Williams, S.D., Funckes-Shippy, C.L., Spath, I.S., Blomme, E.A. Comparison of immunohistochemistry for activated caspase-3 and cleaved cytokeratin 18 with the TUNEL method for quantification of apoptosis in histological sections of PC-3 subcutaneous xenografts. *The Journal of Pathology* 199(2003):221–8.

Eom, H.J., Choi, J. p38 MAPK activation, DNA damage, cell cycle arrest and apoptosis as mechanisms of toxicity of silver nanoparticles in Jurkat T cells. *Environmental Science & Technology* 44(2010):8337–42.

Farh, K.K., Grimson, A., Jan, C., Lewis, B.P., Johnston, W.K., Lim, L.P. et al. The widespread impact of mammalian microRNAs on mRNA repression and evolution. *Science* 310(2005):1817–21.

Farkas, J., Christian, P., Urrea, J.A.G., Roos, N., Hassellov, M., Tollefsen, K.E. et al. Effects of silver and gold nanoparticles on rainbow trout (*Oncorhynchus mykiss*) hepatocytes. *Aquatic Toxicology* 96(2010):44–52.

Funez, A.A., Haza, A.I., Mateo, D., Morales, P. In vitro evaluation of silver nanoparticles on human tumoral and normal cells. *Toxicology Mechanisms and Methods* 23(2013):153–60.

Galdiero, S., Falanga, A., Vitiello, M., Cantisani, M., Marra, V., Galdiero, M. Silver nanoparticles as potential antiviral agents. *Molecules* 16(2011):8894–918.

Garcia, T.X., Costa, G.M.J., Franca, L.R., Hofmann, M.C. Sub-acute intravenous administration of silver nanoparticles in male mice alters Leydig cell function and testosterone levels. *Reproductive Toxicology* 45(2014):59–70.

George, S., Pokhrel, S., Xia, T., Gilbert, B., Ji, Z.X., Schowalter, M. et al. Use of a rapid cytotoxicity screening approach to engineer a safer zinc oxide nanoparticle through iron doping. *ACS Nano* 4(2010):15–29.

Ghavami, S., Hashemi, M., Ande, S.R., Yeganeh, B., Xiao, W., Eshraghi, M. et al. Apoptosis and cancer: Mutations within caspase genes. *Journal of Medical Genetics* 46(2009):497–510.

Gourlay, C.W., Ayscough, K.R. The actin cytoskeleton: A key regulator of apoptosis and ageing? *Nature Reviews Molecular Cell Biology* 6(2005):583-U5.

Griffin, T.J., Gygi, S.P., Ideker, T., Rist, B., Eng, J., Hood, L. et al. Complementary profiling of gene expression at the transcriptome and proteome levels in *Saccharomyces cerevisiae. Molecular & Cellular Proteomics* 1(2002):323–33.

Gu, S., Kay, M.A. How do miRNAs mediate translational repression. *Silence* 1(2010):11.

Hrincius, E.R., Wixler, V., Wolff, T., Wagner, R., Ludwig, S., Ehrhardt, C. CRK adaptor protein expression is required for efficient replication of avian influenza A viruses and controls JNK-mediated apoptotic responses. *Cellular Microbiology* 12(2010):831–43.

Hsin, Y.H., Chena, C.F., Huang, S., Shih, T.S., Lai, P.S., Chueh, P.J. The apoptotic effect of nanosilver is mediated by a ROS- and JNK-dependent mechanism involving the mitochondrial pathway in NIH3T3 cells. *Toxicology Letters* 179(2008):130–9.

Huang, Y., Lü, X.Y. The influence of silver nanoparticle-induced oxidative stress on microRNA expression and cytotoxicity. *Science of Advanced Materials* 6(2014): 1907–18.

Huang, Y., Lü, X.Y., Qu, Y.H., Yang, Y.M., Wu, S. MicroRNA sequencing and molecular mechanisms analysis of the effects of gold nanoparticles on human dermal fibroblasts. *Biomaterials* 37(2015):13–24.

Huang, Y., Lü, X.Y., Ma, J.W. Toxicity of silver nanoparticles to human dermal fibroblasts on microRNA level. *Journal of Biomedical Nanotechnology* 10(2014):3304–17.

Hussain, S.M., Hess, K.L., Gearhart, J.M., Geiss, K.T., Schlager, J.J. In vitro toxicity of nanoparticles in BRL 3A rat liver cells. *Toxicology in Vitro* 19(2005):975–83.

Ip, M., Lui, S.L., Poon, V.K.M., Lung, I., Burd, A. Antimicrobial activities of silver dressings: An in vitro comparison. *Journal of Medical Microbiology* 55(2006):59–63.

Jeyaraj, M., Rajesh, M., Arun, R., MubarakAli, D., Sathishkumar, G., Sivanandhan, G. et al. An investigation on the cytotoxicity and caspase-mediated apoptotic effect of biologically synthesized silver nanoparticles using *Podophyllum hexandrum* on human cervical carcinoma cells. *Colloids and Surfaces B – Biointerfaces* 102(2013):708–17.

Joris, F., Manshian, B.B., Peynshaert, K., De Smedt, S.C., Braeckmans, K., Soenen, S.J. Assessing nanoparticle toxicity in cell-based assays: Influence of cell culture parameters and optimized models for bridging the in vitro–in vivo gap. *Chemical Society Reviews* 42(2013):8339–59.

Kalishwaralal, K., Banumathi, E., Pandian, S.R.K., Deepak, V., Muniyandi, J., Eom, S.H. et al. Silver nanoparticles inhibit VEGF induced cell proliferation and migration in bovine retinal endothelial cells. *Colloids and Surfaces B – Biointerfaces* 73(2009):51–7.

Kang, T.S., Guan, R.F., Song, Y.J., Lyu, F., Ye, X.Q., Jiang, H. Cytotoxicity of zinc oxide nanoparticles and silver nanoparticles in human epithelial colorectal adenocarcinoma cells. *LWT – Food Science and Technology* 60(2015):1143–8.

Kawata, K., Osawa, M., Okabe, S. In vitro toxicity of silver nanoparticles at noncytotoxic doses to HepG2 human hepatoma cells. *Environmental Science & Technology* 43(2009):6046–51.

Kim, S., Choi, J.E., Choi, J., Chung, K.H., Park, K., Yi, J. et al. Oxidative stress-dependent toxicity of silver nanoparticles in human hepatoma cells. *Toxicology in Vitro* 23(2009):1076–84.

Kligys, K., Claiborne, J.N., Debiase, P.J., Hopkinson, S.B., Wu, Y., Mizuno, K. et al. The slingshot family of phosphatases mediates rac1 regulation of cofilin phosphorylation, laminin-332 organization, and motility behavior of keratinocytes. *Journal of Biological Chemistry* 282(2007):32520–8.

Krizkova, S., Kepinska, M., Emri, G., Rodrigo, M.A.M., Tmejova, K., Nerudova, D. et al. Microarray analysis of metallothioneins in human diseases – A review. *Journal of Pharmaceutical and Biomedical Analysis* 117(2016):464–73.

Kulthong, K., Maniratanachote, R., Kobayashi, Y., Fukami, T., Yokoi, T. Effects of silver nanoparticles on rat hepatic cytochrome P450 enzyme activity. *Xenobiotica* 42(2012):854–62.

Kumari, M., Mukherjee, A., Chandrasekaran, N. Genotoxicity of silver nanoparticles in *Allium cepa*. *Science of the Total Environment* 407(2009):5243–6.

Landels, A., Evans, C., Noirel, J., Wright, P.C. Advances in proteomics for production strain analysis. *Current Opinion in Biotechnology* 35(2015):111–7.

Lee, R.C., Feinbaum, R.L., Ambros, V. The *C. elegans* heterochronic gene Lin-4 encodes small RNAs with antisense complementarity to Lin-14. *Cell* 75(1993):843–54.

Li, S., Wang, Y., Wang, H., Bai, Y., Liang, G., Huang, N. et al. MicroRNAs as participants in cytotoxicity of CdTe quantum dots in NIH/3T3 cells. *Biomaterials* 32(2011a):3807–14.

Li, S., Wang, H., Qi, Y., Tu, J., Bai, Y., Tian, T. et al. Assessment of nanomaterial cytotoxicity with SOLiD sequencing-based microRNA expression profiling. *Biomaterials* 32(2011b):9021–30.

Lim, D.H., Jang, J., Kim, S., Kang, T., Lee, K., Choi, I.H. The effects of sub-lethal concentrations of silver nanoparticles on inflammatory and stress genes in human macrophages using cDNA microarray analysis. *Biomaterials* 33(2012):4690–9.

Long, J.C., Caceres, J.F. The SR protein family of splicing factors: Master regulators of gene expression. *Biochemical Journal* 417(2009):15–27.

Long, Y.C., Cheng, Z.Y., Copps, K.D., White, M.F. Insulin receptor substrates Irs1 and Irs2 coordinate skeletal muscle growth and metabolism via the Akt and AMPK pathways. *Molecular and Cellular Biology* 31(2011):430–41.

Lü, X.Y., Lu, H.Q., Zhao, L.F., Yang, Y.M., Lu, Z.H. Genome-wide pathways analysis of nickel ion-induced differential genes expression in fibroblasts. *Biomaterials* 31(2010):1965–73.

Lü, X.Y., Bao, X., Huang, Y., Qu, Y.H., Lu, H.Q., Lu, Z.H. Mechanisms of cytotoxicity of nickel ions based on gene expression profiles. *Biomaterials* 30(2009):141–8.

Lü, X.Y., Huang, Y., Yu, Y.D., Yang, Y.M. Application of genomics/proteomics technologies in the research of biocompatibility of biomaterials. *Journal of Inorganic Materials* 28(2013):21–8.

Ma, J.W., Lü, X. Y., Huang, Y. Genomic analysis of cytotoxicity response to nanosilver in human dermal fibroblasts. *Journal of Biomedical Nanotechnology* 7(2011):263–75.

Melaiye, A., Sun, Z.H., Hindi, K., Milsted, A., Ely, D., Reneker, D.H. et al. Silver(I)-imidazole cyclophane gem–diol complexes encapsulated by electrospun tecophilic nanofibers: Formation of nanosilver particles and antimicrobial activity. *Journal of the American Chemical Society* 127(2005):2285–91.

Miethling-Graff, R., Rumpker, R., Richter, M., Verano-Braga, T., Kjeldsen, F., Brewer, J. et al. Exposure to silver nanoparticles induces size- and dose-dependent oxidative stress and cytotoxicity in human colon carcinoma cells. *Toxicology in Vitro* 28(2014):1280–9.

Mitchison, T.J., Cramer, L.P. Actin-based cell motility and cell locomotion. *Cell* 84(1996):371–9.

Nel, A., Xia, T., Madler, L., Li, N. Toxic potential of materials at the nanolevel. *Science* 311(2006):622–7.

Nel, A.E., Madler, L., Velegol, D., Xia, T., Hoek, E.M.V., Somasundaran, P. et al. Understanding biophysicochemical interactions at the nano-bio interface. *Nature Materials* 8(2009):543–57.

Nishanth, R.P., Jyotsna, R.G., Schlager, J.J., Hussain, S.M., Reddanna, P. Inflammatory responses of RAW 264.7 macrophages upon exposure to nanoparticles: Role of ROS-NF kappa B signalling pathway. *Nanotoxicology* 5(2011):502–16.

Perco, P., Muhlberger, I., Mayer, G., Oberbauer, R., Lukas, A., Mayer, B. Linking transcriptomic and proteomic data on the level of protein interaction networks. *Electrophoresis* 31(2010):1780–9.

Piao, M.J., Kang, K.A., Lee, I.K., Kim, H.S., Kim, S., Choi, J.Y. et al. Silver nanoparticles induce oxidative cell damage in human liver cells through inhibition of reduced glutathione and induction of mitochondria-involved apoptosis. *Toxicology Letters* 201(2011):92–100.

Qin, H., Zhu, C., An, Z.Q., Jiang, Y., Zhao, Y.C., Wang, J.X. et al. Silver nanoparticles promote osteogenic differentiation of human urine-derived stem cells at noncytotoxic concentrations. *International Journal of Nanomedicine* 9(2014):2469–78.

Qiu, J.H., Asai, A., Chi, S., Saito, N., Hamada, H., Kirino, T. Proteasome inhibitors induce cytochrome c-caspase-3-like protease-mediated apoptosis in cultured cortical neurons. *Journal of Neuroscience* 20(2000):259–65.

Qu, Y.H., Huang, Y., Lü, X.Y. Proteomic analysis of molecular biocompatibility of gold nanoparticles to human dermal fibroblasts-fetal. *Journal of Biomedical Nanotechnology* 9(2013):40–52.

Qu, Y.H., Lü, X.Y. Aqueous synthesis of gold nanoparticles and their cytotoxicity in human dermal fibroblasts-fetal. *Biomedical Materials* 4(2009):025007.

Rahman, M.F., Wang, J., Patterson, T.A., Saini, U.T., Robinson, B.L., Newport, G.D. et al. Expression of genes related to oxidative stress in the mouse brain after exposure to silver-25 nanoparticles. *Toxicology Letters* 187(2009):15–21.

Reinhart, B.J., Slack, F.J., Basson, M., Pasquinelli, A.E., Bettinger, J.C., Rougvie, A.E. et al. The 21-nucleotide let-7 RNA regulates developmental timing in *Caenorhabditis elegans*. *Nature* 403(2000):901–6.

Shahare, B., Yashpal, M., Singh, G. Toxic effects of repeated oral exposure of silver nanoparticles on small intestine mucosa of mice. *Toxicology Mechanisms and Methods* 23(2013):161–7.

Soenen, S.J., Rivera-Gil, P., Montenegro, J.M., Parak, W.J., De Smedt, S.C., Braeckmans, K. Cellular toxicity of inorganic nanoparticles: Common aspects and guidelines for improved nanotoxicity evaluation. *Nano Today* 6(2011):446–65.

Takane, K., Kanai, A. Vertebrate virus-encoded microRNAs and their sequence conservation. *Japanese Journal of Infectious Diseases* 64(2011):357–66.

Takekawa, M., Saito, H. A family of stress-inducible GADD45-like proteins mediate activation of the stress-responsive MTK1/MEKK4 MAPKKK. *Cell* 95(1998):521–30.

Takenaka, S., Karg, E., Roth, C., Schulz, H., Ziesenis, A., Heinzmann, U. et al. Pulmonary and systemic distribution of inhaled ultrafine silver particles in rats. *Environmental Health Perspectives* 109(2001):547–51.

Tian, Q., Stepaniants, S.B., Mao, M., Weng, L., Feetham, M.C., Doyle, M.J. et al. Integrated genomic and proteomic analyses of gene expression in mammalian cells. *Molecular & Cellular Proteomics* 3(2004):960–9.

Ueda, K., Arakawa, H., Nakamura, Y. Dual-specificity phosphatase 5 (DUSP5) as a direct transcriptional target of tumor suppressor p53. *Oncogene* 22(2003): 5586–91.

Verano-Braga, T., Miethling-Graff, R., Wojdyla, K., Rogowska-Wrzesinska, A., Brewer, J.R., Erdmann, H. et al. Insights into the cellular response triggered by silver nanoparticles using quantitative proteomics. *ACS Nano* 8(2014):2161–75.

Xia, W., Cao, G., Shao, N. Progress in miRNA target prediction and identification. *Science in China Series C—Life Sciences* 52(2009):1123–30.

Yang, Y.M., Qu, Y.H., Lü, X.Y. Global gene expression analysis of the effects of gold nanoparticles on human dermal fibroblasts. *Journal of Biomedical Nanotechnology* 6(2010):234–46.

Zimmermann, R., Dudek, J. HSPA5 (heat shock 70kDa protein 5 (glucose-regulated protein, 78kDa)). *Atlas of Genetics and Cytogenetics in Oncology and Haematology* 14(2010):1597–604.

11

Methods and Tools for Assessing Nanomaterials and Uses and Regulation of Nanosilver in Europe

Steffen Foss Hansen and Aiga Mackevica

CONTENTS

11.1 Introduction

The increasing advertising using the word 'nano' when it comes to marketing consumer and medical products has gained a lot of public attention and has raised concerns about consumer and environmental safety. The main reason is that there is and has been a general lack of information available regarding how and where nanomaterials are used, the overall safety of nanoparticle-containing products and whether regulation to protect consumers and the environment is adequate. For instance, in 2014, the Center for Food Safety (CFS), a nongovernmental organisation, started a lawsuit against the US Environmental Protection Agency (US EPA) over their inability to regulate nanoparticle-based biocides, as a large number of them were commercially available and there were safety concerns regarding both consumer and environmental health (Center for Food Safety 2014).

In the same year, US EPA banned the production and sales of several silver nanoparticle–containing consumer products, such as plastic food containers, mentioning the lack of proper testing to ensure consumer safety as a reason (Environmental Protection Agency 2014).

In Europe, three specific pieces of regulation are especially relevant to consider when it comes to nanosilver, namely, Europe's chemical regulation known as REACH, the biocidal product regulation known as the 'BPR' and the medical drug and devices regulation. Each of these has been revised in recent years in order to address the unique challenges arising from nanomaterials, and each of them will be discussed in the following.

First, we introduce The Nanodatabase and analyse the uses of nanosilver in the European Union (EU). Second, we explain how nanosilver is regulated in the EU when it comes to REACH, BPR and medical drugs and devices, and then we elaborate on the challenges that nanomaterials present when it comes to regulation. One of the main challenges relates to how to complete risk assessment of nanomaterials; thus, the final part of the chapter discusses the test methods used to complete chemical risk assessment as well as alternative methods and tools that have been explored when it comes to nanosilver (i.e. NanoRiskCat and GreenScreenNano).

11.2 The Applications and Use of Silver Nanoparticles

The use of silver dates back to some of the ancient cultures like the Greeks, Romans and Egyptians, who utilised it to keep water and other liquids sanitary (Hill 2009). Over time, silver was utilised for a wider range of applications including jewellery, coinage, utensils, photography and explosives (Chen and Schluesener 2008). Mainly because of its biocidal properties, silver is still being used in a wide range of applications such as water purification, medicine and a large number of everyday items (Hill 2009).

When it comes to silver in the nanoparticulate form, some of the first documented uses go back to 1897, when silver nanoparticles of 10 nm in size were used for medical applications in a product called 'Collargol' (Nowack et al. 2011). Silver nanoparticle properties are different when compared to larger particles of the same compound, one of the main reasons being the large surface-to-volume ratio (Navarro et al. 2008). Depending on the nanoparticle size, approximately 40%–50% of the atoms are located on the surface of the nanoparticle, which consequently results in much greater reactivity compared to that of bigger particles (Farré et al. 2009). Compared to the bulk form, silver nanoparticles exhibit greater antibacterial activity, higher electrical conductivity and better optical properties (Foldbjerg et al. 2015). Because of these unique physicochemical properties of silver when it is at the nanoscale, silver nanoparticles are being increasingly used for different consumer and medical applications (Wijnhoven et al. 2009). The products cover many different applications, such as dietary supplements and food packaging, body lotions, textiles, air filters, kitchen appliances and even white goods (The Nanodatabase 2015).

Silver nanoparticles have a broad spectrum of biocidal activity, and therefore they are incorporated into various products for antimicrobial purposes. For the biocidal effect to take place, silver ions have to be released. The efficacy of silver nanoparticles as a biocide is strongly associated to the ability to release silver ions (Kumar et al. 2005; Luoma 2008). Silver ions can be toxic through several pathways, such as reacting with thiol groups in proteins and enzymes, inducing oxidative stress and producing reactive oxygen species and inhibiting DNA replication (Luoma 2008; Nel et al. 2006).

11.2.1 Nanosilver and Consumer Products

During the last decade, silver nanoparticle use has become more widespread when it comes to consumer products and everyday items; however, factual information about production volumes, product concentration and so on is hard to come by. In the United States, the US EPA has already registered silver nanoparticles under the name 'colloidal silver' since 1954. In 2011, out of the 92 EPA-registered biocidal silver-containing products, 7% were confirmed to contain silver in the nanoform and 46% were likely containing nanosilver (Nowack et al. 2011). Data for Europe and elsewhere are not available to the best of our knowledge.

Several consumer product databases developed by various academics, semi-governmental think-tanks and NGOs have tried to keep track of the use of nanomaterials in consumer products based on 'nanoclaims' made by producers and retailers. An example is the inventory by Woodrow Wilson International Center for Scholars, which was established in 2006 (The Project on Emerging Nanotechnologies 2015). Over the years, the number of consumer products containing nanoparticles has been increasing, and silver nanoparticles have been the most abundantly used material in these products. To date, there are 442 products claiming to contain silver nanoparticles in this inventory out of 1827 nano-containing products in total, whereas back in 2006, the number of silver nanoparticle-containing products was less than 40 (The Project on Emerging Nanotechnologies 2015).

The USA CFS has generated a database containing food items and food contact materials that are claiming to contain or are positively tested for their nanomaterial content (Center for Food Safety 2015). It contains more than 300 products in total, and the most abundant nanomaterial in these products is silver, which is found in 86 products. These products generally contain silver to attribute antibacterial action for a wide range of items, such as baby bottles, food containers and personal care products, like toothbrushes and toothpastes, and even white goods.

The same trend has also been observed in The Nanodatabase – another nanoproduct inventory that we maintain that focuses mainly on the European

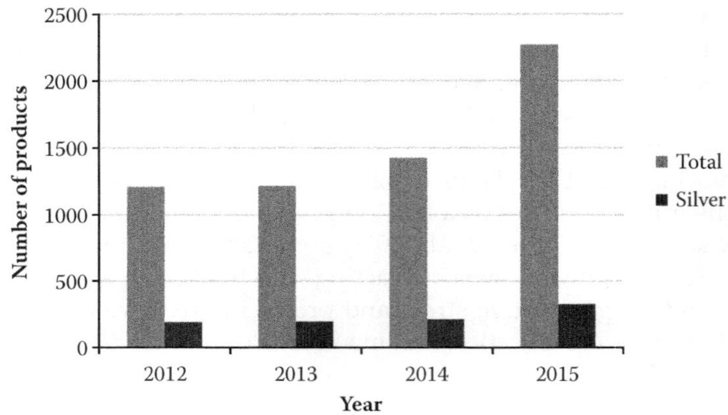

FIGURE 11.1
Total number of products and silver nanoparticle-containing products in The Nanodatabase. (From The Nanodatabase. 2015. http://nanodb.dk [accessed December 2015].)

market, established in 2012 (The Nanodatabase 2015). Both the total number of products and the number of silver nanoparticle–containing products added to the database continue to increase (Figure 11.1), and silver has the largest number of products compared with other types of nanomaterials.

Consumer products can be categorised according to their product category based on their application. The categories are 'Health and Fitness', 'Home and Garden', 'Automotive', 'Electronics and Computers', 'Food and Beverage', 'Appliances' and 'Goods for Children'. Most nanoparticle-containing products fall in the category of 'Health and Fitness' products, representing such items as cleaning sprays, clothing, kitchen equipment and many more. This category, along with most of the other ones, is dominated by silver nanoparticle products (Figure 11.2). When it comes to looking into distributions of silver nanoparticle–containing products into various product types, the most popular ones are personal care products, clothing and cleaning products (Figure 11.3), where the biocidal properties of silver nanoparticles are utilised.

Silver nanoparticles can be incorporated in a product in several different ways. They can be suspended in a liquid (e.g. in lotions and cleaning supplies), embedded in a solid matrix such as plastic, or used as a coating for a solid material.

11.2.2 Medical Devices and the Utilisation of Nanosilver

In medicine, silver has been known as an antibacterial agent for decades. The increasing use of silver in medical supplies has recently become more popular to avoid medical device–related infections without the use of antibiotics

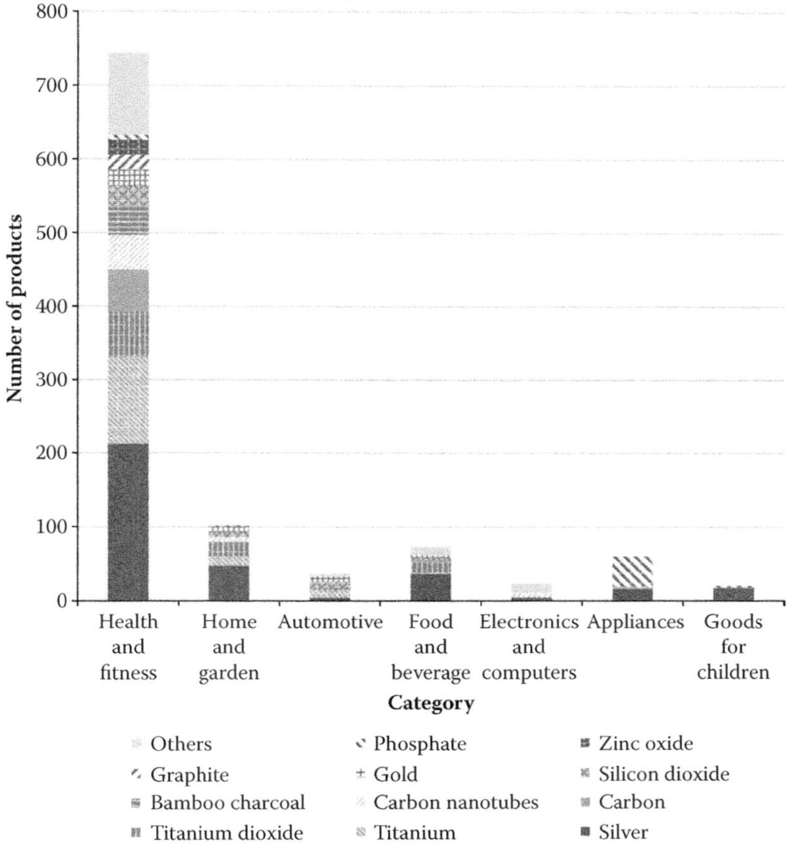

FIGURE 11.2
Nanoparticle use across different product categories. Products where the type of nanomaterial is 'unknown' are excluded. (From The Nanodatabase. 2015. http://nanodb.dk [accessed December 2015].)

(Wijnhoven et al. 2009). Silver has been utilised for different types of medical equipment and textiles, implants and prostheses, catheters and wound treatment, especially to prevent infections for burn victims (Lansdown 2006).

Such devices as catheters, implants and wound dressings are prone to bacterial adhesion and biofilm formation, which may easily lead to infections. Silver salts have been used as coatings to these devices, but the efficacy has not always been satisfactory. Using silver in the nanoparticle form has been found to be more beneficial, as the nano-coatings may be designed to have a more controlled release of silver ions over a longer period, when compared to silver salts (Chaloupka et al. 2010), and a faster silver ion release compared to bulk silver (Lansdown 2006). Silver nanoparticle coatings can be created

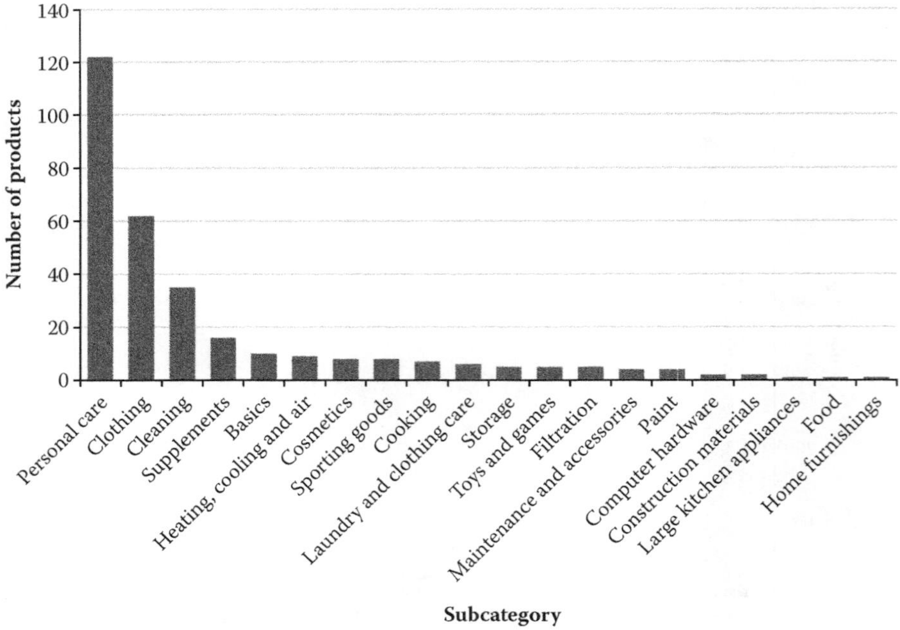

FIGURE 11.3
Silver nanoparticle use for different products. (From The Nanodatabase. 2015. http://nanodb.dk [accessed December 2015].)

and successfully used on a wide range of materials, such as metals, ceramics, polymers, glass and textiles (Wijnhoven et al. 2009). Some of the medical products containing silver nanoparticles are also commercially available and include such applications as wound dressings, ventricular catheters, hand gels, wound dressings, cavity fillers and drug delivery catheters (Chaloupka et al. 2010). Because of the growing need for new antibiotics to fight bacteria that have developed resistance to antibiotics, the use of silver nanotechnology in medicine has become an increasingly popular issue in the recent years (Rai et al. 2009). It has already been shown that silver nanoparticle use for various implantable devices, for example, neurosurgical and venous catheters, has been beneficial as it prevents or reduces the bacterial infections and requires less antibiotic use (Chaloupka et al. 2010). In recent years, silver nanoparticles have also been quite extensively used for medical devices associated with treating wounds, such as burns, chronic wounds, ulcers and meshed skin grafts (reviewed in Wijnhoven et al. 2009). Promising potential applications of silver nanoparticles range from implant technology and drug delivery, to diagnostics and imaging (Wijnhoven et al. 2009), as well as water purification to control and prevent outbreaks of various water-borne diseases (Tran et al. 2013).

11.3 Regulation of Nanosilver in Europe

Three specific pieces of regulation are especially relevant to consider when it comes to nanosilver in Europe, namely, Europe's chemicals regulation known as REACH, the biocidal product regulation known as the BPR and the medical drugs and devices regulation. Each of these has been revised in recent years in order to address the unique challenges arising from nanomaterials and each of them will be discussed in the following sections.

11.3.1 Registration, Evaluation and Authorisation of Chemicals

In mid-2007, Regulation (EC) No. 1907/2006 of the European Parliament and of the Council of the European Union called Registration, Evaluation and Authorisation of Chemicals (REACH) went into force (EP and CEU 2006). Although not originally intended to address nanomaterials, REACH has evolved into one of the key pieces of European legislation affecting nanomaterials (Hansen and Baun 2012). In short, REACH consists of four elements: (1) registration (i.e. data collection on chemical use and toxicity), (2) evaluation (i.e. examination of the need for additional testing and regulation of chemicals by governments), (3) authorisation of chemicals (i.e. requirements for firms to seek permission to use chemicals of high concern) and (4) restrictions or complete ban of certain chemicals that cannot be used safely.

As nothing new, REACH shifts the responsibility in the registration and authorisation phase of REACH onto manufacturers and importers to provide data and information (including downstream users of chemicals). The registration process happened gradually, and on 30 November 2010, manufacturers and importers had to register substances produced or imported in more than 100 tonnes per year. The same applied for substances produced in more than a 100 tonnes that have been classified as very toxic to aquatic organisms and substances produced in more than 1 tonne that have been classified under Category 1 or 2 carcinogens, mutagens or reproductive toxicants. By 1 June 2013, producers or importers of substances in quantities of more than 100 tonnes had to register, and by 1 June 2018, registration of substances produced in more than 10 tonnes has to be completed (EP and CEU 2006). So far, only seven nanomaterials have been registered during the first two registrations (Jones 2013). Although a number of substances (e.g. nanosilver and various forms of carbon nanotubes) have been registered as nanomaterials under REACH, REACH does not specifically mention the word 'nanomaterials' and there is no specific registration or information requirements for nanomaterials (EP and CEU 2006), and this might help explain why so few nanomaterials have been registered under REACH to date. One of the limitations of REACH in regard to nanomaterials is related to whether a nano-equivalent of a substance with different physicochemical and (eco) toxicological properties from the bulk substance would be considered as the same or as another substance under REACH (Chaundry et al. 2006). REACH defines a substance as a 'chemical element and its compounds in the natural state or obtained by any manufacturing process, including any additive necessary to preserve its stability and any impurity deriving from the process used, but excluding any solvent which may be separated without affecting the stability of the substance or changing its composition' (EP and CEU 2006, art. 3).

Whether nanomaterials are considered to be equivalent to or different from the bulk material will have a major impact on the requirements put on manufacturers before placing nanomaterials on the market. If a nanomaterial is considered to be the same as a registered bulk material, the appropriateness of the hazard information data would be open to discussion. On the other hand, if the nanomaterial is considered a different substance, hazard information would have to be generated for the registration dossier if it is produced in more than 1 tonne per year (Chaundry et al. 2006).

Although there is no tonnage-related exemption under REACH for authorisation, restriction or classification and labelling requirements, a second limitation of REACH is that 'Substances manufactured or imported in volumes of less than 1 ton/year do not need to be registered' and hence producers or importers are not required to provide toxicological data and assess environmental exposure. As noted by Chaundry et al. (2006) and Franco et al. (2007), this threshold would hardly be reached for many nanoparticles. Chaundry et al. (2006) estimated that the majority of applications are likely to fall outside the scope of REACH on the basis of the low tonnage currently used in gram to kilogram quantities. Furthermore, the usually low concentration of nanomaterials in the final article could potentially exclude some nanomaterials from the REACH legislation, since no registration is required when the concentrations of a substance in the final article are lower than 0.1% w/w. However, a general lack of access to information about product formulations and nanoparticles concentration hampers determination of concentrations of substances by weight (Franco et al. 2007; Hansen and Baun 2012).

11.3.2 The Biocidal Products Regulation

Chemicals with claimed antibacterial properties such as nanosilver are regulated as biocidal active substances or as biocidal products in the EU under the EU Biocidal Products Regulation (BPR). A key feature of the BPR is the specific provisions regarding nanomaterials (Hansen and Brinch 2014). In the BPR, nanomaterials are defined as 'A natural or manufactured material containing particles, in an unbound state or as an aggregate or as an agglomerate and where, for 50% or more of the particles in the number size distribution, one or more external dimensions is in the size range 1 nm–100 nm' (European Parliament and of the Council 2012). This definition is in line with the recommended definitions from the European Commission for most parts, although 'incidentally created NPs' have been omitted from the BPR definition of NMs; the 50% threshold is replaced by a lower value as well (Hansen and Brinch 2014).

Besides being the first piece of legislation to adopt the definition of NMs recommended by the European Commission, the BPR is also the first to specify that an approval of an active substance does not cover a corresponding NM form, except when this is explicitly mentioned. Furthermore, in order to get an authorisation for a biocidal product containing nanomaterials, a specific risk assessment must be performed separately for the nanomaterial in question, and it is not possible to apply for a simplified authorisation, if the biocidal product contains nanomaterials (European Parliament and of the Council 2012). These requirements were implemented to address concerns about the safety of nanomaterials and, as a result, the BPR provides the most ambitious piece of nanospecific legislation yet to be implemented by European legislators. Before being allowed to commercialise their active substance or biocidal product, a manufacturer has to submit a dossier to the European Chemicals Agency that fulfils specific information requirements, outlined in Annexes of the BPR (European Parliament and of the Council 2012). These information requirements include information on the physicochemical properties of the chemical/nanomaterial in question; which type of products the active substance is to be used; expected exposure patterns as well as toxicological and ecotoxicological information. The information has to be obtained following the methods specified in the Test Methods Regulation (European Parliament and of the Council 2009), which again are equivalent to Organisation for Economic Co-operation and Development (OECD) guidelines for the testing of chemicals (OECD 2015). It is noteworthy that the BPR requires to provide an explanation of the scientific appropriateness of the test when it comes to nanomaterials and, where applicable, of the technical adaptations/adjustments that have been made in order to respond to the specific characteristics of these materials. The BPR furthermore specifies that it is possible to use other scientifically suitable methods if a test method is considered inadequate or not included in the BPR. Justification for the appropriateness of these alternative methods is, however, required (European Parliament and of the Council 2012).

Besides active substances and biocidal products, the BPR also contains provisions that apply to articles, which incorporate a biocidal product or have been treated with one. Articles can only be treated with active substances, which have been approved in the EU for that specific purpose. Treated articles have to be labelled with a label providing information of the names of all nanomaterials contained in the product, followed by the word 'nano' in brackets (e.g. [Ag]). The label furthermore has to include information on any specific related risks of the nanomaterial.

It is not clear which articles commercially available in the EU have been treated with nanomaterials or which incorporate a biocidal form. It is, however, well known that, for instance, nanosilver and nanocopper are used in consumer products because of their antibacterial properties (Hansen and Brinch 2014).

11.3.3 Medical Drugs and Devices

Well-described medicinal products containing nanoparticles in the form of liposomes, polymer protein conjugates, polymeric substances or suspensions have been given Marketing Authorisations within the EU under the existing regulatory framework, for example, Regulation 726/2004 on authorisation and supervision of medicinal products for human and veterinary use, Directive 2001/83/EC on medicinal products for human use, Directive 93/42/EEC concerning medical devices, Directive 90/385/EEC relating to active implantable medical devices and Directive 98/79/EC on in vitro diagnostic medical devices (Council of the European Communities 1990, 1993, 1998, 2001; EP and CEU 2004; Hansen and Baun 2012). Until recently, there was no specific mention of nanomaterial in the EU legislation on medicinal products and devices, tissue engineering and other advanced therapies, but in 2015, the European Commission published a proposal on medical devices in order to amend, among others, Directive 2001/83/EC concerning medicinal products for human use. In the proposal, nanomaterials are defined according to the recommendations made by the European Commission, and in the Annex of the proposal on 'General safety and performance requirements', it states that 'The devices shall be designed and manufactured in such a way as to reduce to a minimum the risks linked to the size and the properties of particles used. Special care shall be applied when devices contain or consist of nanomaterial that can be released into the patient's or user's body' (Council of the European Council 2015a,b). The proposal furthermore specifies that information on the label should provide an indication that the device incorporates or consists of nanomaterial unless the nanomaterial is encapsulated or bound in such a manner that it cannot be released into the patient's or user's body. Notably, the latter only applies when the device is used within its intended purpose (Council of the European Council 2015b). Such devices should also be classified as 'Class III', which constitutes the highest risk classification in the EU and is set aside for the most critical devices for which explicit prior authorisation with regard to conformity is required for them to be placed on the market (Council Directive 93/42/EEC).

Despite recent efforts to address nanomaterials, none of these regulations or directives were written with nanomedicinal applications in mind, and although their scope generally covers nanomedicine, they have been accused of being too general and nonspecific as well as fraught with concerns and difficulties when it comes to dealing with drugs more complex than traditional ones (D'Silva and Van Calster 2008; Editorial 2007; Hansen and Baun 2012). The hope is that pre-market safety assessment ensures that the benefits outweigh any identified risks or the adverse side effects (EGE 2007; N&ET Working Group 2007), but as with REACH and the BPR, concerns have been raised that risk assessment, safety and quality requirements may not be designed to be suitable to address various aspects relating to nanomedicine. According to the European Medicines Agency (2006), this might be especially relevant when it comes to novel applications of nanotechnology such as nanostructure scaffolds for tissue replacement, nanostructures that allow transport across biological barriers, remote control of nanoprobes, integrated implantable sensory nanoelectronic systems and multifunctional chemical structures for drug delivery and targeting of disease. It is furthermore unclear whether novel nanomedicine is to be regulated as a medicinal product or as a medical device (EGE 2007). Currently, the mechanism of action is the key to decide whether a product should be regulated as one or the other; however, nanomedicinal products may exhibit a complex mechanism of action combining mechanical, chemical, pharmacological and immunological properties, and combining diagnostic and therapeutic functions. Hence many of these novel applications are likely to span regulatory boundaries between medicinal products and medical devices (EGE 2007; European Medicines Agency 2006; Hansen and Baun 2012).

11.4 Methods and Tools for Assessing Nanomaterials

As noted above, REACH, the BPR and the European medical legislation rely on our ability to complete chemical risk assessment, which, again, in Europe rely heavily on the applicability of standard OECD guidelines for testing of chemicals.

In 2009, a preliminary OECD review of the current test guidelines for their applicability to nanomaterials was published. In relation to ecotoxicity testing, 24 guidelines were reviewed to evaluate their adequacy in addressing nanomaterials and to identify the need for development of new test guidelines or a revision of existing ones. The key finding of the review was that guidance was insufficient for testing of nanomaterials when it comes to (1) material characterisation, (2) exposure preparation and delivery of substance to test systems, (3) monitoring of stability and consistency of nanomaterials during the tests and (4) measurement and use of dose metrics. It was found, however, that the basic toxicological principles and test endpoints were adequate. The recommendation was, therefore, not to have extensive modification of all OECD guidelines, but instead to address specific issues related to testing of nanomaterials in a separate document. It was also noted that the terminology used in many cases was not applicable to nanomaterials, and these terms also need to be revised. As the preliminary review revealed, a primary failing of the current test guidelines was the lack of guidance on sample preparation. As a result, in 2010, the OECD published a guidance document on sample preparation and dosimetry, and this was reviewed and amended 2 years later (Hansen and Brinch 2014). However, this still does not offer an actual test guideline with specific steps and requirements, but rather an outline of important considerations that manufacturers and researchers should bear in mind in order to obtain meaningful and reproducible test results. The lack of clear and specific guidance on how to complete nano-specific testing creates a significant challenge for registrants when it comes to REACH and the BPR, because how can they demonstrate that they have completed nano-specific testing and risk assessment of the nanomaterial that they wish to register? Similarly, how can the competent authorities assess the appropriateness of the submitted data and whether the risk assessment of the bulk form of a given active substance covers the nanoform as well (Hansen and Brinch 2014)?

When it comes to nanomedicine, a mass-based action level could furthermore be problematic as mass-based concentrations might not be the most relevant metrics to describe the environmental profile of nanomaterials (Baun et al. 2008; Zhang et al. 2007). Establishing the ecotoxicity of nanoparticles currently holds a number of limitations and challenges (Stone et al. 2010) and many of these shortcomings to chemical risk assessment are valid for nanomedical products as well. For instance, in the EU guidelines for risk assessment of medical products, the octanol–water coefficient is used as a surrogate value for bioaccumulation data, but so far, there is no strong evidence that this approach applies to nanomaterials (Baun et al. 2008; Handy et al. 2008; Hansen and Baun 2012; SCENIHR 2007, 2009).

Completing a chemical risk assessment for nanosilver is by no means easy as noted above. As a consequence, many have developed and proposed alternative safety evaluation methods and tools when it comes to nanomaterials. In the following, we will introduce two of them, namely, NanoRiskCat and GreenScreenNano, as these have specifically been completed to explore the risks of nanosilver.

11.4.1 NanoRiskCat and Nanosilver

NanoRiskCat is a tool developed by Hansen et al. (2014) that can be used by companies and risk assessors to categorise nanomaterials considering existing environmental, health and safety information and known possible uncertainties about the exposure risks and hazard of these materials (Hansen et al. 2014).

The final NanoRiskCat evaluation for a specific nanomaterial in a given application is communicated in the form of a short title (e.g. Ag in air purifiers or in an antibacterial soap) describing the use of the nanomaterial and a five-coloured bullet colour code i.e. •••|••. The first three coloured bullets always refer to potential exposure of professional end users, consumers and the environment in that sequence and the last two coloured bullets always refer to the hazard potential for humans and the environment. The colours assigned to the exposure and hazard potential are green, yellow, red and grey, corresponding to none, possible, expected and unknown, respectively.

The exposure potential was evaluated based on (1) the location of the nanomaterial and (2) a judgment of the potential of nanomaterial exposure based on the description and explanation of each process, category and so on (see Hansen et al. 2014).

The hazard potential for humans is evaluated based on whether the nanomaterial in question is known as a compound to have low solubility in water (biodurable), to fulfill the fibre paradigm, to be regulated harder than nuisance materials and to have CMR properties or other adverse effects. On the other hand, the environmental hazard potential is based on whether the nanomaterial in question is known to be readily dispersed, persistent or bioaccumulative or has been reported to be hazardous to environmental species (Hansen et al. 2014).

The first step in the Human Hazard Evaluation is to determine whether the nanomaterial fulfils the HARN paradigm. Normally, nanosilver is commercialised as powder, flakes, grains and so on (Mikkelsen et al. 2011), which do not fulfil the HARN requirements of having a diameter aspect ratio greater than 10 to 1. Furthermore, bulk silver has not been classified according to CLP and neither has nanosilver specifically been reported to be acute toxic (Mikkelsen et al. 2011; Stone et al. 2010). The key question in regard to NanoRiskCat and the human health hazard evaluation of nanosilver is whether there are indications that the nanomaterial causes genotoxic, mutagenic, carcinogenic, respiratory, cardiovascular, neurotoxic or reproductive effects in humans and laboratory animals or organ-specific accumulation has been documented. Here, the answer is yes for a number of reasons. First of all, a number of studies have furthermore associated nanosilver with respiratory tract toxicity (Sung et al. 2008, 2009) and Lee et al. (2008) have demonstrated that inhalation of nanosilver for a period of 14 days changed specific brain gene expressions in mice and caused neuron disorders and neurodegenerative disease, among others. Finally, nanosilver has been observed to be primarily accumulated in the lungs and liver, as well as in the olfactory bulb, brain and kidneys (Kim et al. 2008; Sung et al. 2009). Consequently, Hansen et al. (2014) have concluded that the NanoRiskCat colour code for nanosilver is red when it comes to the human hazard evaluation. When it comes to NanoRiskCat and the environmental hazard evaluation, the first step is to investigate whether silver is classified as CLP Acute 1 or Chronic 1 or Chronic 2 (Annex VI of Regulation [EC] No. 1272/2008 [CLPZ]). Silver is classified as neither. However, both types of nanosilver have been reported to be hazardous to environmental species, that is, LC_{50} or EC_{50} < 10 mg/L. Griffitt et al. (2008) found LC_{50} values of 0.04 mg/L for *Daphnia pulex* and 7.2 mg/L for zebrafish when testing silver nanoparticles. Zhao and Wang (2012) have established that the toxicity of silver nanoparticles is highly dependent on the surface coating and the size of the nanoparticles. The 48 h LC_{50} toward *Daphnia magna* varied from 28.7

to 1.1 μg/L depending on the coating of the silver nanoparticles. Hence, the environmental hazard profile of nanoAg is red (Hansen et al. 2014).

11.4.2 GreenScreen

GreenScreen is a method for comparative Chemical Hazard Assessment that can be used for identifying chemicals of high concern and safer alternatives. The method was developed by the NGO Clean Production Action and builds on the USEPA Design for the Environment Program (DfE) approach as well as OECD testing of chemicals and the Global Harmonized System for Classification and Labelling of Chemicals. GreenScreen includes consideration of feasible and relevant transformation products and has been used by industry, government and NGOs to support product design and development, as well as materials procurement, and as part of an alternative assessment to meet regulatory requirements.

The focus of GreenScreen can be on single chemicals or more complex mixtures and polymeric materials. The GreenScreen procedure consists of three steps: (1) assess and classify hazards, (2) apply benchmarks and (3) make an informed decision. The first step of classifying a given chemical is subject to analysis according to 18 human and environmental health hazard endpoints from Very High (vH) to Very Low (vL). The classification is supposed to be based on scientific research and data collection from all relevant sources coupled with expert judgment, and the 18 endpoints include endpoints such as carcinogenicity, reproductive toxicity, acute aquatic toxicity and chronic aquatic toxicity. For each of the classifications, the level of confidence for each hazard classification has to be determined by using the 'GreenScreen Guidance'. In the final GreenScreen, **bold** letters indicate high confidence, whereas *italic* letters indicate lower confidence, and a data gap is supposed to be assigned only after an exhaustive search has been completed and no hazard classification can be made (Clean Production Action 2015).

In the second step of GreenScreen, benchmarks are determined by analysing specific combinations of hazard classifications generated in step 1 and a final Benchmark score is obtained. The Benchmarks were developed to reflect hazard concerns that have been established by governments nationally and internationally and the Benchmark 1 criteria are, for instance, aligned with the definition of a substance of very high concern (SVHC) under REACH. If the data are insufficient, a Benchmark cannot be assigned and only certain numbers and types of data gaps are allowed for each Benchmark level. In step 3 of GreenScreen, all the classification of hazards and the application of benchmarks come together, aiming at making an informed decision about how to address the chemical of concern. The final decision could aim at changing the product design and development, chemical and material procurement, risk management, workplace safety and so on.

In an attempt to use GreenScreen on silver and nanoscale silver, the Natural Resources Defense Council contracted the NSF International to explore whether adaptations should be made to the GreenScreen approach. Both forms of silver were classified Benchmark 1, which corresponds to the highest concern benchmark score owing to the aquatic toxicity of silver combined with the persistence and acute inhalation toxicity of this material (NRDC 2015; Sass 2013).

11.5 Conclusion and Outlook

A lot of public attention and concern have been raised about the use of nanosilver in consumer products and biocidal products and its medical applications. It has been quite unclear how and to what extent nanosilver was used in consumer products in the EU, but work that we have done establishing The Nanodatabase provides a unique insight into the applications of nanosilver. The Nanodatabase is a nanoproduct inventory focusing on products claimed to entail nanomaterials or to be based on nanotechnology and that are available to European consumers. The Nanodatabase was established in 2012 and analysis of the data in The Nanodatabase shows that nanosilver has the largest number of products compared with other types of nanomaterials. The most popular uses of nanosilver are in personal care products and in clothing and cleaning products where the biocidal properties of silver nanoparticles are utilised. Apart from consumer applications, there is furthermore an increasing use of silver in medical supplies and different kinds of medical equipment and textiles, implants and prostheses, catheters and wound treatment. When it comes to mapping and understanding how widespread the use of nanosilver is, some key challenges remain. First, there might be products and devices on the market where the producers do not make any claims about 'nano', which makes it impossible to identify the products and include them in our database. Second, there might be products in our database, where producers use the word 'nano' as an advertisement stunt and nothing else. Finally, the fact that the product might entail nanosilver does not tell us anything about how much nanosilver the product entails or how much might be released over time, which is vital for any kind of safety evaluation.

Three specific regulations are especially relevant to consider when it comes to nanosilver in Europe, namely, Europe's chemicals regulation known as REACH, the biocidal product regulation known as the BPR and the medical drugs and devices regulation. Each of these has been revised in recent years in order to address the unique challenges concerning nanomaterials. However, they still struggle as they all rely heavily on our ability to complete chemical risk assessments, which require that the OECD tests, which support chemical risk assessment, are used for testing of nanomaterials. OECD testing has major flaws when it comes to assessing nanomaterial safety, as they do not provide enough nano-specific guidance when it comes to, for example, sample preparation and how to ensure reproducibility of the test results. A lot of effort has been made to evaluate the safety of nanosilver, such as adapting the existing OECD test guidelines, but it proved to be futile, as the tests on which chemical risk assessments are based have yet to take the nano-specific properties of these unique materials into account. Alternatives to chemical risk assessment have been explored in recent years (e.g. NanoRiskCat and GreenScreen). The application of the GreenScreen framework resulted in the highest concern benchmark score owing to the aquatic toxicity of silver combined with the persistence and acute inhalation toxicity. Via the application of NanoRiskCat, it was found that *in vivo* and *in vitro* tests have observed a range of potential hazards, including respiratory and genotoxic effects after inhalation of nanosilver. Dermal toxicity after long-term exposure also seems likely. In addition, nanosilver (or dissolved Ag) has a tendency to translocate within the body and accumulate in cells and inner organs. Observed genotoxicity may lead to carcinogenesis, but further investigations are necessary to confirm this. Only few studies have been carried out concerning neurotoxicity, but it is possible that problems can occur whereas no evidence of cardiovascular toxicity has been observed. Consequently, the NanoRiskCat profile of silver is red, reflecting that there is an expected hazard when it comes to human health and the environment.

References

Baun, A., Hartmann, N.B., Grieger, K., Kusk, K.O. 2008. Ecotoxicity of engineered nanoparticles to aquatic invertebrates: A brief review and recommendations for future toxicity testing. *Ecotoxicology* 17 (5): 387–395.

Chaundry, Q., Blackburn, J., Floyd, P., George, C., Nwaogu, T., Boxall, A., Aitken, R. 2006. *A Scoping Study to Identify Gaps in Environmental Regulation for the Products and Applications of Nanotechnologies*. London: Department for Environment, Food and Rural Affairs.

Center for Food Safety. 2014. Press release. Nonprofits Sue EPA for Failure to Regulate Novel Pesticide Products Created with Nanotechnology. http://www.centerforfoodsafety.org/press-releases/3664/nonprofits-sue-epa-for-failure-to-regulate-novel-pesticide-products-created-with-nanotechnology (accessed 28 December 2015).

Center for Food Safety. 2015. Nanotechnology in Our Food. An Interactive Database of Consumer Food Products Containing Nanomaterials. http://salsa3.salsalabs.com/o/1881/p/salsa/web/common/public/content?content_item_KEY=14112 (accessed December 2015).

Chaloupka, K., Malam, Y., Seifalian, A.M. 2010. Nanosilver as a new generation of nanoproduct in biomedical applications. *Trends in Biotechnology* 28 (11): 580–588.

Chen, X., Schluesener, H.J. 2008. Nanosilver: A nanoproduct in medical application. *Toxicology Letters* 176 (1): 1–12.

Clean Production Action. 2015. Guidance and Method Documents. http://www.greenscreenchemicals.org/method/method-documents (accessed December 2015).

Council of the European Communities. 1990. Council Directive 90/385/EEC of 20 June 1990 on the approximation of the laws of the Member States relating to active implantable medical devices. Official Journal L 189 of 20 July 1990, pp. 17–36.

Council of the European Communities. 1993. Council Directive 93/42/EEC of 14 June 1993 concerning medical devices. Official Journal L 169 of 12 July 1993, pp. 1–43.

Council of the European Communities. 1998. Council Directive 98/24/EC of 7 April 1998 on the protection of the health and safety of workers from the risks related to chemical agents at work (fourteenth individual Directive within the meaning of Article 16(1) of Directive 89/391/EEC). Official Journal L 131:23.

Council of the European Communities. 2001. Directive 2001/83/EC of the European Parliament and of the Council of 6 November 2001 on the Community code relating to medicinal products for human use. Official Journal L 311/67-128.

Council of the European Council. 2015a. Proposal for a Regulation of the European Parliament and of the Council on Medical Devices and Amending Directive 2001/83/EC, Regulation (EC) No 178/2002 and Regulation (EC) No 1223/2009. 9769/15. Interinstitutional File: 2012/0266 (COD).

Council of the European Council. 2015b. Proposal for a Regulation of the European Parliament and of the Council on Medical Devices and Amending Directive 2001/83/EC, Regulation (EC) No 178/2002 and Regulation (EC) No 1223/2009. 9769/15 ADD 1. Interinstitutional File: 2012/0266 (COD).

D'Silva, J., Van Calster, G. 2008. Regulating Nanomedicine: A European Perspective. http://ssrn.com/abstract=1286215 (accessed November 2008).

Editorial. 2007. Regulating nanomedicine. *Nature Materials* 6: 249.

EGE 2007. Opinion 21 – On the ethical aspects of nanomedicine, The European Group on Ethics in Science and New Technologies (EGE). http://bookshop.europa.eu/pl/opinion-on-the-ethical-aspects-of-nanomedicine-pbKAAJ06021/downloads/KA-AJ-06-021-EN-C/KAAJ06021ENC_002.pdf;pgid=y8dIS7GUWMdSR0EAlMEUUsWb0000RdsXaP00;sid=6tAftS2q2CEfvH4QMWGBEk-PSBNj5WDJ9KI=?FileName=KAAJ06021ENC_002.pdf&SKU=KAAJ06021ENC_PDF&CatalogueNumber=KA-AJ-06-021-EN-C (accessed December 2015).

Environmental Protection Agency. 2014. News Release: EPA Takes Action to Protect Public from an Illegal Nano Silver Pesticide in Food Containers; Cites NJ Company for Selling Food Containers with an Unregistered Pesticide Warns Large Retailers Not to Sell these Products. http://Yosemite.Epa.Gov/Opa/Admpress.Nsf/0/6469952cdbc19a4585257cac0053e637?OpenDocument (accessed June 2015).

European Medicines Agency. 2006. Guideline on the environmental risk assessment of medicinal products for human use EMEA/CHMP/SWP/4447/00. European Medicines Agency, London, UK.

European Parliament and Council of the European Union. 2004. Regulation (EC) No 726/2004 of the European Parliament and of the Council of 31 March 2004 laying down community procedures for the authorization and supervision of medicinal products for human and veterinary use and establishing a European Medicines Agency.

European Parliament and Council of the European Union. 2006. Regulation (EC) No. 1907/2006 of the European Parliament and of the Council of 18 December 2006 concerning the Registration, Evaluation, Authorization and Restriction of Chemicals (REACH), establishing a European Chemicals Agency, amending Directive 999/45/EC and repealing Council Regulation(EEC) No. 793/93 and Commission.

European Parliament and of the Council. 2009. Commission Regulation EC No 761/2009 of 23 July 2009 amending, for the purpose of its adaptation to technical progress, Regulation (EC) No 440/2008 laying down test methods pursuant to Regulation (EC) No 1907/2006 of the European Parliament and of the Council on the Registration, Evaluation, Authorisation and Restriction of Chemicals (REACH). *Official Journal of the European Union* L 220,1–94.

European Parliament and of the Council. 2012. Regulation EU No 528/2012 of the European Parliament and of the Council of 22 May 2012 concerning the making available on the market and use of biocidal products. *Official Journal of the European Union*, L 167, 1–123.

Farré, M., Gajda-Schrantz, K., Kantiani, L., Barceló, D. 2009. Ecotoxicity and analysis of nanomaterials in the aquatic environment. *Analytical and Bioanalytical Chemistry* 393 (1): 81–95.

Foldbjerg, R., Jiang, X., Miclăuş, T., Chen, C., Autrup, H., Beer, C. 2015. Silver nanoparticles – Wolves in sheep's clothing? *Toxicology Research* 4 (3): 563–575.

Franco, A., Hansen, S.F., Olsen, S.I., Butti, L. 2007. Limits and prospects of the 'incremental approach' and the European Legislation on the Management of Risks related to nanomaterials. *Regulatory Toxicology & Pharmacology* 48: 171–183.

Griffitt, R.J., Luo, J., Gao, J., Bonzongo, J.C., Barber, D.S. 2008. Effects of particle composition and species on toxicity of metallic nanomaterials in aquatic organisms. *Environmental Toxicology & Chemistry* 27 (9): 1972–1978.

Handy, R.D., Owen, R., Valsami-Jones, E. 2008. The ecotoxicology of nanoparticles and nanomaterials: Current status, knowledge gaps, challenges, and future needs. *Ecotoxicology*, 17 (5): 315–325.

Hansen, S.F., Baun, A. 2012. European regulation affecting nanomaterials – Review of limitations and future recommendations. *Dose-Response* 10 (3): 364–383.

Hansen, S.F., Jensen, K.A., Baun, A. 2014. NanoRiskCat: A conceptual tool for categorization and communication of exposure potentials and hazards of nanomaterials in consumer products. *Journal of Nanoparticle Research* 16 (1): 2195. doi:10.1007/s11051-013-2195-z.

Hansen, S.F., Brinch, A. 2014. The biocides market for nano actives. *Chemical Watch* 67: 8–9.

Hill, J.W. 2009. *Colloidal Silver: Medical Uses, Toxicology and Manufacture*. Clear Springs Press, Washington, DC.

Jones, P. 2013. Deadline sees only four nano registrations. https://chemicalwatch.com/15076/2013-deadline-sees-only-four-nano-registrations (accessed 12 December 2015).

Kim, Y.S., Kim, J.S., Cho, H.S., Rha, D.S., Park, J.D., Choi, B.S., Lim, R., Chang, H.K., Chung, Y.H. 2008. Twenty-eight-day oral toxicity, genotoxicity, and gender-related tissue distribution of silver nanoparticles in Sprague–Dawley rats. *Inhalation Toxicology* 20: 575–583.

Kumar, R., Howdle, S., Münstedt, H. Polyamide/silver antimicrobials: Effect of filler types on the silver ion release. 2005. *Journal of Biomedical Materials Research Part B: Applied Biomaterials* 75 (2): 311–319.

Lansdown, A. 2006. Silver in health care: Antimicrobial effects and safety in use. *Current Problems in Dermatology* 33: 17–34.

Lee, C., Kim, J.Y., Lee, W.I., Nelson, K.L., Yoon, J., Sedlak, D.L. 2008. Bacterial effect of zero-valent iron nanoparticles on *Escherichia coli*. *Environmental Science & Technology* 42: 4927–4933.

Luoma, S.N. 2008. Silver nanotechnologies and the environment: Old problems or new challenges? *The Project on Emerging Nanotechnologies*. Washington, DC: Woodrow Wilson International Center for Scholars.

Mikkelsen, S.H., Hansen, E., Christensen, T.B., Baun, A., Hansen, S.F., Binderup, M.-L. 2011. Survey on basic knowledge about exposure and potential environmental and health risks for selected nanomaterials. Environmental Project No. 1370 2011. Copenhagen: Danish Ministry of the Environment. Danish Environmental Protection Agency.

N&ET Working Group. 2007. Report on nanotechnology to the medical devices expert group findings and recommendations. http://ec.europa.eu/DocsRoom/documents/2388/attachments/1/translations/en/renditions/native (accessed December 2015).

Navarro, E., Baun, A., Behra, R., Hartmann, N.B., Filser, J., Miao, A.-J., Quigg, A., Santschi, P.H., Sigg, L. 2008. Environmental behavior and ecotoxicity of engineered nanoparticles to algae, plants, and fungi. *Ecotoxicology* 17 (5): 372–386.

Nel, A., Xia, T., Mädler, L., Li, N. 2006. Toxic potential of materials at the nanolevel. *Science* 311 (5761): 622–627.

Nowack, B., Krug, H.F., Height, M. 2011. 120 years of nanosilver history: Implications for policy makers. *Environmental Science & Technology* 45 (4): 1177–1183.

NRDC. 2015. Powerpoint on GreenScreen and Nano silver GreenScreen™. http://docs.nrdc.org/health/hea_13061001.asp (accessed December 2015).

OECD. 2015. OECD Guidelines for the Testing of Chemicals. http://www.oecd.org/chemicalsafety/testing/oecdguidelinesforthetestingofchemicals.htm (accessed December 2015).

Rai, M., Alka, Y., Aniket, G. Silver nanoparticles as a new generation of antimicrobials. 2009. *Biotechnology Advances* 27 (1): 76–83.

Sass, J. 2013. GreenScreen™ hazard assessment of silver and nanosilver demonstrates what we know, what we don't, and what we'd like to know before we get too cozy with nanomaterials. http://switchboard.nrdc.org/blogs/jsass/greenscreen_hazard_assessment.html (accessed December 2015).

SCENIHR. 2007. The appropriateness of the risk assessment methodology in accordance with the Technical Guidance Documents for new and existing substances for assessing the risks of nanomaterials. European Commission, Scientific Committee on Emerging and Newly Identified Health Risks, June 21–22. http://ec.europa.eu/health/ph_risk/committees/04_scenihr/docs/scenihr_o_010.pdf.

SCENIHR. 2009. Risk assessment of products of nanotechnologies. European Commission, Scientific committee on emerging and newly identified health risks, January 19. http://ec.europa.eu/health/ph_risk/committees/04_scenihr/docs/scenihr_o_023.pdf.

Stone, V., Hankin, S., Aitken, R., Aschberger, K., Baun, A., Christensen, F., Fernandes, T., Hansen, S.F., Hartmann, N.B., Hutchinson, G., Johnston, H., Micheletti, G., Peters, S., Ross, B., Sokull-Kluettgen, B., Stark, D., Tran, L. 2010. Engineered Nanoparticles: Review of Health and Environmental Safety (ENRHES). Available: http://nmi.jrc.ec.europa.eu/project/ENRHES.html (accessed February 2010).

Sung, J.H., Ji, J.H., Park, J.D., Yoon, J.U., Kim, D.S., Jeon, K.S., Song, M.Y., Jeong, J., Han, B.S., Han, J.H., Chung, Y.H., Chang, H.K., Lee, J.H., Cho, M.H., Kelman, B.J., Yu, I.J. 2009. Subchronic inhalation toxicity of silver nanoparticles. *Toxicological Science* 108 (2): 452–461.

Sung, J.H., Ji, J.H., Yoon, J.U., Kim, D.S., Song, M.Y., Jeong, J., Han, B.S., Han, J.H., Chung, Y.H., Kim, J., Kim, T.S., Chang, H.K., Lee, E.J., Lee, J.H., Yu, I.J. 2008. Lung function changes in Sprague–Dawley rats after prolonged inhalation exposure to silver nanoparticles. *Inhalation Toxicology* 20: 567–574.

The Nanodatabase. 2015. http://nanodb.dk (accessed December 2015).

The Project on Emerging Nanotechnologies. 2015. Consumer Products Inventory. http://www.nanotechproject.org/cpi (accessed December 2015).

Tran, Q.H., Nguyen, V.Q., Le, A.-T. 2013. Silver nanoparticles: Synthesis, properties, toxicology, applications and perspectives. *Advances in Natural Sciences: Nanoscience and Nanotechnology* 4 (3): 033001.

Wijnhoven, S.W.P., Peijnenburg, W.J.G.M., Herberts, C.A., Hagens, W.I., Oomen, A.G., Heugens, E.H.W., Roszek, B. et al. 2009. Nano-silver – A review of available data and knowledge gaps in human and environmental risk assessment. *Nanotoxicology* 3 (2): 109–138.

Zhang, L., Jiang, Y., Ding, Y., Povey, M., York, D. 2007. Investigation into the antibacterial behaviour of suspensions of ZnO nanoparticles (ZnO nanofluids). *Journal of Nanoparticle Research, 9* (3): 479-489.

Zhao, C.-M., Wang, W.-X. 2012. Importance of surface coatings and soluble silver in silver nanoparticles toxicity to *Daphnia magna*. *Nanotoxicology* 6 (6): 361–370.

12

Toward Selectively Toxic Silver Nanoparticles

Huiliang Cao

CONTENTS

12.1 Introduction

The use of implantable medical devices has continued to rise as a result of our prolonged life spans; however, these devices, in relation to their extended stay *in vivo*, are challenged by biomaterial-associated infections (BAIs) (Busscher et al. 2012; Gristina 1987). The number of dental implants used in the United States can be 2 million per year, and more than 5% of which may fail because of infections (Ehrlich et al. 2005). Although the infection rate of patients involved in fixation of closed fractures is generally lower (1%–2%), the incidence for fixation of open fractures may exceed 30% (Trampuz and Zimmerli 2006). BAIs cause approximately 55,000 deaths annually in the United States alone, with similar morbidities worldwide (Grainger et al. 2013). The average revision costs were many times more than that of a primary insertion (van Oosten et al. 2013).

BAIs occur because of bacterial contamination and formation of biofilms (Costerton et al. 1999). Administration of various antibiotics was taken as standard precautions against bacterial colonisation, but they faced severe challenges in the crisis of drug resistance, which saw the worldwide spread of antibiotic-resistant pathogens, for example, methicillin-resistant *Staphylococcus aureus* (MRSA). It was reported that more than 50% of the *S. aureus*–mediated orthopaedic infections admitted to the Shanghai Sixth People's Hospital (in China) during 2006 to 2011 were resistant to methicillin (Shen et al. 2014). Because of the emergence of antibiotic-resistant bacteria and clinical selective pressure of antibiotics, silver has gained an established place as a disinfectant (Gemmell et al. 2006). Silver has strong and nonspecific biocidal actions against a broad spectrum of bacterial and fungal species, including antibiotic-resistant strains (Agarwal et al. 2010). It is believed that silver nanoparticles (Ag NPs) are more reactive than bulk metallic forms because of the more active sites that resulted from high specific surface (Cao and Liu 2010); thus, Ag NPs are widely explored for antimicrobial applications (Eckhardt et al. 2013; Ouay and Stellacci 2015; Rizzello and Pompa 2014; Wei et al. 2015). On the other hand, there are also many studies demonstrating that Ag NPs have potential risk to mammalian cells (Soenen et al. 2015), which seriously hinders the real applications of the material. Accordingly, this chapter will focus on the physicochemical properties of Ag NPs and their specific actions to bacterial and mammalian cells, and discuss how to suppress their side effects.

12.2 Overview of Ag NPs

Nanomaterials can be generally classified into nanocrystalline materials and nanoparticles. The former are polycrystalline bulk materials with grain sizes in the nanometre range (less than 100 nm), while the latter refers to ultrafine dispersive particles with different sizes and shapes scaling from 1 to 100 nm (Tjong and Chen 2004). Metallic nanoparticles are often built from full-shell clusters of atoms conforming various crystallographic structures, such as body-centred cubic (BCC), face-centred cubic (FCC), hexagonal close packed (HCP) and so on (Schmidt 2001). During formation, the net gain in surface energy of a nanoparticle will outweigh the strain-energy cost (Howie and Marks 1984; Marks 1984); thus, metallic nanoparticles tend to nucleate and grow into twinned and multiply twinned structures bounded by the lowest-energy facets (Ajayan and Marks 1988).

As to silver (FCC metal), the {111} facets with a surface energy of 1.172 J/m^2 (the lowest among the low-index facets; Vitos et al. 1998) will be preferred at the surface as the size of the particle is decreased into the nanoscale. Other shapes with less stable facets can only be synthesised with the help of chemical capping reagents (Jin et al. 2001; Kirkland et al. 1993; Sun and Xia 2002), and numerous approaches for selective synthesis of silver nanostructures of various shapes were developed. A light-driven method for converting spherical Ag NPs into triangular nanoprisms (Figure 12.1b) was developed by Jin et al. (2001, 2003). Their procedure involves illuminating the bis(*p*-sulphonatophenyl)phenylphosphine dihydrate dipotassium and sodium citrate passivated silver nanospheres with narrowband light source. Nanosilver cubes (Figure 12.1c) and tetrahedrons (with truncated corners or edges) have been prepared by polyol synthesis, that is, reducing silver nitrate with ethylene glycol heated to 148°C in the presence of poly(vinyl pyrrolidone) (PVP), a trace amount of sodium chloride and oxygen (in air) (Wiley et al. 2004, 2007a). Nanosilver bipyramids (Figure 12.1d) were selectively grown by reducing silver nitrate with ethylene glycol heated to 160°C in the presence of PVP and bromide (NaBr), which facilitated the formation of single (111) twinned silver seeds (Wiley et al. 2006, 2007a). By double increasing the amount of bromide relative to that for synthesis of silver bipyramids, one can fabricate silver nanobars (Figure 12.1e), which can be further converted into nanorice (Figure 12.1f) by storing them in water with 5 wt% solution of PVP at room temperature for 1 week (Wiley et al. 2007a,b). In addition to chemical approaches, some physical methods were also established for producing nanostructural silver. Spherical Ag NPs can be manufactured by a physical process in which silver vapour was electrically

FIGURE 12.1
Ag NPs in various shapes: (a) transmission electron microscopy (TEM) image of nanospheres; (b) TEM image of nano prisms; (c) TEM image of nano cubes; (d) SEM image of nano bipyramids; (e) scanning electron microscopy (SEM) image of nano bars; (f) SEM image of nano rices. (a and c through f were adapted with permission from Wiley, B.J. et al. *Acc Chem Res* 40: 1067–76. Copyright 2007 American Chemical Society; b was adapted by permission from McMillan Publishers Ltd. *Nature* Jin et al. 425:487–90, copyright 2003.)

produced from bulk silver and then condensed to form nanoparticles in the presence of inert gas, but free of surface modifiers and stabilisers (Yen et al. 2009). Ion implantation is a powerful and versatile technique for synthesising nanoclusters or crystals and immobilising them in the near-surface of a variety of host materials beyond the normal thermodynamic constraints (Meldrum et al. 2001) and was used to embed silver nanocrystals in silica glasses as early as the 1970s (Arnold and Borders 1977). In order to eliminate the line-of-sight problems of conventional ion implantation, plasma immersion ion implantation (PIII), also known as plasma-based ion implantation or plasma source ion implantation, was proposed in the mid-1980s by Adler and Picraux (1985) and Conrad et al. (1987). During PIII, the target is placed directly in the plasma source and is pulse-biased to a high negative potential, which is relative to the walls of the vacuum chamber, so that the ions in the plasma cloud are accelerated and directed normal to the target surface and further condensed into nanostructural particles, offering an attractive procedure for surface modification of complex-shaped three-dimensional workpieces. By combining PIII with cathodic arc, a process named metal plasma immersion ion implantation and deposition (Anders 1997), silver can be injected into titanium (Cao et al. 2011), polymer (Zhang and Chu 2008; Zhang et al. 2008) and various oxides (Cao et al. 2013, 2014, 2016; Wang et al. 2016), forming Ag NPs for antibacterial applications. Moreover, silver may be deposited on substrates by physical vapour deposition (Ewald et al. 2006), sputtering (Fung et al. 1996), ion beam–assisted deposition (Bosetti et al. 2002; Massè et al. 2000), galvanic deposition (Gosheger et al. 2004; Hardes et al. 2007) and so on, producing integrated coatings that may be composed of silver nanograins (may also have nano size effects to some extent).

Accordingly, in this chapter, by weakening the difference on definition of nanocrystalline materials and nanoparticles, the concerned Ag NPs assemblies were classified into three categories: the diffusive Ag NPs, which are dispersed in liquids or biodegradable materials, ready for cellular uptake (Figure 12.2a); the immobilised Ag NPs, which are dispersed in/on nondegradable substrates (such as titanium and its oxide), repulsive to phagocytosis

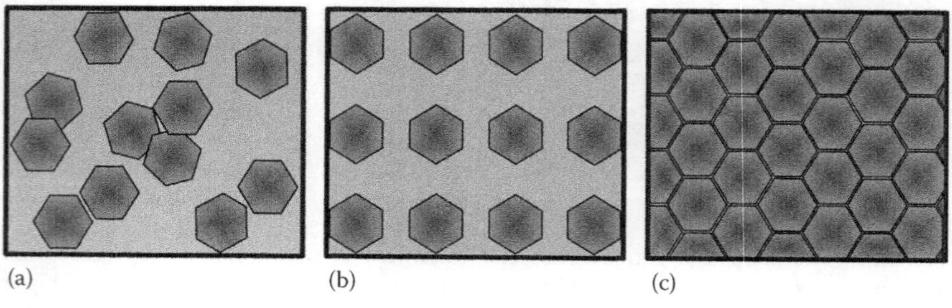

FIGURE 12.2
Schematic illustrations of the three particle assemblies concerned in this discussion: (a) diffusive Ag NPs; (b) immobilised Ag NPs; and (c) bulk silver with nanograins.

(Figure 12.2b) and the bulk silver, which can be coatings or metals (normally called nanocrystalline materials, which can be sintered from nanocrystal powders or be surface self-nanocrystallised silver bulks), consisting of nanograins (Figure 12.2c).

12.3 The Size Matter

Generally, there are two types of size-dependent effects: smoothly scalable ones, which are related to the fraction of atoms at the surface, and quantum effects, which show discontinuous behaviour owing to completion of shells in systems with delocalised electrons (Jortner 1992; Roduner 2006). The unique chemical and physical properties of nanocrystals are determined not only by the large portion of surface atoms but also by the crystallographic structures of the particle surface. The former is determined by the size of the particles and the latter relies on the particle shape. The {111}, {100} and possibly {110} surfaces of FCC metal particles are different not only in the surface atom densities but also in the electronic structure, bonding and chemical reactivities (Wang 2000).

12.3.1 Surface Atoms

One of the most crucial characteristics of nanoparticles is their very high surface (S)-to-volume (V) ratio, resulting in large fractions of surface atoms. A nanoparticle of 10 nm diameter would have ~10% of atoms on the surface, compared to 100% when the diameter is 1 nm (Rao et al. 2000). These surface atoms along with the impacts of ultrafine size and shape result in nanoparticles exhibiting markedly different behaviours from the bulk counterpart.

For a spherical particle with a diameter D, the ratio, S/V can be

$$\frac{S}{V}=\frac{4\pi(D/2)^2}{4\pi(D/2)^3/3}=\frac{6}{D}. \tag{12.1}$$

The total number of atoms (N_T) in the particle scales linearly with volume (V); thus, the size of the particle (D) scales with the inverse third power of the number of atoms (the atomic diameter is D_o), $D=D_o\cdot N_T^{1/3}$. Then, the particle volume, $V=\pi D_o^3 N_T/6$, the surface area, $S=\pi D_o^2 N_T^{2/3}$, and the number of atoms on the surface, N_S, becomes (Jortner 1992)

$$N_S=\frac{S}{\pi(D_o/2)^2}=\frac{\pi D_o^2 N_T^{2/3}}{\pi D_o^2/4}=4N_T^{2/3}. \tag{12.2}$$

Hence, the fraction of atoms in the surface shell, *F*, is (Jortner 1992)

$$F = \frac{N_S}{N_T} = \frac{4N_T^{2/3}}{N_T} = \frac{4}{N_T^{1/3}}. \tag{12.3}$$

According to Equation 12.3, the effect of size scaling on the fraction of atoms at the surface can be roughly quantified. For example, $F \approx 0.4$ for $N_T = 10^3$, $F \approx 0.19$ for $N_T = 10^4$ and $F \approx 0.04$ for $N_T = 10^6$. For other shapes, both the ratios of the surface atoms to N_T and the atoms at corner and edge sites to N_T will be increased rapidly as the particle size reduces in nanoscale. Figure 12.3 shows the situation of the cuboctahedron-shaped FCC model (Cuenya and Behafarid 2015). However, such expressions are only applicable for sufficiently large particles ($N_T > 100$) (Jortner 1992). As to smaller clusters, detailed packing information is required.

Surface atoms differ from atoms in the bulk of the particle in that they have an incomplete set of direct neighbours, which varies with the place where that atom is situated (Hardeveld and van Hartog 1969). The determination of the coordination number (C_N) for an atom in a particle is recognised as an important step to interpret its contribution to the physical and chemical properties of the particles (Carter 1978).

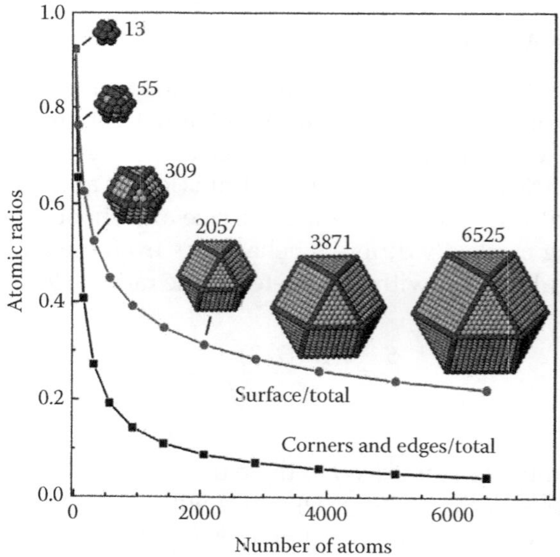

FIGURE 12.3
(See colour insert.) Reducing particle size results in an increased ratio of the surface atoms to the total number of atoms (red circles) and the atoms at corner and edge sites to the total number of atoms (black squares), calculated by using the cuboctahedron-shaped FCC model. (Adapted from *Surf Sci Rep*, 70, Cuenya, B.R. and Behafarid, F., Nanocatalysis: Size- and shape-dependent chemisorption and catalytic reactivity, 135–87, Copyright 2015, with permission from Elsevier.)

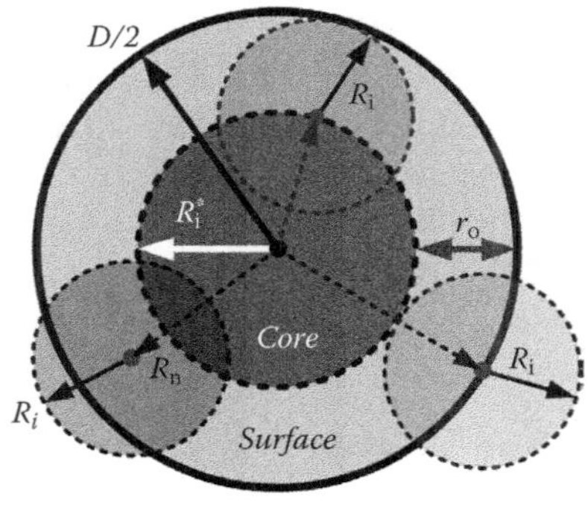

FIGURE 12.4
A shape model illustrating the relative relations between the various regions in a spherical particle (radius $D/2$) and the cutoff radius (R_i) of interatomic forces. (Modified according to *J Catal,* 63, Greegor, R.B. and Lytle, F.W., Morphology of supported metal clusters: Determination by EXAFS and chemisorption, 476–86, Copyright 1980, with permission from Elsevier.)

A sphere model (Figure 12.4) can be used in determining the average coordination number (ACN) for a spherical particle (radius $D/2$). The inner core (radius R_i^*) includes atoms with complete coordination shells that were defined by the cutoff radius (R_i) of interatomic forces, where i = 1, 2 or 3 correspond to the first, second and third coordination shells. Atoms located in the surface shell (thickness r_o) are imperfectly coordinated. For a given cutoff shell (R_i) with coordination number $C_{N,i}$ (R_i and $C_{N,i}$ are determined by the crystal structure), the ACN (which is the average of the coordination numbers of both the interior and surface atoms in the particle), $\overline{C_N}$, can be calculated as follows (Greegor and Lytle 1980):

$$\overline{C_N} = \frac{1}{\left(\frac{D}{2}\right)^3}\left[\left(\frac{D}{2} - R_i\right)^3 C_{N,i} + \sum_n \left(3\Delta \cdot R_n^2 + 3\Delta^2 \cdot R_n + \Delta^3\right) f \cdot C_{N,i}\right] \quad (12.4)$$

where n is an integer representing the coordination shell count beginning with the atom at the centre of the particle. The summation of n is performed so that $(D/2 - R_i) < R_n < D/2$. $R_n = \alpha \cdot \sqrt{n}$, and α is the shortest interatomic distance. The shell increment Δ is the difference between R_n and R_{n+j}. The value of j determines the size of the increment used in the summation. Usually, for $N_t < 10^3$, $j = 1$, and for larger particles, $j > 1$. The fraction f of a given coordination shell in the outer region, which was laid within the particle, was given by (Greegor and Lytle 1980)

$$f = \frac{1}{2}\left[1 + \frac{(D/2)^2 - R_n^2 - R_i^2}{2R_n R_i}\right]. \quad (12.5)$$

According to Equation 12.4, the decrease in the particle size leads to a decrease in the ACN, $\overline{C_N}$. The coordination number concept can be useful to describe many physicochemical phenomena of various materials. It has been found that ACN determines the effective hybridisation and therefore the magnetic moment of the clusters (Datta et al. 2007). A decrease in ACN causes a transition from bulk to atomic or molecular properties (DiCenzo et al. 1988; Rao et al. 2002).

12.3.2 Cohesive Energy

Traditionally, cohesive energy (E_{CE}) describes how strongly atoms or molecules stick together to hold the whole structures of materials in the macro scale (Yaghmaee et al. 2009). A series of theoretical models were developed to describe the size-dependent cohesion energy of nanoparticles (Jiang et al. 2002; Qi and Wang 2002; Vanithakumari and Nanda 2008; Yaghmaee and Shokri 2007). The effects of size on the cohesion energy of metal particles can be prescribed to (Qi and Wang 2002)

$$E_{CE} = E_{CEo}\left(1 - \frac{D_o}{D}\right), \tag{12.6}$$

where E_{CE_o} is the bulk cohesion energy, and it can be defined by

$$E_{CE_o} = k\pi \cdot \gamma_{So} \cdot D_o^2, \tag{12.7}$$

where γ_{So} is the surface energy per unit area at 0 K, k accounts for the difference between real particle (or atoms) and the ideal spheres, and generally one has $k > 1$. As shown in Equation 12.6, the cohesive energy is inversely proportional to the particle size (D), approaching the bulk value (E_{CEo}) as the particles grow large. The cohesive energy of nanoparticles is far lower than the bulk one, which means that the atomic bonds in nanoparticles will be broken much easier, leading to improved reactivity. A more adequate model has been proposed by considering the contribution of the surface atoms to the cohesion energy of nanoparticles (Shandiz et al. 2008).

$$E_{CE} = \frac{1}{2}\varphi\left(\sum_{k=1}^{N_L} C_{NL,k} + \sum_{j=1}^{N_S} C_{NS,j}\right) = \frac{1}{2}\varphi \cdot N_T \cdot \overline{C_N}, \tag{12.8}$$

where φ is the bond strength of the atoms in a particle, and $C_{NL,k}$ and $C_{NS,j}$ are the coordination numbers for the lattice and surface atoms of the particle, respectively. Equation 12.8 demonstrates that the cohesive energy of a nanoparticle varies linearly with its ACN. The computational analysis by

Yaghmaee and Shokri (2007) shows that the cohesion energy of Ag NPs just starts to decrease under 100 nm, and there is a critical size for these clusters; that is, the surface cohesion energy overcomes the inner values below 8 nm. Cohesive energy is an important physical parameter that quantifies various behaviours of a material, such as melting, boiling, solubility and so on. It is directly interrelated to the Gibbs free energy of formation of the particles.

12.3.3 Surface Energy

Surface energy (δ) quantifies the disruption of interatomic bonds involved in creating a new surface. It is an important physical attribute interpreting the surface nature of materials and displays an obvious behaviour dependent on the size of nanoparticles (Yao et al. 2015). The surface energy of a solid is usually measured at high temperatures, and the result is extrapolated to low temperatures (Tyson and Miller 1977). Accordingly, a constant surface energy of 7.2 J/m^2 has been obtained for Ag nanoparticles in the size range studied, which is in excellent agreement with that obtained from the size-dependent lattice parameter of free Ag nanoparticles but higher as compared to that of bulk (1.2–1.4 J/m^2) (Nanda et al. 2002, 2003). Errors of unknown magnitude can be induced by the presence of impurities or creeps at such temperatures, leading to conflict data documented by various researches (Sun 2007). Numerical attempts based on various theoretical approaches, such as *ab initio* calculations, broken bond rule, embedded atom method or the molecular dynamics simulations, are alternative approaches to measurement (Ouyang et al. 2006).

It was demonstrated that the surface energy of noble metals scales accurately with the number of broken bonds between first neighbours (Galanakis et al. 2002a,b). The simplest approach to roughly estimate the value of γ at 0 K is to determine the broken bond number $C_{(hkl)}$ for creating a fresh surface via cutting a crystal along a certain crystallographic plane with a Miller index (*hkl*), $C_{(hkl)} = C_{NL} - C_{NS}$. Multiplying this number with the cohesion energy per bond $E_b = E_{CE}/C_{NL}$ for the non–spin-polarised atom at the temperature, γ is determined by (Jiang et al. 2004)

$$\delta = C_{(hkl)} \cdot E_b = (1 - C_{NS}/C_{NL}) \cdot E_{CE}, \tag{12.9}$$

where γ corresponds actually to the energy loss owing to the reduction of coordination, which is always lower than the cohesive energy of the bulk atom. This estimation provides the order of magnitude of γ and shows a close relationship between γ and atomic binding strength. However, since E_b generally does not scale linearly with C_{NS}, the broken-bond rule seems to contradict the basic knowledge about the electronic structure (Jiang et al. 2004). As the particle size reduces, the bond strength becomes stronger for a surface atom with a smaller coordination number. This effect can be quantified using the tight-binding approximation (Desjonquères and Spanjaard 1996). By assuming that the global crystalline energy is the total contributions of all atomic bonds, the surface energy is suggested to follow the relation (Methfessel et al. 1992)

$$\delta \approx \left(1-\sqrt{C_{NS}/C_{NL}}\right)\cdot E_{CE}. \tag{12.10}$$

Although Equation 12.10 is especially suitable for noble metals, it is incomplete because only attractive forces are taken into account. The aforementioned two models can be improved by taking the arithmetic mean of Equations 12.9 and 12.10 (Jiang et al. 2004).

$$\delta = \frac{\left(2-C_{NS}/C_{NL}-\sqrt{C_{NS}/C_{NL}}\right)\cdot E_{CE}}{2} \tag{12.11}$$

Equation 12.11 implies that δ still depends on the broken-bond rule and is scaled by the coordination number of surface atoms, C_{NS}, which can be determined according to the crystalline structure and geometry of the materials.

12.3.4 Electronic Structure

The electronic structure of a metal particle is critically size dependent. The increasingly large fraction of surface to bulk atoms could change the electronic structure of nanoparticles because of different *d* and *s* orbital hybridisation of surface and bulk atoms (Liu et al. 2005). In the presence of a surface, the wave functions of valence electrons are of three types: the extended states correspond to the state that the electrons move towards the surface and are reflected into the bulk, decaying exponentially into vacuum; the resonance states are some of the extended states in which electrons are fairly localised in the surface region but can leak into the interior bulk; the surface states have localised wave functions decrease exponentially on both the bulk and vacuum of the surface but propagate along the surface, during which the electrons are trapped in the vicinity of the surface (Desjonquères and Spanjaard 1996). For small particles, the electronic states are discrete owing to the quantum confinement of the electron wave functions. The average spacing of successive quantum levels, ω, known as the Kubo gap, is given by $\omega = 4E_F/3N_T$, where E_F is the Fermi energy of the bulk material and N_T is the total number of atoms in the nanocrystal (Kubo 1962). For an individual Ag NP of 3 nm diameter containing approximately 1000 silver atoms, the value of ω would be 5–10 meV (Rao et al. 2000). High-energy spectroscopies, such as x-ray photoelectron spectroscopy, ultraviolet photoelectron spectroscopy and bremsstrahlung isochromat spectroscopy, provide direct access to the electronic structure of metal nanoparticles (Rao et al. 2000). As the particle size decreases, the core-level binding energy in small silver particles increases sharply because of the poor screening of the core hole, while the density of the 5s band decreases, a manifestation of the particle size–dependent metal-insulator transition (Issendorff and Cheshnovsky 2005; Vijayakrishnan et al. 1992).

Theoretical calculations throw light on the size-induced changes in the electronic structure of metal nanocrystals. There are basically two different ways to calculate the electronic structure and total energies of molecules and solids: the wave function–based approaches and the density functional theory (DFT) methods. The fundamental equation upon which electronic structure theories are based is the nonrelativistic Schrödinger equation (Greeley et al. 2002)

$$(H-E)\cdot\psi=0, \tag{12.12}$$

where H is the Hamiltonian operator, E is the total energy of the system and ψ is the wave function that depends on the positions and spins of the electrons. For studying the dynamics of electrons, the atomic nuclei are considered as fixed in space and surrounded by an 'electron gas'. Based on the Born–Oppenheimer approximation, H is (Kohn 1999)

$$H=-\frac{\hbar^2}{2m}\sum_j \nabla_j^2-\sum_{j,l}\frac{Z_l q^2}{|\rho_j-P_l|}+\frac{1}{2}\sum_{j\neq j^*}\frac{q^2}{|\rho_j-\rho_j^*|}, \tag{12.13}$$

where ρ_j and ρ_j^* are the positions of the electrons; P_i and Z_l are the positions and atomic numbers of the nuclei; $\hbar$ is equal to the Planck constant divided by 2π; the m and q are the particle mass and elementary charge, respectively; ∇_j^2 are the Laplacian operators. The solution of Equation 12.12 permits the determination of the structure for an electronic gas, and the resulting total energy is interpreted as a potential energy for the nuclei. In practice, only the potential energy in the ground state is of interest in analyses of the chemical behaviours of nanomaterials. An electron cluster model potential, which consists of a short-range repulsive interaction and a long-range polarisation potential, was proposed by Rosenblit and Jortner to explore the particle size– and dielectric constant–dependent energy and charge distribution of the electronic surface states. It was found that the behaviours of excess electrons on nanoparticles provide key information on the size dependence of the dielectric constant and are of fundamental importance as a probe for the electronic properties of large finite systems (Rosenblit and Jortner 1994).

12.4 The Biocompatibility of Silver

The word *biocompatibility* seems to have been mentioned first by Hegyeli and Homsy et al. in 1970, and it did not begin to be commonly used in scientific literature until almost two decades later (Ratner 2011). Many definitions of biocompatibility have emerged over the years. Biocompatibility was defined in 1987 as 'the ability of a material to perform with an appropriate host response in a specific situation' (Williams 1987). This definition has three major shortcomings: first, it is too general and self-evident to really help in advancing knowledge of biocompatibility; second, it did not lead to a comprehensive understanding of specific mechanisms and individual processes in the innovation of new biomaterials; third, it cannot be applied to all material–tissue interactions that pertain to wide applications varying from drug-eluting stents to joint replacement prostheses or invasive biosensors (Williams 2008). Accordingly, based on the evidence accumulated over the last 50 years through experiment and clinical experience, the definition of biocompatibility was revised by Prof. Williams as 'the ability of a biomaterial to perform its desired function with respect to a medical therapy, without eliciting any undesirable local or systemic effects in the recipient or beneficiary of that therapy, but generating the most appropriate beneficial cellular or tissue response in that specific situation, and optimising the clinically relevant performance of that therapy' (Williams 2008).

Accordingly, biocompatibility should be considered as therapy dependent. The fundamental situation is that biocompatibility is a characteristic of a specific material–biological system and not a property of a material (Williams 2008). The crucial thing to fully understand biocompatibility is to determine which chemical/biochemical, physical/physiological or other mechanisms become operative under a highly specific condition associated with the interactions between biomaterials and the tissues of the body, and what are the consequences of these events (Williams 2008). It should be noted that a material may affect different biological systems in different manners, and it may be time-dependently conditioned after contact and interaction with the tissues. These facts make it crystal clear that 'there is no material with ubiquitous biocompatibility characteristics and no such things as a uniquely biocompatible material', and it is essential to clearly interpret the specific application of a material when discussing biocompatibility (Williams 2014).

In addition, before discussing the biocompatibility of silver, it is important to recognise that there are several mediators involved in regulating the biocompatibility of a material other than the material itself, and if there is more than one biomaterial used for manufacturing the medical implants, the interactions between silver and the co-existing materials may also play a role in the biocompatibility of the whole device; hence, all these interactions should be fully considered.

12.4.1 Silver in Bulk Forms

The implications of *bulk silver* are subjected to the definition in Section 12.2 (Figure 12.2). Silver is well known as an antimicrobial material. Generally, it is considered to be a relatively low toxic threat to humans; hence, silver was used in applications such as wound dressings, sutures, protheses and catheters. Nonetheless, in some forms and concentrations, silver can be toxic to mammalian cells. A comprehensive review on the safety and efficacy of silver and silver compounds in medicine was published by Williams et al. as early as 1989 (Williams et al. 1989). They evaluated the literature (including their own findings) on the physiological events at the interface of silver implants and tissue, the corrosion/degradation effects and the local tissue responses and found that silver induced minimal local tissue response with very little inflammation and cellular activity *in vivo*. Thus, they concluded that silver could be beneficial to medical uses when antibacterial property was required.

BAI is a serious complication in orthopaedic oncology because of immunosuppression related to the underlying disease and also from adjuvant chemotherapy and radiotherapy treatments (Brennan et al. 2015). The reported infection rate is between 5% and 35% despite systemic and local antibiotic prophylaxis, and secondary amputation or hip disarticulation is, in some cases, the only solution to control the infection (Gosheger et al. 2004). Silver-coated devices have proved their efficacy in reducing infections. Elementary silver coating with a thickness ranging from 10 to 15 μm can be deposited on titanium megaprostheses by using a galvanic process (Gosheger et al. 2004). Before deposition of silver, a gold layer with a thickness of 0.2 μm was coated to drive the release of silver ions and to prevent progressive corrosion. The antibacterial property of the silver-coated titanium prosthesis was evaluated by infecting rabbits with *S. aureus*. Compared with the uncoated group, the silver group has shown significantly ($p < 0.05$) lower infection rates (7% vs. 47%). More importantly, significant ($p < 0.05$) lower inflammatory response in the silver group was evidenced by measuring the C-reactive protein, neutrophilic leukocytes, rectal temperature and body weight of the test animals. The silver concentrations in blood and organs were elevated without pathological and histological changes. Therefore, the authors concluded that the silver-coated prosthesis, exhibiting antimicrobial activity without toxicological side effects, might be promising in tumour surgery (Gosheger et al. 2004). Accordingly, various implants galvanically coated of silver were made for further evaluation in human. The studies of Hardes et al. (2007, 2010) demonstrated that the silver-coated megaprosthesis (Figure 12.5a and b) could guarantee a sustained release of silver for disinfection without any local or systemic side effects in patients who had bone metastasis. They found that the silver-coated proximal femur replacement showed no signs of corrosion, local inflammation and argyria (Figure 12.5c and d). The silver levels in the blood did not exceed 56.4 parts per billion (ppb) (can be considered as

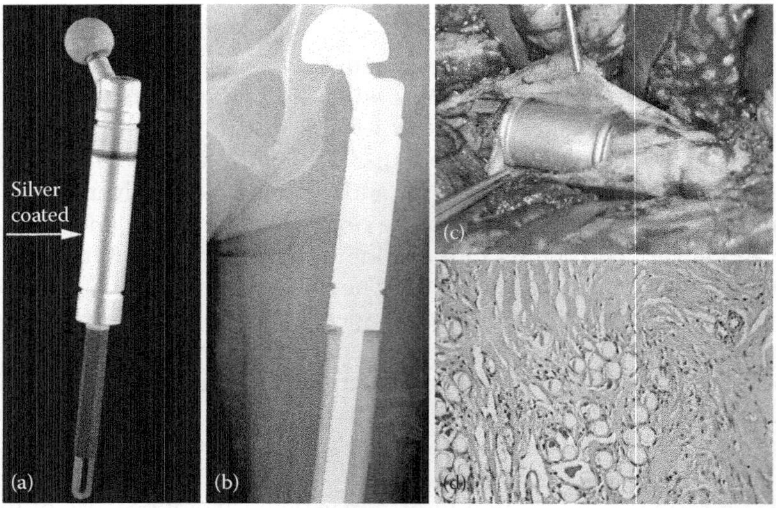

FIGURE 12.5
(See colour insert.) (a) The corpus of the megaprosthesis was elementary-silver coated (the arrow) and the stem was not treated; (b) x-ray of the silver-coated implant placed in bone; (c) a picture of a silver-coated proximal femur replacement showing no signs of corrosion, local inflammation and argyria at 7 months postoperation; (d) histopathological view of the periprosthetic environment (stained by the hematoxylin and eosin assay) showing ingrowth of the polyethylenterepthalate tube in the surrounding tissue without any foreign body granulomas or silver particle depositions. (Adapted from *Biomaterials*, 28, Hardes, J. et al., Lack of toxicological side-effects in silver-coated megaprostheses in humans, 2869–75, Copyright 2007, with permission from Elsevier.)

nontoxic), no significant changes in liver and kidney functions were detected by laboratory values and no signs of foreign body granulomas or chronic inflammation were evidenced by histopathological examination (in 2 of the 20 patients), although the silver concentration was up to 1626 ppb at the prosthetic surface. A study by Henrichs et al. (2015) further demonstrated that silver-coated proximal femur prosthesis for stump lengthening allows optimisation of remnant soft-tissue envelope and can reduce the risk of stump perforation. The silver-coated proximal femur prosthesis can be a standard special rounded end cap (Figure 12.6a) or a custom-made shaft fixed with a femur neck screw (Figure 12.6b); after treatment, the patients could have a good range of motion after stump lengthening (Figure 12.6c). It increasingly seems that the routine use of antibacterial silver-coated tumor prostheses is able to reduce the rate of infection without any toxic side effects, and now the silver-coated implants are already commercially available for patients who suffer from orthopaedic oncology (MUTARS, implantcast, Germany).

Moreover, there are other positive reports on the biocompatibility of silver-coated materials (Table 12.1). In a work of Bosetti et al. (2002), orthopaedic external fixation pins (made of AISI 316L stainless steel rods) were silver

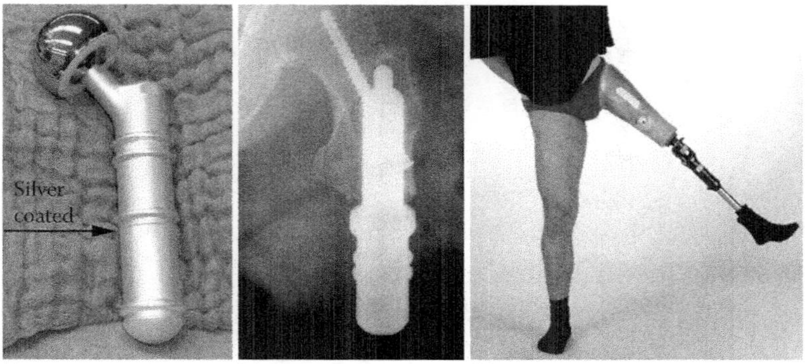

(a) (b) (c)

FIGURE 12.6
(a) The elementary-silver coated proximal femur prosthesis in combination with a special rounded end-cap and a bipolar cup being used as the permanent endoprosthetic stump. (b) In cases of high-thigh amputation, a custom-made shaft was fixed with a femur neck screw (x-ray image). (c) The patients have good range of motion after stump lengthening. (Adapted from *J Arthroplasty*, 30, Henrichs, M.P. et al., Stump lengthening procedure with modular endoprostheses – The better alternative to disarticulations of the hip joint, 681–6, Copyright 2015, with permission from Elsevier.)

coated by ion beam–assisted deposition of the vapour phase. Compared to the uncoated control, there is no statistically significant difference in the frequency of sister chromatid exchanges and micronuclei in human peripheral blood lymphocytes cultured on silver-coated samples. The analysis of lymphocytes suggested that silver coating did no harm to cell cycle. Good osteoblast activity on silver-coated samples, particularly at longer incubation periods, was detected. These results have shown that silver is neither genotoxic nor cytotoxic as compared to the uncoated AISI 316L stainless steel, a material widely used as metal implants. The implant of screws, silver coated by using the same technique as that in the study of Bosetti et al., resulted in a significant increase of silver concentration in serum (up to 11.8 μg/L) that is related to the number of the silver screws (Massè et al. 2000). The study of Fung et al. (1996) demonstrated that the silver-coated (by sputtering) silicone peritoneal dialysis catheter in a porcine model can be firmly fixated to the surrounding tissue, indistinguishable from that of the noncoated ones, revealing that silver coating is a promising technology capable of retarding bacterial colonisation on percutaneous indwelling catheters. Physical vapour deposition (PVD) is an alternative approach that can coat various substrates a silver layer. By using this technique, a 2-μm thickness of silver-contained titanium layer (0.7%–9% silver, measured by energy dispersive x-ray) was coated on titanium (Ewald et al. 2006). The composite coatings released sufficient silver ions (0.5–2.3 ppb) acting against *Staphylococcus epidermidis* and *Klebsiella pneumoniae* strains while no cytotoxic effects on osteoblast and epithelial cells were found. The PVD silver-coated titanium stems showed

TABLE 12.1

Selected Studies Focusing on the Biocompatibility of Bulk Silver

Device/Material	Concentration	Source/Technique	Host/Cell Line	Outcome	Reference
Megaprostheses/titanium–vanadium alloy	The layer thickness ranges from 10 to 15 μm.	Galvanic deposition of elementary silver (purity of 99.7%)	Human	No signs of local inflammation, metallosis or argyria.	Hardes et al. 2007
Megaprostheses/titanium–vanadium alloy	The layer thickness ranges from 10 to 15 μm.	Galvanic deposition of elementary silver (purity of 99.7%)	Rabbit	Reduced infection rates without toxicological side effects.	Gosheger et al. 2004
Pins/AISI 316L	Total dose was 6×10^{17} ions/cm^2. The maximum depth was 150 nm.	Ion beam–assisted deposition of silver from the vapour phase	Human peripheral blood lymphocytes, fibroblasts and osteoblast-like cells	Silver is neither genotoxic nor cytotoxic as compared to stainless steel.	Bosetti et al. 2002
Screws/AISI 316L	Not indicated.	Ion beam–assisted deposition of silver from the vapour phase	Human	Resulted in a significant increase in the silver serum level (related to the number of the silver screws).	Massè et al. 2000
Catheter/silicone	Not indicated.	Sputter-coated	Fat and muscle in pigs	No significant tissue irritant.	Fung et al. 1996
Titanium	Thickness of 2 μm (silver 0.7%–9%).	Physical vapour deposition process	Osteoblast and epithelial cells	No cytotoxic effects.	Ewald et al. 2006
Stem	Silver of 8.1 μg/cm^2 and thickness of up to 300 nm.	Physical vapour deposition process	Canine model	Stable osseous integration evidenced.	Hauschild et al. 2015
Pure silver	4 mm^2 large with a thickness of 0.5 mm.	Commercially pure (99.9%)	Striated muscle and subcutaneous tissue in hamsters	Severe inflammation and massive edema.	Kraft et al. 2000

stable osseous integration in a canine model (revealed by radiological, histological and biomechanical analyses), and organic changes in liver and kidney were excluded (Hauschild et al. 2015), representing a step towards selective toxicity.

However, there are also negative reports. Kraft et al. (2000) comparatively studied the biocompatibility of commercially pure silver, stainless steel and titanium by using the dorsal skinfold chamber model in Syrian golden hamsters. They found that the implantation of pure silver could distinctly and persistently activate leukocytes (massive leukocyte extravasation) and markedly disrupt the integrity of microvascular endothelial lining (considerable venular dilation), whereas stainless steel triggered a moderate increase in these aspects and recuperated later and titanium merely induced a transient (within the first two hours) increase of leukocyte-endothelial cell and no apparent change in macromolecular leakage was detected. Worse, five of six preparations with the silver implants saw severe inflammations and massive edemas 3 days postoperation. Infection is one of the most common complications of blood-contacting devices, such as intravascular catheters, stents and prosthetic heart valves. In 1994, Sioshansi, based on the ion beam–assisted deposition technique, developed a new process (with a trade name SPI-ARGENT) for coating silver on silicone rubber catheters, which demonstrated good antimicrobial activity but excellent biocompatibility in *in vitro*, clinical and simple laboratory studies (Sioshansi 1994). The SPI-ARGENT technology became the basis of Silzone (introduced by St. Jude Medical), which is composed of three layers beginning with titanium, which provides adhesion to the polyester fabric substrate for prosthetic heart valves; then, palladium which serves as an oxygen barrier and an outer layer of metallic silver (Andersen *v.* St. Jude Medical, Inc. 2012). Silzone-coated valves were designed and manufactured to directly reduce the risk of infection while having no side effect on tissue healing as compared to the uncoated ones, and an Artificial Valve Endocarditis Reduction Trial was begun in July 1998, with the original goal of randomising 4400 patients at 7 European and 12 North American centres; however, because of the higher rates of paravalvular leakage in patients receiving the Silzone prosthesis, the recruitment ended 21 January 2000 (Schaff et al. 2002). Although late-event analysis has shown that the additional risks of the Silzone valve diminish over time and disappear by 4 years after implantation (Grunkemeier et al. 2006), these cases brought up a highly debated issue on the potential benefit of using silver-coated medical prostheses.

12.4.2 Diffusive Ag NPs

The size effects on the toxicity of silver were extensively studied by using diffusive (or free) nanoparticles (some typical examples are listed in Table 12.2). Nanomaterials have similar sizes to cellular components or proteins and thus may bypass the biological barriers (such as the cell membrane) and

TABLE 12.2

Selected Publications on the Biocompatibility of Diffusive Ag NPs

Size	Shape	Surface State	Dosage/Duration	Cell Line/Host	Outcome	References
83 ± 22 nm	Spherical	PVP-capped	2–5.91 μg/mL; 1–6 h	Human acute monocytic leukemia cell line (THP-1)	Particles regulate the oxidative stress genes and alter the immune signalling processes in the coelomocytes and THP-1 cells.	Hayashi et al. 2012
2–4, 5–7 and 20–40 nm	Spherical	Bare; zeta-potential was 5.35–13.69 mV	1 and 10 ppm; 24–72 h	Murine macrophages (J774 A1)	Particles enter the cells, but did not up-regulate IL-1, IL-6 and TNF-a.	Yen et al. 2009
5.7–20.4 nm	Spherical	Supported on nanostructural silica	5, 10 and 20 mg/L; 24 h	Murine macrophages (RAW 264.7)	Particle toxicity is mediated by ion release; direct cell–particle interactions dominated the toxicity.	Pratsinis et al. 2013
5 and 100 nm	Round	PVP-coated	2.5 μg/mL; 2 h	Human macrophage cell line (U937)	5-nm particles induced the expression of IL-8 and stress genes, but the 100-nm ones did not.	Lim et al. 2012
5, 28 and 100 nm	Round	PVP-coated	0.15–6.25 μg/mL; 2 h	Human blood monocytes	Both 5- and 28-nm Ag NPs induced inflammasomes to produce IL-1β.	Yang et al. 2012
20, 40 and 80 nm	Spherical	In water	6.25 to 50 μg/cm^3; 0.5–8 h	Primary rat brain microvessel endothelial cells isolated from adult Sprague–Dawley rats	Size- and time-dependent profiles of proinflammatory responses.	Trickler et al. 2010

(Continued)

TABLE 12.2 (CONTINUED)

Selected Publications on the Biocompatibility of Diffusive Ag NPs

Size	Shape	Surface State	Dosage/Duration	Cell Line/Host	Outcome	References
15, 50 and 100 nm	Spherical	In phosphate buffer	1.25, 2.5, 5, 10 and 20 μg/mL; 2 h	Heparin-stabilised fish red blood cells	The middle size particles (50 nm) showed the highest level of adsorption and uptake; the smallest particles (15 nm) displayed a greater ability to induce haemolysis and membrane damage.	Chen et al. 2015
5–30 and 5–20 nm	Spherical	Stabilised by PVA or starch	50, 100 and 400 μg/mL; 1.5 h	Human erythrocytes	Significant lysis, haemagglutination, membrane damage, detrimental morphological variation and cytoskeletal distortions were evidenced; the magnitude of toxicity varied with capping agents (PVA and starch).	Asharani et al. 2010
<100 nm (citrate stabilised); 35 nm; 2000–3500 nm	Spherical	Citrate stabilised or not	22–2200 μg/mL; 210 min	Human blood	High haemolysis level induced by Ag NPs; citrate showed no significant effect on haemolysis.	Choi et al. 2011
10 and 20 nm	Spherical	Citrate-buffered deionised water	0.1, 1.0, 10.0, 50.0 and 100.0 μg/mL; 24 h	Human adipose-derived stem cells	Cause minimal toxicity and do not influence cell differentiation.	Samberg and Loboa 2012

(*Continued*)

TABLE 12.2 (CONTINUED)

Selected Publications on the Biocompatibility of Diffusive Ag NPs

Size	Shape	Surface State	Dosage/Duration	Cell Line/Host	Outcome	References
2–5 nm	Spherical	In distilled water	0–15.75 ppm; 4 h	CHO-K1 cells	1 ppm or lower did not show genotoxicity, acute toxicity and intracutaneous reactivity.	Han et al. 2012
50 nm, 3 µm and 30 µm	Spherical	In the a-MEM	8–500 µg/mL; 72 h	Primary osteoblasts and osteoclasts	Ag NPs are toxic because of silver ion release.	Albers et al. 2013
80 nm	Spherical	PVP-coated	2.5, 5 and 10 µg/mL; 24 h	Human mesenchymal stem cells	Ag NPs attenuate adipogenic and osteogenic differentiation at nontoxic concentrations.	Sengstock et al. 2014
75 nm	Spherical	PVP-coated; zeta potential was approximately −25 mV	5–30 µg/mL; 24 h	Peripheral monocytes and lymphocytes (T-cells)	Uptake of Ag NPs is cell type specific.	Greulich et al. 2011a
80 nm	Spherical	PVP-coated	15, 20, 25, 30 or 50 µg/ml; 24 h	Human mesenchymal stem cells	Uptake of Ag NPs by clathrin-dependent endocytosis and macropinocytosis.	Greulich et al. 2011b
20 nm	Spherical	In deionised water	0.1–64 µg/mL; 24 h	Human urine–derived stem cells	Promote osteogenic differentiation.	Qin et al. 2014b
5 nm	Spherical	Bounded to Fe_3O_4 nanoparticles	~430 mg/L; 24 h	Mice embryonal fibroblasts	No acute cytotoxicity.	Prucek et al. 2011

(*Continued*)

TABLE 12.2 (CONTINUED)

Selected Publications on the Biocompatibility of Diffusive Ag NPs

Size	Shape	Surface State	Dosage/Duration	Cell Line/Host	Outcome	References
20 and 100 nm	–	In phosphate buffer	0.0082–6 mg/kg (body weight) per day; 28 days	Intravenous administration/ Wistar rats	6 mg/kg was well tolerated; particle accumulation was noted in spleen, liver and lymph nodes; striking toxic effect was detected in the natural killer cell in spleen.	De Jong et al. 2013
20, 80 and 110 nm	Spherical	In phosphate buffer	23.8–27.6 μg/mL daily for 5 consecutive days	Wistar rats	The 20-nm group distributed to liver followed by kidneys and spleen; the 80- and 110-nm groups distributed mainly to spleen followed by liver and lung.	Lankveld et al. 2010
11.6 ± 3.5 nm	Spherical	In deionised water	0.04–0.71 nM; 120 h	Zebrafish embryos	Biocompatibility is highly dependent on the dose.	Lee et al. 2007
41.6 ± 9.1 nm	Spherical	In deionised water	0.02–0.7 nM; 120 h	Zebrafish embryos	The larger particles (41.6 ± 9.1 nm) are more toxic than the smaller one (11.6 ± 3.5 nm).	Lee et al. 2012

do harm to living cells, tissues and organs. Engineered nanomaterials are considered as foreigners to the host and may undesirably trigger immune reactions, leading to harmful consequences. Therefore, three major immunological issues must be considered when a nanomaterial is designed for *in vivo* applications: immune-mediated rejection or destruction, which eliminates the nanomaterials administrated; immunotoxicity, which induces pathological changes and damages the host and immunosafety, which relates to engineered nanomaterials that do not interfere with the normal courses of the immune system (Boraschi et al. 2012). Assessing the potential adverse effects on the immune system is a critical component of the whole evaluation of nanotoxicity. Nanomaterials, because of their remarkably different physicochemical properties, may trigger innate and adaptive immune responses in a variety of models (Figure 12.7) (Luo et al. 2015). Nanoparticle properties such as size, charge and hydrophobicity determine their interaction with the immune system (Dobrovolskaia and McNeil 2007). Comprehensive studies showed that Ag NPs can stimulate or suppress the immune responses in size, surface chemistry and time-dependent profiles. It was reported that

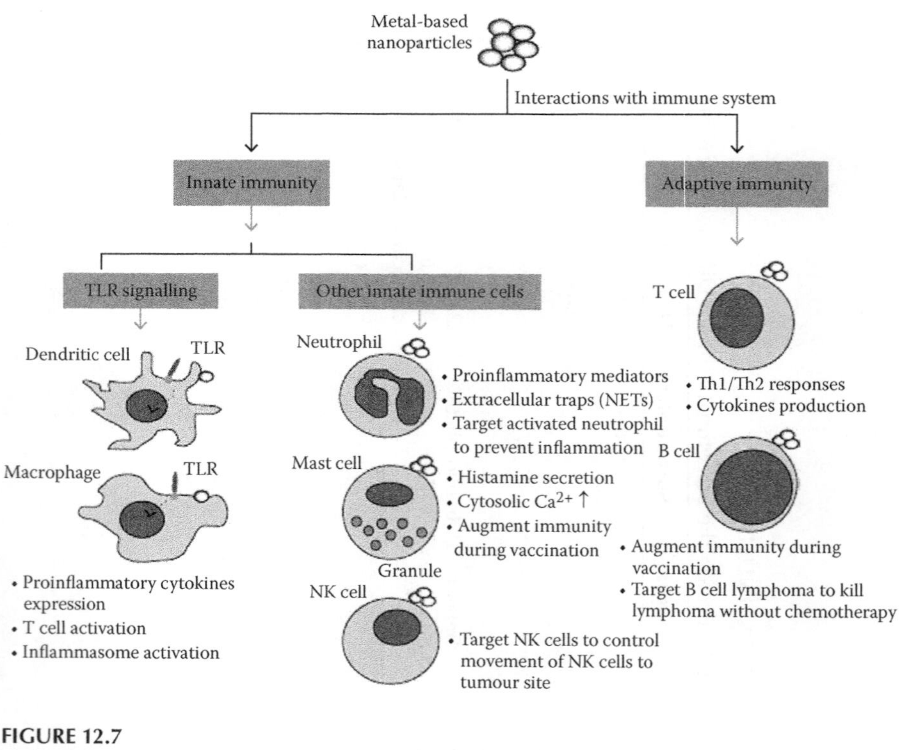

FIGURE 12.7
Metal-based nanoparticles interaction with immune system. (Adapted from Luo, Y.H. et al., *Biomed Res Int* 2015: 143720, copyright 2015, open access article distributed under the Creative Commons Attribution Licence.)

Ag NPs (83 ± 22 nm, spherical powder capped with 0.2 wt%/wt polyvinyl pyrrolidone, PVP) could regulate the oxidative stress genes early and subsequently alter the immune signalling processes in THP-1 cells (a human acute monocytic leukemia cell line), and the differentiated THP-1 cells were more vulnerable than their precursor (Hayashi et al. 2012). The response of murine macrophages (J774 A1, ATCC) to physically produced pure Ag NPs (in three different sizes, 2–4, 5–7 and 20–40 nm, without surface modifiers or stabilisers) was studied by Yen et al. (2009). Although intracellular accumulation of Ag NPs was evidenced by transmission electron microscopy, the expressions of proinflammatory genes interlukin-1 (IL-1), interlukin-6 (IL-6) and tumour necrosis factor (TNF-a) in the cells were not up-regulated. The effects of sublethal concentrations (2.5 μg/mL) of Ag NPs (round and PVP-coated) on inflammatory and stress genes in human macrophages (U937) were studied by using the microarray assay; it was found that small particles (5 nm) induced the expression of IL-8 and stress genes in the human macrophage cell line (U937), but large ones (100 nm) did not (Lim et al. 2012). The immunological effect of Ag NPs on innate immunity was investigated by Yang et al. (2012). They found that both 5- and 28-nm Ag NPs (round and PVP-coated) triggered the production of interleukin 1 beta (IL-1β, a critical cytokine involved in innate immunity) in human blood monocytes, during which two mechanisms may be involved, that is, the cathepsin leakage because of the disintegration of lysosomal membranes and the K^+ efflux owing to the formation of cell membrane pores. In addition, small particles (5 nm) produced more hydrogen peroxide and were more cytotoxic than larger ones (28 nm), indicating that the balance between superoxide and hydrogen peroxide governs the cell fate. It was reported that the toxicity of nanostructural silica–supported Ag NPs to murine macrophages (RAW 264.7, ATCC) was mediated by ion release at small sizes (<10 nm) and dominated by the direct particle–cell interactions at sizes larger than 10 nm (Pratsinis et al. 2013). Ag NPs (25, 40 and 80 nm) induced proinflammatory responses of primary rat brain microvessel endothelial cells in size- and time-dependent profiles, and these events may lead to brain inflammation and neurotoxicity (Trickler et al. 2010). These reports demonstrated that the size and surface properties of Ag NPs should be particularly engineered to accommodate the immune system of the host.

Evaluating the haemocompatibility of nanoparticles is also of great significance because the blood components and the cardiovascular system probably interact directly with the particles during administration. Choi et al. (2011) demonstrated that Ag NPs, compared to microsize particles, could induce higher haemolysis levels because of their large surface-to-volume ratio, increased kinetics in silver ion release and direct activity to red blood cells (RBCs). It was reported that Ag NPs exhibited a size effect on their adsorption and uptake by fish RBCs, and the optimal particle size for passive uptake by RBCs is ~50 nm (Chen et al. 2015). In addition, the toxic effects of Ag NPs on haemolysis, membrane injury and lipid peroxidation were size and dose dependent. In particular, the small particles (15 nm) showed a greater ability to induce haemolysis and membrane damage than large ones (50 and 100 nm). Ag NPs (50 nm, 500 nM) could suppress the vascular endothelial growth factor–induced proliferation and migration in bovine retinal endothelial cells and effectively inhibit the formation of new microvessels. This effect of Ag NPs can serve as a potent anti-angiogenic material that inhibits angiogenesis (Gurunathan et al. 2009). Significant lysis, haemagglutination, membrane damage, detrimental morphological variation and cytoskeletal distortions were evidenced in human erythrocytes exposed to Ag NPs at a concentration of 100 μg/mL for 1.5 h, and multiple pits and depressions can be observed on the membrane of human RBCs that were treated by Ag NPs (50 μg/mL). However, no lysis or deterioration was detected on human RBCs exposed to silver ions (Ag^{+}), suggesting that the observed toxicity is solely particle dependent (Asharani et al. 2010). Moreover, this study showed that the toxic magnitude of Ag NPs varied with capping agents (PVA and starch), although these agents themselves did not result in any visible changes in the morphology of RBCs, opening a window that leads to the optimisation of the toxicity of Ag NPs. In fact, the uptake of Ag NPs is not only dependent on surface chemistry but also related to cell type. Greulich et al. (2011a) compared the uptake of Ag NPs (75 nm, PVP coated) by peripheral monocytes and lymphocytes (T-cells). Accumulation of nanoparticles was evidenced within monocytes but not in T-cells (Figure 12.8) even if both were treated with Ag NPs at a concentration of 5–30 μg/mL. Particle-induced cytotoxicity in monocytes was observed at Ag NPs levels higher than 25 μg/mL, whereas no apparent modulation in the proliferation of T-cells was detected at such concentrations. The cell type–specific behaviour of Ag NPs reminds us that diffusive nanomaterials may not be suitable for every situation that requires antibacterial property.

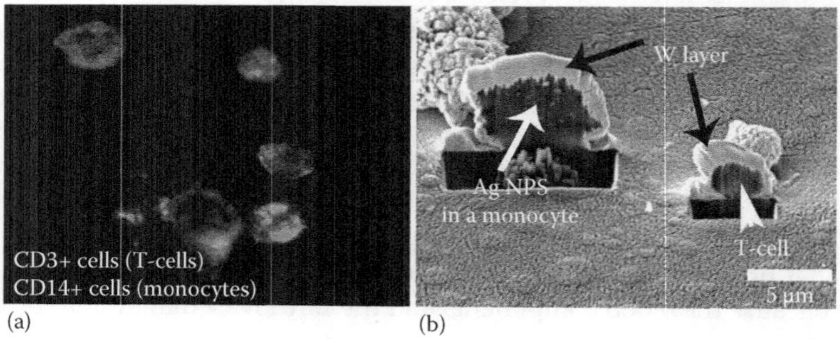

FIGURE 12.8
(See colour insert.) (a) Fluorescence micrograph of the peripheral monocytes (CD14+) and lymphocytes (T-cells, CD3+); (b) detection of the intracellular Ag NPs in monocytes (cultured with 20 μg/mL Ag NPs for 24 h) by focused ion beam, scanning electron microscopy (FIB/SEM) technique; before carrying out the FIB process, the specimens were protected by coating a thin tungsten (W) layer. (Adapted from *Acta Biomater*, 7, Greulich, C. et al., Cell type-specific responses of peripheral blood mononuclear cells to silver nanoparticles, 3505–14, Copyright 2011, with permission from Elsevier.)

Toxic actions of Ag NPs to bone cells were also reported. Albers et al. found that Ag NPs (50 nm) strongly decrease the viability and differentiation of primary osteoblasts and osteoclasts, whereas weak cytotoxic effects of microparticles were observed. The cytotoxicity of Ag NPs was primarily mediated by a size-dependent release of silver ions (Ag^+) (Albers et al. 2013). The concentration-dependent uptake of Ag NPs (80 nm, PVP coated) by human mesenchymal stem cells (hMSCs) was evidenced by Greulich et al. (2011b). The Ag NPs were uptaken by clathrin-dependent endocytosis and macropinocytosis in hMSCs and could attenuate the adipogenic and osteogenic differentiation of the cells even at nontoxic concentrations (Sengstock et al. 2014). It was found that Ag NPs have no significant cytotoxicity to human adipose–derived stem cells (hASCs) and just a minimal dose-dependent toxicity can be detected at antimicrobial concentrations. The biocompatibility of Ag NPs with hASCs laid out the suitability for incorporation of Ag NPs into biomedical devices for the prevention of bacterial contaminations (Samberg and Loboa 2012). The Ag NPs (2–5 nm) at 1 ppm or lower did not induce genotoxicity in CHO-K1 cells (Han et al. 2012). More importantly, Qin et al. (2014b) found that Ag NPs (20 nm) at suitable concentrations (<4 μg/mL) could promote the osteoblastic differentiation of urine-derived stem cells by improving actin polymerisation, increasing cytoskeletal tension and activating RhoA, but the silver ions (in $AgNO_3$ form) could not.

There were also many studies concerning the host responses of Ag NPs. The potential toxicity of Ag NPs (20 and 100 nm) to Wistar-derived rats was studied by intravenous administration (tail vein, once a day for 28 days). The results demonstrated that particle accumulation was noted in spleen, liver and lymph nodes, and the activity of the natural killer (NK) cell in spleen was completely suppressed at high doses (the critical dose for a 5% decrease in NK cell activity was 0.06 mg/kg) (De Jong et al. 2013). Spherical Ag NPs with three different sizes (20, 80 and 110 nm, dispersed in phosphate buffer) were intravenously administrated to Wistar rats (1 mL dispersion in concentrations of 23.8–27.6 μg/mL daily for 5 consecutive days) (Lankveld et al. 2010). Sixteen days after the first injection, the authors found that small particles (the 20-nm group) distributed mainly to liver followed by kidneys and spleen, yet the larger particles (the 80- and 110-nm groups) distributed mainly to spleen followed by liver and lung. Moreover, the silver concentrations in other organs evaluated (kidney, heart, lungs, testes and brain) were much lower and no size-related differences were evidenced. Zebrafish embryo is an effective model available for probing the transport behaviour and dose-dependent biocompatibility of the nanoparticles *in vivo*. Lee et al. (2007) directly visualised the transport of single Ag NPs (11.6 ± 3.5 nm) into zebrafish embryos and characterised their effects on the early development of the embryos in real time. They found that single Ag NPs passed in and out of embryos through chorion pore canals (CPCs) in a Brownian diffusive manner (Figure 12.9). The diffusive particles may be trapped inside CPCs and the inner mass of the embryos, resulting in dose-dependent abnormalities

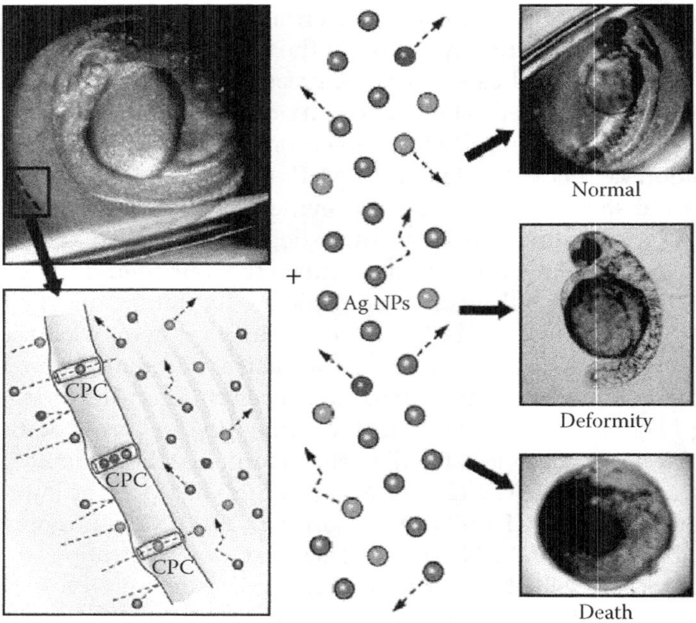

FIGURE 12.9
Illustrating the transport of single Ag NPs via an array of chorion pore canals (CPCs) in embryos. Ag NPs may be trapped inside CPCs and the inner mass of the embryos, such that dose-dependent abnormalities or death is observed in zebrafish. (Adapted with permission from Lee, K.J. et al., *ACS Nano* 1: 133–43. Copyright 2007 American Chemical Society.)

or death, with a critical concentration of 0.19 nM. This particular transport mechanism of Ag NPs in zebrafish embryos may be the answer for the following observations demonstrating that larger particles (41.6 ± 9.1 nm) are more toxic than the smaller ones (11.6 ± 3.5 nm) (Lee et al. 2012).

12.4.3 Supported Ag NPs

The research on the toxic effect of supported (or immobilised) Ag NPs is still undeveloped as compared to that of diffusive ones (typical studies are listed in Table 12.3). Ag NPs can be incorporated into degradable substrates, such as hydroxyapatite (Ciobanu et al. 2014), calcium phosphate (Lee and Murphy 2013), sodium calcium silicates (Esteban-Tejeda et al. 2012) or chemically be linked to or deposited on nondegradable substrates, for example, titanium oxide coatings (Jia et al. 2016; Zhao et al. 2011), glasses (Taglietti et al. 2014) and polymer (Taheri et al. 2014). Although better outcomes on the biocompatibility of composites were evidenced, the biological behaviour of silver particles will likely be similar to that of diffusive ones as the supports degrade gradually or the linkers become weak. For example, Jia et al. reported that Ag NPs (~50 nm, 8.57 ± 1.01 mg/cm^2) can be anchored on TiO_2 by polydopamine.

TABLE 12.3

Typical Studies on the Biocompatibility of Supported Ag NPs

Size	Shape	Substrate/Technique	Silver Content	Cell Line/Host	Outcome	References
~50 nm	Spherical	TiO_2/anchored by polydopamine	8.57 ± 1.01 mg/cm^2	Human osteoblast like cell line MG-63; adult New Zealand white rabbits	Cell adherence, spreading, proliferation and differentiation retained normal or promoted; minimal inflammatory responses	Jia et al. 2016
~2–25 nm	Spherical	Titanium/ion implantation	1.7–2.8 × 10^8 particles per square millimetre	Osteoblast-like cell line MG-63	Proliferation enhanced	Cao et al. 2011
Not indicated	Not indicated	Titanium/ion implantation	1 × 16 ions cm^{-2}	Human osteoblasts	Proliferation enhanced	Fiedler et al. 2011
5–16 nm	Spherical	ASTM F138 stainless steel/ion implantation	2.7–4.17 × 10^8 particles per square millimetre	Human bone marrow stromal cells	Osteogenic differentiation enhanced	Qin et al. 2015
5–40 nm	Spherical	Dental implants (titanium)/ion implantation	Not indicated/covered by a thin layer	Labrador dogs	Bone apposition improved	Qiao et al. 2015
4–25 nm	Spherical	Titanium oxide/ion implantation	~0.058 × 10^3 to 1.34 × 10^3 particles per square micron	MG63 and MC3T3 cells	No significant cytotoxicity and even good cytocompatibility was evidenced	Cao et al. 2013

(Continued)

TABLE 12.3 (CONTINUED)

Typical Studies on the Biocompatibility of Supported Ag NPs

Size	Shape	Substrate/Technique	Silver Content	Cell Line/Host	Outcome	References
3–10 nm	Spherical	Polyethylene/ion implantation	9% relative to C	Human foetal osteoblastic cells	Better adhesion and growth	Zhang et al. 2008
40–50 nm	Spherical	Polyethersulfone/adsorb silver ions through sulfonic groups, and reduced with vitamin C	4.07% ± 1.57%	Human umbilical vein endothelial cells (ECV24)	Good biocompatibility	Cao et al. 2010
5–30 nm	Spherical	Polymerised allylamine/silver particles modified by mercaptosuccinic acid, and deposited through liquid immersion	5.2%–14.6%	Human dermal fibroblasts; primary macrophages	No cytotoxicity	Taheri et al. 2014

The resulting coating had no side effect on (even promoted) the adherence, spreading, proliferation and differentiation of human osteoblast-like cell line MG-63 and induced minimal inflammatory responses in adult New Zealand white rabbits (Jia et al. 2016). However, the connection established by polydopamine was not firm enough and the particles were easily detached by mammalian cells (Jia et al. 2016), having the risk to attack mitochondria and trigger the cascade reactions of toxicity.

In other cases, antibacterial silver nanoparticles were physically immobilised on (or embedded in) various nondegradable substrates, for example, metals (Cao et al. 2011) and semiconductive oxides, such as titanium oxide (Cao et al. 2013, 2014) and tantalum oxide (Cao et al. 2016; Huang et al. 2014; Wang et al. 2016). The direct consequence of such hybridisations is to dramatically reduce the diffusive capability and the subsequent cellular uptake of nanomaterials, resulting in better outcomes on the compatibility to the biological systems (Cao et al. 2011). In addition, according to our previous studies (Cao et al. 2011, 2013, 2014, 2016; Wang et al. 2016), the interaction of Ag NPs and their supports also plays a significant role in the control of the biological actions of the particles. Ag NPs can be *in situ* fabricated and immobilised on titanium by taking advantage of the atomic scale heating effect in silver plasma immersion ion implantation (Ag PIII) process at low (room) temperatures. As shown in Figure 12.10, Ag NPs precipitated on (Figure 12.10b) and underneath (Figure 12.10c) the titanium surface after Ag PIII for 0.5 and 1.5 h, respectively. Because of the difference of standard electrode

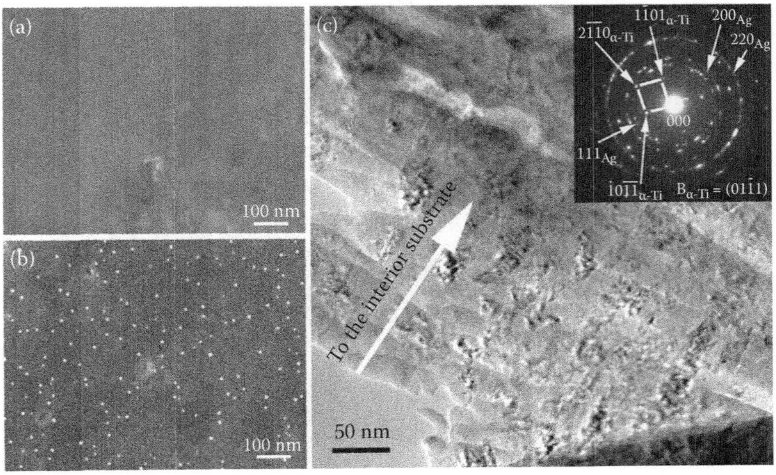

FIGURE 12.10
Immobilising of Ag NPs on titanium by silver plasma immersion ion implantation (Ag PIII) technique: (a) untreated Cp Ti (SEM); (b) Ag PIII treated for 0.5 h (SEM); (c) Ag PIII treated for 1.5 h (TEM). (Reprinted from *Biomaterials*, 32, Cao, H. et al., Biological actions of silver nanoparticles embedded in titanium controlled by micro-galvanic effects, 693–705, Copyright 2011, with permission from Elsevier.)

potential (E°) between titanium and silver (the E° for titanium is −1.630 V, which is markedly more negative than that of silver, 0.7996 V), galvanic reactions are likely triggered when the Ag PIII–treated titanium is immersed in physiological liquids, which is abundant in aggressive ions, such as protons (H^+) and chloride (Cl^-). These reactions may further interfere with the proton electrochemical gradient (proton-motive force [PMF]), depress the activities of various proton pumps or cut off the 'energy supply' in pathogenic microbes (Figure 12.11). Therefore, good antibacterial activity of immobilised Ag NPs was evidenced even if the silver release was minimal (Cao et al. 2011). In fact, the bactericidal efficacy of Ag PIII–treated titanium is determined by two factors, the population of Ag NPs and the density of the titanium substrate. The former determines the overall amount of galvanic couples that are established in titanium surface; the latter influences the total number of couples that really work (the porosity may facilitate the diffusion of those aggressive ions and the activation of the interior couples in titanium surface). The galvanic efficiency of every couple is determined by the current

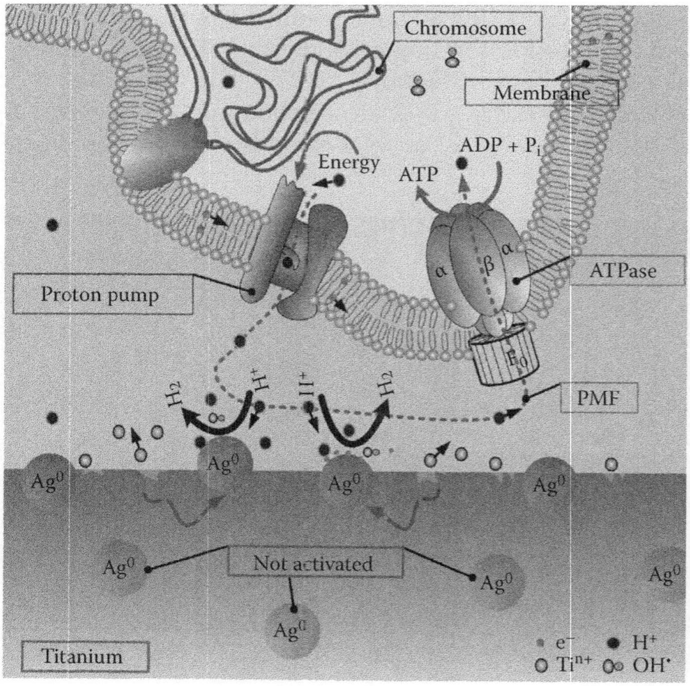

FIGURE 12.11
(See colour insert.) The microgalvanic effects controlled bactericidal actions of titanium surface immobilised of Ag NPs (Ag^0) by silver plasma immersion ion implantation (Ag PIII). PMF denotes the electrochemical gradient of proton-motive force. (Modified according to *Biomaterials*, 32, Cao, H. et al., Biological actions of silver nanoparticles embedded in titanium controlled by micro-galvanic effects, 693–705, Copyright 2011, with permission from Elsevier.)

across the anode and the cathode (Liu and Schlesinger 2009), I_G, which can be expressed theoretically via Equation 12.14 (Song et al. 2004)

$$I_G = (U_C - U_A)/(R_A + R_C + R_S + R_M), \quad (12.14)$$

where U_C and U_A are the open circuit potentials of the cathode and anode, respectively. R_A, R_C, R_S and R_M are the resistances corresponding to the anode, cathode, solution path between the anode and the cathode and metallic path from the anode surface to the cathode surface, respectively. What is important is that these immobilised Ag NPs can inhibit the growth of bacterial cells and reduce the rate of implant-related infections in rats (Qin et al. 2014a) while enhancing the proliferation of the osteoblast-like cell line MG63 (Cao et al. 2011) and human osteoblasts (Fiedler et al. 2011), promoting osteogenic differentiation of human bone marrow stromal cells (hBMSCs) (Qin et al. 2015) and improving the bone apposition around titanium dental implants in dogs (Qiao et al. 2015). These evidences demonstrated that Ag NPs can be a positive stimulus to various biological systems, although the specific answer is still not revealed.

Since the report on the electrochemical photolysis of water by Fujishima et al. in the early 1970s (Fujishima and Honda 1972), titanium oxides have been extensively studied as catalysts for photolysis of bacteria and disinfection. It is generally recognised that the bactericidal action of titanium oxide is closely related to its light-induced charge separation processes (Equation 12.15), which facilitate the simultaneous occurrence of both oxidation and reduction reactions (Hoffmann et al. 1995), that is, the 'hole pools' (h^+) that can react directly with the bacterial membrane in contact or indirectly by reacting with adsorbed hydroxide ions (OH^-) and producing oxidative species (such as hydroxyl radicals, $OH^\bullet$, and hydrogen peroxide, H_2O_2), leading to the chemical transformation of the biomolecules (Equations 12.16 and 12.17) (Sunada et al. 1998; Valentin and Fittipaldi 2013), and the generated electrons (e^-) can be scavenged by acceptor species in the aqueous media, such as protons (H^+), based on Equation 12.18 (Blake et al.1999).

$$M_{sc} + hv \rightarrow h^+ + e^- \quad (12.15)$$

$$h^+ + H_2O \rightarrow OH^\bullet + H^+ \quad (12.16)$$

$$h^+ + OH^- \rightarrow OH^\bullet \quad (12.17)$$

$$2e^- + 2H^+ \rightarrow H_2 \quad (12.18)$$

A minimum photonic energy ($h\nu$) that is equal to the band gap energy of the materials (M_{SC}) is required for exciting the charge separation process (Equation 12.15). This is why ultraviolet (UV) light is usually required in activating the antibacterial capacity of titanium dioxide. In order to reduce the band gap and facilitate the charge separation process, the material can be doped with oxygen vacancies (Chen et al. 2011), nitrogen (Asahi et al. 2001) and noble metals (Murdoch et al. 2011). Among these strategies, loading of Ag NPs to titanium oxide may produce a so-called Schottky barrier owing to the Fermi level alignment at the interface between the two materials (Sze and Ng 2007), endowing the particles with electron trapping capability (Takai and Kamat 2011; Zhang and Yates 2012). In fact, according to the Schottky–Mott model for monitoring metal-semiconductor contacts (Rhoderick 1978), the rectifying behaviour of electron transfer across the boundary between Ag NPs and the substrate can be determined by the Schottky–Mott barrier height (ϕ), which is the difference between the work function of silver, ϕ_{Ag}, and the electron affinity of the tantalum oxide substrate, χ.

$$\phi = \phi_{Ag} - \chi \tag{12.19}$$

As a result, a depletion layer with a thickness of W can be produced because of electron storage on a silver particle with a diameter of D_{Ag}. The number of electrons transferred to a silver particle, Q_{Ag}, is given by (Warren et al. 1990).

$$Q_{Ag} = \frac{2\pi\varepsilon_0\varepsilon_v}{e} \cdot D_{Ag} \cdot \phi \tag{12.20}$$

where e is electron charge, ε_0 is the static dielectric constant of tantalum oxide and ε_v is the vacuum permittivity. Equation 12.20 well illustrates directly the size effect on charging the silver particles and on the establishment of 'pool of holes' (h^+) at the semiconductor side. Accordingly, there is an abundance of studies on utilising the charge separation behaviour of Ag-loaded titanium oxide for visible light–responsive disinfection (Henderson 2011). However, previous studies evidenced that there is a synergistic effect between Ag NPs and semiconductors on disrupting the integration of bacterial cells even without light illumination (Cao et al. 2013, 2014, 2016; Wang et al. 2016). This evidence demonstrated that Equation 12.15 is not a necessary step for antibacterial applications. As a matter of fact, extracellular transport of electrons is an important procedure in bacteria by which they produce adenosine triphosphate (ATP), the energy for maintaining metabolism and growth (Harris et al. 2010; Strahl and Hamoen 2010). Accordingly, the immobilised Ag NPs may collect those bacteria-extruded electrons by taking advantage of the rectifying electron-transfer behaviour of Schottky barriers (the Ag NPs/semiconductor contacts, Figure 12.12) and inducing toxic reactions like that under light illuminations (Equations 12.16 through 12.18), damaging

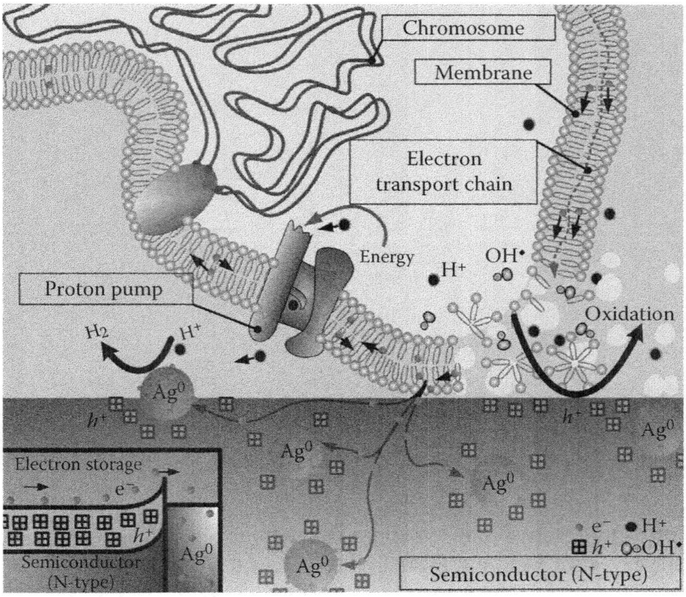

FIGURE 12.12
(See colour insert.) The Schottky–Mott barrier controlled bactericidal actions of a semiconductor (N-type) immobilised of Ag NPs (Ag^o) by silver plasma immersion ion implantation (Ag PIII). That is, the electrons are transferred from the bacterial membranes to the semiconductor surface, stored on the Ag NPs (electron storage) and induce valence-band hole (h^+) accumulation at the semiconductor side answer for the cytosolic content leakage (oxidation) of the adherent bacteria in the dark. (Modified according to *Acta Biomater*, 9, Cao, H. et al., Electron storage mediated dark antibacterial action of bound silver nanoparticles: Smaller is not always better, 5100–10, Copyright 2013, with permission from Elsevier.)

bacterial cells similar to that under light illumination. As shown in Figure 12.13, Ag NPs with different sizes (Figures 12.13a and b) can be immobilised on titanium oxide by manipulating the atomic-scale heating effect of Ag PIII under proper parameters (Cao et al. 2013). It was found that, in the dark, titanium oxide with large silver particles (5–25 nm, Figure 12.13b-1 and b-2) can stimulate tougher oxidation reactions to bacterial cells than small ones (~4 nm, Figure 12.13a-1 and a-2), though the particle distribution density of the latter group is approximately 23 times larger than that of the former one. This result is consistent with the prediction of Equation 12.20, which reveals that large particles are better than small ones in electron trapping. In addition, it was evidenced that the dark antibacterial efficacy of immobilised Ag NPs not only relies on their size-dependent electron storage nature but also is particle spacing dependent. As shown in Figure 12.14, Ag NPs with a similar size (~5 nm) but different distribution density were immobilised on a plasma-sprayed titanium oxide coating by using the Ag PIII technique (Cao et al. 2014). Titanium oxide coatings with a small number of particles

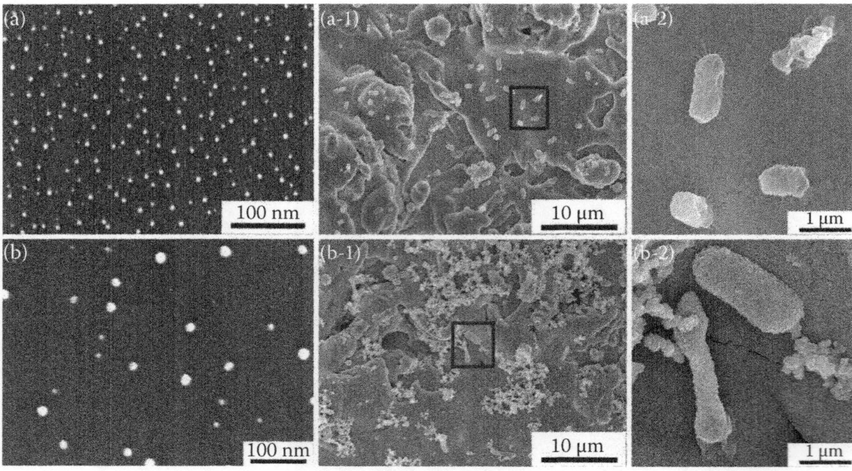

FIGURE 12.13
The size effect on the antibacterial activity of immobilised Ag NPs: (a) titanium oxide coating with particles ~4 nm; (a-1) morphology of the *E. coli* cultured on (a) for 24 h; (a-2) high-magnification images of the circled area in (a-1); (b) titanium oxide coating with particles ~5 to 25 nm; (b-1) morphology of the *E. coli* cultured on (b) for 24 h; (b-2) high-magnification images of the circled area in (b-1); all are SEM images. (Modified according to *Acta Biomater*, 9, Cao, H. et al., Electron storage mediated dark antibacterial action of bound silver nanoparticles: smaller is not always better, 5100–10, Copyright 2013, with permission from Elsevier.)

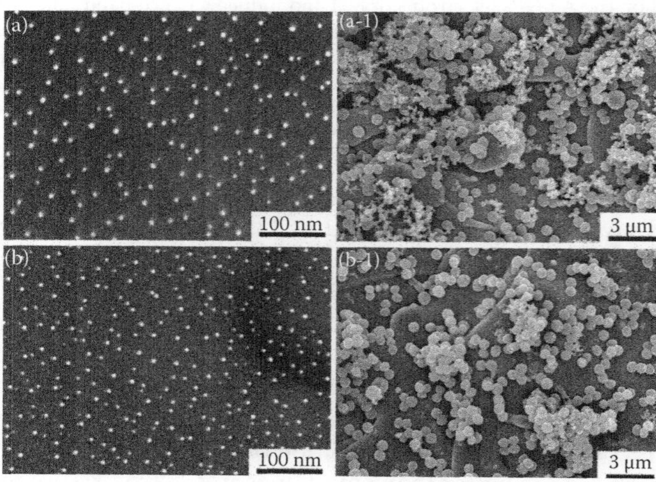

FIGURE 12.14
The spacing effect on the antibacterial activity of immobilised Ag NPs: (a) titanium oxide coating with particles ~5 nm, distribution density ~ 0.97×10^3 particles per square micrometre; (a-1) morphology of the *S. aureus* cultured on (a) for 24 h; (b) titanium oxide coating with particles ~5 nm, distribution density ~ 1.47×10^3 particles per square micrometre; (b-1) morphology of the *S. aureus* cultured on (b) for 24 h; all are SEM images. (Modified with permission from Cao, H. et al., *J Phys Chem Lett* 5: 743–8. Copyright 2014 American Chemical Society.)

(Figure 12.14a-1) were better at disrupting microbes than that with more particles (Figure 12.14b-1), indicating that the immobilised particles were likely interacting with each other and consequently undermine their bactericidal performance. Moreover, although immobilisation of Ag NPs was toxic to bacterial adhesion, a side effect on the adhesion and proliferation of mammalian cells (both MG63 and MC3T3 cells) was not detected (Cao et al. 2013). The aforementioned results suggested that the toxic actions of immobilised Ag NPs are entirely different from those of diffusive ones, and by taking advantage of the interface effect of silver and its support, one may produce bactericidal surfaces with good compatibility.

12.5 Concepts on Selective Toxicity

It was realised that colonisation of bacteria is one of the key processes responsible for the high susceptibility of biomaterials to infections; thus, surface engineering of biomaterials with balanced biological properties (i.e. inhibiting the adhesion of pathogenic microbes but promoting the integration of local tissues) is highly desired for implantable medical devices. For example, inhibiting bacterial adhesion but restoring the functions of bone cells is a demand for orthopaedic implants. However, many of the recent studies in this field have not considered the two modalities in parallel during the development of new orthopaedic coatings (Raphel et al. 2016). Ag NPs are widely studied for antimicrobial applications (Eckhardt et al. 2013; Ouay and Stellacci 2015; Rizzello and Pompa 2014; Wei et al. 2015), whereas the public worries on their potential toxicity to mammalian cells will not be dispelled until they are engineered with selective toxicity. Selective toxicity was defined as 'the injuring of one kind of cell without injuring some other kind of cell' (Albert 1958). The physical basis of selectivity rests on three main aspects, comparative cytology, comparative biochemistry and differences in accumulation (Albert 1981). Accordingly, in the author's opinion, the following aspects should be considered for a safe used of Ag NPs.

12.5.1 Make a Distinction between Mitochondria and Bacteria

Ag NPs possess biocidal actions to pathogenic bacterial cells because the material can directly interact with the bacterial membrane and penetrate the cells, elevating the production of reactive oxygen species (ROS) (Soenen et al. 2015). Ag NPs (1 to 10 nm particles with highly reactive facets, {111}) can directly attach to the surface of and penetrate Gram-negative bacteria (*Escherichia coli, Vibrio cholerae, Pseudomonas aeruginosa* and *Salmonella typhi*), drastically disturbing their normal functions (Morones et al. 2005). By using stress-specific bioluminescent bacteria, Ag NPs (with an average diameter of 10 nm) was found capable of causing oxidative damage via disrupting the bacterial membrane (Hwang et al. 2008). Ag NPs (spherical with a diameter of 6.5–12.1 nm) were shown to destabilise the bacterial outer membrane, collapse the plasma membrane potential and decrease the intracellular ATP levels. These results were consistent with proteomic findings that revealed that a 30-min exposure of *E. coli* cells (wild-type K12 strain, MG1655) to antibacterial concentrations (0.4 and 0.8 nM, with 0.1% bovine serum albumin) of the particle resulted in an accumulation of envelope protein precursors, dissipating their proton electrochemical gradient (PMF) (Lok et al. 2006). The Ag NPs (20–30 nm) immobilising on silicate clay (80–100 nm) released less than 200 ppb silver ions (in a solution of 0.1 wt% hybrid of AgNP/clay, this concentration rules out the silver ion–contributed toxicity to bacteria), but inhibited the growth of dermal pathogens including *S. aureus, Pseudomonas aeruginosa* and *Streptococcus pyogenes*, as well as the methicillin- and oxacillin-resistant *S. aureus* (MRSA and ORSA) by elevating the ROS levels in the cells (Su et al. 2009).

Unfortunately, a large number of reports demonstrated that the cytotoxicity of AgNPs is mediated via cellular uptake, and subsequently, their interactions with the mitochondria in mammalian cells (Peynshaert et al. 2014; Singh and Ramarao 2012) induce the overproduction of ROS, which in turn leads to DNA damage, apoptosis or even cancer initiation (Fu et al. 2014; Nel et al. 2006). Teodoro et al. (2011) found that the transport of nanoparticles (40 and 80 nm) across liver cell membranes into mitochondria statistically significantly decreased the mitochondrial membrane potential and ADP-induced depolarisation, altered the mitochondrial membrane permeability and impaired mitochondrial functions, demonstrating that mitochondrial toxicity played a central role. Ag NPs may decrease the activity of mitochondrial respiratory chain complexes I, II, III and IV in the homogenates from all rat tissues, including brain, skeletal muscle, heart and liver (Costa et al. 2010). After being exposed to Ag NPs (15, 30 and 55 nm) for 24 h, the ROS levels in rat alveolar macrophages were significantly increased, triggering a significant inflammatory response by release of traditional inflammatory mediators, such as tumour necrosis factor (TNF-R), macrophage inhibitory protein (MIP-2) and interleukin-1 (IL-1) (Carlson et al. 2008). Ag NPs induced apoptosis in NIH3T3 fibroblast cells by stimulating the release of cytochrome c into the cytosol and translocation of Bax to mitochondria. This kind of apoptosis was associated with the increase of ROS levels and activation of JNK in mitochondria, and inhibition of either ROS or JNK can attenuate the toxic effects of the particles (Hsin et al. 2008). The toxic behaviours of Ag NPs to human colon carcinoma cells were highly related to their size; as shown in Figure 12.15, the 20-nm nanoparticles induced direct effects on generation of ROS and protein carbonylation, while the 100-nm ones exerted indirect effects via serine/threonine protein kinase (PAK), mitogen-activated protein kinase (MAPK) and phosphatase pathways, since the 20-nm particles can easily be uptaken by the cells while the 100-nm particles can hardly be (Verano-Braga

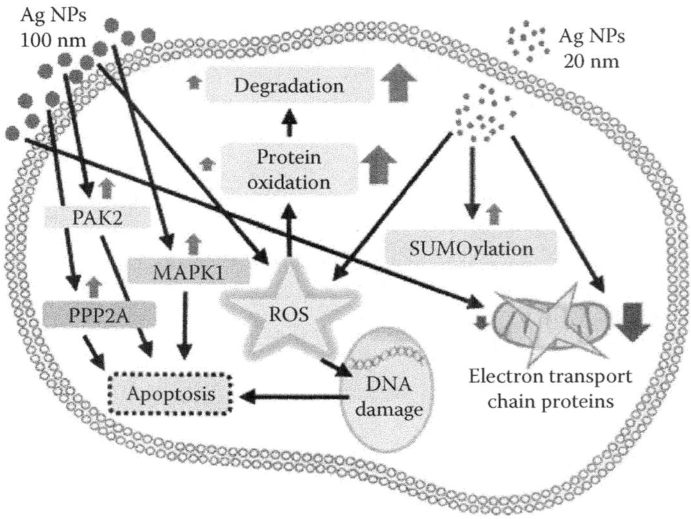

FIGURE 12.15
The size effect on cytotoxicity of diffusive Ag NPs: The 20-nm nanoparticles induced direct effects on generation of reactive oxygen species, while the 100-nm ones exerted indirect effects. (Adapted with permission from Verano-Braga, T. et al., *ACS Nano* 8(3): 2161–75. Copyright 2014 American Chemical Society.)

et al. 2014). Ag NPs can reduce the ATP content in human fibroblasts (IMR-90), cause damage to mitochondria and increase production of ROS in a dose-dependent manner (AshaRani et al. 2009). As shown in Figure 12.16, the possible mechanism involves disruption of the mitochondrial respiratory chain by the uptaken Ag NPs, leading to overproduction of ROS and interruption of ATP synthesis, and in turn cause DNA damage (cell cycle arrest in the G(2)/M phase). This evidence demonstrated that the increase in the generation of ROS by mitochondria is an important mechanism answering for the nanotoxicity of Ag NPs.

Mitochondria, which lie at the heart of eukaryotic cell biology, are found distributing through the cytosol of all mammalian cells apart from anucleate red blood cells (Rich and Maréchal 2010). The main function of the organelles is to generate and supply cellular energy, the ATP; in addition, they are also involved in cell signal transduction, cell cycle control, metabolism and apoptosis (McBride et al. 2006). The number of mitochondria within a cell ranges from a few hundred to thousands, for those requiring the highest energy (Donald et al. 2006). Mitochondria construct their membrane-integrated respiratory system (electron transport chain) by an enzymatic series of electron donors and acceptors, including NADH dehydrogenase (Complex I), succinate dehydrogenase (Complex II), cytochrome bc_1 (Complex III), cytochrome *c* oxidase (Complex IV) and the F_0F_1-ATP synthase (Rich and Maréchal 2010; Sun et al. 2005). Electrons from NADH pass

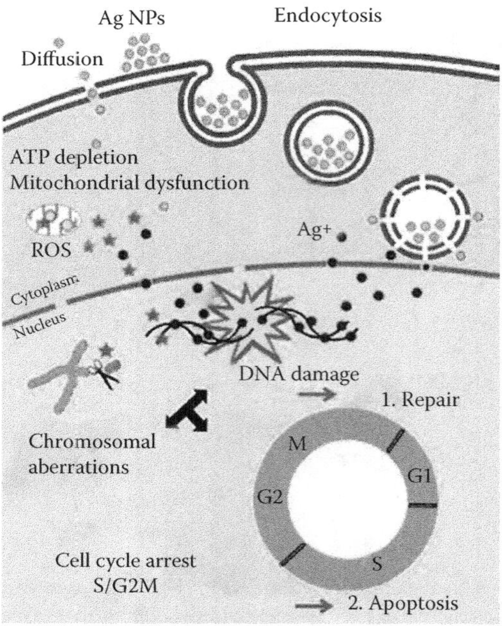

FIGURE 12.16
A possible toxic mechanism of diffusive Ag NPs: It involves disruption of the mitochondrial respiratory chain by the particles, leading to production of ROS and interruption of ATP synthesis, which in turn cause DNA damage (cell cycle arrest in the G(2)/M phase). (Adapted with permission from AshaRani, P.V. et al., *ACS Nano* 3: 279–90. Copyright 2009 American Chemical Society.)

through the respiratory chain to oxygen, which is reduced to water; simultaneously, protons are pumped into the intermembrane space, establishing a proton electrochemical gradient (PMF) that can be used by ATP synthase to produce ATP. During this process, a small amount of oxygen is not reduced completely, resulting in the formation of oxidative by-products, superoxide anion radicals, hydroxyl radicals, singlet oxygen and hydrogen peroxide, which are called ROS; Complexes I and III are shown to be responsible for much of the mitochondrial superoxide generated (Raha and Robinson 2001). Normal levels of ROS play beneficial physiological roles in cellular signalling systems, whereas excess production of ROS disorders cell signalling, doing harm to cell growth and tissue repair (D'Autréaux and Toledano 2007; Ray et al. 2012). Ag NPs can also participate in these oxidation–reduction reactions, bringing about the high ROS levels (Fu et al. 2014; Wei et al. 2015).

The bacterial cytoplasmic membrane, which serves as the respiratory centre, contains integrated protein complexes that establish a similar but somewhat more complicated electron transport chain (Anraku 1988). Membrane dehydrogenases, through the intermediary of ubiquinones and menaquinones, transfer electrons to cytochromes, and electrogenic translocation of protons out of the cytoplasmic membrane that serves for the establishment of a proton motive force to drive ATP synthesis, secondary active solute transport, protein secretion and cell motility, just as that takes place in mitochondria (Rich and Maréchal 2010). Most bacteria have a respiratory chain, but there is a difference between aerobic and anaerobic bacterial cells in the terminal electron acceptor: it is oxygen in aerobic microbes and may be either oxygen or an acceptor of the nitrate or sulfate type in facultative anaerobes (Marreiros et al. 2016). Molecular oxygen adventitiously abstracts electrons from the redox enzymes integrated in the bacterial respiratory chain, continuously forming intracellular superoxide and hydrogen peroxide (ROS), which may further disturb the functions of metalloenzymes and disrupt the integrity of DNA, as that to mitochondria (Imlay 2013). In fact, genome data strongly support the idea that mitochondria are of bacterial ancestry, originating from the bacterial phylum α-proteobacteria (Gray 2012). Phylogenetic reconstructions based on a combined set of mitochondrial NADH dehydrogenase subunits suggest that these are derived from the α-proteobacteria; the core genes (*cox*I, *cox*II and *cox*III) for cytochrome oxidase *c* are always mitochondrially encoded and cluster closely with their α-proteobacterial homologues. The gene order for ATP synthetase in mitochondria is highly conserved among bacterial genomes (Kurland and Andersson 2000).

Therefore, during the design of antibacterial surfaces for medical devices, one should consider the mitochondrial and bacterial similarity in structure and metabolism. Antibacterial actions targeting bacterial membrane functions are promising in preventing and treating bacterial infections (Allison et al. 2011; Hurdle et al. 2011). Ag NPs are known to interact with the membrane constituents causing structural changes, degradation and eventual cell death (Morones et al. 2005). As to releasing-based antibacterial paradigms, although selective or targeted strategies based on lysosomes (Setyawati et al. 2014), external magnetic field (Prucek et al. 2011) and bacteria-specific antibody (Huo et al. 2014) were proposed, Ag NPs still likely induce serious toxic responses in mammalian cells because they can hardly make a distinction between mitochondria and bacteria; however, for contacting-based antimicrobial approaches, Ag NPs may behave better because the probability for cytophagy and subsequent actions to mitochondria is reduced. This may be the reason why positive results are common on supported Ag NPs (Table 12.3). From this point of view, physically immobilising Ag NPs on implantable medical devices (as discussed in Section 12.4.3) is promising for antibacterial applications.

12.5.2 Ag NPs Have Co-Players

There has been some controversy over how Ag NPs (most are diffusive ones) become toxic. Some studies demonstrated that Ag NPs were toxic because of the release of silver ions (Ag^+), the particle-specific toxicity was negligible (Kennedy 2010; Kittler et al. 2010; Levard 2013a; Navarro et al. 2008; Singh and Ramarao 2012; Xiu et al. 2012), while some reports revealed that the particle-specific toxicity did exist and was likely independent on the toxicity of silver ions (Fabrega et al. 2009; Ivask et al. 2014; Kawata et al. 2009; Kim et al. 2009; McQuillan and Shaw 2014). At present, the Ag NPs used for various studies were mostly synthesised via chemical approaches, by which silver particles were commonly obtained through chemical reduction of silver salts dissolved in solutions containing a reducing compound, such as $NaBH_4$, sodium citrate and hydrazine (Desireddy et al. 2013; Marambio-Jones and Hoek 2010). Some of these reductants are considered toxic or hazardous, and the trace residues of such agents may affect the fate of the synthesised silver particles in biological systems. Moreover, the size, morphology and stability of Ag NPs are strongly influenced by the interaction kinetics between silver ions and the reducing agents, as well as the adsorption processes of stabilisers (such as chloride, polyvinylpyrrolidone and NaBr) on the precursors (Sharma et al. 2009; Wiley et al. 2007a); these experimental conditions can hardly be identical among the research groups (even in the same group), thus markedly influencing the physicochemical properties and the biological behaviours of the fabricated Ag NPs.

The physicochemical properties and subsequently the biological potency of Ag NPs are highly dependent on their size, shape and capping agents as well as solution pH, ionic strength, ligands and electrolyte types (El Badawy et al. 2010; Liu et al. 2010; Ouay and Stellacci 2015). Pristine Ag NPs are chemically instable and strongly reactive with inorganic (e.g. molecular oxygen, chloride and sulfide) or organic (such as –SH, thiol, humic acid, –COO and carboxylate) substances. The toxicity of Ag NPs (35.4 nm, amorphous carbon coated) to bacteria increased 2.3-fold after exposure to air for 0.5 h because of the increased levels in silver release (Xiu et al. 2011). Chloride ions (Cl^-) are a ubiquitous species in most physiological environments that can strongly affect toxicity results for Ag NPs. It was found that the dissolution kinetics of silver particles (PVP coated, average diameter of 32.9 nm) were strongly dependent on the Cl/Ag ratio, and the toxicity of AgNPs to *E. coli* was governed by concentrations of Cl^- in the suspensions (Levard et al. 2013a). It was demonstrated that Ag NPs (PVP coated, average diameter of 37 nm) readily react with sulfide to form core–shell particles of $Ag^0@Ag_2S$, decreasing the toxicity of the nanoparticles relative to their pristine counterparts (Levard et al. 2013b). The effect of dissolved organic carbon, –SH (in cysteine) and –COO (in trolox) on the colloidal stability, dissolution rate and toxicity of citrate-coated Ag NPs (hydrodynamic diameter of 14.8 nm) was studied (Pokhrel et al. 2013). The results indicated that these organic ligands can differentially modify the size, surface charge and ion release kinetics of the nanoparticles, consequently attenuating (cysteine and trolox) or promoting (dissolved organic carbon) the toxicity of Ag NPs. More complicated is that the surface states of Ag NPs can transform during storage or cytophagy. The slow dissolution of citrate- and PVP-coated Ag NPs (hydrodynamic diameter of 85 nm) was detected during storage in water (Kittler et al. 2010). The silver particles stored in dispersion for several weeks were more toxic toward hMSCs than that of freshly prepared ones, because the concentration of silver ions in the dispersion was increased during storage. The three-dimensional distribution of Ag NPs (20 nm, dispersed in Tween-20) inside a single human monocyte (THP-1) was constructed by integrating synchrotron radiation-beam transmission x-ray microscopy and SR x-ray absorption near edge structure spectroscopy, and the data revealed that the cytotoxicity of the particles was largely related to the chemical transformation of silver from elemental silver (Ag^0) to silver ions and Ag-O- and then to Ag-S- species (Figure 12.17) (Wang et al. 2015).

Surface stabilisers, such as citrate, PVP and BPEI, were usually used in synthesis of Ag NPs with controlled shape, size and degradation. These agents may be residual on the surface of the Ag NPs produced, as shown in Figure 12.18; the capping layers can be identified on Ag NPs synthesised via the sulfide-mediated polyol process (Cobley et al. 2009) or the sodium citrate–assisted reducing procedure (Zeng et al. 2010). As a result, the physicochemical characteristics of these agents can also influence the biological

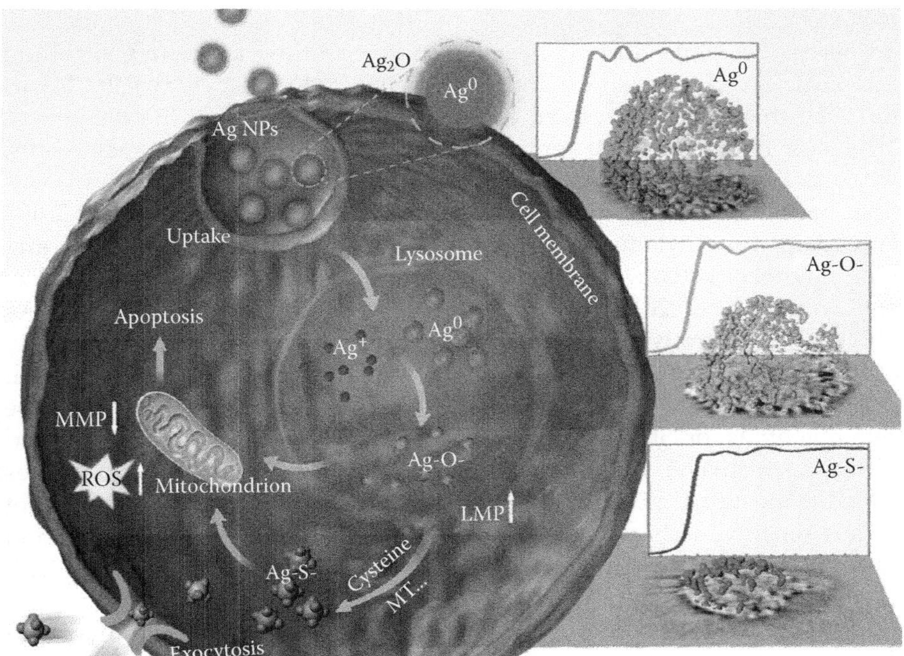

FIGURE 12.17
(See colour insert.) A schematic diagram illustrating the chemical transformation of Ag NPs in human monocytes (THP-1): Ag NPs were uptaken by the cells and trafficked from engulfed vesicles to the lysosomes. Because of the acidic environment in the lysosome, silver transferred from elemental silver (Ag^0) to silver ions and Ag-O-, and then to Ag-S- species. (Adapted with permission from Wang, L. et al., *ACS Nano* 9: 6532–47. Copyright 2015 American Chemical Society.)

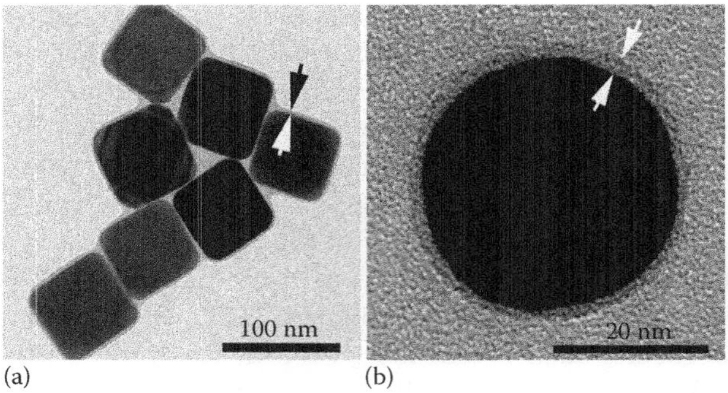

FIGURE 12.18
Ag NPs capped of stabilisers: (a) silver nano cubes produced via a sulfide-mediated polyol process; (b) silver nanosphere synthesised in the presence of sodium citrate. The capping layer can be indentified between the arrows (a was adapted from Cobley, C.M. et al.: Etching and growth: An intertwined pathway to silver nanocrystals with exotic shapes. *Angew Chem Int Ed*. 2009. 48. 4824–7. Copyright Wiley-VCH Verlag GmbH & Co. KGaA. Reproduced with permission.; b was adapted with permission from Zeng, J. et al., *J Am Chem Soc* 132: 8552–3. Copyright 2010 American Chemical Society).

property of Ag NPs and may even be a determining factor in controlling the particle–cell interactions and in inducing/reducing cytotoxicity. It was reported that the citrate-coated colloidal Ag NPs (30 nm) at the 100-μg/mL level were not geno-, cyto- and phytotoxic to human skin keratinocyte cells, whereas the citrate-coated Ag NP powder (dried form colloidal form) was toxic owing to the chemical structure change during drying (Lu et al. 2010). Poly(diallyldimethylammonium)-coated Ag NPs, to both macrophage and lung epithelial cells, were found to be more toxic than uncoated colloidal ones (Suresh et al. 2012). The toxicity of citrate-, PVP- and BPEI-coated Ag NPs was comparatively studied. A direct correlation between the toxicity of the particles and their surface charge was identified, demonstrating that the most negatively charged citrate-coated Ag NPs were the least toxic (the zeta potentials for citrate-, PVP- and BPEI-coated Ag NPs were −40, −12 and 39 mV, respectively), whereas the most positively charged BPEI-coated ones were the most toxic (El Badawy et al. 2011). The property of these coated Ag NPs is sensitive to background conditions, such as pH, ionic strength and electrolyte type (El Badawy et al. 2010), making the problem more difficult to solve.

The aforementioned studies solidly evidenced that the biological potency of Ag NPs can be modified by various surface engineering approaches (Liu et al. 2010; Ouay and Stellacci 2015), which are significant and major steps toward safe applications of the material, but far from selective toxicity. More importantly than all of these, the designed surface modifications and the involved background environments may make the Ag NPs entirely different with its intrinsic nature. Take the changes in surface charge as an example; the zeta potential for physically manufactured (without any surface modifiers or stabilisers) Ag NPs can be positive (change from 5.35 to 13.69 mV as the particle size decreased from 40 to 2 nm, pH not indicated, possibly 7) (Yen et al. 2009), whereas this parameter for biosynthesised particles (–28.5 mV for a particle size of 5–40 nm, pH 7) can be negative (Fayaz et al. 2010) and also is distinct from that for chemically synthesised and citrate-coated Ag NPs (particle size of 19 nm, −40 mV, pH 6.9) (El Badawy et al. 2010) and PVP-coated Ag NPs (particle size of 25.6 nm, −33 mV, pH 6.3) (Yu et al. 2014). These changes brought the complexity and difficulty in analysing the biological actions of Ag NPs and have already made clear that Ag NPs are not alone in the process of interacting with various cells. There are co-players that we should take care of and make use of during engineering of antibacterial Ag NPs with good biocompatibility.

12.5.3 Ag NPs Act as a Team

Particle interactions are considered to be the important ingredients responsible for the emergence of collective effects that are not presented by individual nanoparticles (Hentschel et al. 2010; Mahadevi and Sastry 2016). The interparticle forces can facilitate positioning of Ag NPs to achieve an ordering pattern (Korgel et al. 1998), and the aggregation and assembly of various nanoparticles can be controlled by manipulating the particle interactions (Kim et al. 2005). Because of the strong particle interactions, an apparent red shift in the dipolar surface plasmon resonance was observed as the interparticle space reduced (Gunnarsson et al. 2005) and a cooperative plasmon mode was evidenced by optimising the particle size and interparticle distance of silver (Kinnan and Chumanov 2010). The aggregation state of the nanoparticles is a key player that strongly influences their interactions with various proteins and cells (Albanese and Chan 2011; Lacerda et al. 2010; Walkey et al. 2014) and the subsequent biocompatible or bioadverse outcomes (Nel et al. 2009). Regulation of the interparticle forces reveals the controlled aggregation in charged nanoparticles and can be translated into the trapping and scavenging of toxic ions, such as lead (Pb^{2+}) and cadmium (Cd^{2+}) (Rao et al. 2016). Thus, it can be regarded that a comprehensive understanding of interparticle interactions is essential for technological implementation of sophisticated superstructures with various dimensionalities, unusual nanoscale properties and predictable biological functions (Batista et al. 2015).

Nanoparticles can be held together by strong covalent or metallic, or weak noncovalent bonds, and assembled into diverse ordered or disordered systems, bringing cooperative or anticooperative interparticle interactions (Min et al. 2008). The interactions between diffusive particles are typically described by the classical Derjaguin–Landau–Verwey–Overbeek (DLVO) theory, which treats interparticle forces as a balance of attractive van der Waals forces and repulsive electrical double-layer forces (Ducker et al. 1991). The DLVO approach has provided an adequate prediction for the interactions of gold nanoparticles (50, 100 and 250 nm) electrostatically confined between parallel planar glass surfaces (Eichmann et al. 2008); it is inaccurate at the nanoscale (especially for particles with a diameter of 1 to 20 nm) because of breakdown of common assumptions, such as the total force is a summation for plenty of independent repulsive and attractive components; the size of the background molecules and ions in the suspensions is negligibly smaller than that of the dispersed particles and the particles have simple shapes (typically spherical) (Batista et al. 2015). In fact, when the particle size reduces to a few tens of nanometres and the interparticle gaps are at similar scales, nonadditivity of electrostatic, van der Waals, hydrophobic and other interactions between the particles reveals itself and becomes dominant (Batista et al. 2015). The extraordinary stability of nanoparticle dispersions and the unusual biomimetic behaviour of elaborated nanoparticle geometries in their complexes with enzymes and proteins represent experimental manifestations of nonadditivity (Batista et al. 2015; Cha et al. 2015; Huang et al. 2013; del Pino et al. 2014). Interactions between charged particles are strongly dependent on specific ion effects (SIEs), which stem from a very elaborate set of nonadditive interactions between the ions, the solvent and the interfaces (Boström et al. 2001). These nonadditivities at ionic or molecular levels evolve into the nonadditivity of inter-nanoparticle forces (Batista et al. 2015). It was found that the nonadditive forces played an important role in the stability of silver clusters (Kaplan et al. 1995a,b; Ramírez-Solís et al. 1990); however, despite considerable contributions on fabrication of various Ag NPs and their size, shape, ionic strength, ligand and other factor-dependent impacts on various biological systems (Ouay and Stellacci 2015), the effect of interparticle interactions on the physicochemical property of the whole Ag NP assembly is insignificant. This effect can be exemplified by the aforementioned interparticle gap-dependent antimicrobial action of titanium oxide–supported Ag NPs (Cao et al. 2014). It was demonstrated experimentally and theoretically that the antibacterial efficacy of those Ag NPs relies on their electron storage capability, which is associated with interparticle distance; that is, a particle population with a relatively large spacing distance is superior in disrupting the integrity of bacterial membranes (Figure 12.14). This antibacterial behaviour of supported Ag NPs is inversely dose dependent and can be a typical example to illuminate the collective effect of nonadditivity on the biological action of Ag NPs. The study opens up a new window leading to the efficient use of Ag NPs in the active design of antibacterial surfaces, which is important for selective toxicity.

12.6 Summary

BAI caused by bacterial contamination is becoming a serious and costly complication of implantable medical devices. Ag NPs, as one of the special concerns in disinfection, are capable of acting strongly against the aggression of a broad spectrum of bacteria. Although thousands of papers concerning the antibacterial actions of Ag NPs were published during the past 10 years, their application into medical devices approved for use is impeded because of concerns in cytotoxicity that arose from the ultra-small size and high mobility of the particles. Evidence from many sources revealed that free Ag NPs could also be adversaries to mammalian cells. Therefore, it will be of great significance if Ag NPs of selective toxicity can be engineered, that is, to kill bacteria without harming the host. In order to achieve such a goal, one should sophisticatedly control the transport and reactivity of Ag NPs. At present, there are two paradigms in the application of the antibacterial property of Ag NPs, that is, active release killing and conservative contact killing. Because of the structural and metabolic similarities between bacteria and mitochondria, the former approach can hardly distinguish mammalian cells from microbes while the latter method can be selectively toxic because immobilised particles have little chance to directly interact with mitochondria. Reactivity control is relatively more complicated because it may relate to many aspects of Ag NPs, including size (surface states, electronic structures, packing styles, etc.), background environments (pH, electrolyte type, cell lines, etc.) and interparticle forces (electrostatic, van der Waals, hydrophobic, etc.). The effects of interparticle forces on the physicochemical property and subsequently the biological potency of the whole group of Ag NPs are rarely studied as compared to the former two aspects. This should be addressed in the future because particle interaction is an important contributor to the collective properties of various Ag NP assemblies. Since every coin has two sides, Ag NPs as a type of broad-spectrum antibacterial agent may not be suitable for every situation; however, their biocompatibility depends on what we know and how we engineered them.

Acknowledgements

The work was jointly financially supported by the National Natural Science Foundation of China (31100675, 31370962 and 31670980), the Shanghai Rising-Star Program (15QA1404100) and Youth Innovation Promotion Association CAS (2015204).

References

Adler, R.J., Picraux, S.T. Repetitively pulsed metal ion beams for ion implantation. *Nucl Instrum Methods Phys Res B.* (1985) 6: 123–8.

Agarwal, A., Weis, T.L., Schurr, M.J., Faith, N.G., Czuprynski, C.J. Surfaces modified with nanometer thick silver-impregnated polymeric films that kill bacteria but support growth of mammalian cells. *Biomaterials* 31 (2010): 680–90.

Ajayan, P.M., Marks, L.D. Quasimelting and phases of small particles. *Phys Rev Lett* 60 (1988): 585–7.

Albanese, A., Chan, W.C. Effect of gold nanoparticle aggregation on cell uptake and toxicity. *ACS Nano* 5 (2011): 5478–89.

Albers, C.E., Hofstetter, W., Siebenrock, K.A., Landmann, R., Klenke, F.M. In vitro cytotoxicity of silver nanoparticles on osteoblasts and osteoclasts at antibacterial concentrations. *Nanotoxicology* 7 (2013): 30–6.

Albert, A. Chemical aspects of selective toxicity. *Nature* 182 (1958): 421–3.

Albert, A. *Selective Toxicity: The Physico-chemical Basis of Therapy*. London: Chapman and Hall, 1981.

Allison, K.R., Brynildsen, M.P., Collins, J.J. Metabolite-enabled eradication of bacterial persisters by aminoglycosides. *Nature* 473 (2011): 216–20.

Anders, A. Metal plasma immersion ion implantation and deposition: A review. *Surf Coat Technol* 93 (1997): 158–67.

Andersen *v.* St. Jude Medical, Inc., 2012 ONSC 3660.

Anraku, Y. Bacterial electron transport chains. *Annu Rev Biochem* 57 (1988): 101–32.

Arnold, G.W., Borders, J.A. Aggregation and migration of ion-implanted silver in lithia–alumina–silica glass. *J Appl Phys* 48 (1977): 1488.

Asahi, R., Morikawa, T., Ohwaki, T., Aoki, K., Taga, Y. Visible-light photocatalysis in nitrogen-doped titanium oxides. *Science* 293 (2001): 269–71.

AshaRani, P.V., Low, K., Mun, G., Hande, M.P., Valiyaveettil, S. Cytotoxicity and genotoxicity of silver nanoparticles in human cells. *ACS Nano* 3 (2009): 279–90.

Asharani, P.V., Sethu, S., Vadukumpully, S., Zhong, S., Lim, C.T., Hande, M.P., Valiyaveettil, S. Investigations on the structural damage in human erythrocytes exposed to silver, gold, and platinum nanoparticles. *Adv Funct Mater* 20 (2010): 1233–42.

Batista, C.A., Larson, R.G., Kotov, N.A. Nonadditivity of nanoparticle interactions. *Science* 350 (2015): 1242477.

Blake, D.M., Maness, P.C., Huang, Z., Wolfrum, E.J., Huang, J., Jacoby, W.A. Application of the photocatalytic chemistry of titanium dioxide to disinfection and the killing of cancer cells. *Sep Purif Rev* 28 (1999): 1–50.

Boraschi, D., Costantino, L., Italiani, P. Interaction of nanoparticles with immunocompetent cells: Nanosafety considerations. *Nanomedicine (London)* 7 (2012): 121–31.

Bosetti, M., Massè, A., Tobin, E., Cannas, M. Silver coated materials for external fixation devices: In vitro biocompatibility and genotoxicity. *Biomaterials* 23 (2002): 887–92.

Boström, M., Williams, D.R., Ninham, B.W. Specific ion effects: Why DLVO theory fails for biology and colloid systems. *Phys Rev Lett* 87 (2001): 168103–6.

Brennan, S.A., Ni Fhoghlú, C., Devitt, B.M., O'Mahony, F.J., Brabazon, D., Walsh, A. Silver nanoparticles and their orthopaedic applications. *Bone Joint J* 97B (2015): 582–9.

Busscher, H.J., van der Mei, H.C., Subbiahdoss, G., Jutte, P.C., van den Dungen, J.J., Zaat, S.A., Schultz, M.J., Grainger, D.W. Biomaterial-associated infection: Locating the finish line in the race for the surface. *Sci Transl Med* 4 (2012): 153rv110.

Cao, X., Tang, M., Liu, F., Nie, Y., Zhao, C. Immobilization of silver nanoparticles onto sulfonated polyethersulfone membranes as antibacterial materials. *Colloids Surf B Biointerfaces* 81 (2010): 555–62.

Cao, H., Liu, X. Silver nanoparticles-modified films versus biomedical device-associated infections. *Wiley Interdiscip Rev Nanomed Nanobiotechnol* 2 (2010): 670–84.

Cao, H., Liu, X., Meng, F., Chu, P.K. Biological actions of silver nanoparticles embedded in titanium controlled by micro-galvanic effects. *Biomaterials* 32 (2011): 693–705.

Cao, H., Qiao, Y., Liu, X., Lu, T., Cui, T., Meng, F., Chu, P.K. Electron storage mediated dark antibacterial action of bound silver nanoparticles: Smaller is not always better. *Acta Biomater* 9 (2013): 5100–10.

Cao, H., Qiao, Y., Meng, F., Liu, X. Spacing-dependent antimicrobial efficacy of immobilized silver nanoparticles. *J Phys Chem Lett* 5 (2014): 743–8.

Cao, H., Meng, F., Liu, X. Antimicrobial activity of tantalum oxide coatings decorated with Ag nanoparticles. *J Vac Sci Technol A* 34 (2016): 04C102.

Carlson, C., Hussain, S.M., Schrand, A.M., Braydich-Stolle, L.K., Hess, K.L., Jones, R.L., Schlager, J.J. Unique cellular interaction of silver nanoparticles: Size-dependent generation of reactive oxygen species. *J Phys Chem B* 112 (2008): 13608–19.

Carter, F.L. Quantifying the concept of coordination number. *Acta Cryst B* 34 (1978): 2962–6.

Cha, S.H., Hong, J., McGuffie, M., Yeom, B., VanEpps, J.S., Kotov, N.A. Shape-dependent biomimetic inhibition of enzyme by nanoparticles and their antibacterial activity. *ACS Nano* 9 (2015): 9097–105.

Chen, L.Q., Fang, L., Ling, J., Ding, C.Z., Kang, B., Huang, C.Z. Nanotoxicity of silver nanoparticles to red blood cells: Size dependent adsorption, uptake, and hemolytic activity. *Chem Res Toxicol* 28 (2015): 501–9.

Chen, X., Liu, L., Yu, P.Y., Mao, S.S. Increasing solar absorption for photocatalysis with black hydrogenated titanium dioxide nanocrystals. *Science* 331 (2011): 746–50.

Choi, J., Reipa, V., Hitchins, V.M., Goering, P.L., Malinauskas, R.A. Physicochemical characterization and in vitro hemolysis evaluation of silver nanoparticles. *Toxicol Sci* 123 (2011): 133–43.

Ciobanu, G., Ilisei, S., Luca, C. Hydroxyapatite–silver nanoparticles coatings on porous polyurethane scaffold. *Mater Sci Eng C Mater Biol Appl* 35 (2014): 36–42.

Cobley, C.M., Rycenga, M., Zhou, F., Li, Z.Y., Xia, Y. Etching and growth: An intertwined pathway to silver nanocrystals with exotic shapes. *Angew Chem Int Ed* 48 (2009): 4824–7.

Conrad, J.R., Radtke, J.L., Dodd, R.A., Worzala, F.J., Tran, N.C. Plasma source ion-implantation technique for surface modification of materials. *J Appl Phys* 62 (1987): 4591–6.

Costa, C.S., Ronconi, J.V., Daufenbach, J.F., Gonçalves, C.L., Rezin, G.T., Streck, E.L., Paula, M.M. In vitro effects of silver nanoparticles on the mitochondrial respiratory chain. *Mol Cell Biochem* 342 (2010): 51–6.

Costerton, J.W., Stewart, P.S., Greenberg, E.P. Bacterial biofilms: A common cause of persistent infections. *Science* 284 (1999): 1318–22.

Cuenya, B.R., Behafarid, F. Nanocatalysis: Size- and shape-dependent chemisorption and catalytic reactivity. *Surf Sci Rep* 70 (2015): 135–87.

Datta, S., Kabir, M., Ganguly, S., Sanyal, B., Saha-Dasgupta, T., Mookerjee, A. Structure, bonding, and magnetism of cobalt clusters from first-principles calculations. *Phys Rev B* 76 (2007): 014429.

D'Autréaux, B., Toledano, M.B. ROS as signalling molecules: Mechanisms that generate specificity in ROS homeostasis. *Nat Rev Mol Cell Biol* 8 (2007): 813–24.

De Jong, W.H., Van Der Ven, L.T., Sleijffers, A., Park, M.V., Jansen, E.H., Van Loveren, H., Vandebriel, R.J. Systemic and immunotoxicity of silver nanoparticles in an intravenous 28 days repeated dose toxicity study in rats. *Biomaterials* 34 (2013): 8333–43.

del Pino, P., Pelaz, B., Zhang, Q., Maffre, P., Nienhausb, G.U., Parak, W.J. Protein corona formation around nanoparticles – From the past to the future. *Mater Horiz* 1 (2014): 301–13.

Desireddy, A., Conn, B.E., Guo, J., Yoon, B., Barnett, R.N., Monahan, B.M., Kirschbaum, K., Griffith, W.P., Whetten, R.L., Landman, U., Bigioni, T.P. Ultrastable silver nanoparticles. *Nature* 501 (2013): 399–402.

Desjonquères, M.C., Spanjaard, D. *Concepts in Surface Physics*. Berlin: Springer, 1996.

DiCenzo, S.B., Berry, S.D. and Hartford, E.H. Photoelectron spectroscopy of single-size Au clusters collected on a substrate. *Phys Rev B Condens Matter* 38 (1988): 8465–8.

Dobrovolskaia, M.A., McNeil, S.E. Immunological properties of engineered nanomaterials. *Nature Nanotechnol* 2 (2007): 469–78.

Donald, V., Voet, J.G., Pratt, C.W. *Fundamentals of Biochemistry*. USA: John Wiley & Sons, 2006.

Ducker, W.A., Senden, T.J., Pashley, R.M. Direct measurement of colloidal forces using an atomic force microscope. *Nature* 353 (1991): 239–41.

Eckhardt, S., Brunetto, P.S., Gagnon, J., Priebe, M., Giese, B., Fromm, K.M. Nanobio silver: Its interactions with peptides and bacteria, and its uses in medicine. *Chem Rev* 113 (2013): 4708–54.

Ehrlich, G.D., Stoodley, P., Kathju, S., Zhao, Y., McLeod, B.R., Balaban, N., Hu, F.Z., Sotereanos, N.G., Costerton, J.W., Stewart, P.S., Post, J.C., Lin, Q. Engineering approaches for the detection and control of orthopaedic biofilm infections. *Clin Orthop Relat Res* 437 (2005): 59–66.

Eichmann, S.L., Anekal, S.G., Bevan, M.A. Electrostatically confined nanoparticle interactions and dynamics. *Langmuir* 24 (2008): 714–21.

El Badawy, A.M., Luxton, T.P., Silva, R.G., Scheckel, K.G., Suidan, M.T., Tolaymat, T.M. Impact of environmental conditions (pH, ionic strength, and electrolyte type) on the surface charge and aggregation of silver nanoparticles suspensions. *Environ Sci Technol* 44 (2010): 1260–6.

El Badawy, A.M., Silva, R.G., Morris, B., Scheckel, K.G., Suidan, M.T., Tolaymat, T.M. Surface charge-dependent toxicity of silver nanoparticles. *Environ Sci Technol* 45 (2011): 283–7.

Esteban-Tejeda, L., Cabal, B., Malpartida, F., López-Piriz, R., Torrecillas, R., Saiz, E., Tomsia, A.P., Moya, J.S. Soda-lime glass-coating containing silver nanoparticles on Ti-6Al-4V alloy. *J Eur Ceram Soc* 32 (2012): 2723–9.

Ewald, A., Glückermann, S.K., Thull, R., Gbureck, U. Antimicrobial titanium/silver PVD coatings on titanium. *Biomed Eng Online* 5 (2006): 22.

Fabrega, J., Fawcett, S.R., Renshaw, J.C., Lead, J.R. Silver nanoparticle impact on bacterial growth: Effect of pH, concentration, and organic matter. *Environ Sci Technol* 43 (2009): 7285–90.

Fayaz, A.M., Balaji, K., Girilal, M., Yadav, R., Kalaichelvan, P.T., Venketesan, R. Biogenic synthesis of silver nanoparticles and their synergistic effect with antibiotics: A study against gram-positive and gram-negative bacteria. *Nanomedicine* 6 (2010): 103–9.

Fiedler, J., Kolitsch, A., Kleffner, B., Henke, D., Stenger, S., Brenner, R.E. Copper and silver ion implantation of aluminium oxide-blasted titanium surfaces: Proliferative response of osteoblasts and antibacterial effects. *Int J Artif Organs* 34 (2011): 882–8.

Fu, P.P., Xia, Q., Hwang, H.M., Ray, P.C., Yu, H. Mechanisms of nanotoxicity: Generation of reactive oxygen species. *J Food Drug Anal* 22 (2014): 64–75.

Fujishima, A., Honda, K. Electrochemical photolysis of water at a semiconductor electrode. *Nature* 238 (1972): 37–8.

Fung, L.C., Khoury, A.E., Vas, S.I., Smith, C., Oreopoulos, D.G., Mittelman, M.W. Biocompatibility of silver-coated peritoneal dialysis catheter in a porcine model. *Perit Dial Int* 16 (1996): 398–405.

Galanakis, I., Bihlmayer, G., Bellini, V., Papanikolaou, N., Zeller, R., Blugel, S., Dederichs, P.H. Broken-bond rule for the surface energies of noble metals. *Europhys Lett* 58 (2002a): 751–7.

Galanakis, I., Papanikolaou, N., Dederichs, P.H. Applicability of the broken-bond rule to the surface energy of the fcc metals. *Surf Sci* 511 (2002b): 1–12.

Gemmell, C.G., Edwards, D.I., Frainse, A.P. Guidelines for the prophylaxis and treatment of methicillin-resistant *Staphylococcus aureus* (MRSA) infections in the UK. *J Antimicrob Chemother* 57 (2006): 589–608.

Gosheger, G., Hardes, J., Ahrens, H., Streitburger, A., Buerger, H., Erren, M., Gunsel, A., Kemper, F.H., Winkelmann, W., Von Eiff, C. Silver-coated megaendoprostheses in a rabbit model – An analysis of the infection rate and toxicological side effects. *Biomaterials* 25 (2004): 5547–56.

Grainger, D.W., van der Mei, H.C., Jutte, P.C., van den Dungen, J.J., Schultz M.J., van der Laan, B.F., Zaat, S.A., Busscher, H.J. Critical factors in the translation of improved antimicrobial strategies for medical implants and devices. *Biomaterials* 34 (2013): 9237–43.

Gray, M.W. Mitochondrial evolution. *Cold Spring Harb Perspect Biol* 4 (2012): a011403.

Greegor, R.B., Lytle, F.W. Morphology of supported metal clusters: Determination by EXAFS and chemisorption. *J Catal* 63 (1980): 476–86.

Greeley, J., Nørskov, J.K., Mavrikakis, M. Electronic structure and catalysis on metal surfaces. *Annu Rev Phys Chem* 53 (2002): 319–48.

Greulich, C., Diendorf, J., Gessmann, J., Simon, T., Habijan, T., Eggeler, G., Schildhauer, T.A., Epple, M., Köller, M. Cell type-specific responses of peripheral blood mononuclear cells to silver nanoparticles. *Acta Biomater* 7 (2011a): 3505–14.

Greulich, C., Diendorf, J., Simon, T., Eggeler, G., Epple, M., Köller, M. Uptake and intracellular distribution of silver nanoparticles in human mesenchymal stem cells. *Acta Biomater* 7 (2011b): 347–54.

Gristina, A.G. Biomaterial-centered infection: Microbial adhesion versus tissue integration. *Science* 237 (1987): 1588–95.

Grunkemeier, G.L., Jin, R., Im, K., Holubkov, R., Kennard, E.D., Schaff, H.V. Time-related risk of the St. Jude Silzone heart valve. *Eur J Cardiothorac Surg* 30 (2006): 20–7.

Gunnarsson, L., Rindzevicius, T., Prikulis, J., Kasemo, B., Käll, M., Zou, S., Schatz, G.C. Confined plasmons in nanofabricated single silver particle pairs: Experimental observations of strong interparticle interactions. *J Phys Chem B* 109 (2005): 1079–87.

Gurunathan, S., Lee, K.J., Kalishwaralal, K., Sheikpranbabu, S., Vaidyanathan, R., Eom, S.H. Antiangiogenic properties of silver nanoparticles. *Biomaterials* 30 (2009): 6341–50.

Han, D.W., Woo, Y.I., Lee, M.H., Lee, J.H., Lee, J., Park, J.C. In-vivo and in-vitro biocompatibility evaluations of silver nanoparticles with antimicrobial activity. *J Nanosci Nanotechnol* 12 (2012): 5205–9.

Hardes, J., Ahrens, H., Gebert, C., Streitbuerger, A., Buerger, H., Erren, M., Gunsel, A., Wedemeyer, C., Saxler, G., Winkelmann, W., Gosheger, G. Lack of toxicological side-effects in silver-coated megaprostheses in humans. *Biomaterials* 28 (2007): 2869–75.

Hardes, J., von Eiff, C., Streitbuerger, A., Balke, M., Budny, T., Henrichs, M.P., Hauschild, G., Ahrens, H. Reduction of periprosthetic infection with silver-coated megaprostheses in patients with bone sarcoma. *J Surg Oncol* 101 (2010): 389–95.

Hardeveld, R., van Hartog, F. The statistics of surface atoms and surface sites on metal crystals. *Surf Sci* 15 (1969): 189–230.

Harris, H.W., El-Naggar, M.Y., Bretschger, O., Ward, M.J., Romine, M.F., Obraztsova, A.Y., Nealson, K.H. Electrokinesis is a microbial behavior that requires extracellular electron transport. *Proc Natl Acad Sci USA* 107 (2010): 326–31.

Hauschild, G., Hardes, J., Gosheger, G., Stoeppeler, S., Ahrens, H., Blaske, F., Wehe, C., Karst, U., Höll, S. Evaluation of osseous integration of PVD–silver-coated hip prostheses in a canine model. *Biomed Res Int* (2015): 292406.

Hayashi, Y., Engelmann, P., Foldbjerg, R., Szabó, M., Somogyi, I., Pollák, E., Molnár, L., Autrup, H., Sutherland, D.S., Scott-Fordsmand, J., Heckmann, L.H. Earthworms and humans in vitro: Characterizing evolutionarily conserved stress and immune responses to silver nanoparticles. *Environ Sci Technol* 46 (2012): 4166–73.

Henderson, M.A. A surface science perspective on TiO_2 photocatalysis. *Surf Sci Rep* 66 (2011): 185–297.

Henrichs, M.P., Singh, G., Gosheger, G., Nottrott, M., Streitbuerger, A., Hardes, J. Stump lengthening procedure with modular endoprostheses – The better alternative to disarticulations of the hip joint. *J Arthroplasty* 30 (2015): 681–6.

Hentschel, M., Saliba, M., Vogelgesang, R., Giessen, H., Alivisatos, A.P., Liu, N. Transition from isolated to collective modes in plasmonic oligomers. *Nano Lett* 10 (2010): 2721–6.

Hoffmann, M.R., Martin, S.T., Choi, W., Bahnemann, D.W. Environmental applications of semiconductor photocatalysis. *Chem Rev* 95 (1995): 69–96.

Howie, A., Marks, L.D. Elastic strains and the energy balance for multiply twinned particles. *Philos Mag A* 49 (1984): 95–109.

Hsin, Y.H., Chen, C.F., Huang, S., Shih, T.S., Lai, P.S., Chueh, P.J. The apoptotic effect of nanosilver is mediated by a ROS- and JNK-dependent mechanism involving the mitochondrial pathway in NIH3T3 cells. *Toxicol Lett* 179 (2008): 130–9.

Huang, R., Carney, R.P., Stellacci, F., Lau, B.L.T. Colloidal stability of self-assembled monolayer-coated gold nanoparticles: The effects of surface compositional and structural heterogeneity. *Langmuir* 29 (2013): 11560–6.

Huang, H., Chang, Y., Chen, H., Chou, Y., Lai, C., Chen, M.Y.C. Antibacterial properties and cytocompatibility of tantalum oxide coatings with different silver content. *J Vac Sci Technol A* 23 (2014): 02B117.

Huo, D., Ding, J., Cui, Y.X., Xia, L.Y., Li, H., He, J., Zhou, Z.Y., Wang, H.W., Hu, Y. X-ray CT and pneumonia inhibition properties of gold-silver nanoparticles for targeting MRSA induced pneumonia. *Biomaterials* 35 (2014): 7032–41.

Hurdle, J.G., O'Neill, A.J., Chopra, I., Lee, R.E. Targeting bacterial membrane function: An underexploited mechanism for treating persistent infections. *Nat Rev Microbiol* 9 (2011): 62–75.

Hwang, E.T., Lee, J.H., Chae, Y.J., Kim, Y.S., Kim, B.C., Sang, B.I., Gu, M.B. Analysis of the toxic mode of action of silver nanoparticles using stress-specific bioluminescent bacteria. *Small* 4 (2008): 746–50.

Imlay, J.A. The molecular mechanisms and physiological consequences of oxidative stress: Lessons from a model bacterium. *Nat Rev Microbiol* 11 (2013): 443–54.

Issendorff, B., von Cheshnovsky, O. Metal to insulator transitions in clusters. *Annu Rev Phys Chem* 56 (2005): 549–80.

Ivask, A., Elbadawy, A., Kaweeteerawat, C., Boren, D., Fischer, H., Ji, Z., Chang, C.H., Liu, R., Tolaymat, T., Telesca, D., Zink, J.I., Cohen, Y., Holden, P.A., Godwin, H.A. Toxicity mechanisms in *Escherichia coli* vary for silver nanoparticles and differ from ionic silver. *ACS Nano* 8 (2014): 374–86.

Jia, Z., Xiu, P., Li, M., Xu, X., Shi, Y., Cheng, Y., Wei, S., Zheng, Y., Xi, T., Cai, H., Liu, Z. Bioinspired anchoring AgNPs onto micro-nanoporous TiO_2 orthopedic coatings: Trap-killing of bacteria, surface-regulated osteoblast functions and host responses. *Biomaterials* 75 (2016): 203–22.

Jiang, Q., Li, J.C., Chi, B.Q. Size-dependent cohesive energy of nanocrystals. *Chem Phys Lett* 366 (2002): 551–4.

Jiang, Q., Lu, H.M., Zhao, M. Modelling of surface energies of elemental crystals. *J Phys Condens Matter* 16 (2004): 521–30.

Jin, R., Cao, Y., Mirkin, C.A., Kelly, K.L., Schatz, G.C., Zheng, J.G. Photoinduced conversion of silver nanospheres to nanoprisms. *Science* 294 (2001): 1901–3.

Jin, R., Cao, Y.C., Hao, E., Métraux, G.S., Schatz, G.C., Mirkin, C.A. Controlling anisotropic nanoparticle growth through plasmon excitation. *Nature* 425 (2003): 487–90.

Jortner, J. Cluster size effects. *Z. Phys. D – Atom Mol Cl* 24 (1992): 247–75.

Kaplan, I.G., Santamaría, R., Novaro, O. Non-additive forces in atomic clusters: The case of Agn. *Molecular Physics* 84 (1995a): 105–14.

Kaplan, I.G., Santamaría, R., Novaro, O. Nonadditive interactions and the relative stability of neutral and anionic silver clusters. *Int J Quantum Chem* 55 (1995b): 237–243.

Kawata, K., Osawa, M., Okabe, S. In vitro toxicity of silver nanoparticles at noncytotoxic doses to HepG2 human hepatoma cells. *Environ Sci Technol* 43 (2009): 6046–51.

Kennedy, A.J., Hull, M.S., Bednar, A.J., Goss, J.D., Gunter, J.C., Bouldin, J.L., Vikesland, P.J., Steevens, J.A. Fractionating nanosilver: Importance for determining toxicity to aquatic test organisms. *Environ Sci Technol* 44 (2010): 9571–7.

Kim, S., Choi, J.E., Choi, J., Chung, K., Park, K., Yi, J., Ryu, D.Y. Oxidative stress-dependent toxicity of silver nanoparticles in human hepatoma cells. *Toxicol In Vitro* 23 (2009): 1076–84.

Kim, T., Lee, K., Gong, M.S., Joo, S.W. Control of gold nanoparticle aggregates by manipulation of interparticle interaction. *Langmuir* 21 (2005): 9524–8.

Kinnan, M.K., Chumanov, G. Plasmon coupling in two-dimensional arrays of silver nanoparticles: II. Effect of the particle size and interparticle distance. *J Phys Chem C* 114 (2010): 7496–501.

Kirkland, A.I., Jefferson, D.A., Duff, D.G., Edwards, P.P., Gameson, I., Johnson, B.F.G., Smith, D.J. Structural studies of trigonal lamellar particles of gold and silver. *Proc R Soc London Ser A* 440 (1993): 589–609.

Kittler, S., Greulich, C., Diendorf, J., Köller, M., Epple, M. Toxicity of silver nanoparticles increases during storage because of slow dissolution under release of silver ions. *Chem Mater* 22 (2010): 4548–54.

Kohn, W. Nobel lecture: Electronic structure of matter-wave functions and density functionals. *Rev Mod Phys* 71 (1999): 1253–66.

Korgel, B.A., Fullam, S., Connolly, S., Fitzmaurice, D. Assembly and self-organization of silver nanocrystal superlattices: Ordered 'soft spheres'. *J Phys Chem B* 102 (1998): 8379–88.

Kraft, C.N., Hansis, M., Arens, S., Menger, M.D., Vollmar, B. Striated muscle microvascular response to silver implants: A comparative in vivo study with titanium and stainless steel. *J Biomed Mater Res* 49 (2000): 192–9.

Kubo, R. Electronic properties of metallic fine particles I. *J Phys Soc Jpn* 17 (1962): 975–86.

Kurland, C.G., Andersson, S.G.E. Origin and evolution of the mitochondrial proteome. *Microbiol Mol Biol Rev* 64 (2000): 786–820.

Lacerda, S.H., Park, J.J., Meuse, C., Pristinski, D., Becker, M.L., Karim, A., Douglas, J.F. Interaction of gold nanoparticles with common human blood proteins. *ACS Nano* 4 (2010): 365–79.

Lankveld, D.P., Oomen, A.G., Krystek, P., Neigh, A., Troost-de Jong, A., Noorlander, C.W., Van Eijkeren, J.C., Geertsma, R.E., De Jong, W.H. The kinetics of the tissue distribution of silver nanoparticles of different sizes. *Biomaterials* 31 (2010): 8350–61.

Lee, J.S., Murphy, W.L. Functionalizing calcium phosphate biomaterials with antibacterial silver particles. *Adv Mater* 25 (2013): 1173–9.

Lee, K.J., Browning, L.M., Nallathamby, P.D., Desai, T., Cherukuri, P.K., Xu, X.H. In vivo quantitative study of sized-dependent transport and toxicity of single silver nanoparticles using zebrafish embryos. *Chem Res Toxicol* 25 (2012): 1029–46.

Lee, K.J., Nallathamby, P.D., Browning, L.M., Osgood, C.J., Xu, X.H. In vivo imaging of transport and biocompatibility of single silver nanoparticles in early development of zebrafish embryos. *ACS Nano* 1 (2007): 133–43.

Levard, C., Mitra, S., Yang, T., Jew, A.D., Badireddy, A.R., Lowry, G.V., Brown, G.E. 'Effect of chloride on the dissolution rate of silver nanoparticles and toxicity to *E. coli*.' *Environ Sci Technol* 47 (2013a): 5738–45.

Levard, C., Hotze, E.M., Colman, B.P., Dale, A.L., Truong, L., Yang, X.Y., Bone, A.J., Brown, G.E. Jr., Tanguay, R.L., Di Giulio, R.T., Bernhardt, E.S., Meyer, J.N., Wiesner, M.R., Lowry, G.V. Sulfidation of silver nanoparticles: Natural antidote to their toxicity. *Environ Sci Technol* 47 (2013b): 13440–8.

Lim, D.H., Jang, J., Kim, S., Kang, T., Lee, K., Choi, I.H. The effects of sub lethal concentrations of silver nanoparticles on inflammatory and stress genes in human macrophages using cDNA microarray analysis. *Biomaterials* 33 (2012): 4690–9.

Liu, H.J., Mun, B.S., Thornton, G., Isaacs, S.R., Shon, Y.S., Ogletree, D.F., Salmeron, M. Electronic structure of ensembles of gold nanoparticles: Size and proximity effects. *Phys Rev B* 72 (2005): 155430.

Liu, J., Sonshine, D.A., Shervani, S., Hurt, R.H. Controlled release of biologically active silver from nanosilver surfaces. *ACS Nano* 4 (2010): 6903–13.

Liu, L.J., Schlesinger, M. Corrosion of magnesium and its alloys. *Corr Sci* 51 (2009): 1733–7.

Lok, C.N., Ho, C.M., Chen, R., He, Q.Y., Yu, W.Y., Sun, H., Tam, P.K., Chiu, J.F., Che, C.M. Proteomic analysis of the mode of antibacterial action of silver nanoparticles. *J Proteome Res* 5 (2006): 916–24.

Lu, W., Senapati, D., Wang, S., Tovmachenko, O., Singh, A.K., Yu, H., Ray, P.C. Effect of surface coating on the toxicity of silver nanomaterials on human skin keratinocytes. *Chem Phys Lett* 487 (2010): 92–6.

Luo, Y.H., Chang, L.W., Lin, P. Metal-based nanoparticles and the immune system: Activation, inflammation, and potential applications. *Biomed Res Int* 2015 (2015): 143720.

Mahadevi, A.S., Sastry, G.N. Cooperativity in noncovalent interactions. *Chem Rev* 116 (2016): 2775–825.

Marambio-Jones, C., Hoek, E.M.V. A review of the antibacterial effects of silver nanomaterials and potential implications for human health and the environment. *J Nanopart Res* 12 (2010): 1531–51.

Marks, L.D. Surface structure and energetics of multiply twinned particles. *Philos Mag A* 49 (1984): 81–93.

Marreiros, B.C., Calisto, F., Castro, P.J., Duarte, A.M., Sena, F.V., Silva, A.F., Sousa, F.M., Teixeira, M., Refojo, P.N., Pereira, M.M. Exploring membrane respiratory chains. *Biochimica et Biophysica Acta* 1857 (2016): 1039–67.

Massè, A., Bruno, A., Bosetti, M., Biasibetti, A., Cannas, M., Gallinaro, P. Prevention of pin track infection in external fixation with silver coated pins: Clinical and microbiological results. *J Biomed Mater Res* 53 (2000): 600–4.

McBride, H.M., Neuspiel, M., Wasiak, S. Mitochondria: More than just a powerhouse. *Curr Biol* 16 (2006): R551–60.

McQuillan, J.S., Shaw, A.M. Differential gene regulation in the Ag nanoparticle and Ag (+)-induced silver stress response in *Escherichia coli*: A full transcriptomic profile. *Nanotoxicology* 8 (2014) Suppl 1: 177–84.

Meldrum Al, H., Richard, F., Boatner, L.A., White, C.W. Nanocomposite materials formed by ion implantation. *Adv Mater* 13 (2001): 1431–44.

Methfessel, M., Hennig, D., and Scheffler, M. Trends of the surface relaxations, surface energies, and work functions of the 4 d transition metals. *Phys Rev B* 46 (1992): 4816–29.

Min, Y., Akbulut, M., Kristiansen, K., Golan, Y., Israelachvili, J. The role of interparticle and external forces in nanoparticle assembly. *Nat Mater* 7 (2008): 527–38.

Morones, J.R., Elechiguerra, J.L., Camacho, A., Holt, K., Kouri, J.B., Ramirez, J.T., Yacaman, M.J. The bactericidal effect of silver nanoparticles. *Nanotechnology* 16 (2005): 2346–53.

Murdoch, M., Waterhouse, G.I.N., Nadeem, M.A., Metson, J.B., Keane, M.A., Howe, R.F. et al. The effect of gold loading and particle size on photocatalytic hydrogen production from ethanol over Au/TiO_2 nanoparticles. *Nat Chem* 3 (2011): 489–92.

Nanda, K.K., Kruis, F.E., Fissan, H. Evaporation of free PbS nanoparticles: Evidence of the Kelvin effect. *Phys Rev Lett* 89 (2002): 256103.

Nanda, K.K., Maisels, A., Kruis, F.E., Fissan, H., Stappert, S. Higher surface energy of free nanoparticles. *Phys Rev Lett* 91 (2003): 106102.

Navarro, E., Piccapietra, F., Wagner, B., Marconi, F., Kaegi, R., Odzak, N., Sigg, L., Behra, R. Toxicity of silver nanoparticles to *Chlamydomonas reinhardtii*. *Environ Sci Technol* 42 (2008): 8959–64.

Nel, A., Xia, T., Mädler, L., Li, N. Toxic potential of materials at the nanolevel. *Science* 311 (2006): 622–7.

Nel, A.E., Mädler, L., Velegol, D., Xia, T., Hoek, E.M., Somasundaran, P., Klaessig, F., Castranova, V., Thompson, M. Understanding biophysicochemical interactions at the nano-bio interface. *Nat Mater* 8 (2009): 543–57.

Ouay, B.L., Stellacci, F. Antibacterial activity of silver nanoparticles: A surface science insight. *Nano Today* 10 (2015): 339–54.

Ouyang, G., Tan, X., Yang, G. Thermodynamic model of the surface energy of nanocrystals. *Phys Rev B* 74 (2006): 195408.

Peynshaert, K., Manshian, B.B., Joris, F., Braeckmans, K., De Smedt, S.C., Demeester, J., Soenen, S.J. Exploiting intrinsic nanoparticle toxicity: The pros and cons of nanoparticle-induced autophagy in biomedical research. *Chem Rev* 114 (2014): 7581–609.

Pokhrel, L.R., Dubey, B., Scheuerman, P.R. Impacts of select organic ligands on the colloidal stability, dissolution dynamics, and toxicity of silver nanoparticles. *Environ Sci Technol* 47 (2013): 12877–85.

Pratsinis, A., Hervella, P., Leroux, J.-C., Pratsinis, S.E., Sotiriou, G.A. Toxicity of silver nanoparticles in macrophages. *Small* 9 (2013): 2576–84.

Prucek, R., Tuček, J., Kilianová, M., Panáček, A., Kvítek, L., Filip, J., Kolář, M., Tománková, K., Zbořil, R. The targeted antibacterial and antifungal properties of magnetic nanocomposite of iron oxide and silver nanoparticles. *Biomaterials* 32 (2011): 4704–13.

Qi, W.H., Wang, M.P. Size effect on the cohesive energy of nanoparticle. *J Mater Sci Lett* 21 (2002): 1743–5.

Qiao, S., Cao, H., Zhao, X., Lo, H., Zhuang, L., Gu, Y., Shi, J., Liu, X., Lai, H. Ag-plasma modification enhances bone apposition around titanium dental implants: An animal study in Labrador dogs. *Int J Nanomedicine* 10 (2015): 653–64.

Qin, H., Cao, H., Zhao, Y., Zhu, C., Cheng, T., Wang, Q., Peng, X., Cheng, M., Wang, J., Jin, G., Jiang, Y., Zhang, X., Liu, X., Chu, P.K. In vitro and in vivo anti-biofilm effects of silver nanoparticles immobilized on titanium. *Biomaterials* 35 (2014a): 9114–25.

Qin, H., Cao, H., Zhao, Y., Jin, G., Cheng, M., Wang, J., Jiang, Y., An, Z., Zhang, X., Liu, X. Antimicrobial and osteogenic properties of silver-ion-implanted stainless steel. *ACS Appl Mater Interfaces* 7 (2015): 10785–94.

Qin, H., Zhu, C., An, Z., Jiang, Y., Zhao, Y., Wang, J., Liu, X., Hui, B., Zhang, X., Wang, Y. Silver nanoparticles promote osteogenic differentiation of human urine-derived stem cells at noncytotoxic concentrations. *Int J Nanomedicine* 9 (2014b): 2469–78.

Raha, S., Robinson, B.H. Mitochondria, oxygen free radicals, and apoptosis. *Am J Med Genet* 106 (2001): 62–70.

Ramírez-Solís, A., Daudey, J.P., Novaro, O., Ruíz, M.E. Nonadditivity and the stability of Ag3: A multireference configuration interaction study. *Z Phys D* 15 (1990): 71–8.

Rao, A., Roy, S., Unnikrishnan, M., Bhosale, S.S., Devatha, G., Pillai, P.P. Regulation of interparticle forces reveals controlled aggregation in charged nanoparticles. *Chem Mater* 28 (2016): 2348–55.

Rao, C.N.R., Kulkarni, G.U., Thomas, P.J., Edwards, P.P. Metal nanoparticles and their assemblies. *Chem Soc Rev* 29 (2000): 27–35.

Rao, C.N.R., Kulkarni, G.U., Thomas, P.J., Edwards, P.P. Size-dependent chemistry: Properties of nanocrystals. *Chem Eur J* 8 (2002): 28–35.

Raphel, J., Holodniy, M., Goodman, S.B., Heilshorn, S.C. Multifunctional coatings to simultaneously promote osseointegration and prevent infection of orthopaedic implants. *Biomaterials* 84 (2016): 301–14.

Ratner, B.D. The biocompatibility manifesto: Biocompatibility for the twenty-first century. *J Cardiovasc Trans Res* 4 (2011): 523–7.

Ray, P.D., Huang, B.W., Tsuji, Y. Reactive oxygen species (ROS) homeostasis and redox regulation in cellular signaling. *Cell Signal* 24 (2012): 981–90.

Rhoderick, E.H. *Metal-semiconductor contacts*. UK: Oxford University Press, 1978.

Rich, P.R., Maréchal, A. The mitochondrial respiratory chain. *Essays Biochem* 47 (2010): 1–23.

Rizzello, L., Pompa, P.P. Nanosilver-based antibacterial drugs and devices: Mechanisms, methodological drawbacks, and guidelines. *Chem Soc Rev* 43 (2014): 1501–18.

Roduner, E. Size matters: Why nanomaterials are different. *Chem Soc Rev* 35 (2006): 583–92.

Rosenblit, M., Jortner, J. Excess electron surface states on clusters. *J Phys Chem* 98 (1994): 9365–70.

Samberg, M.E., Loboa, E.G., Oldenburg, S.J., Monteiro-Riviere, N.A. Silver nanoparticles do not influence stem cell differentiation but cause minimal toxicity. *Nanomedicine (Lond)* 7 (2012): 1197–209.

Schaff, H.V., Carrel, T.P., Jamieson, W.R., Jones, K.W., Rufilanchas, J.J., Cooley, D.A., Hetzer, R., Stumpe, F., Duveau, D., Moseley, P., van Boven, W.J., Grunkemeier, G.L., Kennard, E.D., Holubkov, R. Paravalvular leak and other events in silzone-coated mechanical heart valves: A report from AVERT. *Ann Thorac Surg* 73 (2002): 785–92.

Schmidt, G. Metals. In *Nanoscale Materials in Chemistry*, 15–59. USA: John Wiley & Sons, 2001.

Sengstock, C., Diendorf, J., Epple, M., Schildhauer, T.A., Köller, M. Effect of silver nanoparticles on human mesenchymal stem cell differentiation. *Beilstein J Nanotechnol* 5 (2014): 2058–69.

Setyawati, M.I., Yuan, X., Xie, J., Leong, D.T. The influence of lysosomal stability of silver nanomaterials on their toxicity to human cells. *Biomaterials* 35 (2014): 6707–15.

Shandiz, M.A., Safaei, A., Sanjabi, S., Barber, Z.H. Modeling the cohesive energy and melting point of nanoparticles by their average coordination number. *Solid State Comm* 145 (2008): 432–7.

Sharma, V.K., Yngard, R.A., Lin, Y. Silver nanoparticles: Green synthesis and their antimicrobial activities. *Adv Colloid Interface Sci* 145 (2009): 83–96.

Shen, H., Tang, J., Mao, Y., Wang, Q., Wang, J., Zhang, X., Jiang, Y. Pathogenic analysis in different types of orthopedic implant infections. *Chin Med J (Engl)* 127 (2014): 2748–52.

Singh, R.P., Ramarao, P. Cellular uptake, intracellular trafficking and cytotoxicity of silver nanoparticles. *Toxicol Lett* 213 (2012): 249–59.

Sioshansi, P. New processes for surface treatment of catheters. *Artif Organs* 18 (1994): 266–71.

Soenen, S.J., Parak, W.J., Rejman, J., Manshian, B. (Intra) cellular stability of inorganic nanoparticles: Effects on cytotoxicity, particle functionality, and biomedical applications. *Chem Rev* 115 (2015): 2109–35.

Song, G., Johannesson, B., Hapugoda, S., St. John, D. Galvanic corrosion of magnesium alloy AZ91D in contact with an aluminium alloy, steel and zinc. *Corr Sci* 46 (2004): 955–77.

Strahl, H., Hamoen, L.W. Membrane potential is important for bacterial cell division. *Proc Natl Acad Sci USA* 107 (2010): 12281–6.

Su, H.L., Chou, C.C., Hung, D.J., Lin, S.H., Pao, I.C., Lin, J.H., Huang, F.L., Dong, R.X., Lin, J.J. The disruption of bacterial membrane integrity through ROS generation induced by nanohybrids of silver and clay. *Biomaterials* 30 (2009): 5979–87.

Sun, C.Q. Size dependence of nanostructures: Impact of bond order deficiency. *Prog Solid State Chem* 35 (2007): 1–159.

Sun, F., Huo, X., Zhai, Y., Wang, A., Xu, J., Su, D., Bartlam, M., Rao, Z. Crystal structure of mitochondrial respiratory membrane protein complex II. *Cell* 121 (2005): 1043–57.

Sun, Y., Xia, Y. Shape-controlled synthesis of gold and silver nanoparticles. *Science* 298 (2002): 2176–9.

Sunada, K., Kikuchi, Y., Hashimoto, K., Fujishima, A. Bactericidal and detoxification effects of TiO_2 thin film photocatalysts. *Environ Sci Technol* 32 (1998): 726–8.

Suresh, A.K., Pelletier, D.A., Wang, W., Morrell-Falvey, J.L., Gu, B., Doktycz, M.J. Cytotoxicity induced by engineered silver nanocrystallites is dependent on surface coatings and cell types. *Langmuir* 28 (2012): 2727–35.

Sze, S.M., Ng, K.K. *Physics of Semiconductor Devices*. Hoboken, NJ: Wiley, 2007.

Taglietti, A., Arciola, C.R., D'Agostino, A., Dacarro, G., Montanaro, L., Campoccia, D., Cucca, L., Vercellino, M., Poggi, A., Pallavicini, P., Visai, L. Antibiofilm activity of a monolayer of silver nanoparticles anchored to an amino-silanized glass surface. *Biomaterials* 35 (2014): 1779–88.

Taheri, S., Cavallaro, A., Christo, S.N., Smith, L.E., Majewski, P., Barton, M., Hayball, J.D., Vasilev, K. Substrate independent silver nanoparticle based antibacterial coatings. *Biomaterials* 35 (2014): 4601–9.

Takai, A., Kamat, P.V. Capture, store, and discharge. Shuttling photogenerated electrons across TiO_2–silver interface. *ACS Nano* 5 (2011): 7369–76.

Teodoro, J.S., Simões, A.M., Duarte, F.V., Rolo, A.P., Murdoch, R.C., Hussain, S.M., Palmeira, C.M. Assessment of the toxicity of silver nanoparticles in vitro: A mitochondrial perspective. *Toxicol In Vitro* 25 (2011): 664–70.

Tjong, S.C., Chen, H. Nanocrystalline materials and coatings. *Mat Sci Eng R: Reports* 45 (2004): 1–88.

Trampuz, A., Zimmerli, W. Diagnosis and treatment of infections associated with fracture-fixation devices. *Injury* 37 (2006): S59–66.

Trickler, W.J., Lantz, S.M., Murdock, R.C., Schrand, A.M., Robinson, B.L., Newport, G.D., Schlager, J.J., Oldenburg, S.J., Paule, M.G., Slikker, W. Jr., Hussain, S.M., Ali, S.F. Silver nanoparticle induced blood–brain barrier inflammation and increased permeability in primary rat brain microvessel endothelial cells. *Toxicol Sci* 118 (2010): 160–70.

Tyson, W.R., Miller, W.A. Surface free energies of solid metals: Estimation from liquid surface tension measurements. *Surf Sci* 62 (1977): 267–76.

Valentin, C.D., Fittipaldi, D. Hole scavenging by organic adsorbates on the TiO_2 surface: A DFT model study. *J Phys Chem Lett* 4 (2013): 1901–6.

Vanithakumari, S.C., Nanda, K.K. A universal relation for the cohesive energy of nanoparticles. *Phys Lett A* 372 (2008): 6930–4.

van Oosten, M., Schäfer, T., Gazendam, J.A., Ohlsen, K., Tsompanidou, E., de Goffau, M.C., Harmsen, H.J., Crane, L.M., Lim, E., Francis, K.P., Cheung, L., Olive, M., Ntziachristos, V., van Dijl, J.M., van Dam, G.M. Real-time in vivo imaging of invasive- and biomaterial-associated bacterial infections using fluorescently labelled vancomycin. *Nat Commun* 4 (2013): 2584.

Verano-Braga, T., Miethling-Graff, R., Wojdyla, K., Rogowska-Wrzesinska, A., Brewer, J.R., Erdmann, H., Kjeldsen, F. Insights into the cellular response triggered by silver nanoparticles using quantitative proteomics. *ACS Nano* 8 (2014): 2161–75.

Vijayakrishnan, V., Chainani, A., Sarma, D.D., Rao, C.N.R. Metal-insulator transitions in metal clusters: A high-energy spectroscopy study of palladium and silver clusters. *J Phys Chem* 96 (1992): 8679–82.

Vitos, L., Ruban, A.V., Skriver, H.L., Kollar, J. The surface energy of metals. *Surf Sci* 411 (1998): 186–202.

Walkey, C.D., Olsen, J.B., Song, F., Liu, R., Guo, H., Olsen, D.W., Cohen, Y., Emili, A., Chan, W.C. Protein corona fingerprinting predicts the cellular interaction of gold and silver nanoparticles. *ACS Nano* 8 (2014): 2439–55.

Wang, L., Zhang, T., Li, P., Huang, W., Tang, J., Wang, P., Liu, J., Yuan, Q., Bai, R., Li, B., Zhang, K., Zhao, Y., Chen, C. Use of synchrotron radiation-analytical techniques to reveal chemical origin of silver-nanoparticle cytotoxicity. *ACS Nano* 9 (2015): 6532–47.

Wang, M., Cao, H., Meng, F., Zhao, X., Ping, Y., Lü, X., Liu, X. Schottky barrier dependent antimicrobial efficacy of silver nanoparticles. *Mater Lett* 179 (2016): 1–4.

Wang, Z.L. Transmission electron microscopy of shape-controlled nanocrystals and their assemblies. *J Phys Chem B* 104 (2000): 1153–75.

Warren, A.C., Woodall, J.M., Freeouf, J.L., Grischkowsky, D., McInturff, D.T., Melloch, M.R., Otsuka, N. Arsenic precipitates and the semi-insulating properties of GaAs buffer layers grown by low-temperature molecular beam epitaxy. *Appl Phys Lett* 57 (1990): 1331–3.

Wei, L., Lu, J., Xu, H., Patel, A., Chen, Z., Chen, G. Silver nanoparticles: Synthesis, properties, and therapeutic applications. *Drug Discov Today* 20 (2015): 595–601.

Wiley, B.J., Chen, Y., McLellan, J.M., Xiong, Y., Li, Z., Ginger, D.S., Xia, Y. Synthesis and optical properties of silver nanobars and nanorice. *Nano Lett* 7 (2007b): 1032–6.

Wiley, B.J., Herricks, T., Sun, Y., Xia, Y. Polyol synthesis of silver nanoparticles: Use of chloride and oxygen to promote the formation of single-crystal, truncated cubes and tetrahedrons. *Nano Lett* 4 (2004): 1733–9.

Wiley, B.J., Sun, Y., Xia, Y. Synthesis of silver nanostructures with controlled shapes and properties. *Acc Chem Res* 40 (2007a): 1067–76.

Wiley, B.J., Xiong, Y., Li, Z., Yin, Y., Xia, Y. Right bipyramids of silver: A new shape derived from single twinned seeds. *Nano Lett* 6 (2006): 765–8.

Williams, D.F. *Definitions in Biomaterials*. Amsterdam: Elsevier, 1987.

Williams, D.F. On the mechanisms of biocompatibility. *Biomaterials* 29 (2008): 2941–53.

Williams, D.F. There is no such thing as a biocompatible material. *Biomaterials* 35 (2014): 10009–14.

Williams, R., Doherty, P., Vince, D., Grashoff, G., Williams, D. The biocompatibility of silver. *Crit Rev Biocompat* 5 (1989): 221–43.

Xiu, Z.M., Ma, J., Alvarez, P.J. Differential effect of common ligands and molecular oxygen on antimicrobial activity of silver nanoparticles versus silver ions. *Environ Sci Technol* 45 (2011): 9003–8.

Xiu, Z.M., Zhang, Q.B., Puppala, H.L., Colvin, V.L., Alvarez, P.J. Negligible particle-specific antibacterial activity of silver nanoparticles. *Nano Lett* 12 (2012): 4271–5.

Yaghmaee, M.S., Shokri, B. Effect of size on bulk and surface cohesion energy of metallic nano-particles. *Smart Mater Struct* 16 (2007): 349.

Yaghmaee, M.S., Shokri, B., Rahimipour, M.R. Size dependence surface activity of metallic nanoparticles. *Plasma Process Polym* 6 (2009): S876–82.

Yang, E.J., Kim, S., Kim, J.S., Choi, I.H. Inflammasome formation and IL-1β release by human blood monocytes in response to silver nanoparticles. *Biomaterials* 33 (2012): 6858–67.

Yao, Y., Wei, Y., Chen, S. Size effect of the surface energy density of nanoparticles. *Surf Sci* 636 (2015): 19–24.

Yen, H.J., Hsu, S.H., Tsai, C.L. Cytotoxicity and immunological response of gold and silver nanoparticles of different sizes. *Small* 5 (2009): 1553–61.

Yu, S.J., Yin, Y.G., Chao, J.B., Shen, M.H., Liu, J.F. Highly dynamic PVP-coated silver nanoparticles in aquatic environments: Chemical and morphology change induced by oxidation of Ag (0) and reduction of Ag(+). *Environ Sci Technol* 48 (2014): 403–11.

Zeng, J., Zheng, Y., Rycenga, M., Tao, J., Li, Z.Y., Zhang, Q., Zhu, Y., Xia, Y. Controlling the shapes of silver nanocrystals with different capping agents. *J Am Chem Soc* 132 (2010): 8552–3.

Zhang, W., Chu, P.K. Enhancement of antibacterial properties and biocompatibility of polyethylene by silver and copper plasma immersion ion implantation. *Surf Coat Technol* 203 (2008): 909–12.

Zhang, W., Luo, Y., Wang, H., Jiang, J., Pu, S., Chu, P.K. Ag and Ag/N_2 plasma modification of polyethylene for the enhancement of antibacterial properties and cell growth/proliferation. *Acta Biomater* 4 (2008): 2028–36.

Zhang, Z., Yates, J.T. Band bending in semiconductors: Chemical and physical consequences at surfaces and interfaces. *Chem Rev* 112 (2012): 5520–51.

Zhao, L., Wang, H., Huo, K., Cui, L., Zhang, W., Ni, H., Zhang, Y., Wu, Z., Chu, P.K. Antibacterial nano-structured titania coating incorporated with silver nanoparticles. *Biomaterials* 32 (2011): 5706–16.

Section IV

Clinical Demands

13

Orthopaedic Implant–Associated Infections: Pathogenesis, Clinical Presentation and Management

Werner Zimmerli

CONTENTS

13.1 Introduction

Implanted devices have been widely used for more than 70 years. In orthopaedic surgery, the introduction of implants in clinical medicine was a breakthrough not only for patients with bone fractures but also for those with osteoarthritis or those needing spinal fusion (Deyo et al. 2004; Gibson 1954; Hernigou 2014; McLaughlin 1947). With the internal fixation of fractures, the position of broken bones could be optimised and healing could be accelerated by complete stabilisation. In addition, weight charge became possible immediately after surgery. In patients with osteoarthritis or other joint-destructing diseases, arthroplasty with an artificial joint is an efficient means not only to alleviate pain but also to improve function. In 1938, a hip mould was already interposed between refashioned surfaces of acetabulum and femoral head in patients with degenerated hip joints. This procedure was called arthroplasty. The first implants were made from Pyrex; subsequent ones were made from Bakelite and Vitallium (Hernigou 2014; Smith-Petersen 1948). The clinical introduction of total hip replacement, which has been described by Charnley (1961), led to a considerable functional improvement. Rapidly after using this novel surgical technique in patients, implant-associated infection has been recognised as a major problem. Indeed, Roles (1971) reported an infection rate after total hip and knee replacement of 7.4% in 252 patients with osteoarthritis and 10.4% in 201 patients with rheumatoid arthritis as underlying disease. Nowadays, the infection rate during the first 2 years after hip or knee replacement is approximately 0.5%–2% (Zimmerli et al. 2004). Despite major efforts for preventing infection in total joint arthroplasty, periprosthetic joint infection (PJI) cannot be completely avoided (Matar et al. 2010). The reason for this is the high susceptibility of implants to infection. Therefore, there is considerable interest for antibacterial devices (Brennan et al. 2015). In their pioneer study, Elek and Conen (1957) showed in human volunteers that in the vicinity of suture material, the minimal abscess-forming dose is as low as 100 colony-forming units (CFU) of *Staphylococcus aureus*, which is >100,000-fold lower than in the absence of foreign material. Thus, obviously implanted foreign material leads to a compromised host defence in the vicinity of the device.

13.2 Pathogenesis of Implant-Associated Infection

13.2.1 General Aspects

Implanted medical devices are made out of different types of material, mainly metals and polymers, but also biological materials such as devitalised bone and blood vessels. Implant material is also called biomaterial

(Williams 2009, 2015). Whereas vascularised tissues or foreign vital cells are not accepted by the host without immunosuppression, synthetic material and devitalised biological devices are not rejected, as long as they are not infected. Nevertheless, the host reacts to such implants to different degrees, which can be designated as biocompatibility (Anderson and McNally 2011). Any type of implant material increases the risk for infection. In a guinea pig model, we could show that 100 CFU of *S. aureus* were sufficient to infect 95% of subcutaneous implants (tissue cages), whereas $>10^7$ CFU of the same bacterial strain did not produce any abscesses in the absence of foreign material (Zimmerli et al. 1982). In the same animal model, extravascular devices could also be infected by the haematogenous route. With an experimental bacteraemia of 10^3 CFU of *S. aureus* per millilitre of blood, selective seeding to the device was detected in 42% (Zimmerli et al. 1985). This experimental observation reflects the clinical data showing that *S. aureus* sepsis in patients with orthopaedic implants results in prosthetic joint-associated infection in one-third of the patients (Murdoch et al. 2001; Sendi et al. 2011b; Tande et al. 2016).

The type of material is of minor clinical importance regarding the susceptibility of a device to infection. By testing bacterial adherence in vitro, it could be shown that biofilm-forming *Staphylococcus epidermidis* adhered to a higher degree on pure titanium than on stainless steel (Ha et al. 2005). However, this in vitro difference could not be observed in an in vivo model, where no differences in infection rates were observed when titanium and stainless steel implants were challenged with staphylococci (Hudetz et al. 2008). Thus, the immediate coating of the implant by host proteins during surgery seems to be more relevant for bacterial adherence than the type of material.

There are two main pathogenic factors responsible for the high susceptibility to infection and the persistence of such infections, namely, the role of the host and the role of the microorganism (Zimmerli and Moser 2012; Zimmerli and Sendi 2011).

13.2.2 Interaction of the Foreign Material with Phagocytes

As mentioned above, implants are highly susceptible to any type of bacterial and fungal agent (Darouiche 2004; Zimmerli et al. 1982). Elimination of microorganisms depends on efficient phagocytosis and intracellular killing. For rapid ingestion of bacteria, opsonisation of the microorganisms is essential. This involves nonspecific (complement, bacterial remnants) and, in some microorganisms, specific soluble components (antibodies), as well as the corresponding receptors on the phagocytes. The process of phagocytosis involves chemotaxis, cell adherence to the microorganism, ingestion, killing and digestion (Verhoef 1991). If this complex process is impaired, there is an enhanced risk of microbial persistence and therefore infection (Zimmerli et al. 1991). Implant-associated infection is typically characterised by pus formation around the device. Thus, there is an obvious paradox of microbial persistence in the presence of abundant granulocytes around the implant.

Implants interact both with different host factors and with microorganisms. After implantation, a foreign body is immediately covered by host proteins such as fibronectin, fibrinogen and laminin. These proteins increase rather than decrease the risk for infection, because they act as mediators for bacterial adherence (Herrmann et al. 1988; Lopes et al. 1985). In addition, granulocytes and complement directly interact with the implant, which may contribute to inflammation. In an animal model, we could show that granulocytes around a subcutaneous implant are unable to efficiently kill staphylococci, despite their adequate opsonisation (Zimmerli et al. 1982). Also, opsonised particles are inefficiently ingested, and granulocytes are partially degranulated and have a decreased production of oxygen radicals (Zimmerli et al. 1984). We could show in vitro that the interaction of granulocytes with a non-phagocytosable surface continuously activates the respiratory burst and results in the extracellular release of specific granules (Zimmerli et al. 1984). This process is called frustrated phagocytosis (Wright and Gallin 1979).

After arthroplasty, wear particles are produced in variable amounts depending on the biomechanical situation. In addition to the implant itself, these foreign particles also challenge the immune system. Bernard et al. (2007) described an impaired bactericidal activity of neutrophils after interaction with wear particles. They incubated host cells with ultra–high-molecular-weight polyethylene particles that simulated in vivo wear debris. The bactericidal activity of neutrophils decreased in a time- and dose-dependent manner. Granulocytes and macrophages are abundant in the peri-implant tissue, where wear debris is present (Tuan et al. 2008). Macrophages try to eliminate wear particles and liberate cytokines upon phagocytosis. Cytokines, such as interleukin (IL)-1α, IL-1β, tumour necrosis factor-α, macrophage colony-stimulating factor (M-CSF), transforming growth factor (TGF)-α and many others have been detected in tissue surrounding orthopaedic implants (Tuan et al. 2008). Some of these cytokines, such as M-CSF and TGF-α, directly stimulate osteoclastogenesis and therefore favour implant loosening by bone resorption triggered by infection.

13.2.3 Microbial Biofilms

After initial adherence to the implant, microorganisms multiply and form microcolonies, resulting in organised structures with numerous cells, resembling multicellular organisms. These structures are surrounded by a self-produced matrix composed of exopolysaccharides, DNA and proteins (Hoiby et al. 2011). Maturation of the biofilm involves several physiological changes of microbes including regulation of factors such as pili, flagellae and exopolysaccharides (Costerton et al. 1995). Mature biofilms have a so-called quorum sensing (QS) system, which regulates production and release of various virulence factors protecting the biofilm from elimination. In some cases, it increases the microbial virulence, resulting in tissue destruction (Bjarnsholt and Givskov 2007; El-Azizi et al. 2004; Fuqua et al. 2001; Pierce 2005).

Throughout the biofilm, various access to nutrients and oxygen results in gradients generating different growth conditions for the microorganisms (Werner et al. 2004). Such physiological differences result in differentiated behaviour of the microorganisms in the biofilm, especially in the core where the access to nutrients and oxygen is limited (Costerton et al. 1995). This is also the area where microorganisms are most inactive, forming so-called persisters or dormant types (Conlon et al. 2015). In humans, implant-associated infections never spontaneously heal, as long as the biofilm-covered device remains in the body. This is due to the fact that biofilms resist host defence mechanisms (see above) (Hirschfeld 2014; Vaudaux et al. 1985).

In addition to the inefficient elimination by phagocytes, biofilm bacteria are also resistant to most antibiotics (Costerton et al. 1999; Stewart and Costerton 2001). Even long-term antimicrobial therapy frequently fails (Brandt et al. 1997). Antimicrobial activity requires penetration into the biofilm matrix (Stewart et al. 2009). Antibiotics penetrate along a diffusion gradient. In addition, for most antibiotics, there are channels penetrating through the biofilm matrix (Hoiby et al. 2011). The biofilm can be considered as an extra compartment in the tissue. Thus, during antibiotic treatment, there is not only a concentration gradient of antibiotics from the bloodstream to the tissue but also delay of their accumulation. Assuming biofilms as a third compartment, there is an additional concentration gradient as well as a further delay in antibiotic accumulation. If an antibiotic with short half-life and limited penetration abilities is used to treat the biofilm infection, the antibiotic concentration may likely never reach sufficient levels.

Ideally, antibiotics used against implant-associated infections should have bactericidal activity against surface-adhering, slow-growing and biofilm-producing microorganisms (Widmer et al. 1990b; Zimmerli et al. 1994).

Biofilm bacteria are in a stationary phase of growth, because oxygen and glucose are limited in biofilms (Anderl et al. 2003; Bernier et al. 2013). Therefore, successful treatment of implant-associated infection should consider these characteristics of the biofilm. In vitro studies revealed that most antimicrobial agents have a minimal bactericidal concentration (MBC), which is much higher in the stationary than in the logarithmic phase of growth. The high stationary-phase MBCs and the lack of efficacy on adhering bacteria are predictive for the failure of antibiotics in implant-associated infections (Baldoni et al. 2013; Furustrand Tafin et al. 2012; John et al. 2009; Trampuz et al. 2007; Widmer et al. 1990b, 1991; Zimmerli et al. 1994). Unfortunately, to date, only two classes of drugs have shown the properties that are needed for efficacious elimination of biofilm bacteria. Rifampin and other rifamycins act on biofilm staphylococci (Baldoni et al. 2013; Furustrand Tafin et al. 2012; John et al. 2009; Trampuz et al. 2007; Widmer et al. 1990b; Zimmerli et al. 1994), and fluoroquinolones act on Gram-negative bacilli (Rodriguez-Pardo et al. 2014; Widmer et al. 1991).

13.3 Periprosthetic Joint Infections

13.3.1 Introduction

The risk for infection after primary total hip or knee arthroplasty is in the range of 0.5%–2% (Lindeque et al. 2014; Zimmerli et al. 2004). In order to get comparable data from different study groups, well-defined criteria for PJI should be used. There are two standard definitions that are mainly used, namely, the IDSA Definition (Table 13.1) and the MSIS Workgroup Definition (Table 13.2) (Bedair et al. 2011; Deirmengian et al. 2014; Osmon et al. 2013; Schinsky et al. 2008; Trampuz et al. 2004; Zimmerli et al. 2004). The two definitions slightly differ; the one of the MSIS is potentially less sensitive, because some of the criteria (3b, 3c, 3d, 3f) are only diagnostic, if they are present in combination. We prefer the IDSA definition, because PJI should be detected with the best sensitivity possible.

Traditionally, PJIs are classified as early (<3 months after surgery), delayed (3–24 months after surgery) and late infections (>2 years after surgery) (Osmon et al. 2013; Zimmerli et al. 2004). Early and delayed infections are mainly exogenously acquired in the perioperative period, whereas most late PJIs are acquired by the haematogenous route. For clinical purposes, a classification considering the surgical treatment concepts is more useful. Table 13.3 shows a classification according to the duration of infection, which is crucial for the choice of the appropriate surgical strategy (Zimmerli and Sendi 2015). Acute haematogenous PJI of less than 3 weeks duration and early postinterventional PJI (<1 month after surgery) can generally be treated with implant retention (see below) (Osmon et al. 2013; Zimmerli et al. 2004). In contrast, in patients with chronic PJI, the biofilm on implant material can generally not

TABLE 13.1

Infectious Diseases Society of America (IDSA) – Definition of Periprosthetic Joint Infection

- Presence of a sinus tract communicating the prosthetic joint
- Presence of purulence without another known etiology surrounding the prosthetic device
- Acute inflammation consistent with infection at histopathological examination of periprosthetic tissue
- Elevated leukocyte count in the synovial fluid and predominance of neutrophils (Bedair et al. 2011; Schinsky et al. 2008; Trampuz et al. 2004)
- Growth of identical microorganisms in at least two intraoperative cultures or combination of preoperative aspiration and intraoperative cultures

Source: Osmon, D. R., E. F. Berbari, A. R. Berendt, D. Lew, W. Zimmerli, J. M. Steckelberg, N. Rao, A. Hanssen, W. R. Wilson, and America Infectious Diseases Society of. 2013. Diagnosis and management of prosthetic joint infection: Clinical practice guidelines by the Infectious Diseases Society of America. *Clin Infect Dis* 56 (1):e1–e25. doi: 10.1093/cid/cis803.

Note: For the diagnosis of PJI, at least one of the five criteria is required.

TABLE 13.2

Musculoskeletal Infection Society (MSIS) – Definition of Periprosthetic Joint Infection

1. A sinus tract communicating with the prosthesis
2. A pathogen is isolated by culture from two separate tissue or fluid samples obtained from the affected prosthetic joint
3. Four of the following six criteria exist:
   a. Elevated ESR and CRP (ESR > 30 mm/h; CRP > 10 mg/L)
   b. Elevated synovial fluid leukocyte count (>3000/μL)
   c. Elevated synovial fluid neutrophil percentage (>65%)
   d. Presence of purulence in the affected joint
   e. Isolation of a microorganism in one periprothestic tissue or fluid culture
   f. >5 neutrophils per high-power field in 5 high-power fields observed from histologic analysis of periprosthetic tissue at ×400 magnification

Source: Deirmengian, C., K. Kardos, P. Kilmartin, A. Cameron, K. Schiller, and J. Parvizi. 2014. Diagnosing periprosthetic joint infection: Has the era of the biomarker arrived? *Clin Orthop Relat Res* 472 (11):3254–62. Doi: 10.1007/s11999-014-3543-8.

Note: One of the three main criteria must be fulfilled.

TABLE 13.3

Classification of PJI

Type of Infection	Characteristics
Acute hematogenous PJI	Infection with 3 weeks or less of duration of symptoms after an uneventful postoperative period
Early postinterventional PJI	Infection that manifests within 1 month after an invasive procedure such as surgery or arthrocentesis
Chronic PJI	Infection with symptoms that persist for more than 3 weeks and are beyond the early postinterventional period

Source: Zimmerli, W., and P. Sendi. Orthopedic implant-associated infections. In *Mandell, Douglas, and Bennett's Principles and Practice of Infectious Diseases*, 1328–40. Philadelphia: Elsevier Saunders, 2015.

be eliminated by antimicrobial agents (Stewart and Costerton 2001; Zimmerli et al. 1982, 1994). Therefore, all foreign material has to be removed in patients with chronic PJI.

13.3.2 Microbiology

Table 13.4 summarises the type of microorganisms that are found in PJI. Data are from case series published between 2004 and 2012. In each type of PJI, *S. aureus* and coagulase-negative staphylococci are the leading pathogens. Microorganisms that are generally considered as apathogenic can typically cause low-grade PJI. *Propionibacterium acnes* is a typical example. The number of *Propionibacterium* spp. is variable according to the culture technique and to the type of prosthetic device. In six case series, only 13

TABLE 13.4
Microorganisms in PJI

Microorganism[a]	Number	Percentage
Staphylococcus aureus	289	37.5%
Coagulase-negative staphylococci	181	23.5%
Enterococcus spp.	64	8.3%
Streptococcus spp.	60	7.8%
Propionibacterium spp.	13	1.7%
Gram-negative bacilli	103	13.4%
Miscellaneous	14	1.8%

Source: Data from 770 Patients reported in Giulieri et al. 2004; Laffer et al. 2006; Peel et al. 2012; Schinsky et al. 2008; Stefansdottir et al. 2009; Trampuz et al. 2004.

[a] Fractions of polymicrobial and culture-negative PJI are not given in each of the cited references and therefore not reported in the table.

of 770 patients (1.7%) were caused by *Propionibacterium* spp. (Table 13.4). However, with careful anaerobic culturing, we found 6% of cases with this microorganism in a consecutive series of 139 patients with PJI after hip, knee or shoulder arthroplasty (Zappe et al. 2008). In a series with exclusive periprosthetic shoulder infection, the fraction of *Propionibacterium* spp. PJI is even higher, namely, 19% (Singh et al. 2012). This is due to the high prevalence of *P. acnes* in the microbiome of the shoulder region, indicating that PJI generally originates from the patients' own skin microbiome (Sethi et al. 2015). The fraction of polymicrobial PJI goes from 0% to 36%, as reported by Peel et al. (2012). It is especially high in patients with chronic PJI complicated by a sinus tract. According to both case definitions (Tables 13.1 and 13.2), culturing a microorganism is not a prerequisite for the presence of a PJI. The fraction of PJI with negative culture is reported to be between 0% and 10%, mostly around 5% (Berbari et al. 2007; Peel et al. 2012). The frequency mainly depends on the fraction of patients pretreated with antibiotics before diagnostic culturing and on the culture technique (Osmon et al. 2013).

13.3.3 Clinical Presentation

The clinical presentation depends on the type of PJI, which is summarised in Table 13.3. Acute PJIs occurring after haematogenous seeding from the bloodstream are typically preceded by a systemic infection such as sepsis, skin and soft-tissue infection, pneumonia or enterocolitis (Maderazo et al. 1988; Samra et al. 1986; Sendi et al. 2011b). However, the first signs may also be new-onset joint pain, initially without local inflammation after a clinically asymptomatic bacteremia (Widmer et al. 1990a). Only one-third of the patients have a sepsis syndrome. However, in most patients, the C-reactive protein (CRP) is >75 mg/L (Sendi et al. 2011a). The most frequent etiologic agents are *S. aureus*, haemolytic streptococci and Gram-negative bacilli (Rodriguez-Pardo et al. 2014; Sendi et al. 2011b; Zimmerli et al. 2004).

Early postoperative PJIs are typically exogenously acquired either during implantation or in the early postoperative period, when the patient still has drains. The risk is especially high in patients suffering from an oozing or even gaping wound. Local signs of wound infection and pain are predominant. In exogenous staphylococcal PJI, fever >38.3°C is present in only one-quarter, and a sepsis syndrome is present in even <10% of the patients (Sendi et al. 2011a). All patients with acute symptoms, regardless of the time after implantation, require prompt diagnostic workup, because the chance of retaining the implant is only high if the duration of symptoms is short (see below) (Giulieri et al. 2004; Osmon et al. 2013; Zimmerli et al. 2004).

Chronic PJI is either exogenously or haematogenously acquired. Chronic exogenous infections of at least 1 month duration are acquired during the perioperative period. They are typically caused by microorganisms of low virulence, such as coagulase-negative staphylococci or *P. acnes*. These microorganisms generally cause low-grade infections, which are diagnosed with a considerable delay. Chronic PJI is characterised by chronic joint effusion, pain by inflammation or implant loosening, local erythema and hyperthermia and occasionally by recurrent or permanent sinus tracts. Typically, routine follow-up markers such CRP and erythrocyte sedimentation rate (ESR) do not normalise after surgery and fluctuate in a slightly elevated range.

13.3.4 Diagnosis

If there is a clinical suspicion of a PJI because of persistent or new-onset arthralgia or local signs of inflammation, a diagnostic workup should be started without delay (Figure 13.1) (Ryu and Patel 2015). The first steps are a careful case history and a clinical examination (Zimmerli 2015). In addition, as a first diagnostic test, a plain radiograph of the involved prosthetic joint and systemic parameters for inflammation such as CRP indicating inflammation should be performed. In many publications, results from the ESR are also reported. In most European centres, ESR is no longer performed because of its low specificity. In the majority of studies, cutoff values are set at 30 mm/h for ESR and 10 mg/L for CRP. Results below these values (either alone or in combination) have high sensitivity (91%–97%) and hence are helpful in excluding an infection (Berbari et al. 2010; Osmon et al. 2013; Sendi and Zimmerli 2012b). Table 13.5 summarises the sensitivities and specificities of the four most frequently used inflammatory parameters.

Newer serum assays include procalcitonin (PCT), IL-6 and soluble intracellular adhesion molecule-1 (sICAM-1), but only a limited number of studies have analysed these tests. PCT has not been proven to be helpful in differentiating septic from aseptic prosthetic joints (Worthington et al. 2010).

Determination of leukocytes and neutrophil fraction in synovial fluid is important, since it allows the detection of culture-negative PJI according to the

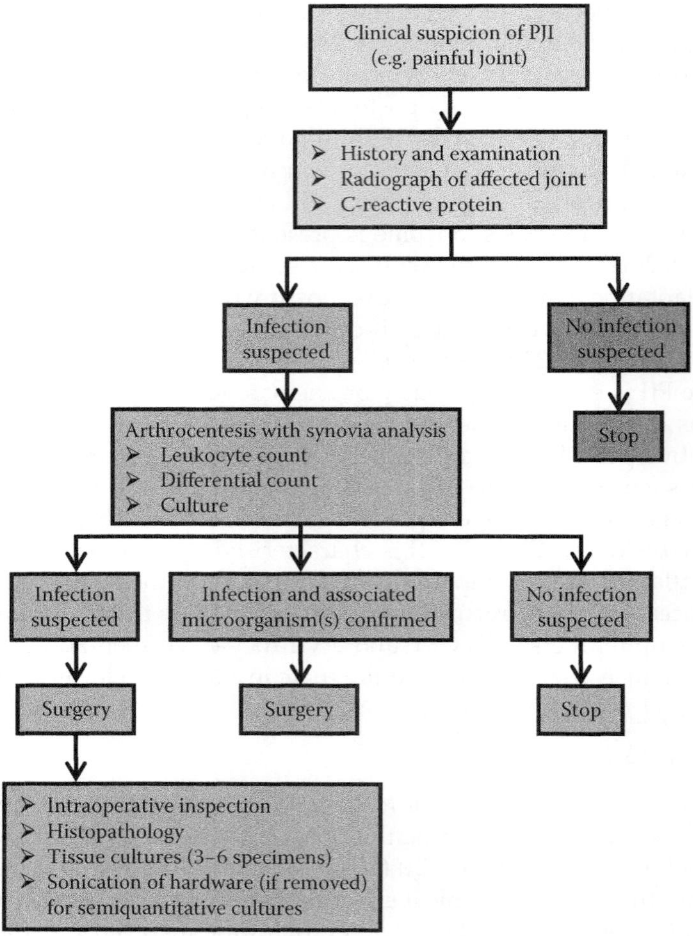

FIGURE 13.1
Diagnostic algorithm in patients with clinical suspicion of periprosthetic joint infection (PJI). (Ryu, S.Y., and R. Patel: *Bone and Joint Infections. From Microbiology to Diagnostics and Treatment*. 325–345. 2015. Copyright Wiley-VCH Verlag GmbH & Co. KGaA. Modified with permission.)

TABLE 13.5
Blood Parameters of Inflammation in PJI

Parameter[a]	Sensitivity	Specificity
Leukocyte counts	45%	87%
Erythrocyte sedimentation rate	75%	70%
C-reactive protein	88%	79%
Interleukin-6	79%	91%

[a] Various threshold in different studies according to a review and meta-analysis of Berbari et al. (2010).

IDSA definition (Table 13.1). The published cutoff values show a sensitivity and specificity of nearly or even more than 90%. In hip arthroplasties, Schinsky et al. (2008) suggested >4200 WBC/μL and >80% polymorphonuclear (PMN) cells for the differential count. In knee arthroplasties, the cutoff values are lower than those in hip arthroplasties. Trampuz et al. (2004) found a value of >1700 WBC/μL and >65% PMN cells for the differential count. If the synovial fluid is examined within the first 6 weeks after surgery, the leukocyte counts are still increased by the surgical trauma and hence difficult to interpret. Proposed cutoff values are >25,000 leukocytes/μL (Bedair et al. 2011). In the future, determination of alpha-defensin, which is a cationic microbicidal peptide in neutrophils, may replace the determination of leukocyte counts in synovia (Deirmengian et al. 2015). However, a direct comparison with synovial leukocytes is still missing.

Conventional microbiological culture of the synovial samples has shown good specificities of up to 100%, though with a moderate sensitivity of 56%–86% (Sendi and Zimmerli 2012b). Hence, a negative culture result from preoperative synovial fluid aspiration does not exclude PJI, particularly not in patients with chronic symptoms. The sample sensitivity can be improved by use of polymerase chain reaction (PCR) (Gallo et al. 2008) or by culturing the synovial fluid in blood culture flasks (Font-Vizcarra et al. 2010). Specific multiplex PCR should be preferred because of their better sensitivity as compared to broad-range PCR (Portillo et al. 2012).

Biopsies that are sampled during surgery should be divided into two parts, one for microbiology and another for histopathology. Comparing pairs of biopsies allows the interpretation of possible contamination, since a positive culture without any signs of tissue inflammation suggests contamination. If granulocytes are present in biopsy specimens without bacterial growth, culture-negative PJI can be diagnosed (Table 13.1). Cultures of biopsy specimens have a higher sensitivity than swab cultures. Swabs should therefore be avoided (Aggarwal et al. 2013).

Microorganisms persist as a biofilm on the implant. Therefore, removed implants or modular parts can be sonicated in order to detach adhering microorganisms. Indeed, sonication has been shown to be more sensitive than biopsy cultures, especially in patients with previous antibiotic therapy (Trampuz et al. 2007).

13.3.5 Treatment

During the last couple of years, considerable progress has been made in the standardisation of the management of PJI (Osmon et al. 2013; Sendi and Zimmerli 2012a; Zimmerli and Sendi 2015; Zimmerli et al. 2004). Traditionally, each PJI has been treated with removal of the device and reimplantation at a later time point (Bengston et al. 1989). Nowadays, individual surgical management according to an algorithm should be preferred (Osmon et al. 2013; Zimmerli and Sendi 2015; Zimmerli et al. 2004). There are five different curative surgical options, namely, (a) debridement and implant retention,

(b) one-stage exchange, (c) two-stage exchange with short interval (2–3 weeks), (d) two-stage exchange with long interval (8 weeks) and (e) removal of the device without replacement (Girdlestone hip and knee arthrodesis, respectively). In case of life-threatening infection, such as necrotising fasciitis, amputation may be needed. In very old and frail patients, surgical intervention can be avoided with palliative suppressive antimicrobial treatment. Lifelong suppressive antibiotic therapy may be a reasonable option to blanket symptoms of infection.

It is crucial to choose the optimal intervention from the beginning, because the functional result is worse after repetitive surgery (Sherrell et al. 2011). Thus, it is not appropriate to start with the least invasive procedure (debridement with implant retention), if the patient does not qualify according to the therapeutic algorithm (Osmon et al. 2013; Zimmerli and Sendi 2015; Zimmerli et al. 2004). Implant retention has only a high cure rate if the patient has an acute haematogenous or early postinterventional PJI (Table 13.3), good bone and soft tissue conditions and no signs of prosthetic loosening. In chronic PJI, all foreign material has to be removed, because the chronic biofilm resists antimicrobial therapy (see Section 13.2.3). In case of implant retention, one-stage replacement or two-stage exchange with a short interval, the patient needs a long-term therapy of approximately 3 month. As a rule, in patients with implant retention, an antibiotic that is active on biofilm bacteria should be used. This is rifampin in combination with a second drug against staphylococci (Baldoni et al. 2013; Furustrand Tafin et al. 2012; John et al. 2009; Trampuz et al. 2007; Widmer et al. 1990b; Zimmerli et al. 1994) and a fluoroquinolone against Gram-negative bacilli (see Section 13.2.3) (Rodriguez-Pardo et al. 2014; Widmer et al. 1991).

13.4 Internal Fixation–Associated Infections

13.4.1 Introduction

Infections associated with internal fixation devices can be classified according to their pathogenesis, namely, exogenous, via bloodstream (haematogenous) and contiguous. Exogenous infections occur either in the perioperative period or as a consequence of a penetrating event. The risk for haematogenous seeding on orthopaedic devices persists lifelong (Law and Stein 1993). However, it is clearly lower on internal fixation devices than on artificial joints (Murdoch et al. 2001). Infections can also be classified according to the time interval between surgery and clinical manifestation. Early infections are mainly caused by virulent microorganisms (e.g. *S. aureus*) and diagnosed within less than 3 weeks after implantation. Delayed infections are typically attributed to low-virulence bacteria, such as coagulase-negative staphylococci, and manifest themselves between 3 and 10 weeks. Finally, late infections occur more than 10 weeks after implantation and are either caused by haematogenous seeding or, alternatively, by recurrence of incorrectly treated early infection (McNally and Sendi 2015).

13.4.2 Microbiology

As in most types of device-associated infections, staphylococci are the most commonly isolated microorganisms in patients with internal fixation device–associated infections. The largest study reporting the spectrum of microorganisms includes 902 patients with surgical device–associated or periprosthetic infections (Lipsky et al. 2007). This study includes 125 (14%) polymicrobial and 777 monomicrobial infections. Table 13.6 summarises the frequency of microbiological isolates in 86% of patients with monomicrobial infection. Approximately three-quarters of the episodes were caused by staphylococci. The fraction of methicillin-resistant *S. aureus* has considerable variations in different countries.

13.4.3 Clinical Presentation

The clinical presentation of infections associated with internal fixation devices is multifaceted (McNally and Sendi 2015; Ochsner et al. 2007; Zimmerli and Sendi 2015). It depends on (a) the preceding trauma or possible surgical procedures, (b) the anatomic localisation, (c) the quality of bone and surrounding soft tissue, (d) the time interval between microbial inoculation (trauma, surgery) and manifestation of infection and (e) the type of microorganism. Early postoperative infection (<3 weeks) is generally characterised by erythema,

TABLE 13.6

Frequency of Microbiological Isolates in 777 Patients with Surgical Device–Associated and Periprosthetic Joint Monomicrobial Infections

Microorganism	Number	Percent
Staphylococcus aureus	338	43.5%
Coagulase-negative staphylococci	256	32.9%
Streptococcus spp.	70	9%
Enterococcus spp.	29	3.7%
Other Gram-positive bacteria	9	1.2%
Gram-negative bacilli	59	6%
Anaerobes	1	0.1%
Fungi	9	1.2%
Other organisms	6	0.7%

Source: Lipsky, B. A., J. A. Weigelt, V. Gupta, A. Killian, and M. M. Peng. 2007. Skin, soft tissue, bone, and joint infections in hospitalized patients: Epidemiology and microbiological, clinical, and economic outcomes. *Infect Control Hosp Epidemiol* 28 (11):1290–8. doi: 10.1086/520743.

local hyperthermia, protracted wound healing and a secreting wet wound. Thus, wound healing disturbance after internal fixation is highly suspicious for early infection and should be managed as such. The first step is always debridement surgery for diagnostic and therapeutic purposes. Delayed (3–10 weeks) or chronic (≥10 weeks) infections are typically attributed to low-virulence microorganisms such as coagulase-negative staphylococci. However, they may also result from inadequate treatment of early infection. If a patient with wound healing disturbance is treated with a short course of antibiotics without debridement surgery, clinical signs of suppressed early infection typically reappear at a later point of time. Delayed and chronic infection manifest with persisting pain and signs of local inflammation, such as erythema, swelling or intermittent drainage of pus (sinus tract).

13.4.4 Diagnosis

In acute internal fixation–associated infection, inflammatory parameters such as ESR, CRP and leukocyte counts are generally not helpful, because they are still increased early after surgical trauma. However, implant-associated infection should be suspected if CRP does not appropriately normalise or if its level rises again after the initial fall (Horst et al. 2015).

Plain radiographs in serial follow-ups allow monitoring bone healing, detection of non-union, implant loosening, migration of devices and bone loss around screws. Implant loosening is suspicious, but not pathognomonic for device-associated infection. It may also have mechanical reasons. Computed tomography allows diagnosis of fluid collection and inflammation around a device. In special cases, positron emission tomography combined with computerised tomography may be useful (Shemesh et al. 2015).

If infection is suspected in an imaging procedure, surgical exploration and sampling for microbiology are crucial. In order to avoid misinterpretation of contamination, biopsies should not only be cultured but also be evaluated in histopathology. Removed hardware can be cultured either directly in enrichment broth or after sonication. With the sonication technique, sensitivity is significantly improved from 57% to 90% as compared to tissue culture. In patients pretreated with antibiotics, the difference is even more important (82% vs. 38%) (Viola et al. 1997).

13.4.5 Treatment

The aims of treatment of internal fixation–associated infection are bone consolidation and control of osteomyelitis. In contrast to the management of PJI, complete elimination of the whole microbial biofilm is not absolutely required, since hardware can be removed after bone consolidation. In general, a multidisciplinary approach is needed, because treatment requires rapid and accurate microbiological diagnosis (microbiologist), appropriate orthopaedic intervention (orthopaedic surgeon), correct soft-tissue management (plastic surgeon) and optimal antimicrobial therapy (infectious disease specialist). Early postoperative infection can generally be completely healed with the combination of appropriate surgical and antibiotic treatment. As in patients with PJI, curative therapy requires an antibiotic, which is active on biofilm bacteria. This is rifampin in combination with a second drug against staphylococci (Baldoni et al. 2013; Furustrand Tafin et al. 2012; John et al. 2009; Trampuz et al. 2007; Widmer et al. 1990b; Zimmerli et al. 1994). In a controlled study, it has been shown that a combination of rifampin with a fluoroquinolone can eliminate biofilm staphylococci from the surface of an implant (Zimmerli et al. 1998). In Gram-negative device-associated infections, fluoroquinolones are able to cure acute device-associated infection (see Section 13.2.3) (Rodriguez-Pardo et al. 2014; Widmer et al. 1991). As a rule, internal fixation devices must not be removed after consolidation if the therapeutic management was curative. In contrast, if complete bacterial elimination from the device is not feasible, hardware should be removed as soon as possible, that is, after stable consolidation. In case of abundant pus formation and lack of bone consolidation, internal fixation has to be changed to external fixation. Details of the surgical management have been recently described by McNally and Sendi (2015).

13.5 Implant-Associated Vertebral Osteomyelitis

13.5.1 Introduction

The most important indications for spinal-fusion surgery are spondylosis, spinal stenosis and disk disorders. In the United States, the use of spinal surgery is even much more rapidly rising than the use of hip and knee arthroplasty (Deyo et al. 2004). In contrast, pediatric or neuromuscular scoliosis, vertebral fractures and vertebral osteomyelitis (Zimmerli 2010) are nowadays rather rare indications for spinal-fusion surgery. Surgical site infection is a feared complication after spinal-fusion surgery. In the literature, different labels are used for the same disease, namely, 'Deep surgical site infection' (Mackenzie et al. 2013; Picada et al. 2000; Pull ter Gunne and Cohen 2009; Sponseller et al. 2000; Weinstein et al. 2000), 'Instrumental spine infection' (Sierra-Hoffman et al. 2010), 'Spinal implant infection' (Kowalski et al. 2007) and 'Implant-associated vertebral osteomyelitis' (Kowalski 2015). We prefer the latter term. Since the implants are integrated in bone, deep surgical site infection after spinal instrumentation has to be considered as vertebral osteomyelitis. Two-thirds of the episodes are diagnosed during the first 30 days, and 90% are diagnosed during the first year (Mackenzie et al. 2013). Therefore, it is reasonable to classify IAVO according to the start of manifestation of infection after surgery into early (≤30 days), delayed (1–12 months) and late (>1 year), as proposed by Kowalski (2015). However, in many publications, only early-presenting (≤30 days) and late-presenting IAVO (>30 days) are differentiated (Kowalski et al. 2007; Sierra-Hoffman et al. 2010). As in other types of surgery, the presence of an implant increases the risk for deep surgical site infection (Massie et al. 1992). In the series of Pull ter Gunne and Cohen (2009), the rate of deep surgical site infection was 1.1% after discectomy, but 8.2% after fusion surgery. In a cohort of 2391 patients undergoing spinal surgery at one single centre, fusion without implant had an infection rate of 0.4%, whereas fusion with hardware had a risk of 3.2% (Weinstein et al. 2000). Furthermore, the infection rate is much higher after primary spinal arthrodesis for neuromuscular scoliosis, as compared to idiopathic scoliosis (13.1% vs. 1.2%) (Mackenzie et al. 2013).

13.5.2 Microbiology

The spectrum of microorganisms causing IAVO differs according to the interval from implantation to manifestation of infection and to the type of indication. In adults without neuromuscular scoliosis, early-presenting IAVO is caused by *S. aureus* (41%), coagulase-negative staphylococci (10%), *Enterococcus* spp. (5%), *Streptococcus* spp. (4%), Gram-negative bacilli (32%) and 7% anaerobes. The most frequent microorganisms causing late-presenting IAVO are coagulase-negative staphylococci (38%) and *Propionibacterium* spp. (41%). *S. aureus* is found in only 12% of the episodes (Kowalski 2015). This indicates that only a minority of late-onset IAVO is haematogenously acquired after the first postoperative year, since the two predominant types of microorganisms are almost never seeded via bloodstream but cause low-grade infection. Thus, obviously, the term 'late-presenting IAVO' is more appropriate than 'late-onset IAVO' since this type of infection starts in most cases by the exogenous route already during the perioperative period.

In paediatric patients and those with neuromuscular scoliosis, staphylococci are rare and bacteria from the stool microbiome predominate: *S. aureus* (6%), coagulase-negative staphylococci (4%), *Streptococcus* spp.(3%), *Enterococcus* spp. (10%), Gram-negative bacilli (43%) and anaereobes (25%), mainly *Bacteroides* spp. (13%) (Kowalski 2015). In addition, in this population, approximately half of the IAVO episodes are polymicrobial (Sponseller et al. 2000). Reasonable explanations for these microbiologic characteristics are the high frequency of faecal and urinary incontinence, as well as the high risk for peri-incisional pressure ulcers owing to the lack of sensation in patients with neuromuscular disorders (Sponseller et al. 2000).

13.5.3 Clinical Presentation

Back pain is the leading symptom in early-presenting (70%–80%) as well as in late-presenting (67%–84%) IAVO (Abbey et al. 1995; Kowalski et al. 2007; Muschik et al. 2004; Sierra-Hoffman et al. 2010). Wound drainage is more frequent in early-presenting than in late-presenting IAVO (90% vs. 31%), whereas a sinus tract is only observed in the latter type (25%–70%) (Kowalski 2015; Kowalski et al. 2007). Erythema and fever are much more frequent in early-presenting than in late-presenting IAVO (Sierra-Hoffman et al. 2010). As a rule, the clinical presentation of late-presenting IAVO is subtle, since it is caused by low-virulence microorganisms at time of implantation in most cases (Kowalski 2015).

13.5.4 Diagnosis

When early-presenting IAVO is clinically suspected (pain, fever, oozing wound), rapid debridement surgery down to the implant is needed. This procedure allows sampling of three to six diagnostic biopsies for culture and microbiological workup. In addition, it is also a prerequisite for the therapeutic management. Because *Propionibacterium* spp. is occasionally also causing early-presenting IAVO, adequate anaerobic culture is also needed in addition to aerobic culture (Collins et al. 2008). If any hardware is removed, its sonication is a good option to improve sensitivity and specificity of cultures. Sampedro et al. (2010) showed that the culture of sonicate fluid is more sensitive and more specific than tissue biopsies (91% vs. 73% and 97% vs. 93%, respectively).

Blood laboratory tests are helpful but nonspecific. In the series of Kowalski et al. (2007), CRP was 71 mg/L (interquartile range [IQR], 30–137) and ESR was 58 mm/h (IQR, 51–81) in 30 patients with early-presenting IAVO. It is useful to draw from two to three pairs of blood cultures. In Kowalski's series, blood cultures were positive in 9 of 30 patients (30%), despite the fact that they were drawn in only 21 of them (Kowalski et al. 2007).

Imaging procedures are of limited value in early-presenting IAVO. Magnetic resonance imaging (MRI) may reveal abscesses or early signs of osteomyelitis. The value of CT scans is limited if beam artefacts by the hardware are not corrected by an appropriate radiological program.

Delayed- and late-presenting IAVO are difficult to suspect in the absence of a sinus tract, since other signs and symptoms are subtle. However, whenever pain is increasing or CRP is rising without another explanation, a diagnostic workup should be started. Unfortunately, the value of inflammatory parameters in blood is limited. In the study of Collins et al. (2008), CRP was normal in 17%, ESR was normal in 45% and leukocyte count was normal even in 95% of the patients. Kowalski et al. (2007) reported a mean CRP of 39 mg/L (IQR, 6–68) and a mean ESR of 45 mm/h (IQR, 20–72) in a series of 71 patients with delayed- and late-presenting IAVO. In their series, 6 of 51 (11.8%) patients had positive blood cultures. During debridement surgery, three to six biopsies should be harvested for histology and culture. Sonication of removed hardware has an excellent sensitivity and specificity, as mentioned above (Sampedro et al. 2010).

Plain radiographs should be performed in order to look for non-union, pseudoarthrosis or implant loosening, which are all signs of late-persisting

IAVO. MRI allows the detection of signs of local inflammation, fluid collection and vertebral osteomyelitis.

13.5.5 Treatment

The goal of the therapeutic management of IAVO is a pain-free patient with a stable spine and an eradicated infection. Details of the therapeutic concepts have been recently published (Kowalski 2015; Kowalski et al. 2007). In brief, all patients with early-presenting IAVO need thorough surgical debridement and retention of the hardware. In addition, they should get a 3- to 12-month course of antibiotics, started intravenously and continued orally. If no rifampin combination regimen is used in staphylococcal IAVO, long-term suppression may be needed (Kowalski et al. 2007). However, in a recent French series, a 12-week therapy with an initial 2-week intravenous course resulted in an 88% 2-year success rate. In contrast to Kowalski et al. (2007), they used rifampin combination regimens, which are active on young biofilm bacteria (see above) (Dubee et al. 2012). If no biofilm-active antimicrobial agents are used, hardware removal should be considered after spinal fusion (Kowalski 2015).

In patients with delayed- or late-presenting IAVO, the hardware should be removed, if there is evidence of spinal fusion. These patients need a 6-week course of antibiotics, similar to patients with non–implant-associated vertebral osteomyelitis (Bernard et al. 2015; Zimmerli 2010). If there is no stable fusion in a patient with a sinus tract or a loose implant, the hardware should be replaced with a one- or two-stage exchange and a 3-month antibiotic course. If the patient has no stable fusion, but no sinus tract and no signs of implant loosening, surgical debridement and implant retention combined with a long-term antibiotic course is the best solution. In this patient group, elective implant removal is recommended after spinal fusion (Kowalski 2015).

13.6 Outlook

Table 13.7 indicates novel strategies against biofilm infections. As mentioned above, systemic antibiotics have only a limited capacity to clear implant-associated infection. Therefore, novel strategies for prevention are needed. Coating of implants with antimicrobial agents has been tested for several years. Among others, antibiotics, bactericidal peptides, disinfectants and silver coating have been evaluated (Gordon et al. 2010; Jennings et al. 2015; Jo et al. 2014; Norowski et al. 2011; Qin et al. 2015; Zhao et al. 2015). In this book,

TABLE 13.7

Novel Strategies against Biofilm Infections

- Coating of biomaterials with different types of antibiotics, bactericidal peptides, disinfectants or silver (Gordon et al. 2010; Jennings et al. 2015; Jo et al. 2014; Norowski et al. 2011; Qin et al. 2015; Zhao et al. 2015)
- Preventive vaccination against antigens that are synthesised during biofilm formation (Achermann et al. 2015; Brady et al. 2011; Flores-Mireles et al. 2014; Lam et al. 2014)
- Quorum-sensing inhibitors (Brackman and Coenye 2013; Brackman et al. 2011; Christensen et al. 2012; Solano et al. 2014)

various aspects of silver nanoparticles for antibacterial devices are presented. Unfortunately, clinical translation of antimicrobial coating of biomaterials is a cumbersome way, as a result of high hurdles of regulatory agencies.

Another novel strategy is the use of an antibiofilm vaccine for the prevention of implant-associated infection. In a rabbit osteomyelitis model, it has been shown that a vaccine containing four staphylococcal antigens, which are upregulated during biofilm formation, was significantly efficacious in clearing staphylococcal osteomyelitis when given together with vancomycin (Brady et al. 2011). In an in vitro test system, it could be shown that staphylococcal PhnD-specific antibodies efficiently blocked biofilm development and favoured biofilm engulfment by neutrophils (Lam et al. 2014). In a recent study, several *P. acnes* proteins have been identified, which are produced during a chronic biofilm-mediated infection. These proteins are potential candidates for a diagnostic test or a vaccine preventing biofilm infections caused by *P. acnes* (Achermann et al. 2015).

Since antibiotics have only limited efficacy against biofilm bacteria, a promising strategy would be the use of antimicrobial agents acting on biofilm integrity. In biofilms, bacteria use QS to coordinate gene expression according to the density of their population. From the literature, it is not very clear whether QS inhibitors synergise or antagonise the elimination of biofilms. On the one hand, QS-deficient *Pseudomonas aeruginosa* biofilms are more susceptible to tobramycin than QS-proficient *P. aeruginosa* biofilms, and the combination treatment with a QS inhibitor and tobramycin synergistically kills in vitro biofilms (Christensen et al. 2012). Furthermore, it has been shown that QS inhibitors increase the susceptibility of bacterial biofilms to different antibiotics in vitro and in vivo (Brackman and Coenye 2013; Brackman et al. 2011). On the other hand, there is clear evidence that QS activates the biofilm dispersion process. The fact that QS inhibitors impair biofilm disassembly indicates that they rather antagonise biofilm therapy (Solano et al. 2014). Taken together, the role of QS inhibitors in biofilm infections is still not clear and therefore has not yet been tested in humans.

References

Abbey, D. M., D. M. Turner, J. S. Warson, T. C. Wirt, and R. D. Scalley. 1995. Treatment of postoperative wound infections following spinal fusion with instrumentation. *J Spinal Disord* 8 (4):278–83.

Achermann, Y., B. Tran, M. Kang, J. M. Harro, and M. E. Shirtliff. 2015. Immunoproteomic identification of in vivo-produced *Propionibacterium acnes* proteins in a rabbit biofilm infection model. *Clin Vaccine Immunol* 22 (5):467–76. doi: 10.1128/CVI.00760-14.

Aggarwal, V. K., C. Higuera, G. Deirmengian, J. Parvizi, and M. S. Austin. 2013. Swab cultures are not as effective as tissue cultures for diagnosis of periprosthetic joint infection. *Clin Orthop Relat Res* 471 (10):3196–203. doi: 10.1007/s11999-013-2974-y.

Anderl, J. N., J. Zahller, F. Roe, and P. S. Stewart. 2003. Role of nutrient limitation and stationary-phase existence in *Klebsiella pneumoniae* biofilm resistance to ampicillin and ciprofloxacin. *Antimicrob Agents Chemother* 47 (4):1251–6.

Anderson, J. M., and A. K. McNally. 2011. Biocompatibility of implants: Lymphocyte/macrophage interactions. *Semin Immunopathol* 33 (3):221–33. doi: 10.1007/s00281-011-0244-1.

Baldoni, D., U. Furustrand Tafin, S. Aeppli, E. Angevaare, A. Oliva, M. Haschke, W. Zimmerli, and A. Trampuz. 2013. Activity of dalbavancin, alone and in combination with rifampicin, against meticillin-resistant *Staphylococcus aureus* in a foreign-body infection model. *Int J Antimicrob Agents* 42 (3):220–5. doi: 10.1016/j.ijantimicag.2013.05.019.

Bedair, H., N. Ting, C. Jacovides, A. Saxena, M. Moric, J. Parvizi, and C. J. Della Valle. 2011. The Mark Coventry Award: Diagnosis of early postoperative TKA infection using synovial fluid analysis. *Clin Orthop Relat Res* 469 (1):34–40. doi: 10.1007/s11999-010-1433-2.

Bengston, S., K. Knutson, and L. Lidgren. 1989. Treatment of infected knee arthroplasty. *Clin Orthop Relat Res* (245):173–8.

Berbari, E. F., C. Marculescu, I. Sia, B. D. Lahr, A. D. Hanssen, J. M. Steckelberg, R. Gullerud, and D. R. Osmon. 2007. Culture-negative prosthetic joint infection. *Clin Infect Dis* 45 (9):1113–9. doi: 10.1086/522184.

Berbari, E., T. Mabry, G. Tsaras, M. Spangehl, P. J. Erwin, M. H. Murad, J. Steckelberg, and D. Osmon. 2010. Inflammatory blood laboratory levels as markers of prosthetic joint infection: A systematic review and meta-analysis. *J Bone Joint Surg Am* 92 (11):2102–9. doi: 10.2106/JBJS.I.01199.

Bernard, L., A. Dinh, I. Ghout, D. Simo, V. Zeller, B. Issartel, V. Le Moing, N. Belmatoug, P. Lesprit, J. P. Bru, A. Therby, D. Bouhour, E. Denes, A. Debard, C. Chirouze, K. Fevre, M. Dupon, P. Aegerter, D. Mulleman, and group Duration of Treatment for Spondylodiscitis study. 2015. Antibiotic treatment for 6 weeks versus 12 weeks in patients with pyogenic vertebral osteomyelitis: An open-label, non-inferiority, randomised, controlled trial. *Lancet* 385 (9971):875–82. doi: 10.1016/S0140-6736(14)61233-2.

Bernard, L., P. Vaudaux, E. Huggler, R. Stern, C. Frehel, P. Francois, D. Lew, and P. Hoffmeyer. 2007. Inactivation of a subpopulation of human neutrophils by exposure to ultrahigh-molecular-weight polyethylene wear debris. *FEMS Immunol Med Microbiol* 49 (3):425–32. doi: 10.1111/j.1574-695X.2007.00222.x.

Bernier, S. P., D. Lebeaux, A. S. DeFrancesco, A. Valomon, G. Soubigou, J. Y. Coppee, J. M. Ghigo, and C. Beloin. 2013. Starvation, together with the SOS response, mediates high biofilm-specific tolerance to the fluoroquinolone ofloxacin. *PLoS Genet* 9 (1):e1003144. doi: 10.1371/journal.pgen.1003144.

Bjarnsholt, T., and M. Givskov. 2007. The role of quorum sensing in the pathogenicity of the cunning aggressor *Pseudomonas aeruginosa*. *Anal Bioanal Chem* 387 (2):409–14. doi: 10.1007/s00216-006-0774-x.

Brackman, G., and T. Coenye. 2013. Comment on: Synergistic antibacterial efficacy of early combination treatment with tobramycin and quorum-sensing inhibitors against *Pseudomonas aeruginosa* in an intraperitoneal foreign-body infection mouse model. *J Antimicrob Chemother* 68 (9):2176–7. doi: 10.1093/jac/dkt151.

Brackman, G., P. Cos, L. Maes, H. J. Nelis, and T. Coenye. 2011. Quorum sensing inhibitors increase the susceptibility of bacterial biofilms to antibiotics in vitro and in vivo. *Antimicrob Agents Chemother* 55 (6):2655–61. doi: 10.1128/AAC.00045-11.

Brady, R. A., G. A. O'May, J. G. Leid, M. L. Prior, J. W. Costerton, and M. E. Shirtliff. 2011. Resolution of *Staphylococcus aureus* biofilm infection using vaccination and antibiotic treatment. *Infect Immun* 79 (4):1797–803. doi: 10.1128/IAI.00451-10.

Brandt, C. M., W. W. Sistrunk, M. C. Duffy, A. D. Hanssen, J. M. Steckelberg, D. M. Ilstrup, and D. R. Osmon. 1997. *Staphylococcus aureus* prosthetic joint infection treated with debridement and prosthesis retention. *Clin Infect Dis* 24 (5):914–9.

Brennan, S. A., C. Ni Fhoghlu, B. M. Devitt, F. J. O'Mahony, D. Brabazon, and A. Walsh. 2015. Silver nanoparticles and their orthopaedic applications. *Bone Joint J* 97-B (5):582–9. doi: 10.1302/0301-620X.97B5.33336.

Charnley, J. 1961. Arthroplasty of the hip: A new operation. *Lancet* 1 (7187):1129–32.

Christensen, L. D., M. van Gennip, T. H. Jakobsen, M. Alhede, H. P. Hougen, N. Hoiby, T. Bjarnsholt, and M. Givskov. 2012. Synergistic antibacterial efficacy of early combination treatment with tobramycin and quorum-sensing inhibitors against *Pseudomonas aeruginosa* in an intraperitoneal foreign-body infection mouse model. *J Antimicrob Chemother* 67 (5):1198–206. doi: 10.1093/jac/dks002.

Collins, I., J. Wilson-MacDonald, G. Chami, W. Burgoyne, P. Vineyakam, T. Berendt, and J. Fairbank. 2008. The diagnosis and management of infection following instrumented spinal fusion. *Eur Spine J* 17 (3):445–50. doi: 10.1007/s00586-007-0559-8.

Conlon, B. P., S. E. Rowe, and K. Lewis. 2015. Persister cells in biofilm associated infections. *Adv Exp Med Biol* 831:1–9. doi: 10.1007/978-3-319-09782-4_1.

Costerton, J. W., Z. Lewandowski, D. E. Caldwell, D. R. Korber, and H. M. Lappin-Scott. 1995. Microbial biofilms. *Annu Rev Microbiol* 49:711–45. doi: 10.1146/annurev.mi.49.100195.003431.

Costerton, J. W., P. S. Stewart, and E. P. Greenberg. 1999. Bacterial biofilms: A common cause of persistent infections. *Science* 284 (5418):1318–22.

Darouiche, R. O. 2004. Treatment of infections associated with surgical implants. *N Engl J Med* 350 (14):1422–9. doi: 10.1056/NEJMra035415.

Deirmengian, C., K. Kardos, P. Kilmartin, A. Cameron, K. Schiller, and J. Parvizi. 2014. Diagnosing periprosthetic joint infection: Has the era of the biomarker arrived? *Clin Orthop Relat Res* 472 (11):3254–62. doi: 10.1007/s11999-014-3543-8.

Deirmengian, C., K. Kardos, P. Kilmartin, A. Cameron, K. Schiller and R.E. Booth, Jr. 2015. The Alpha-defensin test for periprosthetic joint infection outperforms the leukocyte esterase test strip. *Clin Orthop Relat Res* 473 (7):198–203.

Deyo, R. A., A. Nachemson, and S. K. Mirza. 2004. Spinal-fusion surgery – The case for restraint. *N Engl J Med* 350 (7):722–6. doi: 10.1056/NEJMsb031771.

Dubee, V., T. Lenoir, V. Leflon-Guibout, C. Briere-Bellier, P. Guigui, and B. Fantin. 2012. Three-month antibiotic therapy for early-onset postoperative spinal implant infections. *Clin Infect Dis* 55 (11):1481–7. doi: 10.1093/cid/cis769.

El-Azizi, M. A., S. E. Starks, and N. Khardori. 2004. Interactions of *Candida albicans* with other *Candida* spp. and bacteria in the biofilms. *J Appl Microbiol* 96 (5):1067–73.

Elek, S. D., and P. E. Conen. 1957. The virulence of *Staphylococcus pyogenes* for man; a study of the problems of wound infection. *Br J Exp Pathol* 38 (6):573–86.

Flores-Mireles, A. L., J. S. Pinkner, M. G. Caparon, and S. J. Hultgren. 2014. EbpA vaccine antibodies block binding of *Enterococcus faecalis* to fibrinogen to prevent catheter-associated bladder infection in mice. *Sci Transl Med* 6 (254):254ra127. doi: 10.1126/scitranslmed.3009384.

Font-Vizcarra, L., S. Garcia, J. C. Martinez-Pastor, J. M. Sierra, and A. Soriano. 2010. Blood culture flasks for culturing synovial fluid in prosthetic joint infections. *Clin Orthop Relat Res* 468 (8):2238–43. doi: 10.1007/s11999-010-1254-3.

Fuqua, C., M. R. Parsek, and E. P. Greenberg. 2001. Regulation of gene expression by cell-to-cell communication: Acyl-homoserine lactone quorum sensing. *Annu Rev Genet* 35:439–68. doi: 10.1146/annurev.genet.35.102401.09091335/1/439 [pii].

Furustrand Tafin, U., S. Corvec, B. Betrisey, W. Zimmerli, and A. Trampuz. 2012. Role of rifampin against *Propionibacterium acnes* biofilm in vitro and in an experimental foreign-body infection model. *Antimicrob Agents Chemother* 56 (4):1885–91. doi: 10.1128/AAC.05552-11.

Gallo, J., M. Kolar, M. Dendis, Y. Loveckova, P. Sauer, J. Zapletalova, and D. Koukalova. 2008. Culture and PCR analysis of joint fluid in the diagnosis of prosthetic joint infection. *New Microbiol* 31 (1):97–104.

Gibson, A. 1954. Arthroplasty of the hip joint. *Can Med Assoc J* 71 (4):353–6.

Giulieri, S. G., P. Graber, P. E. Ochsner, and W. Zimmerli. 2004. Management of infection associated with total hip arthroplasty according to a treatment algorithm. *Infection* 32 (4):222–8. doi: 10.1007/s15010-004-4020-1.

Gordon, O., T. Vig Slenters, P. S. Brunetto, A. E. Villaruz, D. E. Sturdevant, M. Otto, R. Landmann, and K. M. Fromm. 2010. Silver coordination polymers for prevention of implant infection: Thiol interaction, impact on respiratory chain enzymes, and hydroxyl radical induction. *Antimicrob Agents Chemother* 54 (10):4208–18. doi: 10.1128/AAC.01830-09.

Ha, K. Y., Y. G. Chung, and S. J. Ryoo. 2005. Adherence and biofilm formation of *Staphylococcus epidermidis* and *Mycobacterium tuberculosis* on various spinal implants. *Spine (Phila Pa 1976)* 30 (1):38–43.

Hernigou, P. 2014. Smith-Petersen and early development of hip arthroplasty. *Int Orthop* 38 (1):193–8. doi: 10.1007/s00264-013-2080-5.

Herrmann, M., P. E. Vaudaux, D. Pittet, R. Auckenthaler, P. D. Lew, F. Schumacher-Perdreau, G. Peters, and F. A. Waldvogel. 1988. Fibronectin, fibrinogen, and laminin act as mediators of adherence of clinical staphylococcal isolates to foreign material. *J Infect Dis* 158 (4):693–701.

Hirschfeld, J. 2014. Dynamic interactions of neutrophils and biofilms. *J Oral Microbiol* 6:26102. doi: 10.3402/jom.v6.26102.

Hoiby, N., O. Ciofu, H. K. Johansen, Z. J. Song, C. Moser, P. O. Jensen, S. Molin, M. Givskov, T. Tolker-Nielsen, and T. Bjarnsholt. 2011. The clinical impact of bacterial biofilms. *Int J Oral Sci* 3 (2):55–65. doi: 10.4248/IJOS11026.

Horst, K., F. Hildebrand, R. Pfeifer, K. Koppen, P. Lichte, H. C. Pape, and T. Dienstknecht. 2015. Plate osteosynthesis versus hemiarthroplasty in proximal humerus fractures – Does routine screening of systemic inflammatory biomarkers makes sense? *Eur J Med Res* 20:5. doi: 10.1186/s40001-014-0079-z.

Hudetz, D., S. Ursic Hudetz, L. G. Harris, R. Luginbuhl, N. F. Friederich, and R. Landmann. 2008. Weak effect of metal type and ica genes on staphylococcal infection of titanium and stainless steel implants. *Clin Microbiol Infect* 14 (12):1135–45. doi: 10.1111/j.1469-0691.2008.02096.x.

Jennings, J. A., D. P. Carpenter, K. S. Troxel, K. E. Beenken, M. S. Smeltzer, H. S. Courtney, and W. O. Haggard. 2015. Novel antibiotic-loaded point-of-care implant coating inhibits biofilm. *Clin Orthop Relat Res* 473 (7):2270–82. doi: 10.1007/s11999-014-4130-8.

Jo, Y. K., J. H. Seo, B. H. Choi, B. J. Kim, H. H. Shin, B. H. Hwang, and H. J. Cha. 2014. Surface-independent antibacterial coating using silver nanoparticle-generating engineered mussel glue. *ACS Appl Mater Interfaces* 6 (22):20242–53. doi: 10.1021/am505784k.

John, A. K., D. Baldoni, M. Haschke, K. Rentsch, P. Schaerli, W. Zimmerli, and A. Trampuz. 2009. Efficacy of daptomycin in implant-associated infection due to methicillin-resistant *Staphylococcus aureus*: Importance of combination with rifampin. *Antimicrob Agents Chemother* 53 (7):2719–24. doi: 10.1128/AAC.00047-09.

Kowalski, T. J., E. F. Berbari, P. M. Huddleston, J. M. Steckelberg, J. N. Mandrekar, and D. R. Osmon. 2007. The management and outcome of spinal implant infections: Contemporary retrospective cohort study. *Clin Infect Dis* 44 (7):913–20. doi: 10.1086/512194.

Kowalski, T. J. Implant-associated vertebral osteomyelitis. In *Bone and Joint Infections. From Microbiology to Diagnostics and Treatment,* edited by W. Zimmerli, 325–45. West Sussex: John Wiley & Sons, Inc., 2015.

Laffer, R. R., P. Graber, P. E. Ochsner, and W. Zimmerli. 2006. Outcome of prosthetic knee-associated infection: Evaluation of 40 consecutive episodes at a single centre. *Clin Microbiol Infect* 12 (5):433–9. doi: 10.1111/j.1469-0691.2006.01378.x.

Lam, H., A. Kesselly, S. Stegalkina, H. Kleanthous, and J. A. Yethon. 2014. Antibodies to PhnD inhibit staphylococcal biofilms. *Infect Immun* 82 (9):3764–74. doi: 10.1128/IAI.02168-14.

Law, M. D. Jr., and R. E. Stein. 1993. Late infection in healed fractures after open reduction and internal fixation. *Orthop Rev* 22 (5):545–52.

Lindeque, B., Z. Hartman, A. Noshchenko, and M. Cruse. 2014. Infection after primary total hip arthroplasty. *Orthopedics* 37 (4):257–65. doi: 10.3928/01477447-20140401-08.

Lipsky, B. A., J. A. Weigelt, V. Gupta, A. Killian, and M. M. Peng. 2007. Skin, soft tissue, bone, and joint infections in hospitalized patients: Epidemiology and microbiological, clinical, and economic outcomes. *Infect Control Hosp Epidemiol* 28 (11):1290–8. doi: 10.1086/520743.

Lopes, J. D., M. dos Reis, and R. R. Brentani. 1985. Presence of laminin receptors in *Staphylococcus aureus*. *Science* 229 (4710):275–7.

Mackenzie, W. G., H. Matsumoto, B. A. Williams, J. Corona, C. Lee, S. R. Cody, L. Covington, L. Saiman, J. M. Flynn, D. L. Skaggs, D. P. Roye, Jr., and M. G. Vitale. 2013. Surgical site infection following spinal instrumentation for scoliosis: A multicenter analysis of rates, risk factors, and pathogens. *J Bone Joint Surg Am* 95 (9):800–6, S1-2. doi: 10.2106/JBJS.L.00010.

Maderazo, E. G., S. Judson, and H. Pasternak. 1988. Late infections of total joint prostheses: A review and recommendations for prevention. *Clin Orthop Relat Res* (229):131–42.

Massie, J. B., J. G. Heller, J. J. Abitbol, D. McPherson, and S. R. Garfin. 1992. Postoperative posterior spinal wound infections. *Clin Orthop Relat Res* (284):99–108.

Matar, W. Y., S. M. Jafari, C. Restrepo, M. Austin, J. J. Purtill, and J. Parvizi. 2010. Preventing infection in total joint arthroplasty. *J Bone Joint Surg Am* 92 Suppl 2:36–46. doi: 10.2106/JBJS.J.01046.

McLaughlin, H. L. 1947. An adjustable internal fixation element for the hip. *Am J Surg* 73 (2):150–61.

McNally, M., and P. Sendi. Implant-associated osteomyelitis of long bones. In *Bone and Joint Infections: From Microbiology to Diagnostics and Treatment*, edited by W. Zimmerli, 303–23. West Sussex: John Wiley & Sons, Inc., 2015.

Murdoch, D. R., S. A. Roberts, V. G. Fowler, Jr., M. A. Shah, S. L. Taylor, A. J. Morris, and G. R. Corey. 2001. Infection of orthopedic prostheses after *Staphylococcus aureus* bacteremia. *Clin Infect Dis* 32 (4):647–9. doi: 10.1086/318704.

Muschik, M., W. Luck, and D. Schlenzka. 2004. Implant removal for late-developing infection after instrumented posterior spinal fusion for scoliosis: Reinstrumentation reduces loss of correction. A retrospective analysis of 45 cases. *Eur Spine J* 13 (7):645–51. doi: 10.1007/s00586-004-0694-4.

Norowski, P. A., H. S. Courtney, J. Babu, W. O. Haggard, and J. D. Bumgardner. 2011. Chitosan coatings deliver antimicrobials from titanium implants: A preliminary study. *Implant Dent* 20 (1):56–67. doi: 10.1097/ID.0b013e3182087ac4.

Ochsner, P., M. Sirkin, and A. Trampuz. Acute infections. In *AOPrinciples of Fracture Management (vol 1)*, edited by T. P. Rüedi, R. E. Buckley, and C. G. Moran, 520–40. Stuttgart and New York: Thieme, 2007.

Osmon, D. R., E. F. Berbari, A. R. Berendt, D. Lew, W. Zimmerli, J. M. Steckelberg, N. Rao, A. Hanssen, W. R. Wilson, and America Infectious Diseases Society of America. 2013. Diagnosis and management of prosthetic joint infection: Clinical practice guidelines by the Infectious Diseases Society of America. *Clin Infect Dis* 56 (1):e1–25. doi: 10.1093/cid/cis803.

Peel, T. N., A. C. Cheng, K. L. Buising, and P. F. Choong. 2012. Microbiological aetiology, epidemiology, and clinical profile of prosthetic joint infections: Are current antibiotic prophylaxis guidelines effective? *Antimicrob Agents Chemother* 56 (5):2386–91. doi: 10.1128/AAC.06246-11.

Picada, R., R. B. Winter, J. E. Lonstein, F. Denis, M. R. Pinto, M. D. Smith, and J. H. Perra. 2000. Postoperative deep wound infection in adults after posterior lumbosacral spine fusion with instrumentation: Incidence and management. *J Spinal Disord* 13 (1):42–5.

Pierce, G. E. 2005. *Pseudomonas aeruginosa, Candida albicans*, and device-related nosocomial infections: Implications, trends, and potential approaches for control. *J Ind Microbiol Biotechnol* 32 (7):309–18.

Portillo, M. E., M. Salvado, L. Sorli, A. Alier, S. Martinez, A. Trampuz, J. Gomez, L. Puig, and J. P. Horcajada. 2012. Multiplex PCR of sonication fluid accurately differentiates between prosthetic joint infection and aseptic failure. *J Infect* 65 (6):541–8. doi: 10.1016/j.jinf.2012.08.018.

Pull ter Gunne, A. F., and D. B. Cohen. 2009. Incidence, prevalence, and analysis of risk factors for surgical site infection following adult spinal surgery. *Spine (Phila Pa 1976)* 34 (13):1422–8. doi: 10.1097/BRS.0b013e3181a03013.

Qin, H., H. Cao, Y. Zhao, G. Jin, M. Cheng, J. Wang, Y. Jiang, Z. An, X. Zhang, and X. Liu. 2015. Antimicrobial and osteogenic properties of silver-ion-implanted stainless steel. *ACS Appl Mater Interfaces* 7 (20):10785–94. doi: 10.1021/acsami.5b01310.

Rodriguez-Pardo, D., C. Pigrau, J. Lora-Tamayo, A. Soriano, M. D. del Toro, J. Cobo, J. Palomino, G. Euba, M. Riera, M. Sanchez-Somolinos, N. Benito, M. Fernandez-Sampedro, L. Sorli, L. Guio, J. A. Iribarren, J. M. Baraia-Etxaburu, A. Ramos, A. Bahamonde, X. Flores-Sanchez, P. S. Corona, J. Ariza, and Reipi Group for the Study of Prosthetic Infection. 2014. Gram-negative prosthetic joint infection: Outcome of a debridement, antibiotics and implant retention approach. A large multicentre study. *Clin Microbiol Infect* 20 (11):O911–9. doi: 10.1111/1469-0691.12649.

Roles, N. C. 1971. Infection in total prosthetic replacement of the hip and knee joints. *Proc R Soc Med* 64 (6):636–8.

Ryu, S. Y., and R. Patel. Microbiology of bone and joint infections. In *Bone and Joint Infections: From Microbiology to Diagnostics and Treatment*, edited by W. Zimmerli. West Sussex: John Wiley & Sons, Inc., 325–45, 2015.

Sampedro, M. F., P. M. Huddleston, K. E. Piper, M. J. Karau, M. B. Dekutoski, M. J. Yaszemski, B. L. Currier, J. N. Mandrekar, D. R. Osmon, A. McDowell, S. Patrick, J. M. Steckelberg, and R. Patel. 2010. A biofilm approach to detect bacteria on removed spinal implants. *Spine (Phila Pa 1976)* 35 (12):1218–24. doi: 10.1097/BRS.0b013e3181c3b2f3.

Samra, Y., Y. Shaked, and M. K. Maier. 1986. Nontyphoid salmonellosis in patients with total hip replacement: Report of four cases and review of the literature. *Rev Infect Dis* 8 (6):978–83.

Schinsky, M. F., C. J. Della Valle, S. M. Sporer, and W. G. Paprosky. 2008. Perioperative testing for joint infection in patients undergoing revision total hip arthroplasty. *J Bone Joint Surg Am* 90 (9):1869–75. doi: 10.2106/JBJS.G.01255.

Sendi, P., F. Banderet, P. Graber, and W. Zimmerli. 2011a. Clinical comparison between exogenous and haematogenous periprosthetic joint infections caused by *Staphylococcus aureus*. *Clin Microbiol Infect* 17 (7):1098–100. doi: 10.1111/j.1469-0691.2011.03510.x.

Sendi, P., F. Banderet, P. Graber, and W. Zimmerli. 2011b. Periprosthetic joint infection following *Staphylococcus aureus* bacteremia. *J Infect* 63 (1):17–22. doi: 10.1016/j.jinf.2011.05.005.

Sendi, P., and W. Zimmerli. 2012a. Antimicrobial treatment concepts for orthopaedic device-related infection. *Clin Microbiol Infect* 18 (12):1176–84. doi: 10.1111/1469-0691.12003.

Sendi, P., and W. Zimmerli. 2012b. Diagnosis of periprosthetic joint infections in clinical practice. *Int J Artif Organs* 35 (10):913–22. doi: 10.5301/ijao.5000150.

Sethi, P. M., J. R. Sabetta, S. J. Stuek, S. V. Horine, K. B. Vadasdi, R. T. Greene, J. G. Cunningham, and S. R. Miller. 2015. Presence of *Propionibacterium acnes* in primary shoulder arthroscopy: Results of aspiration and tissue cultures. *J Shoulder Elbow Surg* 24 (5):796–803. doi: 10.1016/j.jse.2014.09.042.

Shemesh, S., Y. Kosashvili, D. Groshar, H. Bernstine, E. Sidon, N. Cohen, T. Luria, and S. Velkes. 2015. The value of 18-FDG PET/CT in the diagnosis and management of implant-related infections of the tibia: A case series. *Injury* 46 (7):1377–82. doi: 10.1016/j.injury.2015.03.002.

Sherrell, J. C., T. K. Fehring, S. Odum, E. Hansen, B. Zmistowski, A. Dennos, N. Kalore, and Consortium Periprosthetic Infection. 2011. The Chitranjan Ranawat Award: Fate of two-stage reimplantation after failed irrigation and debridement for periprosthetic knee infection. *Clin Orthop Relat Res* 469 (1):18–25. doi: 10.1007/s11999-010-1434-1.

Sierra-Hoffman, M., C. Jinadatha, J. L. Carpenter, and M. Rahm. 2010. Postoperative instrumented spine infections: A retrospective review. *South Med J* 103 (1):25–30. doi: 10.1097/SMJ.0b013e3181c4e00b.

Singh, J. A., J. W. Sperling, C. Schleck, W. S. Harmsen, and R. H. Cofield. 2012. Periprosthetic infections after total shoulder arthroplasty: A 33-year perspective. *J Shoulder Elbow Surg* 21 (11):1534–41. doi: 10.1016/j.jse.2012.01.006.

Smith-Petersen, M. N. 1948. Evolution of mould arthroplasty of the hip joint. *J Bone Joint Surg Br* 30B (1):59–75.

Solano, C., M. Echeverz, and I. Lasa. 2014. Biofilm dispersion and quorum sensing. *Curr Opin Microbiol* 18:96–104. doi: 10.1016/j.mib.2014.02.008.

Sponseller, P. D., D. M. LaPorte, M. W. Hungerford, K. Eck, K. H. Bridwell, and L. G. Lenke. 2000. Deep wound infections after neuromuscular scoliosis surgery: A multicenter study of risk factors and treatment outcomes. *Spine (Phila Pa 1976)* 25 (19):2461–6.

Stefansdottir, A., D. Johansson, K. Knutson, L. Lidgren, and O. Robertsson. 2009. Microbiology of the infected knee arthroplasty: Report from the Swedish Knee Arthroplasty Register on 426 surgically revised cases. *Scand J Infect Dis* 41 (11–12):831–40. doi: 10.3109/00365540903186207.

Stewart, P. S., and J. W. Costerton. 2001. Antibiotic resistance of bacteria in biofilms. *Lancet* 358 (9276):135–8.

Stewart, P. S., W. M. Davison, and J. N. Steenbergen. 2009. Daptomycin rapidly penetrates a *Staphylococcus epidermidis* biofilm. *Antimicrob Agents Chemother* 53 (8):3505–7. doi: 10.1128/AAC.01728-08.

Tande, A. M., P. R. Palraj, D. R. Osmon, E. F. Berbari, L. M. Baddour, C. M. Lohse, J. M. Steckelberg, W. R. Wilson, and M. R. Sohail. 2016. Clinical presentation, risk factors, and outcomes of hematogenous prosthetic joint infection in patients with Staphylococcus aureus bacteremia. *Am J Med* 129 (2):221.e11–221.e20.

Trampuz, A., A. D. Hanssen, D. R. Osmon, J. Mandrekar, J. M. Steckelberg, and R. Patel. 2004. Synovial fluid leukocyte count and differential for the diagnosis of prosthetic knee infection. *Am J Med* 117 (8):556–62. doi: 10.1016/j.amjmed.2004.06.022.

Trampuz, A., K. E. Piper, M. J. Jacobson, A. D. Hanssen, K. K. Unni, D. R. Osmon, J. N. Mandrekar, F. R. Cockerill, J. M. Steckelberg, J. F. Greenleaf, and R. Patel. 2007. Sonication of removed hip and knee prostheses for diagnosis of infection. *N Engl J Med* 357 (7):654–63. doi: 10.1056/NEJMoa061588.

Tuan, R. S., F. Y. Lee, Y. Konttinen, J. M. Wilkinson, R. L. Smith, and Group Implant Wear Symposium Biologic Work. 2008. What are the local and systemic biologic reactions and mediators to wear debris, and what host factors determine or modulate the biologic response to wear particles? *J Am Acad Orthop Surg* 16 Suppl 1:S42–8.

Vaudaux, P. E., G. Zulian, E. Huggler, and F. A. Waldvogel. 1985. Attachment of *Staphylococcus aureus* to polymethylmethacrylate increases its resistance to phagocytosis in foreign body infection. *Infect Immun* 50 (2):472–7.

Verhoef, J. 1991. The phagocytic process and the role of complement in host defense. *J Chemother* 3 Suppl 1:93–7.

Viola, R. W., H. A. King, S. M. Adler, and C. B. Wilson. 1997. Delayed infection after elective spinal instrumentation and fusion. A retrospective analysis of eight cases. *Spine (Phila Pa 1976)* 22 (20):2444–50; discussion 2450–1.

Weinstein, M. A., J. P. McCabe, and F. P. Cammisa, Jr. 2000. Postoperative spinal wound infection: A review of 2,391 consecutive index procedures. *J Spinal Disord* 13 (5):422–6.

Werner, E., F. Roe, A. Bugnicourt, M. J. Franklin, A. Heydorn, S. Molin, B. Pitts, and P. S. Stewart. 2004. Stratified growth in *Pseudomonas aeruginosa* biofilms. *Appl Environ Microbiol* 70 (10):6188–96. doi: 10.1128/AEM.70.10.6188-6196.2004.

Widmer, A. F., V. E. Colombo, A. Gachter, G. Thiel, and W. Zimmerli. 1990a. Salmonella infection in total hip replacement: Tests to predict the outcome of antimicrobial therapy. *Scand J Infect Dis* 22 (5):611–8.

Widmer, A. F., R. Frei, Z. Rajacic, and W. Zimmerli. 1990b. Correlation between in vivo and in vitro efficacy of antimicrobial agents against foreign body infections. *J Infect Dis* 162 (1):96–102.

Widmer, A. F., A. Wiestner, R. Frei, and W. Zimmerli. 1991. Killing of nongrowing and adherent *Escherichia coli* determines drug efficacy in device-related infections. *Antimicrob Agents Chemother* 35 (4):741–6.

Williams, D. F. 2009. On the nature of biomaterials. *Biomaterials* 30 (30):5897–909. doi: 10.1016/j.biomaterials.2009.07.027.

Williams, D. F. 2015. Regulatory biocompatibility requirements for biomaterials used in regenerative medicine. *J Mater Sci Mater Med* 26 (2):89. doi: 10.1007s10856-015-5421-7.

Worthington, T., D. Dunlop, A. Casey, R. Lambert, J. Luscombe, and T. Elliott. 2010. Serum procalcitonin, interleukin-6, soluble intercellular adhesin molecule-1 and IgG to short-chain exocellular lipoteichoic acid as predictors of infection in total joint prosthesis revision. *Br J Biomed Sci* 67 (2):71–6.

Wright, D. G., and J. I. Gallin. 1979. Secretory responses of human neutrophils: Exocytosis of specific (secondary) granules by human neutrophils during adherence in vitro and during exudation in vivo. *J Immunol* 123 (1):285–94.

Zappe, B., S. Graf, P. E. Ochsner, W. Zimmerli, and P. Sendi. 2008. *Propionibacterium* spp. in prosthetic joint infections: A diagnostic challenge. *Arch Orthop Trauma Surg* 128 (10):1039–46. doi: 10.1007/s00402-007-0454-0.

Zhao, G., H. Zhong, M. Zhang, and Y. Hong. 2015. Effects of antimicrobial peptides on *Staphylococcus aureus* growth and biofilm formation in vitro following isolation from implant-associated infections. *Int J Clin Exp Med* 8 (1):1546–51.

Zimmerli, W. 2010. Clinical practice. Vertebral osteomyelitis. *N Engl J Med* 362 (11):1022–9. doi: 10.1056/NEJMcp0910753.

Zimmerli, W. Periprosthetic joint infection: General aspects. In *Bone and Joint Infections. From Microbiology to Diagnostics and Treatments*, edited by W. Zimmerli, 113–29. West Sussex: John Wiley & Sons, Inc., 2015.

Zimmerli, W., R. Frei, A. F. Widmer, and Z. Rajacic. 1994. Microbiological tests to predict treatment outcome in experimental device-related infections due to *Staphylococcus aureus*. *J Antimicrob Chemother* 33 (5):959–67.

Zimmerli, W., P. D. Lew, and F. A. Waldvogel. 1984. Pathogenesis of foreign body infection. Evidence for a local granulocyte defect. *J Clin Invest* 73 (4):1191–200. doi: 10.1172/JCI111305.

Zimmerli, W., and C. Moser. 2012. Pathogenesis and treatment concepts of orthopaedic biofilm infections. *FEMS Immunol Med Microbiol* 65 (2):158–68. doi: 10.1111/j.1574-695X.2012.00938.x.

Zimmerli, W., and P. Sendi. 2011. Pathogenesis of implant-associated infection: The role of the host. *Semin Immunopathol* 33 (3):295–306. doi: 10.1007/s00281-011-0275-7.

Zimmerli, W., and P. Sendi. Orthopedic implant-associated infections. In *Mandell, Douglas, and Bennett's Principles and Practice of Infectious Diseases*, edited by J. E. Bennett, R. Dolin, and M. J. Blaser, 1328–40. Philadelphia: Elsevier Saunders, 2015.

Zimmerli, W., A. Trampuz, and P. E. Ochsner. 2004. Prosthetic-joint infections. *N Engl J Med* 351 (16):1645–54. doi: 10.1056/NEJMra040181.

Zimmerli, W., F. A. Waldvogel, P. Vaudaux, and U. E. Nydegger. 1982. Pathogenesis of foreign body infection: Description and characteristics of an animal model. *J Infect Dis* 146 (4):487–97.

Zimmerli, W., A. F. Widmer, M. Blatter, R. Frei, and P. E. Ochsner. 1998. Role of rifampin for treatment of orthopedic implant-related staphylococcal infections: A randomized controlled trial. Foreign-Body Infection (FBI) Study Group. *JAMA* 279 (19):1537–41.

Zimmerli, W., O. Zak, and K. Vosbeck. 1985. Experimental hematogenous infection of subcutaneously implanted foreign bodies. *Scand J Infect Dis* 17 (3):303–10.

Zimmerli, W., A. Zarth, A. Gratwohl, and B. Speck. 1991. Neutrophil function and pyogenic infections in bone marrow transplant recipients. *Blood* 77 (2):393–9.

14

Dental Implant Infection: Typical Causes and Control

Shichong Qiao and Yingxin Gu

CONTENTS

14.1 Introduction

Dental implant treatment was introduced in the 1960s; over the years, with the development of material and technology, implants made of titanium and its alloys have been documented to have successful and predictable outcomes of osseointegration (Figure 14.1) (Buser et al. 1997; Lekholm et al. 2006; Pikner et al. 2009). Dental implants with many more advantages over traditional prostheses are becoming an overwhelmingly preferred form of treatment in dentistry. Especially in the most recent two decades, oral rehabilitation with dental implants has become a routine treatment with high survival and success rates, which provide a contemporary option for the rehabilitation of

FIGURE 14.1
(See colour insert.) Titanium dental implants with ideal osseointegration.

edentate and partially dentate patients (Jung et al. 2008; Pjetursson et al. 2007, 2012). The increasing demand for implants by society and the continuously growing range of clinicians result in a significant increase in the number of dental implants placed over the last 20 years, and this is likely to continue (Armas et al. 2013).

As the worldwide volume of implants increases, the number of patients/implants affected by peri-implant diseases increase markedly. Peri-implant disease, one of the most common complications that may lead to failure of dental implant treatment, has aroused increasingly more attention. The disease refers to the inflammatory lesions that develop in the soft and hard tissues around dental implants, including peri-implant mucositis and peri-implantitis (Figure 14.2). Peri-implant mucositis is recognised as reversible inflammatory reactions in the mucosa adjacent to an implant, whereas peri-implantitis is characterised as an inflammatory process affecting the tissues around an osseointegrated implant in function, resulting in loss of supporting bone (Albrektsson and Isidor 1994). Peri-implant diseases are considered to be infection diseases, which have been shown to have a close association with bacterial contamination (Costerton et al. 1999; Glinel et al. 2012).

The prevalence of peri-implantitis varied depending on the bone loss threshold or probing depth threshold used for case diagnosis, because of the considerable variations in diagnostic criteria of peri-implant diseases in the published literature (Lang and Berglundh 2011). A most recent systematic review on the epidemiology of peri-implant diseases has demonstrated an 'estimated weighted mean prevalence of peri-implant mucositis and peri-implantitis of 43% and 22%, respectively' (Derks and Tomasi 2015).

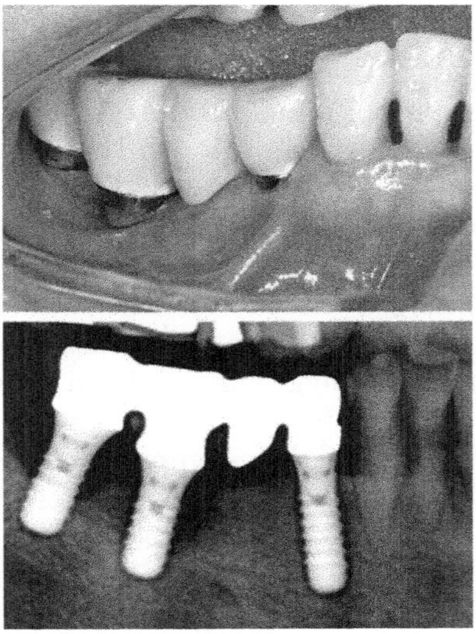

FIGURE 14.2
Titanium dental implants with peri-implantitis and exposed rough surface.

In order to prevent and treat peri-implantitis, various clinical protocols have been proposed, including mechanical debridement, the use of antiseptics and local or systemic antibiotics, as well as surgical access and regenerative procedures (Heitz-Mayfield and Mombelli 2014). However, there is no reliable evidence that can help recommend the most effective intervention for treating peri-implantitis (Esposito et al. 2012). No established and predictable concepts for the treatment of peri-implantitis are available; prevention is of key importance. The management of peri-implant mucositis is one of the most cost-effective preventive measures for the onset of peri-implantitis (Jepsen et al. 2015). Bacteria plaque control is becoming the primary objective, since plaque accumulation is the main etiological factor that causes peri-implant mucositis (Renvert and Polyzois 2015b; Schwarz et al. 2014).

14.2 Anatomy of Peri-Implant Tissues

Since the specific anatomy of the peri-implant soft and hard tissues can influence the course of peri-implant infection, it is fundamental to understand the physiological characteristics of normal peri-implant tissue structures. Essentially, the tissue around the implants can be divided into the peri-implant mucosa and the surrounding alveolar bone. Thus, this chapter will include a brief description of two sections: the transmucosal aspect and the endosseous part of titanium dental implant.

14.2.1 Transmucosal Aspect

Peri-implant mucosa is composed of well-keratinised oral epithelium, sulcular epithelium and junctional epithelium, as well as underlying connective tissue (Berglundh et al. 1991). The oral gingival epithelium faces the oral cavity and the oral sulcular epithelium faces the implant surface without contact. The histological construction of the peri-implant oral gingival epithelium is generally comparable with the marginal periodontium. It is a multilayered squamous epithelium, which can be divided into the following layers (Listgarten 1972): stratum basale (with cylindrical or cubical mitotic active cells), stratum spinosum, stratum granulosum and stratum corneum. In general, the junctional epithelium on the implant with a length of approximately 2 mm appeared to have an expansion comparable to a tooth. It was further observed that the junctional epithelium takes on a stable position under an inflammation-free condition and ends approximately 1 mm above the crestal bone level. Between the implant surface and the epithelial cell are hemidesmosomes and internal basal lamina comparable to a tooth surface. It can be seen from animal experiments that, on the surfaces of titanium and epoxy resin, as well as in the area of the abutment of aluminium oxide ceramic, a junctional epithelium was formed. The soft tissue interface is made up of the epithelium and the underlying connective tissue, which includes the biologic zone known as the biologic width, referring to the height of the dentogingival attachment apparatus encircling the tooth. The term *biologic width* is based on the work of Gargiulo et al. (1995), who described the dimensions of the dentogingival junction in human cadavers. The average dimension of 2.04 mm (1.07 ± 0.97 mm) is composed of supra-alveolar connective tissue and junctional epithelial attachment. In analogy with a tooth, the dentogingival complex additionally contains part of the gingival sulcus. Berglundh and Lindhe were able to show in an animal study that a supracrestal implant surface with an apical coronal expansion of at least 3 mm is necessary for the development of a stable biological width. Functionally, in a clinical sense, there must not be any encroachment within 2 mm of the bone that surrounds the tooth (Dhir et al. 2013). However, a crestal peri-implant bone resorption must be expected below this distance. This, again, could be beneficial for peri-implant plaque accumulation in the exposure of structured implant surfaces.

The proliferative capacity of the junctional epithelium leads to the rapid migration of the epithelial cells as soon as the fibrin clot/granulation tissue starts forming at the implant installation. Once the cells reach the implant surface, their attachment occurs rapidly through the basal lamina and the hemidesmosomes. Another possible attachment modality hypothesised is an indirect epithelium to implant contact. The peri-implant sulcus shares structural, ultrastructural and functional characteristics with the gingival tissues. Human studies have demonstrated that epithelium surrounding dental implants possesses similar patterns of differentiation and function to gingival tissues. The presence of granulation tissue adhering to the surface of the transmucosal components is considered the principal factor that stops the epithelium from migrating down apically. Berlundh speculated that the epithelium not migrating down apically is likely attributed to the interaction between the titanium oxide film and the collagenous connective tissue. A further explanation for the limitation of the proliferation of the junctional epithelium could be the increased fibroblasts over a width of approximately 40 μm in the area of the inner zone, as histologically proven in an animal experimental investigation.

This observation was confirmed in one-stage (open healing) and two-stage (open healing) surgical procedures. Weber et al. (1996), however, showed that the distance between apical extension of the epithelial attachment and the bordering alveolar bone was smaller after closed healing than after open healing. The apical extension of the epithelial attachment can be further encouraged by a manipulation of the abutment (removal and renewed attachment) or by specific material characteristics.

Generally, the stability of a developed physiological biological width does not appear to be primarily dependent on functional stress. During the first year of loading, however, two-piece implants in particular were frequently associated with crestal bone changes of approximately 1.5 to 2.0 mm (Hermann et al. 2000). Furthermore, previous results from an experimental animal study have indicated that remodeling and resorption after implant placement was more pronounced at the buccal than at the lingual aspect of the alveolar bone crest. Moreover, biomechanical aspects, such as interfacial shear strengths, as well as the influence of the implant design itself (e.g. macro- and micro-structure), have also been discussed. In particular, machined titanium implant surfaces located below the bone crest level revealed significantly higher bone changes. Jung et al. (1996) observed a correlation for the amount of bone resorption and the length of the machined neck (the longer the machined neck, the higher the bone resorption). So far, however, the optimal ratio of machined and roughened surfaces at the neck of implants is still rather unclear.

Connective tissue adhesion of the healing wounds involves the following steps: formation and adhesion of the fibrin clots to the implant surface, adsorption of the fibrin clot to the implant surface, adsorption of the extracellular matrix (ECM) proteins and connective tissue cells at the implant surface, transformation of the clot into granulation tissue and migration of epithelial cells on top of the fibrin clot/granulation tissue. The connective tissue zone next to the implant surface is primarily divided into two parts: an inner zone and an outer zone. The inner zone (approximately 50 to 100 μm wide) is described as a dense and weak vascularised collagen fibre–containing structure, resembling scar tissue, which, in close contact with the titanium surface, maintains the seal between the peri-implant bone and the oral environment. Controversial statements have been made in the literature concerning the alignment of the collagen fibres in relation to the surface of the implant. While several authors describe a mainly circular and parallel alignment of the collagen fibres to the implant surface in this area, others report a functional orientation with perpendicular inserting fibres. Buser et al. (1992) further showed in an experimental animal study that the alignment of the collagen fibres was dependent on whether the transmucosal implant area was in a keratinised or nonkeratinised mucosa. The authors were able to observe that the formation of perpendicular inserting fibres in the nonkeratinised area was solely detected parallel to the implant surface. In contrast, the outer zone, which borders on this inner zone, showed collagen fibres with most various alignment directions and a strong vascularisation. In comparison with a tooth, this zone shows, in regard to its ultrastructural configuration, patterns comparable to collagen types I, III and IV; laminin; fibronectin and vascular structures; however, there is an increased presence of collagen type V. Although Hansson et al. and Gould et al. were generally able to prove the formation of a junctional epithelium with internal basal lamina and hemidesmosomes, as well as collagen fibres in subepithelial connective tissue also in human specimens, connective tissue cells and the collagen fibre bundles are separated from the TiO_2 surface with a 20-nm-wide proteoglycan layer (Gould et al. 1981; Hansson et al. 1983). The immunohistochemically proven presence of B- and T-lymphocytes, also under clinical symptom-free peri-implant conditions, suggests a high immunogenic competence of these tissue structures.

14.2.2 Endosseous Part of the Titanium Implants

Osseointegration, defined as a 'direct structural and functional connection between ordered, living bone and the surface of a load bearing implant', is critical for implant stability, and is considered a prerequisite for implant loading and long-term success of endosseous dental implants. The implant–bone interface is an extremely dynamic region of interaction. This complex interaction involves not only biomaterial and biocompatibility issues but also alteration of mechanical environment. The processes of osseointegration involve an initial interlocking between alveolar bone and the implant body, and later, biological fixation through continuous bone apposition and remodelling toward the implant. The process itself is quite complex and there are many factors listed below that influence the formation and maintenance of bone at the implant surface.

14.2.2.1 Stages of Osseointegration

Direct bone healing, as it occurs in defects, primary fracture healing and osseointegration, is activated by any lesion of the pre-existing bone matrix. When the matrix is exposed to extracellular fluid, noncollagenous proteins and growth factors are set free and activate bone repair (Schenk and Buser 1998).

Once activated, osseointegration follows a common, biologically determined programme that is divided into three stages (Berglundh et al. 2003):

1. Incorporation via woven bone formation
2. Adaptation of bone mass to load (lamellar and parallel fibred bone deposition)
3. Adaptation of bone structure to load (bone remodelling)

14.2.2.2 Factors That Influence Implant–Bone Interface

Osseointegration is the basis of a successful endosseous implant. To fully understand what influences osseointegration, it is important first to examine more closely the interface, the most common surfaces used and studied, titanium oxide and the traits of a surface that allow for improved osseointegration.

14.2.2.2.1 Implant–Bone Interface

Osseointegration is a striking phenomenon in which bone directly opposes the implant surface without any interposing collagen or fibroblastic matrix (Albrektsson and Jansson 1986). Numerous studies have all concluded that the strength of an osseointegrated implant is far greater than that of a fibrous encapsulated implant. According to Albrektsson et al. (2003), it is the intimate contact of the bone to the implant, and he referred to it as 'functional ankylotic' adaptation. According to the American Academy of Implant Dentistry glossary of terms, it is a contact established between normal and remodelled bone and an implant surface without the interposition of the nonbone or connective tissue (American Academy of Implant Dentistry 1986). There is never a 100% bone-to-implant interface. The strength of the interface between bone and implant increases soon after implant placement (0–3 months). Other factors that may affect the strength of the interface are biophysical stimulation and time allowed for healing. Studies have shown that measurable increases in bone–implant interactions take place for at least 3 years.

14.2.2.2.2 The Titanium Oxide Layer

Commercially, titanium (Ti) and its alloys are extensively used as the material of dental or orthopaedic implants because of their good load-bearing properties, excellent biocompatibility and high corrosion resistance. When Ti or Ti alloys are exposed to air or normal physiologic environments, there is a reaction with the oxygen that causes an oxide layer to be formed. Usually, the oxide is in the form of TiO, TiO_2 or TiO_3 and is formed in three different crystal structures with various stoichiometric characteristics, preventing direct contact between the metal and the surrounding medium (Kasemo and Lausmaa 1985). It can, therefore, be considered as a biological autonomic surface. Depending on the preconditions under which the oxide film was formed and the manner in which the free bond valences are saturated, biocompatibility can be influenced. Under normal atmospheric conditions, an impurity film forms on the oxide film through saturation of these valences with the molecular impurities found in the air. High surface tension and thereby the biocompatibility of these surfaces are dependent on the reactivity of the pure oxide. Calcium and phosphate ions have been found in the oxide layers, which suggest that there is an active exchange of ions at the bone–implant interface. Porous surfaces have been shown to enhance ionic interactions, initiate a double physical and chemical anchor system and augment load-bearing capacity. Also, it can increase the tensile strength via growth of bone three-dimensionally as well as increased healing rates. Thus, increased bone contact is achieved and the ability to form a three-dimensional interconnection is enhanced.

14.2.2.2.3 Surface Design of the Endosseous Implant Part

The most common type of macro-retention of the implant body occurs through screw threads. These ensure solid anchoring and high mechanical stability immediately after insertion (primary stability). Micro-retentions play a key role in the optimisation of bioadhesion (Ahmad et al. 1999). Micro-retentive surface modifications primarily serve to increase the implant–bone contact surface. A decisive factor for bioadhesion is the surface tension of the implant material and the wetting liquid, which is blood in the case of endosseous implants. An initial wetting of the implant with blood and its molecular protein components indicates a high wettability of the implant with a good prognosis for the attachment of cellular components. It has been shown that the healing of peri-implant tissue is often quicker on porous surfaces, which can be caused by the ingrowth of the bone in the irregularities, which leads to a connection of the implant with the bone (ankylosis). Ankylosis creates the occurrence of very high shearing strength and an optimal transmission of force in the peri-implant bone. In this manner, beneficial conditions are provided for the functional integration of endosseous implants. Potential drawbacks of roughening the implant surface include problems with peri-implantitis and a greater risk of ionic leakage. In recent years, a modSLA titanium implant surface (SLActive, Institut Straumann) with hydrophilic characteristics that could further improve the bone connection in comparison with conventional SLA implants was introduced (Schwarz et al. 2009). The specific production process of the modSLA surface (which means processing under an N_2 atmosphere and storing in an isotonic saline solution) leads to a hydroxylated/hydrated surface, which only showed small portions of hydrocarbon and carbon. The resulting surface is characterised by a direct wettablity and ultrahydrophilic features owing to the contact angle of approximately 0° compared with 139.9° for conventional SLA surfaces (Rupp et al. 2006). Preliminary in vitro studies have indicated that the specific properties noted for modSLA titanium surfaces gave a significant influence on cell differentiation and growth factor production. Animal experiments have shown that hydrophilic surfaces improve early stages of soft and hard tissue integration of either nonsubmerged or submerged titanium implants. These data were also corroborated by the results from preliminary clinical studies.

14.2.2.2.4 Implant Bed

A healthy implant host site is required. However, in the clinical reality, the host bed may have suffered from osteoporosis and resorbed alveolar ridges. Such clinical states may constitute an indication for ridge augmentation with bone grafts. In jaws with insufficient bone volume for implant installation, a grafting technique has been recommended in order to increase the amount of hard tissues. To create more alveolar bone without grafting, some new surgical techniques were tested, relying on the biologic principle of guided tissue regeneration. It is of great value in situations with insufficient alveolar bone volume.

Other common clinical host bed problems involve previous irradiation and osteoporosis, to mention some undesirable states for implantation (Parithimarkalaignan et al. 2013). Previous irradiation need not be an absolute contraindication for the insertion of oral implants. However, it is preferable that some delay is allowed before an implant is inserted into a previously irradiated bed. Furthermore, some 10%–15% poorer clinical results must be anticipated after a therapeutical dose of irradiation because of vascular damage, at least in part (Parithimarkalaignan et al. 2013). Smoking is another factor that has been reported to yield significantly lower success rates with oral implants. The mechanism behind this lowered success is unknown, but vasoconstriction may play a role.

14.2.2.2.5 Loading Conditions

The primary factor for success at the time of placement is achieving primary stability (Hsu et al. 2016). Any micromotion during the initial phases of bone healing will cause a lack of integration. Failure is most often caused by overloading attributed to transmucosal forces of removable appliance over the implant site. Any attempt to keep a patient functioning with fixed provisional restoration during the healing phases of treatment will allow for easier patient management. If immediate loading at the time of final definitive implant placement is to be considered, not only should the initial stability be extremely tight, but control of the occlusion on the provisional interim restoration must be adjusted and monitored carefully through the initial healing period.

14.3 Primary Etiological Causes

14.3.1 Etiological Cause and Risk Factors

In accordance with epidemiological view, the prevalence of peri-implant infections should be calculated from a cross-sectional study and reported on a subject-level basis. The result of longitudinal studies can only provide the incidence rate during a particular period. However, long-term cross-sectional studies of peri-implant infection are scarce and the results of longitudinal studies are sometimes considered as prevalence data of peri-implant infection. In addition, because of the respective diagnostic criteria adopted in these different studies, various results concerning the prevalence of peri-implant diseases have been reported. The prevalence of peri-implant mucositis ranged from 38.8% (Mir-Mari et al. 2012) to 64.6% (Ferreira et al. 2006) while the prevalence of peri-implantitis ranged from 6% (Dierens et al. 2012) to 47.1% (Koldsland et al. 2010).

There is more and more evidence indicating that plaque accumulation is the main etiological cause of peri-implant mucositis (Renvert and Polyzois 2015a; Schwarz et al. 2014). Some independent risk factors may increase the probability of the disease occurring, including systemic/patient-related (i.e. diabetics, smoking, etc.) and local (i.e. residual cement, dimension of the keratinised tissue, surface roughness) risk indicators. In fact, the disturbances in the balance between bacterial contamination and host defence responses lead to the occurrence of peri-implant infections (Heitz-Mayfield 2008; Heitz-Mayfield and Lang 2010). There are plenty of studies that indicated that tissue response to the plaque formation at the surface of teeth and dental implants is similar. Lang et al. (1993) established animal models of peri-implant diseases and periodontal diseases and revealed similar clinical, radiographic, microbiological and histological findings. In addition, an experimental study of peri-implant mucositis in humans has proven that there is a direct cause–effect relationship between plaque accumulation and peri-implant mucositis, similar to that which occurs around natural teeth (Pontoriero et al. 1994). However, there are also several obvious differences between dental implants and natural teeth. Since dental implants are artificial medical devices, peri-implant infections can also be triggered by iatrogenic factors, such as excessive cement, misfit of abutments, unfavourable prosthetic design and various technical complications (Lang and Berglundh 2011).

Many studies have revealed that there are several risk factors associated with the development and progression of peri-implant infections, such as diabetes, a history of periodontitis, poor oral hygiene, smoking, alcohol consumption, genetic traits, absence of keratinised mucosa and implant surfaces (Heitz-Mayfield 2008). Among all the risk factors, strong evidence has been identified for poor oral hygiene, a history of periodontitis and cigarette smoking, which will be beneficial to plaque accumulation. It is well known that poor oral hygiene is intimately associated with plaque accumulation in an oral environment, which is an etiological factor of peri-implant diseases. In fact, it has already been proven that oral hygiene is one of the most important factors affecting peri-implant bone loss (Ferreira et al. 2006). Unfavourable implant-prosthetic design may lead to inadequate access to achieve a positive oral hygiene result, which has been verified to be related to an increased occurrence of peri-implant infection. Serino and Strom (2009) reported that 48% of peri-implantitis–involved implants had no accessibility for proper oral hygiene, while there were only 4% of the infected implants with good accessibility (Serino and Strom 2009). Periodontitis is one of the main causes of tooth loss, which is similar to peri-implant diseases with clinical, radiographic, microbiological and histological aspects. Therefore, it is assumed that patients who are susceptible to periodontitis should also be susceptible to peri-implantitis, owing to the same host-related factors. The problem of the risk of previous periodontitis on the development of peri-implantitis has been a hot area of research for several years. Although there is inadequate evidence about the negative effect of the history of periodontitis on the survival of dental implants, a higher prevalence of peri-implantitis was expected for the long-term result with a history of periodontitis. Patients previously treated for chronic periodontitis and rehabilitated with dental implants showed stable peri-implant variables and survival rates, as well as stable radiographic bone levels after 5 and 10 years, if patients were engaged in a regular periodontal maintenance programme (Meyle et al. 2014). Otherwise, it is confirmed that the absence of maintenance treatment will result in a higher incidence of peri-implantitis (Costa et al. 2012). As one of the primary risk factors of periodontal diseases, smoking is confirmed to have a significant negative impact on dental implants. It is indicated that smoking is related to a higher prevalence of peri-implantitis. Cigarette smoking demonstrated a significant adverse effect on the maintenance of oral hygiene around dental implants, which is the main risk factor of peri-implant infections. Therefore, a significantly higher failure rate of osseointegration has been confirmed (Pesce et al. 2014). However, how to deal with implant treatment for smokers still needs further study.

Peri-implant health depends on the balance between microorganisms and the host response. The host immune system is active in a healthy status, and the disruption in the expression of inflammatory mediators will result in the destruction of tissues surrounding dental implants, including soft tissue and bone. All the risk factors, leading to poor plaque control around dental implants, may trigger the pathological process.

14.3.2 Development of Plaque Biofilms and Typical Etiological Microbes

There are lots of similarities between peri-implant infection and periodontal diseases. Therefore, the microbial etiology study of periodontal diseases provides essential indicative information for studying peri-implant infection. Socransky et al. compared plaque composition between periodontitis and periodontally healthy patients. Five different microbial complexes that are associated with periodontitis were identified (Figure 14.3). The yellow, green and purple complexes were the initial colonisers in the subgingival sulcus and were predominant in gingival health status while the orange and red complexes were later colonisers and were found in greater numbers in inflamed than in healthy gingivae (Socransky et al. 1998).

Similar to natural teeth, dental implants provide a 'hard surface' for bacterial colonisation since the implants are inserted in the oral cavity. As inhabitants of the oral cavity, bacteria were found to reside in saliva, oral mucous and the periodontal area. In different areas, the bacterial species are different. As a result, bacterial composition in the oral cavity of fully edentulous patients is different from that in partial dentate patients because there is no periodontal area. Mombelli et al. have studied the early-stage bacterial colonisation around dental implants in fully edentulous patients and revealed that bacterial colonisation around dental implants occurred in the first weeks after insertion (Mombelli et al. 1988). A streptococcal microflora with the absence of spirochetes and black-pigmented bacteroides was confirmed in submucosal microbiota, while in the oral cavity of partial dentate patients, the periodontal pockets may serve as a reservoir for bacteria, where the composition is different from an edentulous environment. Periodontal pathogenic Gram-negative anaerobic rods were detected more early compared to fully edentulous patients (van Winkelhoff et al. 2000). Bacterial

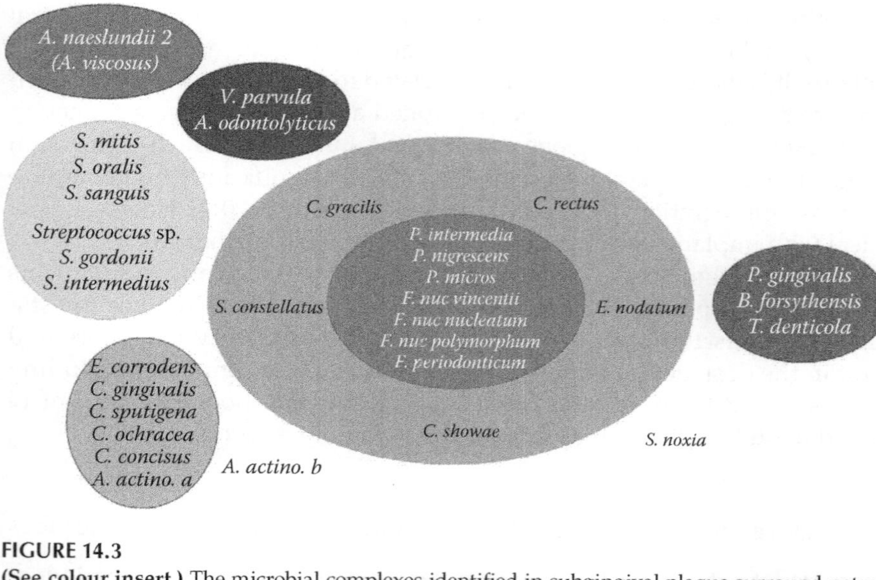

FIGURE 14.3
(See colour insert.) The microbial complexes identified in subgingival plaque surround natural teeth. (Adapted from Socransky et al.: Microbial complexes in subgingival plaque. *J Clin Periodontol.* 1998. 25. 134–44. Copyright Wiley-VCH Verlag GmbH & Co. KGaA. Reproduced with permission.)

colonisation around implants was observed as early as 30 min after installation (Furst et al. 2007), with similar composition of the pathogens to those found around natural teeth, and remained at the same levels at the 6-month follow-up (De Boever et al. 2006; Quirynen et al. 2006).

Aiming for a better understanding of the microbiological environment surrounding dental implants, significant research has been made to compare the microflora between dental implants and natural teeth. Common periodontal pathogens were found at healthy implant sites, and the composition of the microbiota on the remaining teeth was indicated to have a major impact on the composition of the microbiota around dental implants (Lee et al. 1999; Leonhardt et al. 1993). Since dental implants were inserted, typical periodontal bacteria, such as *Porphyromonas gingivalis*, *Aggregatibacter actinomycetemcomitans* and *Prevotella intermedia*, reached similar levels to natural teeth 6 months later, and remained at the same level. In healthy mucosa, the bacterial complexity performed as a scattered, submucosal microbiota dominated by facultative Gram-positive cocci and rods with low levels of anaerobic/aerobic species, Gram-negative species and 'periodontopathogenic' bacteria (Heitz-Mayfield and Lang 2000; Shibli et al. 2008). Around failing dental implants, microbiota share similar compositions to those of periodontitis teeth, with a high proportion of Gram-negative anaerobic rods. Many studies have revealed that the microbiota around infection-involved dental implants share much similarity with periodontitis, including members of the red complex species (*P. gingivalis*, *Treponema denticola* and *Tannerella forsythia*) and orange complex species (*Fusobacterium* sp. and *P. intermedia*) (Mombelli et al. 1988; Persson et al. 2006; Renvert et al. 2007). However, the composition of microbiota is not all the same around dental implants and natural teeth. Substantial differences in the microbial diversity were identified around implants with mucositis and teeth with gingivitis in human, which indicated that the transmission of bacteria was not simply a duplication of the complete bacterial community from teeth to dental implants (Heuer et al. 2012). In a series of studies, distinct community compositions for peri-implant and periodontal microbiomes in both health and disease revealed that the microbial community in peri-implantitis sites was dominated by Gram-negative species, which was less complex than that of periodontitis (Dabdoub et al. 2013; Kumar et al. 2012). Studies have also been performed to compare the microbiota complexity around dental implants with differing severities of peri-implant disease. It is reported that as the peri-implant infection advanced, more frequent and larger numbers of bacteria were identified (Sato et al. 2011). In addition, an increased diversity of species was also identified within the peri-implant microbial communities in an association study (Al-Radha et al. 2012). Remarkable differences in the composition of the microbiota were identified between implants with healthy and inflamed mucosa (da Silva et al. 2014). Significantly more pathogenic bacterial species were found in the inflamed tissues. However, not all the species followed the pattern of 'peri-implantitis > mucositis > health' and 'periodontitis > gingivitis > health' (Cortelli et al. 2013). Differences in the detection frequencies were larger between peri-implant/periodontal health and peri-implantitis/periodontitis than between mucositis/gingivitis and peri-implantitis/periodontitis, indicating similar bacterial etiological species of peri-implant mucositis and peri-implantitis.

Besides, bacteria from other organisms may be involved in peri-implantitis. A high level of *Staphylococcus aureus* infection was identified in the deep, suppurative peri-implant pockets in many studies (Albertini et al. 2015), although *S. aureus* is not strongly associated with chronic periodontitis but rather with therapy-resistant cases of periodontitis. More and more evidence suggests that *S. aureus* plays an important role in the initiation of some cases of peri-implantitis, which is already known as a major pathogen associated with medical device–related infections (Harris and Richards 2004). It is confirmed that *S. aureus* infections are related to rapid bone destruction in some pathogens, including osteomyelitis, bacterial arthritis and infected orthopaedic implant failure (Nair et al. 1995). A specific affinity to titanium surfaces of *S. aureus* was identified (Harris and Richards 2006). First, *S. aureus* adhered to ECM components and then to plasma proteins deposited on biomaterial surfaces, eventually leading to biofilm formation, which is a critical step in the development of peri-implant infections (Cramton et al. 1999). Furthermore, subjects with early implant failures displayed statistically significant lower serum antibody titers to *S. aureus*, indicating an impaired host response to this particular microorganism (Kronstrom et al. 2000).

Therefore, microbiota colonisation around dental implants occurs within hours after dental implant installation. Variable results have been reported for the composition of the microbiota found around periodontally involved teeth and implants with peri-implantitis. Microbiota contamination was confirmed as the etiological cause of peri-implant infections. However, the exact species of bacteria resulting in peri-implant infection still needs further study.

14.4 Therapy

14.4.1 Primary Objective Therapy

Similar to chronic periodontitis, peri-implant infections are also classified as disease processes associated with microorganisms. Therefore, the removal of bacterial plaque biofilms is significantly prerequisite to preventing disease progression. Surface modification is the key property for osseointegration. Many different implant surfaces and their new modifications are commercially available (Padial-Molina et al. 2011). There are not enough data to ensure that implant surface characteristics can have a significant effect on the initiation of peri-implantitis, but rough surfaces tend to accumulate more biofilm and are more difficult to clean. Therefore, many studies have arrived at the consensus that once exposed to the oral environment, rough surfaces are more likely to develop peri-implantitis and are more susceptible to disease progression than smooth or minimally rough surfaces (Albouy et al. 2011). In all treatment approaches, adequate plaque control by the patient and sufficient supportive care must be considered as prerequisites for a successful therapy.

14.4.2 Treatment of Peri-Implant Diseases

The removal of bacteria biofilm should be performed as an initial preparative measure for peri-implant infection treatments. The treatment of peri-implant infections comprises conservative (nonsurgical) and surgical approaches. Depending on the severity of the peri-implant disease (mucositis, moderate or severe peri-implantitis), a nonsurgical therapy alone might be sufficient or a stepwise approach with a nonsurgical therapy followed by a surgical treatment may be necessary. In fact, the removal of biological contamination from common implant surfaces is difficult to achieve, however, because of various surface modifications. In this context, apart from the mechanical removal of the biofilm, decontamination or conditioning of the exposed implant surface is also encouraged in order to optimise the removal of bacterial contaminants from the microstructured implant surface. The indication for the appropriate treatment strategy has been developed and documented as the 'cumulative interceptive supportive therapy (CIST)' concept (Lang et al. 2004; Mombelli 1997; Mombelli and Lang 1998). In the consensus conference of the International Team for Implantology, as the milestone meeting of modern dental implantology, the CIST was modified and called AKUT concept (Table 14.1) (Lang et al. 2004). The basis of this concept is a regular

TABLE 14.1

AKUT Protocol for Peri-Implant Infection Treatment

Stage	Result	Therapy
	Pocket depth (PD) <3 mm, no plaque or bleeding	No therapy
A	PD < 3 mm, plaque or bleeding on probing	Mechanically cleaning, polishing, oral hygienic instructions
B	PD 4–5 mm, radiologically no bone loss	Mechanically cleaning, polishing, oral hygienic instructions plus local anti-infective therapy (e.g. CHX)
C	PD > 5 mm, radiologically bone loss < 2 mm	Mechanically cleaning, polishing, microbiological test, local and systemic anti-infective therapy
D	PD > 5 mm, radiologically bone loss > 2 mm	Resective or regenerative surgery

Source: Adapted from Smeets et al. *Head & Face Medicine* 10:34, copyright 2014, open access article distributed under the Creative Commons Attribution Licence.

recall of the implanted patients and repeated assessment of plaque, bleeding, suppuration, pockets and radiological evidence of bone loss.

The principal step in any treatment option for peri-implant diseases consists of debridement of the tissue defect and decontamination of the affected implant surface. Largely, the treatment may be divided into two categories (Warreth et al. 2015):

1. Targeting peri-implant mucositis (Stages A and B)
2. Treatment of peri-implantitis (Stages C and D)

As shown in Table 14.1, the treatment of mucositis is nonsurgical and the treatment of peri-implantitis may be surgical or nonsurgical, depending on several factors such as the severity of the disease, aesthetic requirement and so on. However, because of the lack of prospective randomised long-term follow-up studies, a number of approaches have been described but there was no consensus on the 'ideal peri-implantitis therapy'. Different study designs in different populations with different materials have been performed, but the sample sizes are often not large enough and the follow-up is too short. Prevention is still the most important instrument for the treatment or control of peri-implant infection. Above all, attention should be paid to risk factors such as poor oral hygiene, smoking and previous periodontitis. In nonsurgical therapy, combinations of mechanical cleaning with curettes and air polishing systems are recommendable. Adjuvant antiseptic rinses and local or systemic antibiotics are effective for short-term bacteria eradication; laser and photodynamic therapy are additional treatment options. Surgical therapy with resective and augmentative procedures can be used in order to eliminate peri-implant defects, to re-establish hygienic abilities and to reduce or even stop peri-implantitis progression. A graded systematic treatment planning according to the CIST protocol can be recommended (Sousa et al. 2016). In fact, there is no 'ideal peri-implantitis therapy', but there is a sum of approaches leading to an individual therapy regime concerning multifactorial etiology, treatment options and study results.

14.4.2.1 Treatment of Peri-Implant Mucositis

In order to stop further tissue destruction, the peri-implant microbial community should be decreased and changed to the level of those associated with healthy tissue. Management of mucositis (Figure 14.4, Stages A and B) involves mechanical debridement and polishing of the restoration–abutment surface in addition to oral hygiene education and follow-up. The effect of mechanical debridement could be improved when it is combined with application of antiseptic agents, mostly antimicrobial mouth rinse (Renvert et al. 2008).

Peri-implant mucositis is a reversible inflammation that occurs in the soft tissue around dental implants. Mechanical debridement, supplemented with

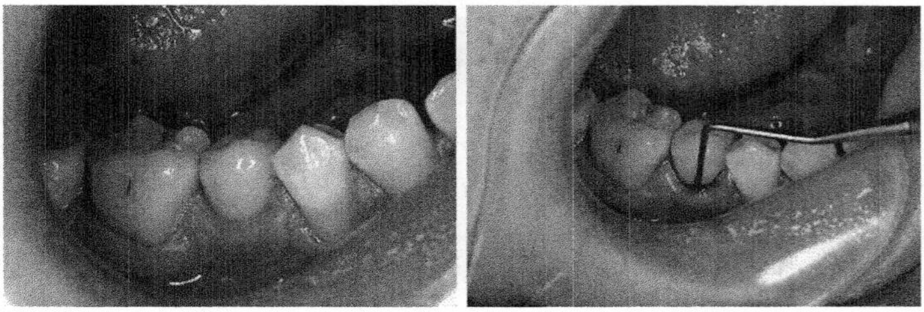

FIGURE 14.4
Dental implants with peri-implant mucositis.

or without chlorhexidine, resulted in a reduction of plaque and inflammation, and was effective in suppressing or eradicating the pathogenic bacteria that are often associated with peri-implant inflammation (Porras et al. 2002). Since the transmucosal part of implants are designed with a smooth surface, which controls the plaque more easily, mechanical debridement with plastic instruments, which are softer than implant materials and will not jeopardise the smooth surface, is effective and could lead to the reduction in peri-implant mucosal inflammation. Furthermore, a positive effect was documented when antimicrobial mouth rinses were used as an adjunct to the mechanical intervention (Ji et al. 2014; Warreth et al. 2015).

14.4.2.2 Treatment of Peri-Implantitis

The primary objective of peri-implantitis treatment is to prevent further peri-implant tissue destruction and to establish healthy soft and hard tissues around dental implants. The secondary objective is to achieve bone fill of the defective bone and re-osseointegration of exposed implant surfaces, which remains controversial and much more difficult. Several treatment protocols have been suggested for the remedy of peri-implantitis. Most of the strategies for peri-implantitis therapy are based on the treatments used for teeth with periodontitis, because the bacterial colonisation of dental and implant surfaces follows similar principles and the microbial biofilm plays an analogous role in the development of peri-implant infections. These strategies are based on several factors, such as degree and extent of the disease and morphology of bone defect as shown in Table 14.1. They can be divided into two main categories (Mishler et al. 2014):

1. The nonsurgical approaches: mechanical debridement or other applications, either alone or combined with antiseptic or antibiotic agents
2. The surgical approaches: open flap access to debridement the infection tissue and implant surface, with or without resective or regenerative techniques; extract the implant in certain conditions

To date, there is still no general agreement on the best method of treatment. Because of lack of sufficient evidence, a recommendation of a specific protocol for the treatment of peri-implantitis is inappropriate. Nevertheless, the first step in the treatment of any peri-implant disease is subgingival debridement and implant surface decontamination with the use of antimicrobial agents and oral hygiene reinforcement. This approach will control inflammation and prepare the site for surgery.

14.4.2.2.1 Nonsurgical Approaches

This approach involves mechanical debridement of the peri-implant tissues and the affected implant surface without raising a flap. The suggested options include medication, manual treatment (e.g. with curettes, ultrasonic and air polishing systems) and innovative techniques such as laser-supported and photodynamic therapy methods.

In order to avoid modifying or roughening the surface of dental implants, it has been recommended that the material of the manual treatment curettes should be softer than titanium (Unursaikhan et al. 2012). Therefore, conventional curettes should be avoided. Basic manual treatment can be provided by Teflon, carbon, plastic and titanium curettes (Figure 14.5). However, the outcome of nonsurgical manual treatment alone of peri-implantitis was not predictable and it is documented that the treatment may be efficient when the pocket depth is shallow (Lang et al. 2004), but not enough when the pockets are deep with exposed implant threads (Karring et al. 2005). Depending on the surface topography of the implants, different therapeutic methods have been recommended (Table 14.2). It is possible to reduce bleeding on probing, plaque index and probing depths after at least 6 months. Significantly lower numbers of bacteria with partial reduction of plaque and bleeding scores after mechanical curettage have been reported (Renvert et al. 2009). While using ultrasonic methods, residual biofilm areas can be reduced 30%–40%. The used medium of air polishing systems has significantly affected the

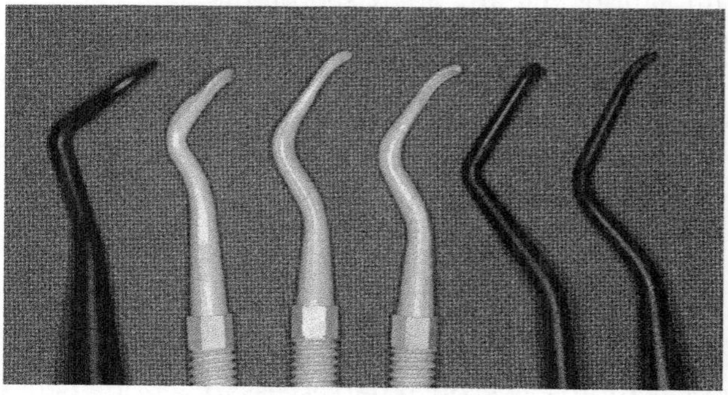

FIGURE 14.5
The instruments used for clinical treatment to avoid scratching and damaging the implant surface.

TABLE 14.2

Qualitative Effectiveness (Y, yes; N, no) of Different Cleaning Methods Depending on Implant Surface

	Smooth Surface	Sandblasted and Acid-Etched Surface (SLA)	Plasma-Sprayed Surface
Rubber cap	N	N	N
Metallic curette, rotating titanium brush	N	Y	Y
Plastic curette	N	N	N
Ultrasonic systems with metallic tips	Y (polished)		
Ultrasonic systems with plastic tips	N	Y	Y
Air polishing	Y	Y	Y

Source: Adapted from Smeets et al. *Head & Face Medicine* 10:34, copyright 2014, open access article distributed under the Creative Commons Attribution License.

treatment outcome in the following order: hydroxylapatite/tricalcium phosphate > hydroxylapatite > glycine > titanium dioxide > water and air (control group) > phosphoric acid (Tastepe et al. 2013). However, the use of mechanical debridement alone was not found to achieve considerable re-osseointegration, which is an important treatment outcome. Even the abrasive air polishing medium may modify the surface of implants. After air powder treatment, cell response to the surface of implants was decreased compared with the original surfaces (Tastepe et al. 2012), although the occurrence of bleeding on probing, one of the qualitative parameters in the presence of a peri-implantitis, could be significantly reduced.

Therefore, there is a general agreement that it is rational to combine mechanical debridement with chemical antiseptic agents. The following therapies can be distinguished:

1. Antiseptic rinses in relation to different parameters
2. Application of systemic and locally delivered antibiotics in relation to pocket depth or different parameters.

In a clinical study of oral implants with moderate peri-implantitis, the use of carbon curettes combined with chlorhexidine antiseptic was compared with the use of air-abrasive devices alone (Persson et al. 2010). Both treatment measures led to comparable but limited reductions of the infection symptom. However, the result of the study indicated that the first treatment regimen was less effective in decreasing the bleeding on probing than the second one. In fact, the addition of antiseptic therapy to mechanical debridement does not provide adjunctive benefits in shallow peri-implant lesions (mean pocket depth, <4 mm). However, in peri-implant lesions with a pocket depth ≥5 mm, the combination of mechanical debridement and antiseptic therapy may provide an improvement in clinical parameters. However, the peri-implant defects remain after the therapy, and additional surgical treatments are still required. Therefore, it may be concluded that the use of antiseptic agents as an adjuvant to mechanical debridement is needed in deep pocket depth. However, surgical intervention may also be required. Local or systemic antibiotics are an additional therapy option. In combination with other conservative or surgical treatments, it results in more efficient reductions of clinical peri-implantitis symptoms. Just administration of antibiotics is no treatment option.

Since the main composition of microbiota plaque around infected dental implants is anaerobic bacteria, photodynamic therapy generates reactive oxygen species by multiplicity with the help of a high-energy single-frequency light (e.g. diode lasers) in combination with photosensitisers (e.g. toluidine blue), in order to enhance plaque control. In a wavelength range of 580 to 1400 nm and toluidine blue concentrations between 10 and 50 μg/mL, photodynamic therapy exhibited bactericidal effects against aerobic and anaerobic bacteria (Figure 14.6). However, the treatment outcomes of photodynamic therapy still need further study. In a randomised clinical study, after manual debridement by titanium curettes and glycine air powder treatment, half of the patients received adjunctive photodynamic therapy and the other half received minocycline microspheres into implant pockets. Twelve months later, the amount of bacteria and the level of IL-1β decreased significantly in both groups without significant differences (Bassetti et al. 2014). In a study on the effectiveness of phototherapy of the moderate and severe peri-implantitis, both clinical attachment level and bleeding on probing index

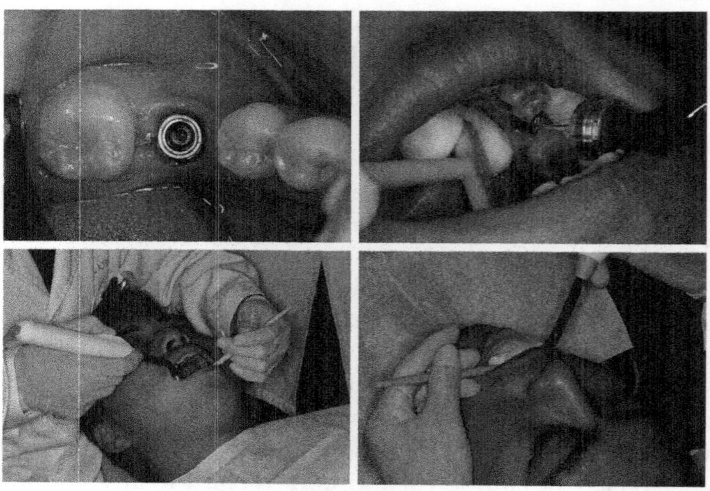

FIGURE 14.6
Nonsurgical therapy of peri-implantitis with photodynamic therapy.

were significantly reduced, suggesting that severe cases still resulted in bone resorption (Deppe et al. 2013). It is generally considered that photodynamic therapy should be considered as an additional treatment option. Because it is a relatively new approach, there are rarely any data and there are no long-term studies available. Further evaluations and prospective clinical trials are needed for evaluation.

14.4.2.2.2 Surgical Therapy

After the nonsurgical treatment of peri-implantitis, acute infection has been resolved and proper oral hygiene should be established, but the peri-implant defect remains and the infection in both soft and hard tissue still need to be controlled in further treatment. The primary aim of surgical therapy of peri-implantitis is to get direct access to the affected site and the implant surface, so that the decontamination of the implant surface could be carried out and the granulation tissue could be eliminated. The selected surgical protocol also depends on the degree and morphology of the peri-implant bony defect. The amount and quality of the remaining peri-implant soft tissue may play a role in surgical protocol selection. The surgical approach can be categorised as follows (Lang et al. 2011):

1. Access surgery
2. Resective surgery with or without implant surface modification
3. Regenerative approach

The appropriate treatment strategy is shown in Table 14.1. At the very beginning of the treatment, oral hygienic conditions have to be improved and mechanical cleaning and local anti-infective treatments are applied. If non-surgical treatment outcome is not good enough, surgical intervention with open debridement and resective or regenerative therapy is recommended.

In order to facilitate decontamination of the implant surface and eliminate infected tissue, access surgery should be carried out with a raising flap, which provides direct vision and access to the infected peri-implant tissue and to the unexposed implant surface. Antiseptic agents are recommended as an adjunctive treatment. In a study on the treatment of moderate to advanced peri-implantitis, 36 implants in 24 partially dentate patients were recruited (Heitz-Mayfield et al. 2012). All infected lesions were treated with open flap surgery, and implant surface decontamination was carried out with titanium-coated Gracey curettes or carbon fibre curettes. Amoxicillin and metronidazole were prescribed as adjunctive systemic antibiotics. The treatment outcomes were analysed at 3, 6 and 12 months. Forty-seven percent of the affected implants had complete resolution of inflammation (BoP negative) and stable crestal bone levels or bone gain, which was seen in 92% of implants. In an animal study, it was reported that several bacterial species that are believed to be associated with peri-implantitis were significantly reduced after access surgery treatment (Hayek et al. 2005). It was documented that the treatment protocol was effective if a strict oral hygiene protocol was followed. In summary, the open flap technique offered direct access into the affected site, which facilitated evaluation of the bony defect and debridement of the implant surface and eliminate the affected tissues. This approach is necessary when the peri-implant pocket is deep or when the angulation of the implant body is in an inconvenient position.

Resective surgery is used to correct soft and hard tissue defects around natural teeth for the treatment of periodontal diseases. The periodontal pocket was eliminated by apical repositioning flap and pocket reduction, to make the periodontal area accessible for cleaning. This type of surgery often involves an osseous resection for the removal of defective bone tissue, whereas for the treatment of peri-implantitis, resective surgery may involve correction of the peri-implant soft tissue when the bone loss is mainly of the horizontal type, with an apical repositioning flap. However, the resective approach should be carried out cautiously as the amount of removed peri-implant tissues may compromise the aesthetic or mechanical results of the implant and the neighbouring teeth. Additionally, smoothening and polishing of the supracrestal implant surface may be applied, which is called implantoplasty. However, the severity of initial peri-implant bone loss may affect the treatment outcome and the stability of the achieved improvement. Serino and Turri (2011) studied surgical pocket elimination and bone resection in combination with plaque control before and after surgery. Thirty-one subjects with clinical signs of peri-implantitis were recruited, and 42% of the implants still had the disease after 2 years of treatment with bone resection and pocket elimination and plaque control before and after the treatment. Seventy-four percent of the implants with an initial bone loss of 2–4 mm showed no sign of peri-implantitis during the 2-year period in comparison with 40% of the implants that had a greater bone loss. Resective surgery is recommended to be combined with implantoplasty for the treatment of peri-implantitis, which involves the use of rotary instruments to smooth the exposed implant surfaces in order to reduce formation of plaque on the implant surface and to facilitate its removal. The marginal bone loss after resective surgery with implantoplasty was significantly lower than after resective therapy only (Romeo et al. 2007). The adjuvant use of antimicrobial substances led to an initially less anaerobic bacteria contamination but did not improve the clinical outcome (de Waal et al. 2013). Ostectomy and osteoplasty combined with implantoplasty exhibit an effective treatment option to reduce or even stop peri-implantitis progression. However, this therapy may increase postoperative soft and hard tissue recessions; it is not suitable for highly aesthetic sensitive areas.

The regenerative approach consists of flap elevation, mechanical implant surface debridement and placement of a graft material, either alone or combined with a membrane. The membrane protects the graft material and provides a confined space for formation of the desired tissues. When the membrane is used with a graft material, the surgical method is known as guided bone regeneration (GBR; Figure 14.7). There are many studies that reported that GBR was efficient for achieving re-osseointegration (Machtei et al. 2016; Renvert et al. 2015; Subramani and Wismeijer 2012). In general, GBR alone and bone fill alone have been shown to be more effective than debridement alone for achieving bone regeneration and re-osseointegration. Many studies reported that the combination of membranes and bone graft materials was superior to using membranes or bone grafts alone. However, there is a high variability in the amount of bone fill as a result of different investigation protocols and measurements, and not all studies showed that there was a benefit for these treatments compared to debridement alone. The clinical study of Schwarz et al. (2005) revealed that using bong graft materials (nanocrystalline hydroxyapatite [Ostim or BioOss]) combined with collagen membrane can significantly improve the treatment outcomes after 6 months of healing (Schwarz et al. 2005). However, the use of graft material without a membrane may be considered when the graft material can be retained within the bony defect, such as in a circumferential bone defect. The membrane may be used when the bony defect morphology does not retain the graft material, but long-term, well-controlled randomised clinical studies are recommended.

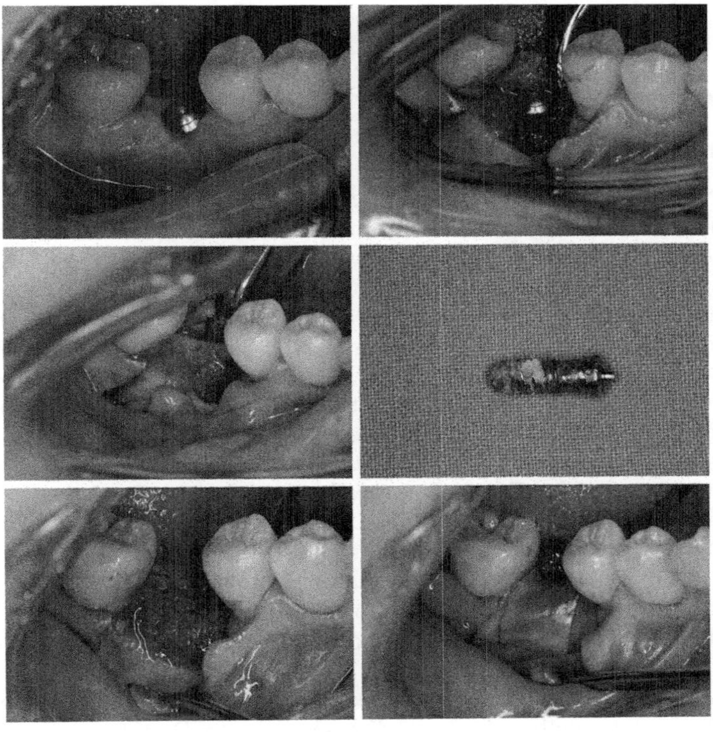

FIGURE 14.7
Regenerative treatment with the extraction of infected dental implants.

14.5 Summary

For bone regeneration, various measurements have been described with various success rates. It can be deduced that xenograft materials in combination with collagen membranes might have advantages in terms of re-osseointegration. After peri-implantitis therapy, tissue recession and consequently exposure of the implant surface are common. Clinicians and patients should be aware of these complications before prospective therapy is carried out. Since the exposed rough implant surface may facilitate plaque accumulation and may be difficult to remove, it may lead to further inflammation and may endanger the implant. Furthermore, removal of part of the peri-implant bone may jeopardise aesthetic outcomes.

Finally, we should remark once again that every implant patient, healthy or not, should be carefully instructed on oral hygiene techniques and counselled on the risk factors for peri-implant disease development. Meanwhile, clinicians should have a thorough peri-implant diagnosis, treatment planning and maintenance protocols, which are significant for achieving successful implant therapy.

References

Ahmad, M., Gawronski, D., Blum, J., Goldberg, J., Gronowicz, G. Differential response of human osteoblast-like cells to commercially pure (cp) titanium grades 1 and 4. *Journal of Biomedical Materials Research* 1(1999):121–31.

Albertini, M., Lopez-Cerero, L., O'Sullivan, M.G., Chereguini, C.F., Ballesta, S., Rios, V. et al. Assessment of periodontal and opportunistic flora in patients with peri-implantitis. *Clinical Oral Implants Research* 26(2015):937–41.

Albouy, J.P., Abrahamsson, I., Persson, L.G., Berglundh, T. Implant surface characteristics influence the outcome of treatment of peri-implantitis: An experimental study in dogs. *Journal of Clinical Periodontology* 38(2011):58–64.

Albrektsson, T., Berglundh, T., Lindhe, J. Osseointegration: *Historic Background and Current Concepts in Clinical Periodontology and Implant Dentistry*. pp. 809–20, Oxford: Blackwell Publishers Ltd, 2003.

Albrektsson, T., Isidor, F. Consensus report of session IV. In: Lang, N., Karring, T., editors. *Proceedings of the 1st European Workshop on Periodontology*. pp. 365–9, London: Quintessence Publishing Co., 1994.

Albrektsson T., Jansson T. Osseointegrated dental implants. *Dental Clinics of North America* 30(1986):151–74.

Al-Radha, A.S., Pal, A., Pettemerides, A.P., Jenkinson, H.F. Molecular analysis of microbiota associated with peri-implant diseases. *Journal of Dentistry* 40(2012):989–98.

American Academy of Implant Dentistry. Glossary of implant terms. *Journal of Oral Implantology* 12(1986):284–94.

Armas, J., Culshaw, S., Savarrio, L. Treatment of peri-implant diseases: A review of the literature and protocol proposal. *Dental Update* 40(2013):472–4, 6–8, 80.

Bassetti, M., Schar, D., Wicki, B., Eick, S., Ramseier, C.A., Arweiler, N.B. et al. Anti-infective therapy of peri-implantitis with adjunctive local drug delivery or photodynamic therapy: 12-month outcomes of a randomized controlled clinical trial. *Clinical Oral Implants Research* 25(2014):279–87.

Berglundh, T., Abrahamsson, I., Lang, N. P., Lindhe, J. De novo alveolar bone formation adjacent to endosseous implants. *Clinical Oral Implants Research* 3(2003):251–62.

Berglundh, T., Lindhe, J., Ericsson, I., Marinello, C.P., Liljenberg, B., Thomsen, P. The soft tissue barrier at implants and teeth. *Clinical Oral Implants Research* 2(1991):81–90.

Buser, D., Mericske-Stern, R., Bernard, J.P., Behneke, A., Behneke, N., Hirt, H.P. et al. Long-term evaluation of non-submerged ITI implants. Part 1: 8-year life table analysis of a prospective multi-center study with 2359 implants. *Clinical Oral Implants Research* 8(1997):161–72.

Buser, D., Weber, H.P., Donath, K., Fiorellini, J.P., Paquette, D.W., Williams, R.C. Soft tissue reactions to non-submerged unloaded titanium implants in beagle dogs. *Journal of Periodontology* 3(1992):225–35.

Cortelli, S.C., Cortelli, J.R., Romeiro, R.L., Costa, F.O., Aquino, D.R., Orzechowski, P.R. et al. Frequency of periodontal pathogens in equivalent peri-implant and periodontal clinical statuses. *Archives of Oral Biology* 58(2013):67–74.

Costa, F.O., Takenaka-Martinez, S., Cota, L.O., Ferreira, S.D., Silva, G.L., Costa, J.E. Peri-implant disease in subjects with and without preventive maintenance: A 5-year follow-up. *Journal of Clinical Periodontology* 39(2012):173–81.

Costerton, J.W., Stewart, P.S., Greenberg, E.P. Bacterial biofilms: A common cause of persistent infections. *Science* 284(1999):1318–22.

Cramton, S.E., Gerke, C., Schnell, N.F., Nichols, W.W., Gotz, F. The intercellular adhesion (ica) locus is present in *Staphylococcus aureus* and is required for biofilm formation. *Infection and Immunity* 67(1999):5427–33.

da Silva, E.S., Feres, M., Figueiredo, L.C., Shibli, J.A., Ramiro, F.S., Faveri, M. Microbiological diversity of peri-implantitis biofilm by Sanger sequencing. *Clinical Oral Implants Research* 25(2014):1192–9.

Dabdoub, S.M., Tsigarida, A.A., Kumar, P.S. Patient-specific analysis of periodontal and peri-implant microbiomes. *Journal of Dental Research* 92(2013):168s–75s.

De Boever, A.L., De Boever, J.A. Early colonization of non-submerged dental implants in patients with a history of advanced aggressive periodontitis. *Clinical Oral Implants Research* 17(2006):8–17.

de Waal, Y.C., Raghoebar, G.M., Huddleston Slater, J.J., Meijer, H.J., Winkel, E.G., van Winkelhoff, A.J. Implant decontamination during surgical peri-implantitis treatment: A randomized, double-blind, placebo-controlled trial. *Journal of Clinical Periodontology* 40(2013):186–95.

Deppe, H., Mucke, T., Wagenpfeil, S., Kesting, M., Sculean, A. Nonsurgical antimicrobial photodynamic therapy in moderate vs severe peri-implant defects: A clinical pilot study. *Quintessence International* 44(2013):609–18.

Derks, J., Tomasi, C. Peri-implant health and disease: A systematic review of current epidemiology. *Journal of Clinical Periodontology* 42(2015):S158–71.

Dhir, S., Mahesh, L., Kurtzman, G.M., Vandana, K.L. Peri-implant and periodontal tissues: A review of differences and similarities. *Compendium of Continuing Education in Dentistry* (Jamesburg, NJ: 1995) 7(2013):e69–75.

Dierens, M., Vandeweghe, S., Kisch, J., Nilner, K., De Bruyn, H. Long-term follow-up of turned single implants placed in periodontally healthy patients after 16-22 years: Radiographic and peri-implant outcome. *Clinical Oral Implants Research* 23(2012):197–204.

Esposito, M., Grusovin, M.G., Worthington, H.V. Interventions for replacing missing teeth: Treatment of peri-implantitis. *The Cochrane Database of Systematic Reviews* 1(2012):Cd004970.

Ferreira, S.D., Silva, G.L., Cortelli, J.R., Costa, J.E., Costa, F.O. Prevalence and risk variables for peri-implant disease in Brazilian subjects. *Journal of Clinical Periodontology* 33(2006):929–35.

Furst, M.M., Salvi, G.E., Lang, N.P., Persson, G.R. Bacterial colonization immediately after installation on oral titanium implants. *Clinical Oral Implants Research* 18(2007):501–8.

Gargiulo, A., Krajewski, J., Gargiulo, M. Defining biologic width in crown lengthening. *CDS Review* 5(1995):20–3.

Glinel, K., Thebault, P., Humblot, V., Pradier, C.M., Jouenne, T. Antibacterial surfaces developed from bio-inspired approaches. *Acta Biomater* 8(2012):1670–84.

Gould, T.R., Brunette, D.M., Westbury, L. The attachment mechanism of epithelial cells to titanium in vitro. *Journal of Periodontal Research* 6(1981):611–6.

Hansson, H.A., Albrektsson, T., Branemark, P.I. Structural aspects of the interface between tissue and titanium implants. *The Journal of Prosthetic Dentistry* 1(1983):108–13.

Harris, L.G., Richards, R.G. Staphylococci and implant surfaces: A review. *Injury* 37(2006):S3–14.

Harris, L.G., Richards, R.G. *Staphylococcus aureus* adhesion to different treated titanium surfaces. *Journal of Materials Science: Materials in Medicine* 15(2004): 311–4.

Hayek, R.R., Araujo, N.S., Gioso, M.A., Ferreira, J., Baptista-Sobrinho, C.A., Yamada, A.M. et al. Comparative study between the effects of photodynamic therapy and conventional therapy on microbial reduction in ligature-induced peri-implantitis in dogs. *Journal of Periodontology* 76(2005):1275–81.

Heitz-Mayfield, L.J. Peri-implant diseases: Diagnosis and risk indicators. *Journal of Clinical Periodontology* 35(2008):S292–304.

Heitz-Mayfield, L.J., Lang, N.P. Comparative biology of chronic and aggressive periodontitis vs. peri-implantitis. *Periodontology 2000* 53(2010):167–81.

Heitz-Mayfield, L.J., Mombelli, A. The therapy of peri-implantitis: A systematic review. *The International Journal of Oral & Maxillofacial Implants* 29(2014): S325–45.

Heitz-Mayfield, L.J., Salvi, G.E., Mombelli, A., Faddy, M., Lang, N.P. Anti-infective surgical therapy of peri-implantitis: A 12-month prospective clinical study. *Clinical Oral Implants Research* 2(2012):205–10.

Hermann, J.S., Buser, D., Schenk, R.K., Cochran, D.L. Crestal bone changes around titanium implants. A histometric evaluation of unloaded non-submerged and submerged implants in the canine mandible. *Journal of Periodontology* 71(2000):1412–24.

Heuer, W., Kettenring, A., Stumpp, S.N., Eberhard, J., Gellermann, E., Winkel, A. et al. Metagenomic analysis of the peri-implant and periodontal microflora in patients with clinical signs of gingivitis or mucositis. *Clinical Oral Investigations* 16(2012):843–50.

Hsu, A., Seong, W.J., Wolff, R., Zhang, L., Hodges, J., Olin, P.S. et al. Comparison of initial implant stability of implants placed using bicortical fixation, indirect sinus elevation, and unicortical fixation. *The International Journal of Oral & Maxillofacial Implants* 2(2016):459–68.

Jepsen, S., Berglundh, T., Genco, R., Aass, A.M., Demirel, K., Derks, J. et al. Primary prevention of peri-implantitis: Managing peri-implant mucositis. *Journal of Clinical Periodontology* 42(2015) Suppl 16:S152–7.

Ji, Y.J., Tang, Z.H., Wang, R., Cao, J., Cao, C.F., Jin, L.J. Effect of glycine powder air-polishing as an adjunct in the treatment of peri-implant mucositis: A pilot clinical trial. *Clinical Oral Implants Research* 25(2014):683–9.

Jung, R.E., Pjetursson, B.E., Glauser, R., Zembic, A., Zwahlen, M., Lang, N.P. A systematic review of the 5-year survival and complication rates of implant-supported single crowns. *Clinical Oral Implants Research* 19(2008):119–30.

Jung, Y.C., Han, C.H., Lee, K.W. A 1-year radiographic evaluation of marginal bone around dental implants. *The International Journal of Oral & Maxillofacial Implants* 6(1996):811–8.

Karring, E.S., Stavropoulos, A., Ellegaard, B., Karring, T. Treatment of peri-implantitis by the Vector system. *Clinical Oral Implants Research* 16(2005):288–93.

Kasemo, B., Lausmaa, J. Aspects of surface physics on titanium implants. *Swedish Dental Journal Supplement* (1985):19–36.

Koldsland, O.C., Scheie, A.A., Aass, A.M. Prevalence of peri-implantitis related to severity of the disease with different degrees of bone loss. *Journal of Periodontology* 81(2010):231–8.

Kronstrom, M., Svensson, B., Erickson, E., Houston, L., Braham, P., Persson, G.R. Humoral immunity host factors in subjects with failing or successful titanium dental implants. *Journal of Clinical Periodontology* 27(2000):875–82.

Kumar, P.S., Mason, M.R., Brooker, M.R., O'Brien, K. Pyrosequencing reveals unique microbial signatures associated with healthy and failing dental implants. *Journal of Clinical Periodontology* 39(2012):425–33.

Lang, N.P., Berglundh, T. Periimplant diseases: Where are we now? – Consensus of the Seventh European Workshop on Periodontology. *Journal of Clinical Periodontology* 38(2011):S178–81.

Lang, N.P., Berglundh, T., Heitz-Mayfield, L.J., Pjetursson, B.E., Salvi, G.E., Sanz, M. Consensus statements and recommended clinical procedures regarding implant survival and complications. *The International Journal of Oral & Maxillofacial Implants* 19(2004):S150–4.

Lang, N.P., Bragger, U., Walther, D., Beamer, B., Kornman, K.S. Ligature-induced peri-implant infection in cynomolgus monkeys. I. Clinical and radiographic findings. *Clinical Oral Implants Research* 4(1993):2–11.

Lee, K.H., Maiden, M.F., Tanner, A.C., Weber, H.P. Microbiota of successful osseointegrated dental implants. *Journal of Periodontology* 70(1999):131–8.

Lekholm, U., Grondahl, K., Jemt, T. Outcome of oral implant treatment in partially edentulous jaws followed 20 years in clinical function. *Clinical Implant Dentistry and Related Research* 8(2006):178–86.

Leonhardt, A., Adolfsson, B., Lekholm, U., Wikstrom, M., Dahlen, G. A longitudinal microbiological study on osseointegrated titanium implants in partially edentulous patients. *Clinical Oral Implants Research* 4(1993):113–20.

Listgarten, M.A. Normal development, structure, physiology and repair of gingival epithelium. *Oral Sciences Reviews* (1972):3–67.

Machtei, E.E., Kim, D.M., Karimbux, N., Zigdon-Giladi, H. The use of endothelial progenitor cells combined with barrier membrane for the reconstruction of peri-implant osseous defects: An animal experimental study. *Journal of Clinical Periodontology* 3(2016):289–97.

Meyle, J., Gersok, G., Boedeker, R.-H., Gonzales, J.R. Long-term analysis of osseointegrated implants in non-smoker patients with a previous history of periodontitis. *Journal of Clinical Periodontology* 41(2014):504–12.

Mir-Mari, J., Mir-Orfila, P., Figueiredo, R., Valmaseda-Castellon, E., Gay-Escoda, C. Prevalence of peri-implant diseases. A cross-sectional study based on a private practice environment. *Journal of Clinical Periodontology* 39(2012):490–4.

Mishler, O.P., Shiau, H.J. Management of peri-implant disease: A current appraisal. *Journal of Evidence-Based Dental Practice* (2014):53–9.

Mombelli, A. Etiology, diagnosis, and treatment considerations in peri-implantitis. *Current Opinion in Periodontology* 4(1997):127–36.

Mombelli, A., Buser, D., Lang, N.P. Colonization of osseointegrated titanium implants in edentulous patients. Early results. *Oral Microbiology and Immunology* 3(1988):113–20.

Mombelli, A., Lang, N.P. The diagnosis and treatment of peri-implantitis. *Periodontology 2000* 17(1998):63–76.

Nair, S., Song, Y., Meghji, S., Reddi, K., Harris, M., Ross, A. et al. Surface-associated proteins from *Staphylococcus aureus* demonstrate potent bone resorbing activity. *Journal of Bone and Mineral Research: The Official Journal of the American Society for Bone and Mineral Research* 10(1995):726–34.

Padial-Molina, M., Galindo-Moreno, P., Fernandez-Barbero, J.E., O'Valle, F., Jodar-Reyes, A.B., Ortega-Vinuesa, J.L. et al. Role of wettability and nanoroughness on interactions between osteoblast and modified silicon surfaces. *Acta Biomaterialia* 7(2011):771–8.

Parithimarkalaignan, S., Padmanabhan, T.V. Osseointegration: An update. *Journal of Indian Prosthodontic Society* 1(2013):2–6.

Persson, G.R., Salvi, G.E., Heitz-Mayfield, L.J., Lang, N.P. Antimicrobial therapy using a local drug delivery system (Arestin) in the treatment of peri-implantitis. I: Microbiological outcomes. *Clinical Oral Implants Research* 4(2006):386–93.

Persson, G.R., Samuelsson, E., Lindahl, C., Renvert, S. Mechanical non-surgical treatment of peri-implantitis: A single-blinded randomized longitudinal clinical study. II. Microbiological results. *Journal of Clinical Periodontology* 37(2010):563–73.

Pesce, P., Menini, M., Tealdo, T., Bevilacqua, M., Pera, F., Pera, P. Peri-implantitis: A systematic review of recently published papers. *The International Journal of Prosthodontics* 27(2014):15–25.

Pikner, S.S., Grondahl, K., Jemt, T., Friberg, B. Marginal bone loss at implants: A retrospective, long-term follow-up of turned Branemark System implants. *Clinical Implant Dentistry and Related Research* 11(2009):11–23.

Pjetursson, B.E., Bragger, U., Lang, N.P., Zwahlen, M. Comparison of survival and complication rates of tooth-supported fixed dental prostheses (FDPs) and implant-supported FDPs and single crowns (SCs). *Clinical Oral Implants Research* 18(2007):S97–113.

Pjetursson, B.E., Thoma, D., Jung, R., Zwahlen, M., Zembic, A. A systematic review of the survival and complication rates of implant-supported fixed dental prostheses (FDPs) after a mean observation period of at least 5 years. *Clinical Oral Implants Research* 23(2012):S22–38.

Pontoriero, R., Tonelli, M.P., Carnevale, G., Mombelli, A., Nyman, S.R., Lang, N.P. Experimentally induced peri-implant mucositis. A clinical study in humans. *Clinical Oral Implants Research* 5(1994):254–9.

Porras, R., Anderson, G.B., Caffesse, R., Narendran, S., Trejo, P.M. Clinical response to 2 different therapeutic regimens to treat peri-implant mucositis. *Journal of Periodontology* 73(2002):1118–25.

Quirynen, M., Vogels, R., Peeters, W., van Steenberghe, D., Naert, I., Haffajee, A. Dynamics of initial subgingival colonization of "pristine" peri-implant pockets. *Clinical Oral Implants Research* 17(2006):25–37.

Renvert, S., Polyzois, I. Risk indicators for peri-implant mucositis: A systematic literature review. *Journal of Clinical Periodontology* 42(2015a):S172–86.

Renvert, S., Polyzois, I.N. Clinical approaches to treat peri-implant mucositis and peri-implantitis. *Periodontology 2000* 1(2015b):369–404.

Renvert, S., Roos-Jansaker, A.M., Claffey, N. Non-surgical treatment of peri-implant mucositis and peri-implantitis: A literature review. *Journal of Clinical Periodontology* 35(2008):S305–15.

Renvert, S., Roos-Jansaker, A.M., Lindahl, C., Renvert, H., Rutger Persson, G. Infection at titanium implants with or without a clinical diagnosis of inflammation. *Clinical Oral Implants Research* 4(2007):509–16.

Renvert, S., Samuelsson, E., Lindahl, C., Persson, G.R. Mechanical non-surgical treatment of peri-implantitis: A double-blind randomized longitudinal clinical study. I: Clinical results. *Journal of Clinical Periodontology* 36(2009):604–9.

Romeo, E., Lops, D., Chiapasco, M., Ghisolfi, M., Vogel, G. Therapy of peri-implantitis with resective surgery. A 3-year clinical trial on rough screw-shaped oral implants. Part II: Radiographic outcome. *Clinical Oral Implants Research* 18(2007):179–87.

Rupp, F., Scheideler, L., Olshanska, N., de Wild, M., Wieland, M., Geis-Gerstorfer, J. Enhancing surface free energy and hydrophilicity through chemical modification of microstructured titanium implant surfaces. *Journal of Biomedical Materials Research Part A* 2(2006):323–34.

Sato, J., Gomi, K., Makino, T., Kawasaki, F., Yashima, A., Ozawa, T. et al. The evaluation of bacterial flora in progress of peri-implant disease. *Australian Dental Journal* 56(2011):201–6.

Schenk, R., Buser, D. Osseointegration: A reality. *Periodontology 2000* 17(1998):22–35.

Schwarz, F., Mihatovic, I., Golubovic, V., Eick, S., Iglhaut, T., Becker, J. Experimental peri-implant mucositis at different implant surfaces. *Journal of Clinical Periodontology* 41(2014):513–20.

Schwarz, F., Sculean, A., Rothamel, D., Schwenzer, K., Georg, T., Becker, J. Clinical evaluation of an Er:YAG laser for nonsurgical treatment of peri-implantitis: A pilot study. *Clinical Oral Implants Research* 16(2005):44–52.

Schwarz, F., Wieland, M., Schwartz, Z., Zhao, G., Rupp, F., Geis-Gerstorfer, J. et al. Potential of chemically modified hydrophilic surface characteristics to support tissue integration of titanium dental implants. *Journal of Biomedical Materials Research Part B, Applied Biomaterials* 2(2009):544–57.

Serino, G., Strom, C. Peri-implantitis in partially edentulous patients: Association with inadequate plaque control. *Clinical Oral Implants Research* 20(2009):169–74.

Serino, G., Turri, A. Outcome of surgical treatment of peri-implantitis: Results from a 2-year prospective clinical study in humans. *Clinical Oral Implants Research* 22(2011):1214–20.

Shibli, J.A., Melo, L., Ferrari, D.S., Figueiredo, L.C., Faveri, M., Feres, M. Composition of supra- and subgingival biofilm of subjects with healthy and diseased implants. *Clinical Oral Implants Research* 19(2008):975–82.

Smeets, R., Henningsen, A., Jung, O., Heiland, M., Hammächer, C., Stein, J.M. Definition, etiology, prevention and treatment of peri-implantitis – A review. *Head & Face Medicine* 10(2014):34.

Socransky, S.S., Haffajee, A.D., Cugini, M.A., Smith, C., Kent, R.L. Jr. Microbial complexes in subgingival plaque. *Journal of Clinical Periodontology* 25(1998):134–44.

Sousa, V., Mardas, N., Farias, B., Petrie, A., Needleman, I., Spratt, D. et al. A systematic review of implant outcomes in treated periodontitis patients. *Clinical Oral Implants Research* 27(2016):787–844.

Subramani, K., Wismeijer, D. Decontamination of titanium implant surface and re-osseointegration to treat peri-implantitis: A literature review. *The International Journal of Oral & Maxillofacial Implants* 5(2012):1043–54.

Tastepe, C.S., Liu, Y., Visscher, C.M., Wismeijer, D. Cleaning and modification of intraorally contaminated titanium discs with calcium phosphate powder abrasive treatment. *Clinical Oral Implants Research* 24(2013):1238–46.

Tastepe, C.S., van Waas, R., Liu, Y., Wismeijer, D. Air powder abrasive treatment as an implant surface cleaning method: A literature review. *The International Journal of Oral & Maxillofacial Implants* 27(2012):1461–73.

Unursaikhan, O., Lee, J.S., Cha, J.K., Park, J.C., Jung, U.W., Kim, C.S. et al. Comparative evaluation of roughness of titanium surfaces treated by different hygiene instruments. *Journal of Periodontal & Implant Science* 42(2012):88–94.

van Winkelhoff, A.J., Goene, R.J., Benschop, C., Folmer, T. Early colonization of dental implants by putative periodontal pathogens in partially edentulous patients. *Clinical Oral Implants Research* 11(2000):511–20.

Warreth, A., Boggs, S., Ibieyou, N., El-Helali, R., Hwang, S. Peri-implant diseases: An overview. *Dental Update* 2015;42:166–8, 71–4, 77–80 passim.

Weber, H.P., Buser, D., Donath, K., Fiorellini, J.P., Doppalapudi, V., Paquette, D.W. et al. Comparison of healed tissues adjacent to submerged and non-submerged unloaded titanium dental implants: A histometric study in beagle dogs. *Clinical Oral Implants Research* 1(1996):11–9.

15

Guidelines for Nanosilver-Based Antibacterial Devices

Loris Rizzello and Pier Paolo Pompa

CONTENTS

15.1 Introduction

The global burden of infection diseases, together with the constant increase in bacterial strain resistance to many available antibiotics, highlights the urgent need for the commercialisation of new classes of antibacterial agents (Morens et al. 2010; Powers 2004; Spellberg et al. 2008a,b). The current inefficacy of treatments is related to the bacterial aptitude of rapidly evolving molecular determinants that interact with the drugs, resulting in their rapid inactivation (Andersson and Hughes 2010; Levy and Marshall 2004; Schwaber et al. 2004). The scenario of drug resistance becomes even more dramatic taking into consideration the field of antibacterial drug discovery, where big pharma are losing interest in the low remunerative market of antibiotics, with a consequent reduction of new active molecules available (Kresse et al. 2007; Projan and Shlaes 2004). This dangerous synergism between the rapid evolution of drug resistance and the loss of interest in antibiotic R&D is creating great concern, especially in Third World countries (Boucher et al. 2009; Rice 2008; Spellberg et al. 2004; Taubes 2008). Several research councils, such as the BBSRC and the MRC in the United Kingdom, have also recently discussed the issue of the drug resistance increase. The primary aim is to try to reduce the number of patient deaths attributed to the inefficacy of therapies, by means of providing higher economical support to the research in the field. Despite the typical delays national governments experience in recognising such dramatic issues and the relative consequences, there is now a common agreement in finding a new, and possibly definitive, solution to a problem that will otherwise represent a serious challenge in the near future. The tangible final risk is, in fact, a possible downfall in a pre-antibiotic-like era. Hence, for the first time, several researchers from significantly different fields, from physics to biology, from nanotechnology to medicine, are merging their efforts, knowledge and expertise to solve a common issue. Such a multidisciplinary approach, which is nowadays mostly focused on nanomaterials-driven solutions, might represent a good chance for the realisation of a new class of antibacterial drugs and drug delivery systems. Among all the categories of nanomaterials, those based on silver have raised particular interest in the scientific community for several reasons: silver possesses a prominent broad range of antibacterial activity even at very low dose, it is relatively cheap and it can be easily integrated within several nanomaterials. The application of Ag as antimicrobial agent is not a recent discovery (Klasen 2000a,b; Liau et al. 1997). However, nanotechnology-based tools now allow one to finely control and guide the assembly of submolecular structures. Consequently, the production of nanomaterials having controlled physicochemical properties at the nanoscale (in terms of size, shape, dispersity and surface properties) is a well-established technology (Dahl et al. 2007). Ag-based nanomaterials include both Ag-based colloidal nanoparticles (NPs) and nanoengineered nanocomposites. The former are emerging in applications such as the treatment of systemic infections, thanks to the ability of NPs to bypass several biological barriers and to reach even the most peripheral tissues. NPs have, in fact, many advantages compared to classic drugs, such as the possibility of delivery only in localised areas, long-term efficacy, the specificity of action and the low cost of production. The latter are, on the other hand, investigated for their potential ability of preventing more topical/localised infections, such as in the case of wound dressings or implant devices (e.g. bone screw, catheters, pacemakers), where even minimal blood retention may promote bacterial adhesion and proliferation.

This chapter aims to give an overview and critically assess the most relevant advances in the area of Ag-based NPs and nanocomposites as biomedical devices for the treatment of infections. In fact, the interest in the field has been constantly increasing in the last decades, as confirmed by more than 8000 research and review articles produced with an exponential trend (Figure 15.1) and by the annual production of nanosilver (ca. 320 tonnes/year)

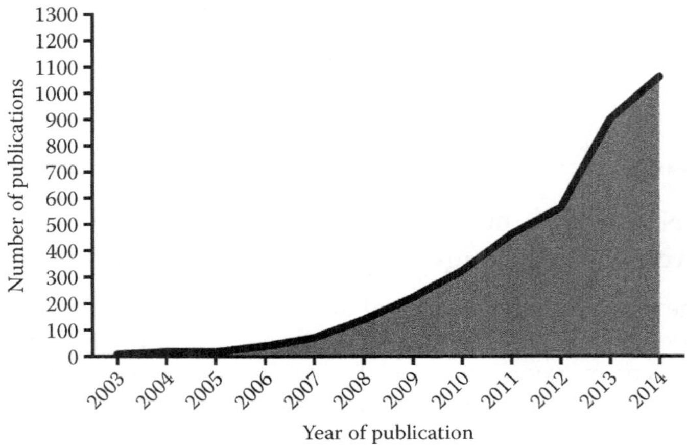

FIGURE 15.1
Number of published papers, from 2003 to 2014, on the use of nanosilver as antibacterial agent. [Data from Web of Knowledge. Research criteria: Topic = (silver nanoparticles) AND Topic = (antibacterial); data of search: June 2015.]

(Kumar et al. 2008; Nowack et al. 2011). We focused our analysis on two main topics. The first part deals with the use of Ag NPs as antimicrobial compounds. We reviewed the most remarkable research in the field, discussing the molecular mechanisms of Ag NP action, as well as the open questions, especially in terms of methodological approaches. This aspect is not trivial. Many of the available data present significant discrepancies concerning the real final lethal dose, the physicochemical parameters influencing NP bactericidal activity and the action of nanosilver and its main molecular targets in bacteria (Chernousova and Epple 2013; Eckhardt et al. 2013; Hajipour et al. 2012; Lemire et al. 2013; Rizzello and Pompa 2014). In this respect, we analysed the causes behind such literature disagreements, which mainly arise from the fact that some studies lack important characterisation techniques (both on the NPs and biological side).

After discussing the role of Ag NPs as a potential tool for the next generation of antimicrobial agents, the second part of this chapter overviews the applications of Ag-based devices, especially in the framework of biomedical applications. While Ag NPs can reach deep and peripheral body compartments by exploiting the blood circulation system, solid-state devices are important for the treatment of more localised infections. This is of crucial importance especially for implantology, where bacterial biofilm-associated persistent infections affect several patients with intracorporeal devices (i.e. pacemakers, bone screws, catheters, orthopaedic bone plates, etc.), usually leading to the surgical removal of the implant, followed by intense therapies. Also in this case, we reported the most interesting findings, critically addressing the experimental drawbacks, especially concerning biological and bio-safety issues and suggesting future applications and research opportunities.

15.2 Ag NPs as Antimicrobial Drugs: Mechanisms of Action, Advantages, Open Issues and Guidelines

Among the available nontraditional antibacterial agents, Ag NPs are currently recognised as promising alternatives to conventional antibiotics to defeat different microorganism-related pathologies, owing to their strong and broad-spectrum activity. Ag NPs are exploited in several commercial materials, ranging from clothing to household water filters, cosmetics, contraceptives, children's toys and biomedical devices (Alt et al. 2004; Bayston et al. 2007; Bhol and Schechter 2005, 2007; Bhol et al. 2004; Chen et al. 2006; Elechiguerra et al. 2005; Galiano et al. 2008; Jin et al. 2010; Kumar et al. 2008; Li et al. 2006; Podsiadlo et al. 2005; Skirtach et al. 2006; Sun et al. 2005; Weisbarth 2007). However, despite the huge commercial use of Ag NPs, a definitive understanding of their effects on microorganisms is not yet available, mainly because of the lack of standard NP materials and assays employed for characterising their effects. In Section 15.2.1, we start reviewing the current data on the biocidal effects of Ag NPs. Then, we describe the proposed mechanisms of Ag NP action on microorganisms at the molecular level, showing the open issues regarding the drawbacks in the employed methods and the lack of standardised tests. Finally, we provide some guidelines to overcome possible experimental artefacts and to design antibacterial devices based on nanosilver.

15.2.1 Ag NPs as Antimicrobial Agents

We start the discussion by examining the role played by the physicochemical properties of Ag NPs (e.g. size, shape and surface chemistry) in inducing antimicrobial effects. It is agreed that size plays a pivotal role in the antibacterial properties of Ag NPs; in particular, small NPs (i.e. in the range of 5–30 nm) are more effective compared to bigger particles (above 60–70 nm). This has been observed, for instance, by Choi and coworkers, who observed the more pronounced activity of 5- to 20-nm NPs with respect to 100-nm particles, AgCl colloids and free Ag^+ ions (silver salt). They also related the toxicity to the production of reactive oxygen species (ROS) (Choi and Hu 2008). Other studies came to similar conclusions and highlighted that Ag NPs are more effective against Gram-negative bacteria, suggesting Ag^+ ions as the real bactericidal agent of Ag NPs (Morones et al. 2005; Sondi and Salopek-Sondi 2004).

The shape is another fundamental physicochemical property demonstrated to tailor the antibacterial activity of Ag NPs. In particular, a study exploring the effect of spherical, tubular and triangular (i.e. with a 111 lattice plane) Ag NPs showed that these latter displayed the strongest effects (Pal et al. 2007). However, the bactericidal behaviour was mainly related to a combination of both shape and surface charge (Figure 15.2) (Pal et al. 2007). In this respect, the role of charge is also important, as positive charge elicits stronger antibacterial activity compared to negatively charged NPs (El Badawy et al. 2011). Very likely, the electrostatic interactions occurring at the Ag NP bacterial membrane interface (positively and negatively charged, respectively) are the main reason behind such experimental evidence.

However, the correlation between a specific physicochemical characteristic of Ag NPs and the final effect to bacteria does not provide an explanation of the underlying toxicity mechanism. We may assume that small, triangular, positively charged Ag NPs might be an ideal choice to obtain the highest

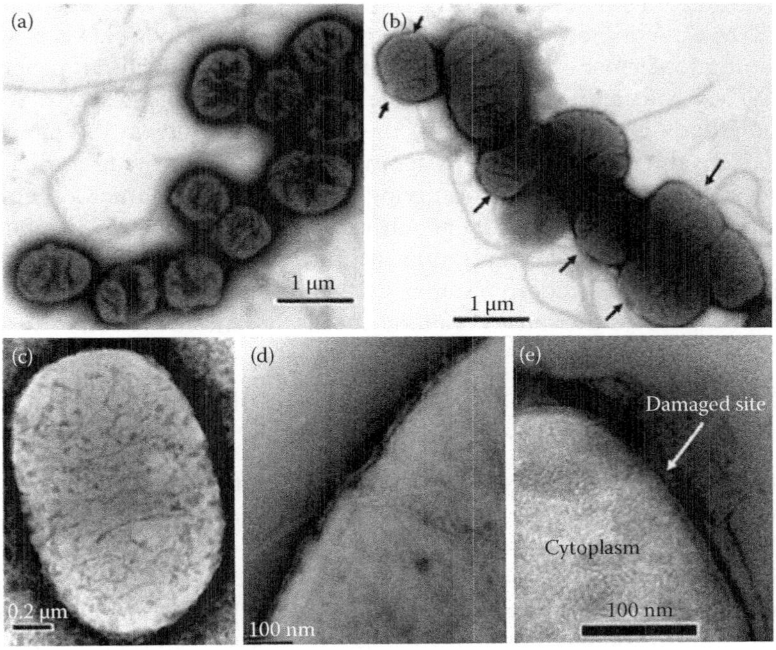

FIGURE 15.2
EFTEM images of *E. coli* cells. (a) Untreated and (b) treated with $AgNO_3$. Arrows indicate partially damaged membranes. These cells are viable. (c) *E. coli* treated with triangular silver nanoplates. Silver NPs appear as dark irregular pits on the cell surface. (d) *E. coli* treated with spherical silver NPs. (e) Enlarged image of part of the bacterial cell membrane treated with triangular silver NPs. The cell membrane is damaged in multiple locations. (Adapted from Pal et al., *Appl Environ Microbiol* 73:1712–1720, copyright 2007, with permission from the American Society for Microbiology.)

bactericidal effects, although no mechanistic information is clearly provided. Xiu and coworkers recently solved this disputed issue, showing that the principal contribution of the antibacterial activity of Ag NPs is attributed to Ag^+ ions, rather than to metallic silver (Xiu et al. 2012). Their experimental strategy was based on incubating bacteria with Ag NPs under conditions that can, or cannot, promote the oxidation process of the NPs in the growth media, with a consequent release of Ag^+ ions from their surface. In particular, they observed that bacteria growing under aerobic conditions, where oxygen stimulates the oxidation process of the particles, were much more affected by Ag NPs than those growing under an anaerobic environment, where the absence of oxygen prevents the silver ions' release (Liu et al 2010a,b). In light of such observations, it is evident that the previously described physico-chemical properties (i.e. size, shape and surface chemistry) can tune NP toxicity, in terms of promoting or inhibiting the overall process of Ag^+ release in the bacterial culture medium.

Several other research studies have been carried out on the bactericidal activity of Ag NPs (Kim et al. 2008, 2009; Navarro et al. 2008; Panacek et al. 2006, 2009; Smetana et al. 2008; Vertelov et al. 2008). However, it is worth mentioning that most of these studies exploited the antibacterial properties of Ag NPs only as a final application, as, for instance, in the case of new synthesis methods of Ag NPs. None of them really focused on the molecular effects, from the microbiology viewpoint, nor did they provide mechanistic insights about the interactions occurring between NPs and microorganisms. In addition, several data are rather contrasting, especially in terms of the dose for minimal inhibitory concentration (MIC), the bacterial molecular targets and the mechanisms underlying toxicity. All these drawbacks share similar reasons; we address the causes of literature discrepancies in Section 15.2.2.

15.2.2 Mechanisms of Action, Methodological Drawbacks and Experimental Guidelines

Direct membrane damage, induced by chemical interactions between silver ions and membrane constituents (mainly proteins), is considered to be the most likely possibility. The binding between silver ions and sulfur-rich proteins is a well-established paradigm, in agreement with Pearson's hard/soft theory (HSAB). This explains how soft ligands (e.g. the protein sulfur groups) strongly bind to soft cations (like Ag^+) in a quasi-covalent bond. In particular, coordination complexes between Ag^+ and several amino acids (AA) may occur, each one having its calculated binding affinity (Jover et al. 2008, 2009; Kasuga et al. 2012; Nomiya et al. 2000). The Ag^+–AA coordination complex would be one of the main reasons leading to the loss of functionality of the bacterial respiratory chain. This latter is a pool of proteins at the membrane level having pivotal importance in electron transport and ATP production, which are at the basis of the correct cell homeostasis. The Ag^+-related perturbation of ATP synthase function (the principal protein of the respiratory chain) results in (i) a lower level of intracellular ATP and (ii) the dissipation of the related proton motive force, with a consequent loss of membrane integrity. Bacteria will inevitably undergo a loss of metabolic activity on one side (caused by the lack of ATP), together with membrane permeability on the other. The membrane will thus be damaged, because of the impossibility of resisting the external osmotic pressure (Dibrov et al. 2002; Liau et al. 1997). Such collapse is also simultaneously promoted by direct Ag^+-related break of β–1→4 glycosidic bonds between the peptidoglycan blocks *N*-acetylglucosamine and *N*-acetylmuramic acid (Li et al. 2011; Mirzajani et al. 2011), which are the main constituents of the membrane.

It is worth mentioning that bacterial membrane might represent itself as a promoter of the antibacterial activity of Ag NPs. It is well known that at the membrane/environment interface, there is a local pH dropdown, which is attributed to the activity of the ATP synthase–related proton motive force. Such local decrease in pH promotes the oxidation processes and the Ag^+ release from the particle surface, with a consequent enhancement of the Ag^+ effective dose and related bactericidal effects. Free silver ions may also access the cytosol through the pre-induced pores, leading to further damage. As in the case of membrane proteins, Ag^+ ions may strongly bind several intracellular structural proteins and enzymes, inducing unfolding processes or loss of functionality (Li et al. 2011). Metalloproteins represent an important class of proteins that can be affected by the presence of Ag^+, as metal displacement may occur at the protein-binding site. Another intracellular target is DNA, as Ag^+ ions possess good binding affinity to guanine N7 and adenine N7 (Arakawa et al. 2011). This may elicit an unpredictable and wrong DNA condensation, followed by mistakes in replication and transcription and by random protein mutations upon the translational processes. It is evident that these are all direct Ag^+-induced damages: the ions will directly bind to several biomolecules impairing their function *in situ*, and the bacterial homeostasis will thus be significantly affected. However, in addition to direct damage, Ag^+ ions are also supposed to affect the metabolism and tune the toxicity, through several indirect ways. One of the most important processes is the Ag^+-related ROS production. It is well known how metal surfaces catalyse the production of ROS, and that the high surface-to-volume ratio of Ag NPs further promotes the process. These ROS, in turn, may damage DNA and even membrane phospholipids, through the phenomenon of oxidative stress. The big family of ROS includes H_2O_2, the singlet oxygen, the hydroxyl radical and the superoxide radical anion. They are known to severely affect both DNA and RNA, usually leading to lethal mutations and membrane phospholipids and proteins (Cabiscol et al. 2000). A summary of the Ag^+-related effects is reported in Figure 15.3. On the other hand, we should consider that bacteria evolved several molecular determinants to resist environmental stresses. As one of the first forms of life on earth, microorganisms had to inevitably interact with the harsh environmental conditions of the beginning of life (e.g. high temperatures, presence of heavy/toxic elements); thus, they

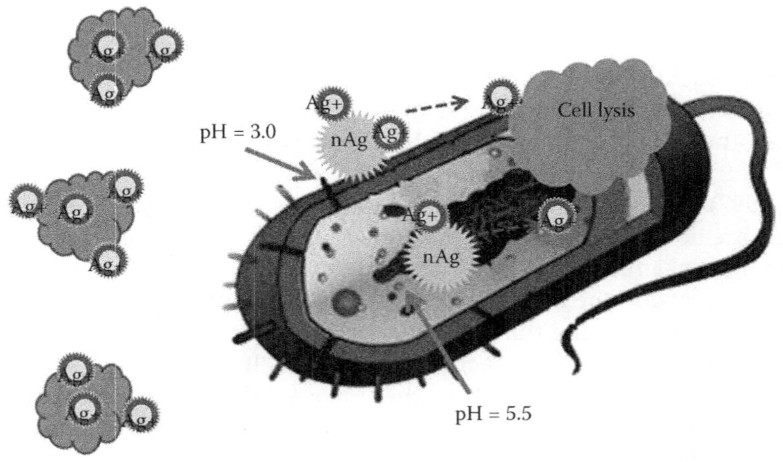

FIGURE 15.3
Schematic of Ag NPs, Ag^+ and cell interactions. Ag NPs may serve as a vehicle to deliver Ag^+ more effectively (being less susceptible to binding and reduced bioavailability by common natural ligands) to the bacterial membrane, whose proton motive force would decrease the local pH (as low as pH 3.0) and enhance Ag^+ release. (Adapted with permission from Xiu et al., *Nano Letters*, 12:4271–4275. Copyright 2012 American Chemical Society.)

developed several strategies to overcome them. As a result, those bacteria evolving detoxification systems (such as superoxide dismutase, peroxidase and catalase enzymes) were able to survive ROS-related stress and provide future offspring (Fang 2004). It is still debated whether all the detoxification systems might represent a chance to resist the indirect Ag^+ damage, and this is probably one other reason behind the literature data disagreement, so that some studies confirmed that silver ions kill bacteria through ROS, while others deny such hypothesis on the basis of the molecular detoxification systems (Choi and Hu 2008; Hwang et al. 2008; Inoue et al. 2002; Sintubin et al. 2011; Xiu et al. 2011).

Another open issue is related to the current unavailability of a reference standard material of Ag NPs, in terms of highly controlled physicochemical properties. This has a deep impact on the final biological outcomes, because of material variability. In order to give a few examples, some studies used Ag NPs with a very broad size distribution, which means that bacteria interact with a pool of inhomogeneous particles. The same applies for shape and charge/surface chemistry, so that the particle batch will include an uncontrolled mixture of spherical, rod-shaped and triangular NPs having different surface charges and inhomogeneous functionalisations. It is thus reasonable to understand the origin of several discrepancies, for example, the presence of contrasting opinions concerning the real final dose required (MIC) or which physicochemical parameter really affects the microbial growth.

The issue of particle variability, however, is not trivial, as the production of high-quality Ag NPs has been a challenge for several years. Some good methods have been implemented only recently to achieve highly controlled NPs with narrow size and shape distributions (Belser et al. 2009; Burda et al. 2005; Liang et al. 2010; Upert et al. 2012; Wennemers 2012). Unfortunately, many bacterial experiments were performed before the development of proper methods for Ag NP production, resulting in the consequent issue of contrasting results. Another aspect entails the analytical methods used to characterise the NPs. Some research, in fact, strongly lacks proper particle characterisation, which is a crucial priority before carrying out any further biological assays. Particle size, size distribution, dispersion status (e.g. presence of primary particles or agglomerates/aggregates), surface charge and accurate concentration are all parameters that significantly affect the biological results. However, there are reports lacking a proper panel of characterisation techniques, both immediately after NP synthesis and upon inoculating them within the bacterial growth media. This is also not trivial. Colloidal NPs completely change their physicochemical properties upon incubation with complex biological media having variable ionic strength and containing mixtures of (usually undefined) proteins and salts. NPs will thus become a different nano-object in biological fluids, and their behaviour has been demonstrated to significantly change compared to the as-synthesised ones (Maiorano et al. 2010; Monopoli et al. 2011a,b; Sabella et al. 2014; Walczyk et al. 2010). The colloidal stability of NPs in biological growth media is another parameter to control, as aggregates and precipitates of NPs affect the effective dose of silver and, consequently, the NP efficacy. Another remarkable aspect is the quantification of NP oxidation in the incubation media, a topic that is typically underestimated. Since the toxicity is driven by Ag^+ ions, the kinetics of silver ion release from the particle surfaces is strictly dependent on specific experimental conditions (Zook et al. 2011). For instance, the ageing of Ag NP batches may play a strong role in antibacterial activity experiments.

We would like now to focus the reader's attention on some biological aspects. Basically, all the studies related to the antibacterial effects of Ag NPs have been carried out under conditions that are significantly far from real biological conditions. In particular, NPs are usually dispersed in a broth containing a predetermined amount of colony-forming units (CFUs). However, several bacteria live within host cells (intracellular pathogens), such that all the data we currently have on the effect of Ag NPs on those bacteria are quite limited, and the experiments should be revised in order to have eukaryotic cells infected with pathogens and then treated with Ag NPs. Beyond these *in vitro* approaches, there is a serious lack of *in vivo* data, where model organisms for infections should be used. This would represent a serious demonstration of the real efficacy of Ag NPs, and it would provide crucial information on both NP toxicity and potential induction of localised or even systemic activations of the immune system.

Despite the evident lack of approaches addressing the big question whether Ag NPs can be exploited for the future treatment of *in vivo* infections in humans, it is also worth stressing that these nanomaterials possess important advantages compared to free drugs. First, Ag NPs are intrinsically a reservoir of Ag^+ ions, so they can be engineered in order to tune the kinetics of ion release or to promote the release only under specific environmental conditions (e.g. pH, temperature, ionic strength, presence of specific molecules). Hence, the possibility of controlled long-term release is a concrete opportunity. Second, NPs have the ability to cross, via a Trojan horse effect, biological barriers (e.g. cell membranes, the reticuloendothelial system, the blood–brain barrier and biological membranes in general), which usually inhibit classical charged molecules to access the cell cytosol or important body compartments (De Matteis et al. 2015; Sabella et al. 2014). Third, Ag NPs may be engineered to target specific cells, upon surface functionalisation. Hence, it is theoretically possible to reduce some typical limitations of classical drugs.

These important properties might be of interest to pharmaceutical companies for real applications, although some additional considerations should be taken into account, depending on the specific antibacterial target/treatment. This is because, while Ag^+-related drugs represent most likely the preferential choice in case of acute infections, where a big pool of ions would immediately stop the bacterial growth, Ag NPs are ideal candidates for persistent/chronic infections, owing to the possibility of controlled long-term ion release. Another key issue is the rise in bacterial resistance to silver. Akin to standard antibiotics, there is evidence that some strains of *E. coli* and *Salmonella* spp. have a specific operon called *sil* that encodes for a panel of proteins providing those bacteria survival mechanisms in the presence of silver ions (Gupta et al. 1998, 1999, 2011). One of the *sil* products is a periplasmic binding protein able to complex the Ag^+ ions (a chaperonine). Its main role is to locally reduce the concentration of free silver, thus increasing the organism survival chances. In addition, this chaperonine has been found to deliver the bonded Ag^+ to a transmembrane efflux pump, which is another product of the *sil* operon. The pump enables the ejection of silver ions from both the cytoplasm and periplasmic space to the extracellular side of microorganisms. Although the phenomenon of silver resistance is still confined to very few bacteria, there is the possibility of horizontal gene transfer with other more dangerous species in the near future.

15.3 Silver-Based Nanocomposites: A New Generation of Antibacterial Devices

In this section, we discuss the approaches for the design of solid-state silver-based nanocomposites, which is a fundamental point for the fabrication of safe and effective intracorporeal devices (Rizzello et al. 2013). It should, in fact, be considered that almost all abiotic surfaces are prone to adhesion and proliferation of bacteria, possibly leading to the formation of biofilms (Costerton et al. 2007; Davey and O'Toole 2000; de Nys and Steinberg 2002; Hall-Stoodley et al. 2004). Bacterial biofilms are hazardous colonies of several strains of microorganisms embedded within a slime matrix. They are commonly recognised as a serious concern in several fields, including food packaging, sea transport, medicine and manufacturing (Callow and Callow 2000, 2011; Chew and Lange 2009; Flemming and Wingender 2010). The biofilm matrix is composed of a complex (and almost unique) mixture of exopolysaccharides, DNA and catalytic proteins secreted by adhering bacteria (Figure 15.4) (Flemming and Wingender 2010; Gotz 2002; Hall-Stoodley et al. 2004; Ma et al. 2009; O'Toole and Stewart 2005; Skillman et al. 1998; Sutherland 2011). In this specific condition, microorganisms are able to proliferate and behave like a quasi-multicellular organism. For instance, specific secreted enzymes may degrade solid biopolymers present at the interface with the adjacent environment, thus acting like a digestive system. Additionally, the biofilm matrix enables bacteria to resist several external physicochemical stress conditions, such as drastic temperature and pH variations, mechanical stimuli, UV radiation, antibiotic treatment and scraping. For all these reasons, it is widely accepted that the best way to eradicate biofilms is to prevent their formation, namely, through suppression of the early stage of bacterial adhesion, rather than by subsequent drug-based treatments.

In this framework, an effective strategy to fabricate effective nanosilver-based device includes the functionalisation of either natural polymers or

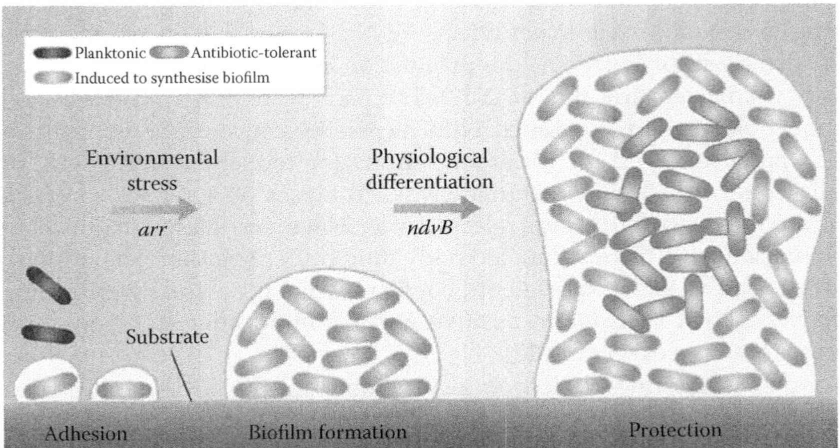

FIGURE 15.4
(See colour insert.) General scheme (for both Gram-positive and -negative bacteria) conceptualising the biofilm development and its behaviours. (Reprinted by permission from Macmillan Publishers Ltd. *Nat Biotech* O'Toole, G.A. and Stewart, P.S. 23:1378–1379, copyright 2005.)

their derivatives (e.g. starch, gelatin, cellulose, sodium alginate and chitosan) or synthetic polymers (e.g. polyvinyl alcohol and polyvinyl pyrollidone) with silver in the form of ions or Ag NPs (Bajpai et al. 2007; Jubya et al. 2012; Kong and Jang 2008; Thomas et al. 2009; Vasilev et al. 2010; Vimala et al. 2010). In particular, a common approach to realising Ag NP–functionalised polymer matrices consists of entrapping Ag^+ ions within the chains of the polymers, followed by *in situ* reduction with specific reducing agents (e.g. $NaBH_4$ or UV radiation). Unlike the mixing of the pre-synthesised Ag NPs within the polymer chains, such *in situ* method has an advantage in that the specific characteristics of the polymer chains may finely tune Ag NP size and shape. Additionally, the macromolecular chains of polymer may improve the quality of NP size distribution (and avoid uncontrolled agglomeration). In the following paragraphs, we review the most interesting studies about Ag NP–functionalised natural (or bioinspired) and synthetic polymers.

15.3.1 Biopolymers as Substrates for the Fabrication of Ag NP–Based Antimicrobial Devices

Concerning the category of naturally inspired polymers, Vimala et al. (2009) fabricated semi-interpenetrating hydrogel networks, based on cross-linked polyacrylamide, by means of a redox polymerisation of *N,N*-methylenebisacrylamide in the presence of different carbohydrate polymers (i.e. carboxymethyl cellulose, gum acacia and starch). At the same time, the reduction of Ag^+ ions entrapped within the polymer chains was performed with $NaBH_4$ (Vimala et al. 2009). The authors found good antibacterial activity of polymers having lower cross-linking networks (as a result of the more pronounced Ag NPs and Ag^+ release), while highly cross-linked polymers showed a comparatively lower effect. Ag NP–loaded gelatin hydrogel pads have also been exploited for the production of antibacterial wound dressings (Rattanaruengsrikul et al. 2012). The pads were prepared from a gelatin aqueous solution, combined with increasing concentrations of $AgNO_3$, which has been aged for different periods for reduction to Ag NPs, and finally cross-linked with glutaraldehyde. Analyses of Ag^+ release revealed that ca. 50%–60% of silver was released after 24 h of incubation in phosphate-buffered saline (PBS) or simulated body fluid buffer solution. The inhibition assays, based on CFU experiments, confirmed that these pads were strongly effective against both Gram-positive and Gram-negative microorganisms (Rattanaruengsrikul et al. 2012).

Another interesting work took inspiration from the adhesive proteins of natural mussels to synthesise water-soluble polyethylene glycol (PEG) polymers containing reactive catechol moieties (Fullenkamp et al. 2012). The authors employed $AgNO_3$ to oxidise polymer catechols of the PEG polymers, leading to hydrogel formation (in the form of a covalent cross-linking) combined with the simultaneous reduction of Ag^+ ions. These devices were found to constantly release Ag^+ for periods of at least 2 weeks in PBS solution, thus inhibiting the growth of microorganisms, while mammalian cell viability remained unaffected (Fullenkamp et al. 2012).

In a smart approach, Bayer et al. (2011) developed a direct and effective procedure to functionalise cellulose with different ethyl-cyanoacrylate nanocomposite shells. In particular, the authors were able to surround the single cellulose fibres (of commercially available sheets) with different nanomaterials: $MnFe_2O_4$ NPs (to provide magnetic activity to the paper), CdSe/ZnS quantum dots (for light emission), polytetrafluoroethylene particles or submicrometre wax (to render the paper superhydrophobic) and finally Ag NPs to give the substrates antibacterial characteristics (Bayer et al. 2011). The great advantage of this multifold approach is that it uses a cheap post-production method, which maintains the original properties of the sheets completely unperturbed. Figure 15.5 shows the paper sheets modified with several nanomaterials, and some nice applications of this effective multifunctional paper.

Many other studies exploited biodegradable cellulose matrices (both of bacterial and vegetable origin) as backbone of the antimicrobial device, while silver reduction was usually performed under UV radiation (Cranston and Gray 2006; Czaja et al. 2007; Klemm et al. 2005; Nadagouda and Varma 2007). The great advantage of these approaches lies in the use of naturally inspired polymers, combined with UV radiation, which enable one to obtain green substrates without any dangerous chemicals and reducing/capping agents (e.g. $NaBH_4$, hydroxylamine hydrochloride and several surfactants). In addition, they are cost-effective and their supply is unrestricted, since these polymers are widely produced and available in nature. On the other hand, biopolymer-based antibacterial devices have limitations, and they require difficult organic reactions for their fabrication.

15.3.2 Synthetic Polymers as Template Materials for the Fabrication of Antimicrobial Ag NP–Based Nanocomposites

Among synthetic polymers, polyurethanes are promising materials, since they are currently exploited in several applications for textiles, adhesives, furniture and biomedicine. In particular, their high chemical and mechanical resistance, combined with their high rubber-like elasticity, has made thermoplastic polyurethanes appropriate for several medical applications. For instance, Shah et al. (2008) included Ag NPs within polyethyleneglycol–polyurethane–TiO_2 (PEG–PU–TiO_2), which displayed excellent activity against both *Bacillus subtilis* and *Escherichia coli*. The authors synthesised PEG–PU–TiO_2 by a simple solution casting technique, while Ag NO_3 was reduced by a photochemical reaction, facilitated by the presence of TiO_2 (Shah et al. 2008). An interesting observation is that the antibacterial activity of silver in polymer–titania nanocomposite films displayed a reasonable activity even when they were tested in the microbial liquid broth. In another work, polymethyl methacrylate (PMMA)/silver nanocomposite microspheres, having specific

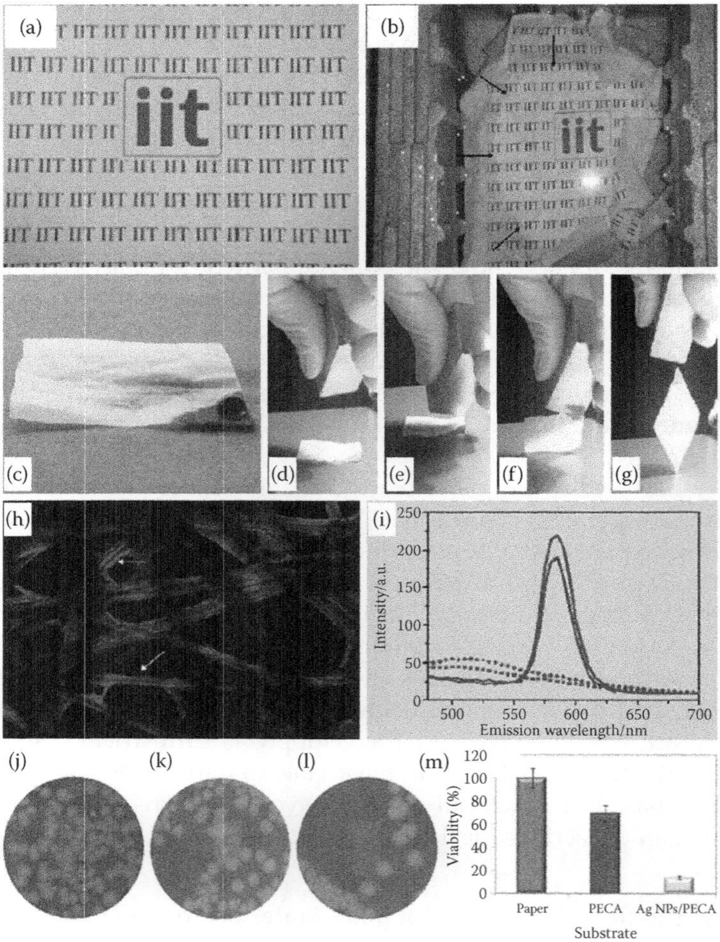

FIGURE 15.5
(a) Photograph of an ordinary copy paper locally treated with the wax/PECA nanocomposite, demonstrating no visible difference in appearance and printing quality. (b) Photograph of the paper shown in (a) immersed in a water bath. Fifteen minutes after immersion, the untreated paper is disintegrated. The treated region remains intact with the original printing on it. (c) Photo showing the difference in the wetting properties between the corner of a sheet treated with nanocomposite of $MnFe_2O_4$NPs in PECA (hydrophobic) and the untreated inherently hydrophilic part. (d through g) Magnetic actuation of the treated sheet. A simple magnet attracts the corner of the cellulose sheet treated with the magnetic nanocomposites. (h) Confocal microscope image showing emission from a cellulose sheet after treatment with the QDs/PECA nanocomposite. (i) Characteristic emission spectra of the QDs identified on the fibres. (j through l) Antibacterial effects after treatment of cellulose sheets with Ag NPs/PECA nanocomposites demonstrated in representative photographs of *E. coli* bacterial growth (after 24 h) on (j) control sample, (k) PECA-treated sheet and (l) Ag NPs/PECA-treated sheet. (m) Quantitative analysis of the population of bacteria grown on the PECA-treated sheet and the Ag NPs/PECA-treated sheet as compared to the control sample. (Adapted with permission from Bayer et al., *ACS Appl Mater Interfaces* 3:4024–4031. Copyright 2011 American Chemical Society.)

multi-hollow structures, were prepared by suspension polymerisation in the presence of dual dispersion agents (Lee et al. 2008). In particular, the authors used a lipophilic emulsifier, the PEG dipolyhydroxystearate, which has been demonstrated to stabilise the water-in-oil (W/O) emulsion and to convert Ag NPs from being hydrophilic to becoming lipophilic at the same time. Upon the addition of a polymerisation dispersion agent (the poly(vinyl alcohol)) to the W/O emulsion, a water-in-oil-in-water suspension was formed with Ag NPs dispersed in the oil phase. The obtained PMMA/Ag microspheres, characterised by various hollow structures, displayed high antibacterial ability (Figure 15.6) (Lee et al. 2008).

PMMA nanofibres containing Ag NPs were also synthesised by radical-mediated dispersion polymerisation and applied as antibacterial agent (Kong and Jang 2008). The authors demonstrated that these Ag NPs/PMMA nanofibres have enhanced antimicrobial efficacy, as compared to silver sulfadiazine and silver nitrate, at the same silver concentration (Kong and Jang 2008). In addition to polyurethanes and PMMA, many other research strategies have been developed towards the exploitation of dendrimers. These appeared as ideal candidates to fulfil the requirements of water solubility and biocompatibility, because of their specific characteristics such as symmetry, canonical structure and monodispersity. Dendrimers are, in fact,

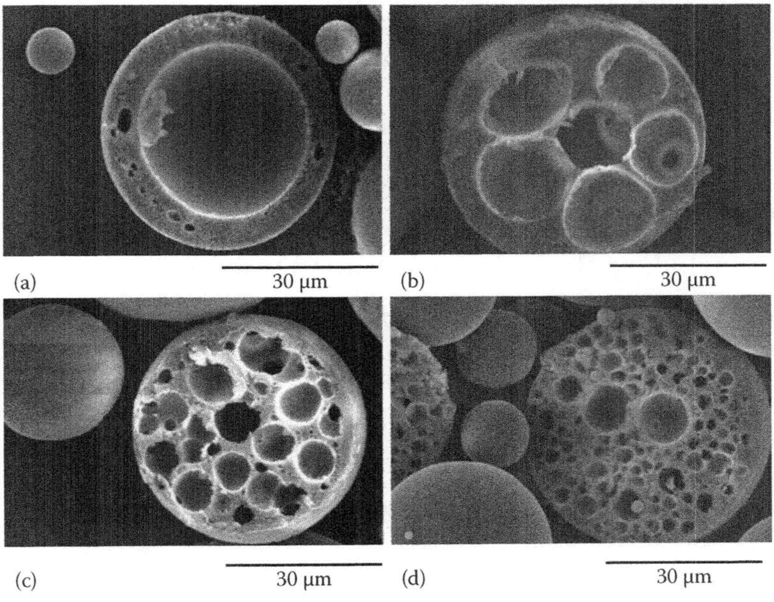

FIGURE 15.6
Various hollow structures of PMMA/silver nanocomposite microspheres with (a) 0.01 wt%, (b) 0.03 wt%, (c) 0.06 wt% and (d) 0.09 wt% surfactant concentration. (Adapted with kind permission from Springer Science+Business Media: *Colloid Polym Sci*, Multihollow structured poly(methyl methacrylate)/silver nanocomposite microspheres prepared by suspension polymerization in the presence of dual dispersion agents, 286, 2008, 1379–1385, Lee et al.)

monodispersed molecules having a regular symmetric and defined spatial architecture. In this framework, many studies exploited their unique properties for synthetising and encapsulating Ag NPs for antibacterial assays (Balogh et al. 2000; Castonguay and Kakkar 2010; Lesniak et al. 2005; Sun et al. 2004; Tang et al. 2013).

It is evident that all these polymers have the great advantage of having a quite simple chemistry (unlike natural or bioinspired polymers), which enables an overall flexibility in the fabrication process. On the other hand, there is a serious risk of adverse effects and immunogenic reactions. It should be, in fact, considered that most of the syntheses employ a strong chemical reduction to obtain Ag NPs, which may cause toxicity. Hence, the inclusion of pre-synthesised Ag NPs into polymeric matrices and using *in situ* photoreduction methods are probably the most promising strategies to overcome the concern of human toxicity.

Finally, it should be considered that in Ag^+- and Ag NP–containing polymers (as well as in natural polymers), the Ag^+ release rate depends mostly on the rate of water diffusion in the polymer matrix (Kumar and Munstedt 2005). Hence, several strategies attempted to control such release, including engineering the tridimensional structure of the polymer matrix (Kumar et al. 2005), the Ag NPs size and shape (Damm et al. 2008), the silver concentration and the physicochemical characteristics of the final nanocomposite (Kumar and Munstedt 2005). In particular, all these parameters can be finely tuned in order to increase the antimicrobial activity while decreasing the chances of Ag^+-related toxicity.

15.4 Concluding Remarks and Future Outlook

The field of Ag NP–based nanocomposites is attracting significant interest, because of their great potential as antimicrobial coatings/agents, especially for intracorporeal devices and wound dressing. However, it should be considered that many fabrication procedures also have important limitations. For instance, Ag NP–functionalised natural (or bioinspired) polymers are the most promising substrates thanks to their intrinsic biocompatibility and their considerably low cost (thanks to their wide natural distribution). On the other hand, 'plastic-like' polymers may elicit adverse toxic effects to mammalians, although their synthesis is quite feasible and reproducible. A theoretical goal could be that of identifying the optimal method to fabricate Ag NP–based composites with a biodegradable, biocompatible and nontoxic matrix, prepared with nontoxic precursors/monomers, and having strongly bonded Ag NPs, which should have a good dispersion state. In this framework, future efforts should be directed towards the improvement of the available technologies, especially in terms of controlling their long-term release, which is a crucial parameter for real applications in implant devices.

References

Alt, V., Bechert, T., Steinrucke, P. et al. An in vitro assessment of the antibacterial properties and cytotoxicity of nanoparticulate silver bone cement. *Biomaterials* 25 (2004): 4383–4391.

Andersson, D. I., Hughes, D. Antibiotic resistance and its cost: Is it possible to reverse resistance? *Nat Rev Microbiol* 8 (2010): 260–271.

Arakawa, H., Neault, J. F., Tajmir-Riahi, H. A. Silver(I) complexes with DNA and RNA studied by Fourier transform infrared spectroscopy and capillary electrophoresis. *Biophys J* 81 (2011): 1580–1587.

Bajpai, S. K., Mohan, Y. M., Bajpai, M., Tankhiwale, R., Thomas, V. Synthesis of polymer stabilized silver and gold nanostructures. *J Nanosci Nanotechnol* 7 (2007): 2994–3010.

Balogh, L., Swanson, D. R., Tomalia, D. A., Hagnauer, G. L., McManus, A. T. Dendrimer–silver complexes and nanocomposites as antimicrobial agents. *Nano Lett* 1 (2000): 18–21.

Bayer, I. S., Fragouli, D., Attanasio, A. et al. Water-repellent cellulose fiber networks with multifunctional properties. *ACS Appl Mater Interfaces* 3 (2011): 4024–4031.

Bayston, R., Ashraf, W., Fisher, L. Prevention of infection in neurosurgery: Role of 'antimicrobial' catheters. *J Hosp Infect* 65 (2007): 39–42.

Belser, K., Slenters, T. V., Pfumbidzai, C. et al. Silver nanoparticle formation in different sizes induced by peptides identified within split-and-mix libraries. *Angew Chem Int Ed Engl* 48 (2009): 3661–3664.

Bhol, K. C., Alroy, J., Schechter, P. J. Anti-inflammatory effect of topical nanocrystalline silver cream on allergic contact dermatitis in a guinea pig model. *Clin Exp Dermatol* 29 (2004): 282–287.

Bhol, K. C., Schechter, P. J. Topical nanocrystalline silver cream suppresses inflammatory cytokines and induces apoptosis of inflammatory cells in a murine model of allergic contact dermatitis. *Br J Dermatol* 152 (2005): 1235–1242.

Bhol, K. C., Schechter, P. J. Effects of nanocrystalline silver (NPI 32101) in a rat model of ulcerative colitis. *Dig Dis Sci* 52 (2007): 2732–2742.

Boucher, H. W., Talbot, G. H., Bradley, J. S. et al. Bad bugs, no drugs: No ESKAPE! An update from the Infectious Diseases Society of America. *Clin Infect Dis* 48 (2009): 1–12.

Burda, C., Chen, X., Narayanan, R., El-Sayed, M. A. Chemistry and properties of nanocrystals of different shapes. *Chem Rev* 105 (2005): 1025–1102.

Cabiscol, E., Tamarit, J., Ros, J. Oxidative stress in bacteria and protein damage by reactive oxygen species. *Int Microbiol* 3 (2000): 3–8.

Callow, J. A., Callow, M. E. Trends in the development of environmentally friendly fouling-resistant marine coatings. *Nat Commun* 2 (2011): 244.

Callow, M. E., Callow, J. A. Substratum location and zoospore behaviour in the fouling alga Enteromorpha. *Biofouling* 15 (2000): 49–56.

Castonguay, A., Kakkar, A. K. Dendrimer templated construction of silver nanoparticles. *Adv Colloid Interface Sci* 160 (2010): 76–87.

Chen, W., Liu, Y., Courtney, H. S. et al. In vitro anti-bacterial and biological properties of magnetron co-sputtered silver-containing hydroxyapatite coating. *Biomaterials* 27 (2006): 5512–5517.

Chernousova, S., Epple, M. Silver as antibacterial agent: Ion, nanoparticle, and metal. *Angew Chem Int Edit* 52 (2013): 1636–1653.

Chew, B. H., Lange, D. Ureteral stent symptoms and associated infections: A biomaterials perspective. *Nat Rev Urol* 6 (2009): 440–448.

Choi, O., Hu, Z. Size dependent and reactive oxygen species related nanosilver toxicity to nitrifying bacteria. *Environ Sci Technol* 42 (2008): 4583–4588.

Costerton, J. W., Montanaro, L., Arciola, C. R. Bacterial communications in implant infections: A target for an intelligence war. *Int J Artif Organs* 30 (2007): 757–763.

Cranston, E. D., Gray, D. G. Morphological and optical characterization of polyelectrolyte multilayers incorporating nanocrystalline cellulose. *Biomacromolecules* 7 (2006): 2522–2530.

Czaja, W. K., Young, D. J., Kawecki, M., Brown, R. M. Jr. The future prospects of microbial cellulose in biomedical applications. *Biomacromolecules* 8 (2007): 1–12.

Damm, C., Münstedt, H., Rösch, A. The antimicrobial efficacy of polyamide 6/silver-nano- and microcomposites. *Mater Chem Phys* 108 (2008): 61–66.

Dahl, J. A., Maddux, B. L., Hutchison, J. E. Toward greener nanosynthesis. *Chem Rev* 107 (2007) 2228–2269.

Davey, M. E., O'Toole G. A. Microbial biofilms: From ecology to molecular genetics. *Microbiol Mol Biol Rev* 64 (2000): 847–867.

De Matteis, V., Malvindi, M. A., Galeone A. et al. Negligible particle-specific toxicity mechanism of silver nanoparticles: The role of Ag^+ ion release in the cytosol. *Nanomed Nanotech Biol Med* 11 (2015): 731–739.

de Nys, R., Steinberg, P. D. Linking marine biology and biotechnology. *Curr Opin Biotechnol* 13 (2002): 244–248.

Dibrov, P., Dzioba, J., Gosink, K. K., Hase, C. C. Chemiosmotic mechanism of antimicrobial activity of Ag(+) in *Vibrio cholerae*. *Antimicrob Agents Chemother* 46 (2002): 2668–2670.

Eckhardt, S., Brunetto, P. S., Gagnon, J. et al. Nanobio silver: Its interactions with peptides and bacteria, and its uses in medicine. *Chem Rev* 113 (2013): 4708–4754.

El Badawy, A. M., Silva, R. G., Morris, B. et al. Surface charge-dependent toxicity of silver nanoparticles. *Environ Sci Technol* 45 (2011): 283–287.

Elechiguerra, J. L., Burt, J. L., Morones, J. R. et al. Interaction of silver nanoparticles with HIV-1. *J Nanobiotechnology* 3 (2005): 6–16.

Fang, F. C. Antimicrobial reactive oxygen and nitrogen species: Concepts and controversies. *Nat Rev Microbiol* 2 (2004): 820–832.

Flemming, H. C., Wingender, J. The biofilm matrix. *Nat Rev Microbiol* 8 (2010): 623–633.

Fullenkamp D. E., Rivera J. G., Gong Y. K. et al. Mussel-inspired silver-releasing antibacterial hydrogels. *Biomaterials* 33 (2012): 3783–3791.

Galiano, K., Pleifer, C., Engelhardt, K. et al. Silver segregation and bacterial growth of intraventricular catheters impregnated with silver nanoparticles in cerebrospinal fluid drainages. *Neurol Res* 30 (2008): 285–287.

Gotz, F. Staphylococcus and biofilms. *Mol Microbiol* 43 (2002): 1367–1378.

Gupta, A., Maynes, M., Silver, S. Effects of halides on plasmid-mediated silver resistance in *Escherichia coli*. *Appl Environ Microbiol* 64 (1998): 5042–5045.

Gupta, A., Matsui, K., Lo, J. F., Silver, S. Molecular basis for resistance to silver cations in Salmonella. *Nat Med* 5 (1999): 183–188.

Gupta, A., Phung, L. T., Taylor, D. E., Silver, S. Diversity of silver resistance genes in IncH incompatibility group plasmids. *Microbiology* 147 (2011): 3393–3402.

Hajipour, M. J., Fromm, K. M., Ashkarran, A. A. et al. Antibacterial properties of nanoparticles. *Trends Biotechnol* 30 (2012): 499–511.

Hall-Stoodley, L., Costerton, J. W., Stoodley, P. Bacterial biofilms: From the natural environment to infectious diseases. *Nat Rev Microbiol* 2 (2004): 95–108.

Hwang, E. T., Lee, J. H., Chae, Y. J. et al. Analysis of the toxic mode of action of silver nanoparticles using stress-specific bioluminescent bacteria. *Small* 4 (2008): 746–750.

Inoue, Y., Hoshino, M., Takahashi, H. et al. Bactericidal activity of Ag-zeolite mediated by reactive oxygen species under aerated conditions. *J Inorg Biochem* 92 (2002): 37–42.

Jin, X., Li, M., Wang, J. et al. High-throughput screening of silver nanoparticle stability and bacterial inactivation in aquatic media: Influence of specific ions. *Environ Sci Technol* 44 (2010): 7321–7328.

Jover, J., Bosque, R., Sales, J. A comparison of the binding affinity of the common amino acids with different metal cations. *Dalton Trans* 45 (2008): 6441–6453.

Jover, J., Bosque, R., Sales, J. Quantitative structure–property relationship estimation of cation binding affinity of the common amino acids. *J Phys Chem A* 113 (2009): 3703–3708.

Jubya, K. A., Dwivedia, C., Kumara, M., Kotab, S., Misrab, H. S., Bajaja, P. N. Silver nanoparticle-loaded PVA/gum acacia hydrogel: Synthesis, characterization and antibacterial study. *Carbohyd Polym* 89 (2012): 906–913.

Kasuga, N. C., Yoshikawa, R., Sakai, Y., Nomiya, K. Syntheses, structures, and antimicrobial activities of remarkably light-stable and water-soluble silver complexes with amino acid derivatives, silver(I) *N*-acetylmethioninates. *Inorg Chem* 51 (2012): 1640–1647.

Kim, K. J., Sung, W. S., Suh, B. K. et al. Antifungal activity and mode of action of silver nano-particles on *Candida albicans*. *Biometals* 22 (2009): 235–242.

Kim K. J., Sung W. S., Moon S. K., Choi J. S., Kim J. G., Lee D. G. Antifungal effect of silver nanoparticles on dermatophytes. *J Microbiol Biotechnol* 18 (2008): 1482–1484.

Klasen, H. J. A historical review of the use of silver in the treatment of burns. II. Renewed interest for silver. *Burns* 26 (2000a): 131–138.

Klasen, H. J. Historical review of the use of silver in the treatment of burns. I. Early uses. *Burns* 26 (2000b): 117–130.

Klemm, D., Heublein, B., Fink, H. P., Bohn, A. Cellulose: Fascinating biopolymer and sustainable raw material. *Angew Chem Int Ed Engl* 44 (2005): 3358–3393.

Kong, H., Jang, J. Antibacterial properties of novel poly(methyl methacrylate) nanofiber containing silver nanoparticles. *Langmuir* 24 (2008): 2051–2056.

Kresse, H., Belsey, M. J., Rovini, H. The antibacterial drugs market. *Nat Rev Drug Discov* 6 (2007): 19–20.

Kumar, R., Howdle, S., Munstedt, H. Polyamide/silver antimicrobials: Effect of filler types on the silver ion release. *J Biomed Mater Res B Appl Biomater* 75 (2005): 311–319.

Kumar, R., Munstedt, H. Silver ion release from antimicrobial polyamide/silver composites. *Biomaterials* 26 (2005): 2081–2088.
Kumar, A., Vemula, P. K., Ajayan, P. M., John, G. Silver-nanoparticle-embedded antimicrobial paints based on vegetable oil. *Nat Mater* 7 (2008) 236–241.
Lee, E., Lee, W. H., Park, J. H. et al. Multihollow structured poly(methyl methacrylate)/silver nanocomposite microspheres prepared by suspension polymerization in the presence of dual dispersion agents. *Colloid Polym Sci* 286 (2008): 1379–1385.
Lemire, J. A., Harrison, J. J., Turner, R. J. Antimicrobial activity of metals: Mechanisms, molecular targets and applications. *Nat Rev Microbiol* 11 (2013) 371–384.
Lesniak, W., Bielinska, A. U., Sun, K. et al. Silver/dendrimer nanocomposites as biomarkers: Fabrication, characterization, in vitro toxicity, and intracellular detection. *Nano Lett* 5 (2005): 2123–2130.
Levy, S. B., Marshall, B. Antibacterial resistance worldwide: Causes, challenges and responses. *Nat Med* 10 (2004): S122–129.
Li, W. R., Xie, X. B., Shi, Q. S., Duan, S. S., Ouyang, Y. S., Chen, Y. B. Antibacterial effect of silver nanoparticles on *Staphylococcus aureus*. *Biometals* 24 (2011): 135–141.
Li, Y., Leung, P., Yao, L., Song, Q. W., Newton, E. Antimicrobial effect of surgical masks coated with nanoparticles. *J Hosp Infect* 62 (2006): 58–63.
Liang, H., Wang, W., Huang, Y., Zhang, S., Wei, H., Xu, H. Controlled synthesis of uniform silver nanospheres. *J Phys Chem C* 114 (2010): 7427–7431.
Liau, S. Y., Read, D. C., Pugh, W. J., Furr, J. R., Russell, A. D. Interaction of silver nitrate with readily identifiable groups: Relationship to the antibacterial action of silver ions. *Lett Appl Microbiol* 25 (1997): 279–283.
Liu, J., Sonshine, D. A., Shervani, S., Hurt, R. H. Controlled release of biologically active silver from nanosilver surfaces. *ACS Nano* 4 (2010a): 6903–6913.
Liu, J., Hurt, R. H. Ion release kinetics and particle persistence in aqueous nano-silver colloids. *Environ Sci Technol* 44 (2010b): 2169–2175.
Ma, L., Conover, M., Lu, H., Parsek, M. R., Bayles, K., Wozniak, D. J. Assembly and development of the *Pseudomonas aeruginosa* biofilm matrix. *PLoS Pathog* 5(2009): e1000354.
Maiorano, G., Sabella, S., Sorce, B. et al. Effects of cell culture media on the dynamic formation of protein–nanoparticle complexes and influence on the cellular response. *ACS Nano* 4 (2010): 7481–7491.
Mirzajani, F., Ghassempour, A., Aliahmadi, A., Esmaeili, M. A. Antibacterial effect of silver nanoparticles on *Staphylococcus aureus*. *Res Microbiol* 162 (2011): 542–549.
Monopoli, M. P., Bombelli, F. B., Dawson, K. A. Nanobiotechnology: Nanoparticle coronas take shape. *Nat Nanotechnol* 6 (2011b): 11–12.
Monopoli, M. P., Walczyk, D., Campbell, A. et al. Physical–chemical aspects of protein corona: Relevance to in vitro and in vivo biological impacts of nanoparticles. *J Am Chem Soc* 133 (2011a): 2525–2534.
Morens, D. M., Folkers, G. K., Fauci, A. S. The challenge of emerging and re-emerging infectious diseases. *Nature* 463 (2010): 122–122.
Morones, J. R., Elechiguerra, J. L., Chamacho, A. et al. The bactericidal effect of silver nanoparticles. *Nanotechnology* 16 (2005): 2346–2353.
Nadagouda, M. N., Varma, R. S. Synthesis of thermally stable carboxymethyl cellulose/metal biodegradable nanocomposites for potential biological applications. *Biomacromolecules* 8 (2007): 2762–2767.
Navarro, E., Piccapietra, F., Wagner, B. et al. Toxicity of silver nanoparticles to *Chlamydomonas reinhardtii*. *Environ Sci Technol* 42 (2008): 8959–8964.

Nomiya, K., Takahashi, S., Noguchi, R., Nemoto, S., Takayama, T., Oda, M. Synthesis and characterization of water-soluble silver(I) complexes with L-histidine (H2his) and (*S*)-(–)-2-pyrrolidone-5-carboxylic acid (H2pyrrld) showing a wide spectrum of effective antibacterial and antifungal activities: Crystal structures of chiral helical polymers $[Ag(Hhis)]_n$ and $([Ag(Hpyrrld)]2)_n$ in the solid state. *Inorg Chem* 39 (2000): 3301–3311.

Nowack, B., Krug, H. F., Height, M. 120 years of nanosilver history: Implications for policy makers. *Environ Sci Technol* 45 (2011): 1177–1183.

O'Toole, G. A., Stewart, P. S. Biofilms strike back. *Nat Biotech* 23 (2005): 1378–1379.

Pal, S., Tak, Y. K., Song, J. M. Does the antibacterial activity of silver nanoparticles depend on the shape of the nanoparticle? A study of the Gram-negative bacterium *Escherichia coli*. *Appl Environ Microbiol* 73 (2007): 1712–1720.

Panacek, A., Kolar, M., Vecerova, R. et al. Antifungal activity of silver nanoparticles against *Candida* spp. *Biomaterials* 30 (2009): 6333–6340.

Panacek, A. Kvítek, L., Prucek, R. et al. Silver colloid nanoparticles: Synthesis, characterization, and their antibacterial activity. *J Phys Chem B* 110 (2006): 16248–16253.

Podsiadlo, P., Paternel, S., Rouillard, J. M. et al. Layer-by-layer assembly of nacre-like nanostructured composites with antimicrobial properties. *Langmuir* 21 (2005): 11915–11921.

Powers, J. H. Antimicrobial drug development – The past, the present, and the future. *Clin Microbiol Infect* 10 (2004): 23–31.

Projan, S. J., Shlaes, D. M. Antibacterial drug discovery: Is it all downhill from here? *Clin Microbiol Infect* 10 (2004): 18–22.

Rattanaruengsrikul, V., Pimpha, N., Supaphol, P. In vitro efficacy and toxicology evaluation of silver nanoparticle-loaded gelatin hydrogel pads as antibacterial wound dressings. *J Appl Polym Sci* 124 (2012): 1668–1682.

Rice, L. B. Federal funding for the study of antimicrobial resistance in nosocomial pathogens: No ESKAPE. *J Infect Dis* 197 (2008): 1079–1081.

Rizzello, L., Cingolani, R., Pompa, P. P. Nanotechnology tools for antibacterial materials. *Nanomedicine-UK* 8 (2013): 807–821.

Rizzello, L., Pompa, P. P. Nanosilver-based antibacterial drugs and devices: Mechanisms, methodological drawbacks, and guidelines. *Chem Soc Rev* 43 (2014): 1501–1518.

Sabella, S., Carney, R. P., Brunetti, V., Malvindi, M. A., Al-Juffali, N., Vecchio, G. A general mechanism for intracellular toxicity of metal-containing nanoparticles. *Nanoscale* 6 (2014): 7052–7061.

Schwaber, M. J., De-Medina, T., Carmeli, Y. Epidemiological interpretation of antibiotic resistance studies. What are we missing? *Nat Rev Microbiol* 2 (2004): 979–983.

Shah, M. S. A. S., Nag, M., Kalagara, T., Singh, S., Manorama, S. V. Silver on PEG-PU-TiO_2 Polymer nanocomposite films: An excellent system for antibacterial applications. *Chem Mater* 20 (2008): 2455–2460.

Sintubin, L., De Gusseme, B., Van der Meeren, P., Pycke, B. F., Verstraete, W., Boon, N. The antibacterial activity of biogenic silver and its mode of action. *Appl Microbiol Biotechnol* 91 (2011): 153–162.

Skillman, L. C., Sutherland, I. W., Jones, M. V. The role of exopolysaccharides in dual species biofilm development. *J Appl Microbiol* 85 (1998): 13S–18S.

Skirtach, A. G., Javier, A. M., Kreft, O. et al. Laser-induced release of encapsulated materials inside living cells. *Angew Chem Int Ed Engl* 45 (2006): 4612–4617.

Smetana, A. B., Klabunde, K. J., Marchin, G. R., Sorensen, C. M. Biocidal activity of nanocrystalline silver powders and particles. *Langmuir* 24 (2008): 7457–7464.

Sondi, I., Salopek-Sondi, B. Silver nanoparticles as antimicrobial agent: A case study on *E. coli* as a model for Gram-negative bacteria. *J Colloid Interf Sci* 275 (2004): 177–182.

Spellberg, B., Powers, J. H., Brass, E. P., Miller, L. G., Edwards, J. E. Trends in antimicrobial drug development: Implications for the future. *Clin Infect Dis* 38 (2004): 1279–1286.

Spellberg, B., Stewart, W. H. Mistaken or maligned? *Clin Infect Dis* 47 (2008a): 294.

Spellberg, B., Guidos, R., Gilbert, D. et al. The epidemic of antibiotic-resistant infections: A call to action for the medical community from the Infectious Diseases Society of America. *Clin Infect Dis* 46 (2008b): 155–164.

Sun, R. W., Chen, R., Ching, N. P. et al. Silver nanoparticles fabricated in Hepes buffer exhibit cytoprotective activities toward HIV-1 infected cells. *Chem Commun (Camb)* (2005): 5059–5061.

Sun, X., Dong, S., Wang, E. One-step preparation and characterization of poly(propyleneimine) dendrimer-protected silver nanoclusters. *Macromolecules* 37 (2004): 7105–7108.

Sutherland, I. W. The biofilm matrix. An immobilized but dynamic microbial environment. *Trends Microbiol* 9 (2011): 222–227.

Tang, J., Chen, W., Su, W., Li, W., Deng, J. Dendrimer-encapsulated silver nanoparticles and antibacterial activity on cotton fabric. *J Nanosci Nanotechnol* 13 (2013): 2128–2135.

Taubes, G. The bacteria fight back. *Science* 321 (2008): 356–361.

Thomas, V., Yallapu, M. M., Sreedhar, B., Bajpai, S. K. Fabrication, characterization of chitosan/nanosilver film and its potential antibacterial application. *J Biomater Sci Polym Ed* 20 (2009): 2129–2144.

Upert, G., Bouillere, F., Wennemers, H. Oligoprolines as scaffolds for the formation of silver nanoparticles in defined sizes: Correlating molecular and nanoscopic dimensions. *Angew Chem Int Ed Engl* 51 (2012): 4231–4234.

Vasilev, K., Sah, V., Anselme, K. et al. Tunable antibacterial coatings that support mammalian cell growth. *Nano Lett* 10 (2010): 202–207.

Vertelov, G. K., Krutyakov, Y. A., Efremenkova, O. V., Olenin, A. Y., Lisichkin, G. V. A versatile synthesis of highly bactericidal Myramistin(R) stabilized silver nanoparticles. *Nanotechnology* 19 (2008): 355707.

Vimala, K., Samba Sivudu, K., Murali Mohan, Y., Sreedhar, B., Mohana Raju, K. Controlled silver nanoparticles synthesis in semi-hydrogel networks of poly(acrylamide) and carbohydrates: A rational methodology for antibacterial application. *Carbohyd Polym* 75 (2009): 463–471.

Vimala, K., Mohan, Y. M., Sivudu, K. S. et al. Fabrication of porous chitosan films impregnated with silver nanoparticles: A facile approach for superior antibacterial application. *Colloid Surface B* 76 (2010): 248–258.

Walczyk, D., Bombelli, F. B., Monopoli, M. P., Lynch, I., Dawson, K. A. What the cell 'sees' in bionanoscience. *J Am Chem Soc* 132 (2010): 5761–5768.

Weisbarth, R. E. The academy and future change. *Optom Vis Sci* 84 (2007): 2–3.

Wennemers, H. Peptides as asymmetric catalysts and templates for the controlled formation of Ag nanoparticles. *J Pept Sci* 18 (2012): 437–441.

Xiu, Z. M., Ma, J., Alvarez, P. J. Differential effect of common ligands and molecular oxygen on antimicrobial activity of silver nanoparticles versus silver ions. *Environ Sci Technol* 45 (2011): 9003–9008.

Xiu, Z. M., Zhang, Q. B., Puppala, H. L., Colvin, V. L., Alvarez, P. J. Negligible particle-specific antibacterial activity of silver nanoparticles. *Nano Lett* 12 (2012): 4271–4275.

Zook, J. M., Long, S. E., Cleveland, D., Geronimo, C. L., MacCuspie, R. I. Measuring silver nanoparticle dissolution in complex biological and environmental matrices using UV-visible absorbance. *Anal Bioanal Chem* 401 (2011): 1993–2002.

Index

Page numbers followed by f and t indicate figures and tables, respectively.

B

C

D

E

G

H

I

K

L

N